ORGANIZING A STATISTICAL PROBLEM: A FOUR-STEP PROCESS

STATE: What is the practical question, in the context of the real-world setting?

PLAN: What specific statistical operations does this problem call for?

SOLVE: Make the graphs and carry out the calculations needed for this problem.

CONCLUDE: Give your practical conclusion in the setting of the real-world problem.

CONFIDENCE INTERVALS: THE FOUR-STEP PROCESS

STATE: What is the practical question that requires estimating a parameter?

PLAN: Identify the parameter, choose a level of confidence, and select the type of confidence interval that fits your situation.

SOLVE: Carry out the work in two phases:

1. **Check the conditions** for the interval you plan to use.
2. Calculate the **confidence interval.**

CONCLUDE: Return to the practical question to describe your results in this setting.

TESTS OF SIGNIFICANCE: THE FOUR-STEP PROCESS

STATE: What is the practical question that requires a statistical test?

PLAN: Identify the parameter, state null and alternative hypotheses, and choose the type of test that fits your situation.

SOLVE: Carry out the test in three phases:

1. **Check the conditions** for the test you plan to use.
2. Calculate the **test statistic.**
3. Find the *P*-value.

CONCLUDE: Return to the practical question to describe your results in this setting.

FIRST EDITION

Essential Statistics

DAVID S. MOORE

Purdue University

W. H. Freeman and Company

New York

Senior Publisher: **Craig Bleyer**
Publisher: **Ruth Baruth**
Senior Acquisitions Editor: **Roland Cheyney**
Senior Development Editor: **Shona Burke**
Executive Marketing Manager: **Jennifer Somerville**
Market Development Manager: **Kirsten Watrud**
Media Editor: **Laura Capuano**
Associate Editor: **Katrina Wilhelm**
Assistant Media Editor: **Andy Lawler**
Editorial Assistant: **Catriona Kaplan**
Photo Editor: **Cecilia Varas**
Text Designer: **Vicki Tomaselli**
Cover Illustrator: **Mark Chickinelli**
Senior Project Editor: **Mary Louise Byrd**
Production Manager: **Paul W. Rohloff**
Composition: **Aptara**
Printing and Binding: **Quebecor World**

TI-83™ screen shots are used with permission of the publisher: © 1996, Texas Instruments Incorporated. TI-83™ Graphing Calculator is a registered trademark of Texas Instruments Incorporated. Minitab is a registered trademark of Minitab, Inc. Microsoft © and Windows © are registered trademarks of the Microsoft Corporation in the United States and other countries. Excel screen shots are reprinted with permission from the Microsoft Corporation. S-PLUS is a registered trademark of the Insightful Corporation.

Library of Congress Cataloging-in-Publication Data

Moore, David S.
   Essential statistics / David S. Moore.—1st ed.
      p. cm.
   Includes index.
   ISBN 1-4292-3369-9
   1. Mathematical statistics.   I. Title.
   QA276.12.M649 2009
   519.5—dc22

                 2009018396

ISBN: 1-4292-3369-9, 1-4292-3446-6 (book + CD)
EAN: 978-1-4292-3369-9, 978-1-4292-3446-7 (book + CD)
ISBN: 1-4292-3970-0, 1-4292-3977-8 (instructor comp book + CD)
EAN: 978-1-4292-3970-7, 978-1-4292-3977-6 (instructor comp book + CD)

W. H. Freeman and Company
41 Madison Avenue
New York, NY 10010
Houndmills, Basingstoke RG21 6XS, England
www.whfreeman.com

To the Instructor: About This Book

To the Student: What Lies Ahead in This Book

PART I:
Exploring Data | 1

EXPLORING DATA: VARIABLES AND DISTRIBUTIONS

CHAPTER 1 Picturing Distributions with Graphs   3

CHAPTER 2 Describing Distributions
with Numbers   29

CHAPTER 3 The Normal Distributions   51

EXPLORING DATA: RELATIONSHIPS

CHAPTER 4 Scatterplots and Correlation   73

CHAPTER 5 Regression   91

CHAPTER 6 Exploring Data: Part I Review   115

PART II:
From Exploration to Inference | 127

PRODUCING DATA

CHAPTER 7 Producing Data: Sampling   129

CHAPTER 8 Producing Data: Experiments   145

PROBABILITY AND SAMPLING DISTRIBUTIONS

CHAPTER 9 Introducing Probability   163

CHAPTER 10 Sampling Distributions   183

CHAPTER 11 General Rules of Probability*   199

CHAPTER 12 Binomial Distributions*   217

INTRODUCING INFERENCE

CHAPTER 13 Introduction to Inference   231

CHAPTER 14 Thinking about Inference   257

CHAPTER 15 From Exploration to Inference:
Part II Review   273

PART III:
Inference about Variables | 283

QUANTITATIVE RESPONSE VARIABLE

CHAPTER 16 Inference about a Population Mean   285

CHAPTER 17 Two-Sample Problems   307

CATEGORICAL RESPONSE VARIABLE

CHAPTER 18 Inference about a
Population Proportion   327

CHAPTER 19 Comparing Two Proportions   341

CHAPTER 20 Inference about Variables:
Part III Review   353

PART IV:
Inference about Relationships | 363

CHAPTER 21 Two Categorical Variables:
The Chi-Square Test   365

CHAPTER 22 Inference for Regression   393

CHAPTER 23 One-Way Analysis of Variance:
Comparing Several Means   421

Additional Material (available on the *Essential Statistics* CD and Web site www.whfreeman.com/essentialstats)

CHAPTER 24 Nonparametric Tests

Commentary: Data Ethics

Applets for Interactive Learning

---

* Starred material is not required for later parts of the text.

CONTENTS

To the Instructor: About This Book

To the Student: What Lies Ahead in This Book

PART I:
Exploring Data | 1

CHAPTER 1
Picturing Distributions with Graphs 3

Individuals and variables / 3
Categorical variables: pie charts and bar graphs / 5
Quantitative variables: histograms / 10
Interpreting histograms / 12
Quantitative variables: stemplots / 16
Time plots / 19

CHAPTER 2
Describing Distributions with Numbers 29

Measuring center: the mean / 29
Measuring center: the median / 31
Comparing the mean and the median / 32
Measuring spread: the quartiles / 33
The five-number summary and boxplots / 34
Measuring spread: the standard deviation / 37
Choosing measures of center and spread / 39
Using technology / 40
Organizing a statistical problem / 40

CHAPTER 3
The Normal Distributions 51

Density curves / 51
Describing density curves / 54
Normal distributions / 55
The 68−95−99.7 rule / 57
The standard Normal distribution / 59
Finding Normal proportions / 61
Using the standard Normal table / 62
Finding a value given a proportion / 65

CHAPTER 4
Scatterplots and Correlation 73

Explanatory and response variables / 73
Displaying relationships: scatterplots / 74
Interpreting scatterplots / 76
Measuring linear association: correlation / 79
Facts about correlation / 80

CHAPTER 5
Regression 91

Regression lines / 91
The least-squares regression line / 94
Using technology / 95
Facts about least-squares regression / 97
Residuals / 98
Influential observations / 101
Cautions about correlation and regression / 103
Association does not imply causation / 105

CHAPTER 6
Exploring Data: Part I Review 115

Part I Summary / 115
Review Exercises / 116
Supplementary Exercises / 121

PART II:
From Exploration to Inference | 127

CHAPTER 7
Producing Data: Sampling 129

Population versus sample / 129
How to sample badly / 131
Simple random samples / 132
Inference about the population / 136
Cautions about sample surveys / 137

CHAPTER 8
Producing Data: Experiments 145

Observation versus experiment / 145
Subjects, factors, treatments / 147
How to experiment badly / 149
Randomized comparative experiments / 150
The logic of randomized comparative experiments / 153
Cautions about experimentation / 154
Matched pairs designs / 156

CHAPTER 9
Introducing Probability 163

The idea of probability / 164
Probability models / 166
Probability rules / 168
Discrete probability models / 171
Continuous probability models / 172
Random variables / 176

Starred material is not required for later parts of the text.

CHAPTER 10
Sampling Distributions   183
  Parameters and statistics / 183
  Statistical estimation and the law of
    large numbers / 184
  Sampling distributions / 187
  The mean and standard deviation of $\bar{x}$ / 189
  The central limit theorem / 190

CHAPTER 11
General Rules of Probability*   199
  Independence and the multiplication rule / 199
  The general addition rule / 203
  Conditional probability / 205
  The general multiplication rule / 207
  Tree diagrams / 208

CHAPTER 12
Binomial Distributions*   217
  The binomial setting and
    binomial distributions / 217
  Binomial distributions in
    statistical sampling / 218
  Binomial probabilities / 219
  Binomial mean and standard deviation / 221
  The Normal approximation to binomial
    distributions / 223

CHAPTER 13
Introduction to Inference   231
  The reasoning of statistical estimation / 232
  Confidence intervals for a
    population mean / 235
  The reasoning of statistical tests / 238
  Stating hypotheses / 241
  P-values / 242
  Tests for a population mean / 245
  Statistical significance / 248

CHAPTER 14
Thinking about Inference   257
  Conditions for inference in practice / 257
  How confidence intervals behave / 261
  Sample size for confidence intervals / 263
  How significance tests behave / 264

CHAPTER 15
From Exploration to Inference: Part II Review   273
  Part II Summary / 273
  Review Exercises / 275
  Supplementary Exercises / 279
  Optional Exercises / 281

PART III:
Inference about Variables | 283

CHAPTER 16
Inference about a Population Mean   285
  Conditions for inference about a mean / 285
  The t distributions / 286
  The one-sample t confidence interval / 288
  The one-sample t test / 291
  Using technology / 293
  Matched pairs t procedures / 295
  Robustness of t procedures / 297

CHAPTER 17
Two-Sample Problems   307
  Comparing two population means / 308
  Two-sample t procedures / 310
  Using technology / 315
  Robustness again / 317

CHAPTER 18
Inference about a Population Proportion   327
  The sample proportion $\hat{p}$ / 328
  Large-sample confidence intervals
    for a proportion / 330
  Choosing the sample size / 332
  Significance tests for a proportion / 334

CHAPTER 19
Comparing Two Proportions   341
  Two-sample problems: proportions / 341
  The sampling distribution of a difference between
    proportions / 342
  Large-sample confidence intervals for
    comparing proportions / 343
  Using technology / 344
  Significance tests for comparing
    proportions / 346

CHAPTER 20
Inference about Variables: Part III Review   353
  Statistics in Outline / 353
  Part III Summary / 354
  Review Exercises / 356
  Supplementary Exercises / 359

PART IV:
Inference about Relationships | 363

CHAPTER 21
Two Categorical Variables: The Chi-Square Test   365
  Two-way tables / 365
  Is there a relationship? Expected cell counts / 370
  The chi-square test / 372
  Data analysis for chi-square / 374
  Another use of the chi-square test / 378
  The chi-square distributions / 380
  The chi-square test for goodness of fit / 382

CHAPTER 22
Inference for Regression   393
  Conditions for regression inference / 395
  Estimating the parameters / 396
  Using technology / 399
  Testing the hypothesis of no linear relationship / 401
  Testing lack of correlation / 403
  Confidence intervals for the regression slope / 404
  Inference about prediction / 405
  Checking the conditions for inference / 408

CHAPTER 23
One-Way Analysis of Variance:
Comparing Several Means   421
  The analysis of variance F test / 423
  Using technology / 425

The idea of analysis of variance / 429
Conditions for ANOVA / 431
F distributions and degrees of freedom / 435

NOTES AND DATA SOURCES / 445

TABLES / 463
  TABLE A   Standard Normal Probabilities / 464
  TABLE B   Random Digits / 466
  TABLE C t Distribution Critical Values / 467
  TABLE D   Chi-Square Distribution Critical Values / 468

ANSWERS TO SELECTED EXERCISES / 469

INDEX / 495

Additional Material (available on the *Essential Statistics* CD and Web site www.whfreeman.com/essentialstats)

CHAPTER 24
Nonparametric Tests
  Comparing two samples: the Wilcoxon rank
    sum test
  The Normal approximation for W
  Using technology
  What hypotheses does Wilcoxon test?
  Dealing with ties in rank tests
  Matched pairs: the Wilcoxon signed rank test
  The Normal approximation for W^+
  Dealing with ties in the signed rank test

Commentary: Data Ethics

Applets for Interactive Learning

About This Book

Essential Statistics is what its name suggests: a basic introduction to statistical ideas and methods that aims to equip students to carry out common statistical procedures and to follow statistical reasoning in their fields of study and in their future employment.

Guiding principles

The book is based on three principles: balanced content, the importance of ideas, and experience with data.

Balanced content. Statistics courses have traditionally emphasized probability-based *inference* (confidence intervals and significance tests). *Essential Statistics* provides a careful introduction to inference, but also introduces the ideas and methods of *data analysis* and *data production*. Data analysis is the systematic exploration of data to extract overall patterns and important deviations from those patterns. It is an essential preliminary to inference (because inference requires clean data) and also applies in many settings not suitable for formal inference. Designing data production is also at the heart of statistics in practice. Random sampling and randomized comparative experiments are the most important contributions of statistics to science. Inference is most reliable in these settings, and flaws in the production of data are by far the most common serious statistical sins.

The importance of ideas. A first course in statistics introduces many skills, from making a stemplot and calculating a correlation to choosing and carrying out a significance test. Anyone who makes serious use of statistics will need some specific procedures not taught in her college stat course. And we all need to understand and evaluate statistical arguments more often than we need to "do statistics" ourselves. For these reasons, a firm grasp of basic ideas—the influence of outliers, observation versus experiment, what statistical significance does and doesn't say—is the most important goal of an introduction to statistics. Formulas without guiding principles do students little good once the final exam is past. It is worth the time to slow down a bit and explain the ideas.

Experience with data. Ideas are best learned in context, not in the abstract. Because statistics is the science of data, statistical ideas are best learned in the context of working with data. Moreover, even quite basic statistical skills are very often useful in academics and in employment. *Essential Statistics* is a practical text, full of data from many fields of study and from everyday life. Experience with data means more than experience manipulating numbers, because data are more than mere numbers. Data are numbers with a context that should play a role in making sense of the numbers and in stating conclusions. I hope that students will both learn to make correct calculations and graphs and to then draw conclusions that connect the data back to their context.

Accessibility

Essential Statistics is a straightforward text that presents "just the basics" in a logical order with little adornment and uses a number of pedagogical devices to help students learn. One principle of writing for beginners is not to try to tell your students everything you know. Another principle is to offer frequent stopping points. *Essential Statistics* presents its content in relatively short chapters, each ending with a summary and two levels of exercises. Within chapters, a few "Apply Your Knowledge" exercises follow each new idea or skill for a quick check of basic mastery—and also to mark off digestible bites of material. Each of the first three parts of the book ends with a review chapter that presents many additional exercises without the "I just studied that" context, thus asking for another level of learning. Many instructors will find that the review chapters appear at the right points for pre-examination review. The text also provides a number of summary aids to learning. Look, for example, at the flowcharts and summary boxes inside the front cover and at the figures that illustrate the key idea of a sampling distribution (pages 188 and 329).

There are two qualifications to the "just the basics" principle. First, "the basics" include ideas as well as methods. Knowing how to carry out the mechanics of a *t* test without being able to explain what a significant test result means is of little lasting value to a student. Important ideas appear in the exposition of data analysis and data production, and students find these straightforward. Inference is harder, so that the introduction to inference in Chapters 13 and 14 is the most challenging part of the text. I have tried to ease the way by isolating this introduction from the important practical issues of inference, and the concepts are reinforced in later chapters. But these chapters do require concentration.

The second qualification concerns the place of probability in a course dedicated to data-oriented statistics. It is common to present considerably more probability than is needed to grasp the statistical content. I offer "just the basics" in Chapters 9 and 10. Chapter 9 is a quite informal introduction to probability. Chapter 10 concentrates on the key idea of a sampling distribution, including the law of large numbers and the central limit theorem. I prefer to proceed directly from Chapter 10 to the presentation of inference in Chapter 13. This avoids expending students' limited supply of mental stamina on the difficult but less essential topic of formal probability theory. Instructors who need more probability will find it in the optional Chapters 11 and 12.

Preparation

Essential Statistics is designed to be accessible to two-year and four-year college and university students with limited quantitative background. The basic requirement is the ability to read and use simple equations without having each step parsed. Each new formula is immediately illustrated by a concrete example, and the making and interpretation of statistical graphics receive the same attention.

Automating calculations and graphics increases students' ability to complete problems, reduces their frustration, and helps them concentrate on ideas and problem recognition rather than mechanics. For calculations, a "two-variable statistics" calculator, with functions for correlation and the least-squares regression line as well as for the mean and standard deviation, is adequate for all but the more elaborate procedures in Part IV. Because "always look at your data" is one of the first commandments of practical statistics, graphs are almost as common as calculations. A graphing calculator or software that automates graphing as well as calculations is therefore very helpful.

Essential Statistics does not assume or require use of software except in Part IV. Even there, exercises based on output provided in the text allow basic coverage without software. The text does accommodate software use and tries to convince students that they are gaining knowledge that will enable them to read and use output from almost any source. The regular "Using Technology" sections display and comment on output from the same three technologies, representing graphing calculators (the Texas Instruments TI-83 or TI-84), spreadsheets (Microsoft Excel), and statistical software (Minitab). The output always concerns one of the main teaching examples, so that students can compare text and output.

Origins

Instructors who have seen my other texts will recognize that *Essential Statistics* is based on the new 5th edition of the successful text *The Basic Practice of Statistics* (*BPS*). It is more than 30% shorter than *BPS* in word count, and the physical size and cost of the book have been further reduced by devices such as setting exercises in two columns and reducing the size of figures. In addition to removing almost all of the optional material in *BPS*, I have carefully rewritten the text to shorten and simplify explanations. Although the reduction in length and detail is often subtle, there are considerable savings in places. The key Chapters 13 and 14 that introduce inference, for example, are about 25% shorter than the corresponding chapters in *BPS*.

Some instructors will find the shorter-and-simpler book ideal for their students. Others will miss some of the fine points and added material that appear in *BPS*. Two features of *BPS* that are loved by some instructors and ignored by others have been moved to the text CD and Web site. These are the essay on data ethics and 28 exercises that guide use of a set of interactive applets to aid learning. I like and use both of these features, but the applets in particular naturally belong to electronic, rather than print, media.

Why did you do that?

There is no single best way to organize our presentation of statistics to beginners. That said, my choices reflect thinking about both content and pedagogy. Here are comments on several "frequently asked questions" about the order and selection of material in *Essential Statistics*.

Why does the distinction between population and sample not appear in Part I? There is more to statistics than inference. In fact, statistical inference is appropriate only in rather special circumstances. The chapters in Part I present tools and tactics for describing data—any data. These tools and tactics do not depend on the idea of inference from sample to population. Many data sets in these chapters (for example, the several sets of data about the 50 states) do not lend themselves to inference because they represent an entire population. John Tukey of Bell Labs and Princeton, the philosopher of modern data analysis, insisted that the population-sample distinction be avoided when it is not relevant. He used the word "batch" for data sets in general. I see no need for a special word, but I think Tukey was right.

Why not begin with data production? It is true that the natural flow of a planned study is from design to data analysis to inference. But in their future employment most students will use statistics mainly in settings other than planned research studies. Doing data analysis first emphasizes that data-analytic techniques apply to any data. This order also calms students made nervous by the word "statistics," who find data analysis relatively easy and clearly useful. Data production (Chapters 7 and 8) then opens Part II. The role of random selection in sampling and experimentation motivates the study of probability and leads on to inference.

Why do Normal distributions appear in Part I? Density curves such as the Normal curves are just another tool to describe the distribution of a quantitative variable, along with stemplots, histograms, and boxplots. Professional statistical software offers to make density curves from data just as it offers histograms. I prefer not to suggest that this material is essentially tied to probability, as the traditional order does. And I find it helpful to break up the indigestible lump of probability that troubles students so much. Meeting Normal distributions early does this and strengthens the "probability distributions are like data distributions" way of approaching probability.

Why not delay correlation and regression until late in the course, as was traditional? *Essential Statistics* begins by offering experience working with data and gives a conceptual structure for this nonmathematical but essential part of statistics. Students profit from more experience with data and from seeing the conceptual structure worked out in relations among variables as well as in describing single-variable data. Correlation and least-squares regression are very important descriptive tools and are often used in settings where there is no population-sample distinction, such as studies of all of a firm's employees. I want students to think about what relationships lie behind the data (confounding, lurking variables, association doesn't imply causation, and so on). Inference in the correlation and regression setting is a bit complex, demands software, and often comes right at the end of the course. I find that delaying all mention of correlation and regression to that point means that students often don't master the basic uses and properties of these methods. I consider Chapters 4 and 5 (correlation and regression) essential and Chapter 22 (regression inference) optional.

Why use the *z* procedures for a population mean to introduce the reasoning of inference? This is a pedagogical issue, not a question of statistics in practice. I hope that introducing the reasoning of inference in isolation from the complications of its use in practice will help students grasp this essential but subtle topic. Chapter 13 therefore introduces inference about a population mean under Simple Conditions (see page 232): true simple random sample, exactly Normal population, and known population standard deviation σ. All three conditions are unrealistic. All the issues of practice—robustness against lack of Normality and application when the data aren't an SRS, as well as the need to estimate σ—are put off until, with the reasoning in hand, we discuss the practically useful t procedures. This separation of initial reasoning from messier practice works well.

The primary alternative is to begin with inference about a population proportion. This introduces many distractions: no exact Normal sampling distribution, but a Normal approximation to a discrete distribution; use of $\hat{p}$ in both the numerator and denominator of the test statistic, to estimate both the parameter p and $\hat{p}$'s own standard deviation; loss of the direct link between test and confidence interval; and the need to avoid small and moderate sample sizes because the Normal approximation for the test is quite unreliable.

Why didn't you cover Topic X? Introductory texts ought not to be encyclopedic. I chose topics on two grounds: they are the most commonly used in practice, and they are suitable vehicles for learning broader statistical ideas. Students who have completed the core of the book, Chapters 1 to 10 and 13 to 20, will have little difficulty moving on to more elaborate methods. Chapters 21 to 23 offer a choice of slightly more advanced topics.

I have enjoyed the opportunity to once again rethink how to help beginning students achieve a practical grasp of basic statistics. What students actually learn is not identical to what we teachers think we have "covered," so the virtues of concentrating on the essentials are considerable. I hope that *Essential Statistics* offers a mix of concrete skills and clearly explained concepts that will help many teachers guide their students toward useful knowledge.

I am grateful to colleagues from two-year and four-year colleges and universities who commented on *Essential Statistics*:

Murray Besler,
    Langara College
Patti B. Collings,
    Brigham Young University
Karen A. Estes,
    St. Petersburg College
Patricia B. Humphrey,
    Georgia Southern University

Linda M. Myers,
    Brookdale Community College
Mary R. Parker,
    Austin Community College
Robb Sinn,
    North Georgia College & State University
Dave Tomkins,
    Thompson Rivers University
Mikhail Turegun,
    Oklahoma City Community College

I would also like to thank the reviewers of *The Basic Practice of Statistics*, 5th edition, upon which *Essential Statistics* is based:

Brad Bailey,
    North Georgia College and State University
E. N. Barron,
    Loyola University, Chicago
Jennifer Beineke,
    Western New England College
Diane Benner,
    Harrisburg Area Community College
Zoubir Benzaid,
    University of Wisconsin, Oshkosh
Jennifer Borrello,
    Baylor University
Smiley Cheng,
    University of Manitoba, Winnipeg
Patti Collings,
    Brigham Young University

Tadd Colver,
    Purdue University
James Curl,
    Modesto Junior College
Jonathan Duggins,
    Virginia Tech
Chris Edwards,
    University of Wisconsin, Oshkosh
Margaret Elrich,
    Georgia Perimeter College
Karen Estes,
    St. Petersburg College
Eugene Galperin,
    East Stroudsburg University
Mark Gebert,
    Eastern Kentucky University

Kim Gilbert,
Clayton State University

Aaron Gladish,
Austin Community College

Ellen Gundlach,
Purdue University

Arjun Gupta,
Bowling Green State University

Jeanne Hill,
Baylor University

Dawn Holmes,
*University of California,
Santa Barbara*

Patricia Humphrey,
Georgia Southern University

Thomas Ilvento,
University of Delaware

Mark Jacobson,
University of Northern Iowa

Marc Kirschenbaum,
John Carroll University

Greg Knofczynski,
Armstrong Atlantic State University

Zhongshan Li,
Georgia State University

Michael Lichter,
University of Buffalo

Tom Linton,
Central College

William Liu,
Bowling Green—Firelands College

Amy Maddox,
Grand Rapids Community College

Steve Marsden,
Glendale Community College

Darcy Mays,
*Virginia Commonwealth
University*

Andrew McDougall,
Montclair State University

Bill Meisel,
*Florida Community College at
Jacksonville*

Nancy Mendell,
*State University of New York,
Stony Brook*

Lynne Nielsen,
Brigham Young University

Melvin Nyman,
Alma College

Darlene Olsen,
Norwich University

Eric Packard,
Mesa State University

Mary Parker,
*Austin Community College, Rio Grande
Campus*

Don Porter,
Beloit College

Bob Price,
East Tennessee State University

Sarah Quesen,
West Virginia University

Asoka Ramanayake,
University of Wisconsin, Oshkosh

Eric Rdurud,
St. Cloud State University

Christoph Richter,
Queens University

Scott Richter,
*University of North Carolina,
Greensboro*

Corlis Robe,
East Tennessee State University

Deborah Rumsey,
Ohio State University

Therese Shelton,
Southwestern University

Eric Shulz,
Walla Walla Community College

Rob Sinn,
*North Georgia College & State
University*

Eugenia Skirta,
East Stroudsburg University

Dianna Spence,
*North Georgia College and State
University*

Suzhong Tian,
Husson College

Suzanne Tourville,
Columbia College

Christopher Tripler,
Endicott College

Gail Tudor,
Husson College

Ramin Vakilian,
  California State University, Northridge
David Vlieger,
  Northwest Missouri State University
Joseph Walker,
  Georgia State University

Steve Waters,
  Pacific Union College
Yuanhui Xiao,
  Georgia State University
Yichuan Zhao,
  Georgia State University

Special thanks are due to Brigitte Baldi (California State University, Long Beach) and Bradley Hartlaub (Kenyon College) for providing exercises, and to Ann Cannon (Cornell College) for carefully checking the manuscript.

I am also grateful to Craig Bleyer, Ruth Baruth, Bruce Kaplan, Shona Burke, Mary Louise Byrd, Vicki Tomaselli, Pamela Bruton, and the other editorial and design professionals who have contributed greatly to the attractiveness of this book.

Finally, I am indebted to the many statistics teachers with whom I have discussed the teaching of our subject over many years; to people from diverse fields with whom I have worked to understand data; and especially to students whose compliments and complaints have changed and improved my teaching. Working with teachers, colleagues in other disciplines, and students constantly reminds me of the importance of hands-on experience with data and of statistical thinking in an era when computer routines quickly handle statistical details.

David S. Moore

For Students

NEW! STATS P⦿RTAL

courses.bfwpub.com/essentialstats

(**Access code or online purchase required.**) *StatsPortal*® is the digital gateway to *Essential Statistics*, designed to enrich the course and enhance students' study skills through a collection of Web-based tools. *StatsPortal* integrates a rich suite of diagnostic, assessment, tutorial, and enrichment features, enabling students to master statistics at their own pace. It is organized around three main teaching and learning components:

1. Interactive eBook integrates a complete and customizable online version of the text with all of its media resources. Students can quickly search the text and can personalize the eBook just as they would the print version, with highlighting, bookmarking, and note-taking features. Instructors can add, hide, and reorder content, integrate their own material, and highlight key text.

2. Resources organizes all of *Essential Statistics* resources into one location:

Student Resources

- **StatTutor** provides tutorials tied directly to the textbook and contains videos, applets, and animations.
- **Statistical Applets** help students master key concepts.
- **Stats@Work Simulations** put students in the role of consultants, helping them better understand statistics within the context of real-life scenarios.
- **EESEE Case Studies** developed by The Ohio State University Statistics Department teach students to apply their statistical skills by exploring actual case studies, using real data, and answering questions about the study.
- **CrunchIt! 2.0**℠
- **Data sets** are provided in ASCII, Excel, JMP, Minitab, TI, SPSS, and S-Plus.
- **Student Study Guide with Selected Solutions** includes explanations of crucial concepts with step-by-step models of important statistical techniques.
- **Statistical Software Manuals** for TI-83/84, Minitab, Excel, JMP, and SPSS provide instruction, examples, and exercises using specific statistical software packages.
- **Interactive Table Reader** allows students to quickly find values in any of the statistical tables used in the course.

- **Tables and Formulas** provide each table and formula from each chapter.
- **Additional Material:** Chapter 24 Nonparametric Tests, Data Ethics Commentary, and Applet-based Exercises.

Resources for Instructors only

- **Instructor's Guide with Solutions** offers teaching suggestions and chapter comments.
- **Test Bank** offers hundreds of multiple-choice questions.
- **Lecture PowerPoint Slides** offer a detailed lecture presentation for each chapter of *Essential Statistics*.
- **Activities and Projects** offer ideas for projects for Web-based exploration that encourage students to write critically about statistics.
- **i>clicker Questions** help instructors query students using i>clicker.
- **SolutionMaster** is a Web-based version of the solutions in the Instructor's Guide with Solutions. This easy-to-use tool allows instructors to generate a solution file for any set of homework exercises. Solutions can be downloaded in PDF format for convenient printing and posting. For more information or a demonstration, contact your local W. H. Freeman sales representative.

3. Assignment Center (**For Instructors Only**) organizes assignments and guides instructors through an easy-to-create assignment process with access to questions from the Test Bank, Web Quizzes, and exercises from the text, including many algorithmic problems.

Online Study Center 2.0
www.whfreeman.com/osc/essentialstats
(**Access code or online purchase required.**)
This premium Web-based study alternative helps students pinpoint where their study time should be focused, then provides all the resources needed to improve their comprehension of troublesome areas. Before beginning each chapter, students take a **Self-Test** to assess their knowledge of the material. The OSC then generates a **Detailed Study Plan** linking to the online resources relevant to the questions they answered incorrectly.

The OSC includes all the student and instructor resources included in *StatsPortal*, except for the Assignment Center and the eBook.

Book Companion Site at www.whfreeman.com/essentialstats, featuring

- Interactive statistical applets
- Data sets
- Exercises and self-quizzes to help students prepare for tests
- Key tables and formulas summary sheet
- Tables appendix from the text in PDF format for quick, easy reference
- Additional material: Chapter 24 Nonparametric Tests, Data Ethics Commentary, and Applet-based Exercises

Interactive Student CD-ROM

Included with every new copy of *Essential Statistics*, the CD contains access to the additional material, applets, and data sets found on the Companion Web site.

Software Manuals

Software manuals covering Minitab, JMP, Excel, SPSS, and TI-83/84 are offered within *StatsPortal* and the Online Study Center. These manuals are available in printed versions through custom publishing.

Study Guide with Selected Solutions, 1-4292-3394-X

This guide offers students explanations of crucial concepts in each section of *Essential Statistics*, plus detailed solutions to key text problems and stepped-through models of important statistical techniques.

For Instructors

The Instructor's Web site, www.whfreeman.com/essentialstats

Password protected, the instructor's Web site features access to all student Web materials on the companion Web site, plus

- Instructor version of EESEE (Electronic Encyclopedia of Statistical Examples and Exercises), with solutions to the exercises in the student version.
- PowerPoint slides containing all textbook figures and tables.
- Lecture PowerPoint slides offering a detailed lecture presentation of statistical concepts covered in each chapter of *Essential Statistics*.
- Full answers to the supplementary applet-based exercises on the student Web site.

Instructor's Guide with Solutions, 1-4292-3393-1

This printed guide includes full solutions to all exercises and provides video and Internet resources and sample examinations. It also contains brief discussions of the *Essential Statistics* approach for each chapter.

Test Bank, printed, 1-4292-3494-6; CD (Windows and Mac on one disk), 1-4292-3550-0

The Test Bank contains hundreds of multiple-choice questions. With the CD version, questions can easily be downloaded, edited, and resequenced.

Enhanced Instructor's Resource CD-ROM, 1-4292-3395-8

Allows instructors to search and export (by key term or chapter) all the material from the student CD, plus

- All text images and tables
- Instructor's Guide with Solutions
- PowerPoint files and lecture slides
- Test Bank files

Course Management Systems

W. H. Freeman and Company provides course cartridges for Blackboard, WebCT (Campus Edition and Vista), and Angel course management systems. Upon request, we also provide courses for users of Desire2Learn and Moodle.

i>clicker Radio Frequency Classroom Response System
www.iclicker.com

Developed for educators by educators, i>clicker is the easiest-to-use and most flexible classroom response system available.

What Lies Ahead in This Book

What genes are active in a tissue? Answering this question can unravel basic questions in biology, distinguish cancer cells from normal cells, and distinguish between closely related types of cancer. To learn the answer, apply the tissue to a "microarray" that contains thousands of snippets of DNA arranged in a grid on a chip about the size of your thumb. As DNA in the tissue binds to the snippets in the array, special recorders pick up spots of light of varying color and intensity across the grid and store what they see as numbers.

What's hot in popular music this week? SoundScan knows. SoundScan collects data electronically from the cash registers in more than 14,000 retail outlets and also collects data on download sales from Web sites. When you buy a CD or download a digital track, the checkout scanner or Web site is probably telling SoundScan what you bought. Sound-Scan provides this information to *Billboard* magazine, MTV, and VH1, as well as to record companies and artists' agents.

Should women take hormones such as estrogen after menopause, when natural production of these hormones ends? In 1992, several major medical organizations said "Yes." In particular, women who took hormones seemed to reduce their risk of a heart attack by 35% to 50%. The risks of taking hormones appeared small compared with the benefits. But in 2002, the National Institutes of Health declared these findings wrong. Use of hormones after menopause immediately plummeted. Both recommendations were based on extensive studies. What happened?

DNA microarrays, SoundScan, and medical studies all produce data (numerical facts), and lots of them. Using data effectively is a large and growing part of most professions. Reacting to data is part of everyday life. That's why statistics is important:

> **STATISTICS IS THE SCIENCE OF LEARNING FROM DATA**

Data are numbers, but they are not "just numbers." **Data are numbers with a context.** The number 10.5, for example, carries no information by itself. But if we hear that a friend's new baby weighed 10.5 pounds at birth, we congratulate her on the healthy size of the child. The context engages our background knowledge and allows us to make judgments. We know that a baby weighing 10.5 pounds is quite large, and that a human baby is unlikely to weigh 10.5 ounces or 10.5 kilograms. The context makes the number informative.

The purpose of *Essential Statistics* is to give you a working knowledge of the ideas and tools of practical statistics. We will divide practical statistics into three main areas:

1. **Data analysis** concerns methods and strategies for exploring, organizing, and describing data using graphs and numerical summaries. Your thoughtful exploration allows data to illuminate reality. Part I of this book (Chapters 1 to 6) discusses data analysis.

2. **Data production** provides methods for producing data that can give clear answers to specific questions. Where data come from is often the most important limitation on

their usefulness. Basic concepts about how to select samples and design experiments are the most influential ideas in statistics. These concepts are the subject of Chapters 7 and 8.

3. **Statistical inference** moves beyond the data in hand to draw conclusions about some wider universe. Statistical conclusions aren't Yes or No answers—they must take into account variability among people, animals, or objects and uncertainty in data. To describe variation and uncertainty, inference uses the language of probability, introduced in Chapters 9 and 10. Because we are concerned with practice rather than theory, we need only a limited knowledge of probability. Chapters 11 and 12 offer more probability for those who want it. Chapters 13 and 14 discuss the reasoning of statistical inference. These chapters are the key to the rest of the book. Chapters 16 to 20 present inference as used in practice in the most common settings. Chapters 21 to 23 concern more advanced or specialized kinds of inference.

Because data are numbers with a context, doing statistics means more than manip-ulating numbers. You must **state** a problem in its real-world context, **plan** your specific statistical work in detail, **solve** the problem by making the necessary graphs and calcu-lations, and **conclude** by explaining what your findings say about the real-world setting. We'll make regular use of this four-step process to encourage good habits that go beyond graphs and calculations to ask, "What do the data tell me?"

Statistics does involve lots of calculating and graphing. The text presents the tech-niques you need, but you should use technology to automate calculations and graphs as much as possible. Because the big ideas of statistics don't depend on any particular level of access to technology, *Essential Statistics* docs not require software or a graphing calcula-tor until we reach the more advanced methods in Part IV of the text. Even if you make little use of technology, you should look at the "Using Technology" sections throughout the book. You will see at once that you can read and apply the output from almost any technology used for statistical calculations. The ideas really are more important than the details of how to do the calculations.

Unless you have constant access to software or a graphing calculator, *you will need a basic calculator with some built-in statistical functions.* Specifically, your calculator should find means and standard deviations and calculate correlations and regression lines. Look for a calculator that claims to do "two-variable statistics" or mentions "regression."

Although ability to carry out statistical procedures is very useful in academics and em-ployment, the most important asset you can gain from the study of statistics is an under-standing of the big ideas about working with data. *Essential Statistics* tries to explain the most important ideas of statistics, not just teach methods. Some examples of big ideas that you will meet (one from each of the three areas of statistics) are "always plot your data," "randomized comparative experiments." and "statistical significance."

You learn statistics by doing statistical problems. As you read, you will see several levels of exercises, arranged to help you learn. Short "Apply Your Knowledge" problem sets appear after each major idea. These are straightforward exercises that help you solidify the main points as you read. Be sure you can do these exercises before going on. The end-of-chapter exercises begin with multiple-choice "Check Your Skills" exercises (with all answers in the back of the book). Use them to check your grasp of the basics. The regular "Chapter Exercises" help you combine all the ideas of a chapter. Finally, the three Part Review chapters (Chapters 6, 15, and 20) look back over major blocks of learning, with many review exercises. At each step you are given less advance knowledge of exactly what statistical ideas and skills the problems will require, so each type of exercise requires more understanding.

The key to learning is persistence. The main ideas of statistics, like the main ideas of any important subject, took a long time to discover and take some time to master. The gain will be worth the pain.

Exploring Data

PART I

EXPLORING DATA:
Variables and
Distributions

CHAPTER 1 Picturing
Distributions with Graphs

CHAPTER 2 Describing
Distributions with Numbers

CHAPTER 3 The Normal
Distributions

EXPLORING DATA:
Relationships

CHAPTER 4 Scatterplots and
Correlation

CHAPTER 5 Regression

CHAPTER 6 Part I Review

 hat do the data say?" is the first question we ask in any statistical study. *Data analysis* answers this question by open-ended exploration of the data. The tools of data analysis are graphs such as histograms and scatterplots and numerical measures such as means and correlations. At least as important as the tools are principles that organize our thinking as we examine data. The six chapters in Part I present the principles and tools of statistical data analysis. They equip you with skills that are immediately useful whenever you deal with numbers.

These chapters reflect the strong emphasis on exploring data that characterizes modern statistics. Sometimes we hope to draw conclusions that apply to a setting that goes beyond the data in hand. This is *statistical inference*, the topic of much of the rest of the book. Data analysis is essential if we are to trust the results of inference, but data analysis isn't just preparation for inference. Roughly speaking, you can always do data analysis but inference requires rather special conditions.

One of the organizing principles of data analysis is to first look at one thing at a time and then at relationships. Our presentation follows this principle. In Chapters 1, 2, and 3 you will study *variables and their distributions*. Chapters 4 and 5 concern *relationships among variables*. Chapter 6 reviews this part of the text.

AP Photo/Gracy Altaffer

New citizens take the oath of allegiance. Many Americans were born in other countries (Example 1.4).

Picturing Distributions with Graphs

IN THIS CHAPTER
WE COVER...

- Individuals and variables
- Categorical variables: pie charts and bar graphs
- Quantitative variables: histograms
- Interpreting histograms
- Quantitative variables: stemplots
- Time plots

Statistics is the science of data. To work with data, we begin by organizing our thinking.

Individuals and variables

Any set of data contains information about some group of *individuals*. The information is organized in *variables*.

> **INDIVIDUALS AND VARIABLES**
>
> **Individuals** are the objects described by a set of data. Individuals may be people, but they may also be animals or things.
>
> A **variable** is any characteristic of an individual. A variable can take different values for different individuals.

When you examine a set of data, ask *what individuals* the data describe and *what variables* the data contain. Some variables, like a person's sex or college major, simply place individuals into categories. Others, like height and grade point average, take numerical values for which we can do arithmetic. It makes sense to give an average income for a company's employees, but it does not make sense to give an "average" sex.

CATEGORICAL AND QUANTITATIVE VARIABLES

A **categorical variable** places an individual into one of several groups or categories.

A **quantitative variable** takes numerical values for which arithmetic operations such as adding and averaging make sense. The values of a quantitative variable are usually recorded in a **unit of measurement** such as seconds or kilograms.

EXAMPLE 1.1 The American Community Survey

The Census Bureau's American Community Survey collects data from 3,000,000 households each year, chosen at random from all the households in the country. You can view the detailed data online, though of course the identities of people and households are protected. If you choose the file of data on people, the *individuals* are the people living in the households contacted by the survey. Over 100 variables are recorded for each individual. Figure 1.1 displays a small part of the data. Most data tables follow this format—each row records data on one individual, and each column contains the values of one *variable* for all the individuals.

Translated from the Census Bureau's abbreviations, the variables are

SERIALNO   An identifying number for the household.
PWGTP   Weight in pounds.
AGEP   Age in years.
JWMNP   Travel time to work in minutes.
SCHL   Highest level of education. The categories are designated by numbers. For example, 9 = high school graduate, 10 = some college but no degree, and 13 = bachelor's degree.
SEX   Sex, designated by 1 = male and 2 = female.
WAGP   Wage and salary income last year, in dollars.

Look at the highlighted row in Figure 1.1. This individual is a 53-year-old man who weighs 234 pounds, travels 10 minutes to work, has a bachelor's degree, and earned $83,000 last year.

FIGURE 1.1

A spreadsheet displaying data from the American Community Survey, for Example 1.1.

	SERIALNO	PWGTP	AGEP	JWMNP	SCHL	SEX	WAGP
1	SERIALNO	PWGTP	AGEP	JWMNP	SCHL	SEX	WAGP
2	283	187	66		6	1	24000
3	283	158	66		9	2	0
4	323	176	54	10	12	2	11900
5	346	339	37	10	11	1	6000
6	346	91	27	10	10	2	30000
7	370	234	53	10	13	1	83000
8	370	181	46	15	10	2	74000
9	370	155	18		9	2	0
10	487	233	26		14	2	800
11	487	146	23		12	2	8000
12	511	236	53		9	2	0
13	511	131	53		11	1	0
14	515	213	38		11	2	12500
15	515	194	40		9	1	800
16	515	221	18	20	9	1	2500
17	515	193	11		3	1	

Each row in the spreadsheet contains data on one individual.

In addition to the household serial number, there are six variables. Education and sex are categorical variables. The values for education and sex are stored as numbers, but these numbers are just labels for the categories and have no units of measurement. The other four variables are quantitative. Their values do have units. These variables are weight in pounds, age in years, travel time in minutes, and income in dollars. ■

When you examine data, pay attention to the *exact definition* of each variable. You might, for example, look into exactly what the Census Bureau means by "wage and salary income." Pay attention also to the *unit of measurement* of each quantitative variable. Weight in Example 1.1 is measured in pounds, but most countries would measure weight in kilograms.

APPLY YOUR KNOWLEDGE

1.1 Fuel economy. Here is a small part of a data set that describes the fuel economy (in miles per gallon) of 2008 model motor vehicles:

Make and model	Vehicle type	Transmission type	Number of cylinders	City mpg	Highway mpg
Aston Martin Vantage	Two-seater	Manual	8	12	19
Honda Civic	Subcompact	Automatic	4	25	36
Toyota Prius	Midsize	Automatic	4	48	45
Chevrolet Impala	Large	Automatic	6	18	29

(a) What are the individuals in this data set?

(b) For each individual, what variables are given? Which of these variables are categorical and which are quantitative?

1.2 Students and TV. You plan to study the television-viewing habits of college students. Describe two categorical variables and two quantitative variables that you might measure for each student. Give the units of measurement for the quantitative variables.

Categorical variables: pie charts and bar graphs

Statistical tools and ideas help us examine data in order to describe their main features. This examination is called **exploratory data analysis.** Like an explorer crossing unknown lands, we want first to simply describe what we see. Here are two principles that help us organize our exploration of a set of data.

exploratory data analysis

1. Begin by examining each variable by itself. Then move on to study the relationships among the variables.
2. Begin with a graph or graphs. Then add numerical summaries of specific aspects of the data.

We will follow these principles in organizing our learning. Chapters 1 to 3 present methods for describing a single variable. We study relationships among several variables in Chapters 4 and 5. In each case, we begin with graphical displays, then add numerical summaries for more complete description.

The proper choice of graph depends on the nature of the variable. To examine a single variable, we usually want to display its *distribution*.

DISTRIBUTION OF A VARIABLE

The **distribution** of a variable tells us what values it takes and how often it takes these values.

The values of a categorical variable are labels for the categories. The **distribution of a categorical variable** lists the categories and gives either the count or the percent of individuals that fall in each category.

EXAMPLE 1.2   **Which major?**

About 1.6 million first-year students enroll in colleges and universities each year. What do they plan to study? Here are data on the percents of first-year students who plan to major in several discipline areas:[1]

Field of study	Percent of students
Arts and humanities	12.8
Biological sciences	7.6
Business	17.4
Education	9.9
Engineering	8.3
Physical sciences	3.1
Professional	14.6
Social science	10.7
Technical	1.2
Other majors	14.1
Total	99.7

It's a good idea to check data for consistency. The percents should add to 100%. In fact, they add to 99.7%. What happened? Each percent is rounded to the nearest tenth. The exact percents would add to 100, but the rounded percents only come close. This is **roundoff error.** Roundoff errors don't point to mistakes in our work, just to the effect of rounding off results. ■

roundoff error

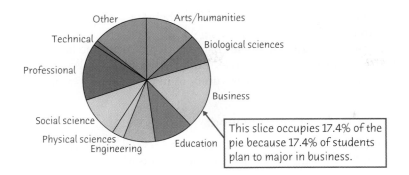

This slice occupies 17.4% of the pie because 17.4% of students plan to major in business.

FIGURE 1.2
You can use a pie chart to display the distribution of a categorical variable. Here is a pie chart of the distribution of intended majors of students entering college.

Columns of numbers take time to read. You can use a pie chart or a bar graph to display the distribution of a categorical variable more vividly. Figures 1.2 and 1.3 illustrate these displays for the distribution of intended college majors.

Pie charts show the distribution of a categorical variable as a "pie" whose slices are sized by the counts or percents for the categories. Pie charts are awkward to make by hand, but software will do the job for you. *A pie chart must include all the categories that make up a whole. Use a pie chart only when you want to emphasize each category's relation to the whole.* We need the "Other majors" category in Example 1.2 to complete the whole (all intended majors) and allow us to make the pie chart in Figure 1.2.

Bar graphs represent each category as a bar. The bar heights show the category counts or percents. Bar graphs are easier to make than pie charts and also easier to read. Figure 1.3 displays two bar graphs of the data on intended majors. The first orders the bars alphabetically by field of study (with "Other" at the end). It is often better to arrange the

pie chart

bar graph

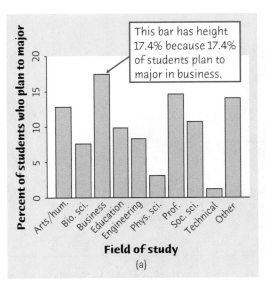

This bar has height 17.4% because 17.4% of students plan to major in business.

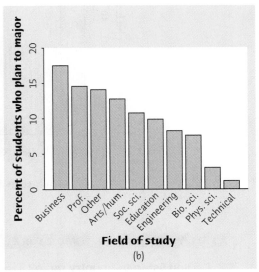

FIGURE 1.3
Bar graphs of the distribution of intended majors of students entering college. In (a), the bars follow the alphabetical order of fields of study. In (b), the same bars appear in order of height.

bars in order of height, as in Figure 1.3(b). This helps us immediately see which majors appear most often.

Bar graphs are more flexible than pie charts. Both pie charts and bar graphs can display the distribution of a categorical variable. But a bar graph can also compare any set of quantities that are measured in the same units, as in the following example.

EXAMPLE 1.3   I love my iPod!

The rating service Arbitron asked adults who used several high-tech devices and services whether they "loved" using them. Here are the percents who said they did:[2]

Device or service	Percent of users who love it
Blackberry or similar device	21
Broadband Internet access	41
Cable TV	20
Digital video recorder	32
High-definition television	34
iPod	45
MP3 player other than iPod	25
Pay TV channels (such as HBO)	16
Satellite radio	33

We can't make a pie chart to display these data. Each percent in the table refers to a different device or service, not to parts of a single whole. Figure 1.4 is a bar graph comparing the nine devices and services. We have again arranged the bars in order of height. ■

FIGURE 1.4

You can use a bar graph to compare quantities that are not part of a whole. This bar graph compares the percents of users who say they "love" using various devices or services, for Example 1.3.

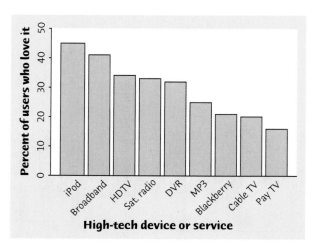

APPLY YOUR KNOWLEDGE

1.3 Do you listen to country radio? The rating service Arbitron places U.S. radio stations into more than 50 categories that describe the kind of programs they broadcast. Which formats attract the largest audiences? Following are Arbitron's measurements of the share of the listening audience (aged 12 and over) for the most popular formats.[3]

Format	Audience share
Country	12.6%
News/Talk/Information	10.4%
Adult Contemporary	7.1%
Pop Contemporary Hit	5.5%
Classic Rock	4.7%
Rhythmic Contemporary Hit	4.2%
Urban Contemporary	4.1%
Urban Adult Contemporary	3.4%
Oldies	3.3%
Hot Adult Contemporary	3.2%
Mexican Regional	3.1%

(a) What is the sum of the audience shares for these formats? What percent of the radio audience listens to stations with other formats?

(b) Make a bar graph to display these data. Be sure to include an "Other format" category.

(c) Would it be correct to display these data in a pie chart? Why?

1.4 Canadian students rate their universities. The National Survey of Student Engagement asked students at many universities, "How would you evaluate your entire educational experience at this university?" Here are the percents of senior-year students at Canada's 10 largest primarily English-speaking universities who responded "Excellent":[4]

University	Excellent rating
Toronto	21%
York	18%
Alberta	23%
Ottawa	11%
Western Ontario	38%
British Columbia	18%
Calgary	14%
McGill	26%
Waterloo	36%
Concordia	21%

(a) The list is arranged in order of undergraduate enrollment. Make a bar graph with the bars in order of student rating.

(b) Explain carefully why it is not correct to make a pie chart of these data.

1.5 Never on Sunday? Births are not evenly distributed across the days of the week. Here are the average numbers of babies born on each day of the week in the United States in a recent year:[5]

Day	Births
Sunday	7,374
Monday	11,704
Tuesday	13,169
Wednesday	13,038
Thursday	13,013
Friday	12,664
Saturday	8,459

Present these data in a well-labeled bar graph. Would it also be correct to make a pie chart? Suggest some possible reasons why there are fewer births on weekends.

Quantitative variables: histograms

histogram

Quantitative variables often take many values. The distribution tells us what values the variable takes and how often it takes these values. A graph of the distribution is clearer if nearby values are grouped together. The most common graph of the distribution of one quantitative variable is a **histogram.**

AP Photo/Gracy Altaffer

EXAMPLE 1.4   Making a histogram

What percent of your home state's residents were born outside the United States? The country as a whole has 12.5% foreign-born residents, but the states vary from 1.2% in West Virginia to 27.2% in California. Table 1.1 presents the data for all 50 states and the District of Columbia.[6] The *individuals* in this data set are the states. The *variable* is the percent of a state's residents who are foreign-born. It's easier to see how your state compares with other states from a graph than from the table. To make a histogram of the distribution of this variable, proceed as follows:

Step 1. Choose the classes. Divide the range of the data into classes of equal width. The data in Table 1.1 range from 1.2 to 27.2, so we decide to use these classes:

percent foreign-born between 0.1 and 5.0

percent foreign-born between 5.1 and 10.0

.
.
.

percent foreign-born between 25.1 and 30.0

TABLE 1.1 Percent of state population born outside the United States

STATE	PERCENT	STATE	PERCENT	STATE	PERCENT
Alabama	2.8	Louisiana	2.9	Ohio	3.6
Alaska	7.0	Maine	3.2	Oklahoma	4.9
Arizona	15.1	Maryland	12.2	Oregon	9.7
Arkansas	3.8	Massachusetts	14.1	Pennsylvania	5.1
California	27.2	Michigan	5.9	Rhode Island	12.6
Colorado	10.3	Minnesota	6.6	South Carolina	4.1
Connecticut	12.9	Mississippi	1.8	South Dakota	2.2
Delaware	8.1	Missouri	3.3	Tennessee	3.9
Florida	18.9	Montana	1.9	Texas	15.9
Georgia	9.2	Nebraska	5.6	Utah	8.3
Hawaii	16.3	Nevada	19.1	Vermont	3.9
Idaho	5.6	New Hampshire	5.4	Virginia	10.1
Illinois	13.8	New Jersey	20.1	Washington	12.4
Indiana	4.2	New Mexico	10.1	West Virginia	1.2
Iowa	3.8	New York	21.6	Wisconsin	4.4
Kansas	6.3	North Carolina	6.9	Wyoming	2.7
Kentucky	2.7	North Dakota	2.1	Dist. of Columbia	12.7

Be sure to specify the classes precisely so that each individual falls into exactly one class. Pennsylvania, with 5.1% foreign-born, falls into the second class, but a state with 5.0% would fall into the first.

Step 2. Count the individuals in each class. Here are the counts:

Class	Count
0.1 to 5.0	20
5.1 to 10.0	13
10.1 to 15.0	10
15.1 to 20.0	5
20.1 to 25.0	2
25.1 to 30.0	1

Check that the counts add to 51, the number of individuals in the data (the 50 states and the District of Columbia).

Step 3. Draw the histogram. Mark the scale for the variable whose distribution you are displaying on the horizontal axis. That's the percent of a state's residents who are foreign-born. The scale runs from 0 to 30 because that is the span of the classes we chose. The vertical axis contains the scale of counts. Each bar represents a class. The base of the bar covers the class, and the bar height is the class count. Draw the bars with no horizontal space between them unless a class is empty, so that its bar has height zero. Figure 1.5 is our histogram. ■

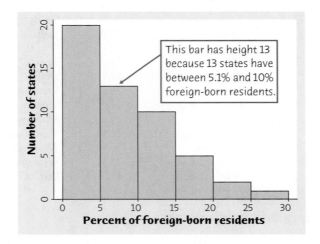

This bar has height 13 because 13 states have between 5.1% and 10% foreign-born residents.

FIGURE 1.5
Histogram of the distribution of the percent of foreign-born residents in the 50 states and the District of Columbia, for Example 1.4.

Although histograms resemble bar graphs, their details and uses are different. A histogram displays the distribution of a quantitative variable. The horizontal axis of a histogram is marked in the units of measurement for the variable. A bar graph compares the sizes of different quantities. The horizontal axis of a bar graph need not have any measurement scale but simply identifies the quantities being compared. Draw bar graphs with blank space between the bars to separate the quantities being compared. Draw histograms with no space, to indicate that all values of the variable are covered.

Our eyes respond to the *area* of the bars in a histogram.[7] Because the classes are all the same width, bar areas are proportional to heights, that is, to the class counts. So our eyes see an accurate picture of the distribution. There is no one right choice of the classes in a histogram. You must use your judgment in choosing classes to display the shape of a distribution. Statistics software will choose the classes for you. The software's choice is usually a good one, but you can change it if you want.

APPLY YOUR KNOWLEDGE

1.6 Traveling to work. How long must you travel each day to get to work or school? Table 1.2 gives the average travel times to work for workers in each state who are at least 16 years old and don't work at home.[8] Make a histogram of the travel times using classes of width 2 minutes starting at 14 minutes. That is, the first bar covers 14.0 to 15.9 minutes, the second covers 16.0 to 17.9 minutes, and so on. (Make this histogram by hand even if you have software, to be sure you understand the process. You may then want to compare your histogram with your software's choice.)

TABLE 1.2 Average travel time to work (minutes) for adults employed outside the home

STATE	TIME	STATE	TIME	STATE	TIME
Alabama	23.6	Louisiana	25.1	Ohio	22.1
Alaska	17.7	Maine	22.3	Oklahoma	20.0
Arizona	25.0	Maryland	30.6	Oregon	21.8
Arkansas	20.7	Massachusetts	26.6	Pennsylvania	25.0
California	26.8	Michigan	23.4	Rhode Island	22.3
Colorado	23.9	Minnesota	22.0	South Carolina	22.9
Connecticut	24.1	Mississippi	24.0	South Dakota	15.9
Delaware	23.6	Missouri	22.9	Tennessee	23.5
Florida	25.9	Montana	17.6	Texas	24.6
Georgia	27.3	Nebraska	17.7	Utah	20.8
Hawaii	25.5	Nevada	24.2	Vermont	21.2
Idaho	20.1	New Hampshire	24.6	Virginia	26.9
Illinois	27.9	New Jersey	29.1	Washington	25.2
Indiana	22.3	New Mexico	20.9	West Virginia	25.6
Iowa	18.2	New York	30.9	Wisconsin	20.8
Kansas	18.5	North Carolina	23.4	Wyoming	17.9
Kentucky	22.4	North Dakota	15.5	Dist. of Columbia	29.2

Interpreting histograms

Making a statistical graph is not an end in itself. *The purpose of graphs is to help us understand the data.* After you make a graph, always ask, "What do I see?" Once you have displayed a distribution, you can see its important features as follows.

EXAMINING A HISTOGRAM

In any graph of data, look for the **overall pattern** and for striking **deviations** from that pattern.

You can describe the overall pattern of a histogram by its **shape, center,** and **spread.**

An important kind of deviation is an **outlier,** an individual value that falls outside the overall pattern.

One way to describe the center of a distribution is by its *midpoint,* the value with roughly half the observations taking smaller values and half taking larger values. For now, we will describe the spread of a distribution by giving the *smallest and largest values.* We will learn better ways to describe center and spread in Chapter 2.

EXAMPLE 1.5 **Describing a distribution**

Look again at the histogram in Figure 1.5. **Shape:** The distribution has a *single peak* at the left, which represents states in which between 0% and 5% of residents are foreign-born. The distribution is *skewed to the right.* A majority of states have no more than 10% foreign-born residents, but several states have much higher percents, so that the graph extends quite far to the right of its peak. **Center:** Arranging the observations from Table 1.1 in order of size shows that 6.3% (Kansas) is the midpoint of the distribution. There are 25 states with smaller percents foreign-born and 25 with larger. **Spread:** The spread is from 1.2% to 27.2%.

Outliers: Figure 1.5 shows no observations outside the overall single-peaked, right-skewed pattern of the distribution. Figure 1.6 is another histogram of the same distribution, with classes half as wide. Now California, at 27.2%, stands a bit apart to the right of the rest of the distribution. Is California an outlier or just the largest observation in a strongly skewed distribution? Unfortunately, there is no rule. Let's agree to call attention to only strong outliers that suggest something special about an observation—or an error such as typing 10.1 as 101. California is certainly not a strong outlier. ■

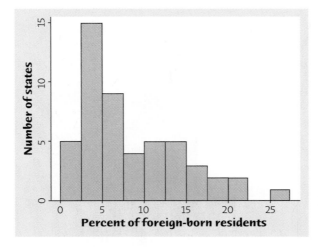

FIGURE 1.6

Another histogram of the distribution of the percent of foreign-born residents, with classes half as wide as in Figure 1.5. Histograms with more classes show more detail but may have a less clear pattern.

Figures 1.5 and 1.6 remind us that interpreting graphs calls for judgment. We also see that *the choice of classes in a histogram can influence the appearance of a distribution.* Because of this, and to avoid worrying about minor details, concentrate on the main features of a distribution. Look for major peaks, not for minor ups and downs, in the bars of the histogram. (For example, don't conclude that Figure 1.6 shows a second peak between 10% and 15%.) Look for clear outliers, not just for the smallest and largest observations. Look for rough *symmetry* or clear *skewness.*

> **SYMMETRIC AND SKEWED DISTRIBUTIONS**
>
> A distribution is **symmetric** if the right and left sides of the histogram are approximately mirror images of each other.
>
> A distribution is **skewed to the right** if the right side of the histogram (containing the half of the observations with larger values) extends much farther out than the left side. It is **skewed to the left** if the left side of the histogram extends much farther out than the right side.

Here are more examples of describing the overall pattern of a histogram.

EXAMPLE 1.6 **Iowa Test scores**

Figure 1.7 displays the scores of all 947 seventh-grade students in the public schools of Gary, Indiana, on the vocabulary part of the Iowa Test of Basic Skills.[9] Notice that the vertical scale is not the *count* of students but the *percent* of students in each histogram class. The distribution is *single-peaked* and *symmetric*. In mathematics, the two sides of symmetric patterns are exact mirror images. Real data are almost never exactly symmetric. We are content to describe Figure 1.7 as symmetric. The center (half above, half below) is close to 7. This is seventh-grade reading level. The scores range from 2.0 (second-grade level) to 12.1 (twelfth-grade level). ∎

FIGURE 1.7

Histogram of the Iowa Test vocabulary scores of all seventh-grade students in Gary, Indiana, for Example 1.6. This distribution is single-peaked and symmetric.

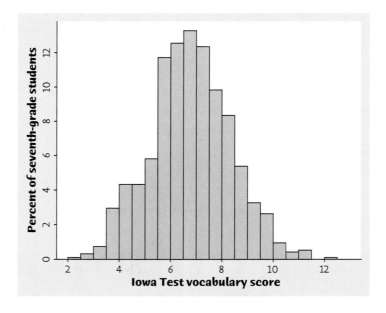

EXAMPLE 1.7 **Who takes the SAT?**

Figure 1.8 is a histogram of the percent of high school graduates in each state who took the SAT Reasoning test.[10] The histogram shows two peaks, a high peak at the left and a lower but broader peak centered in the 60% to 80% class. The presence of several peaks

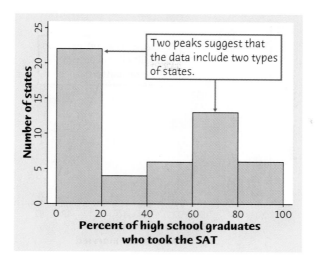

Two peaks suggest that the data include two types of states.

FIGURE 1.8
Histogram of the percent of high school graduates in each state who took the SAT Reasoning test, for Example 1.7. The graph shows two groups of states: ACT states (where few students take the SAT) at the left and SAT states at the right.

suggests that a distribution mixes several kinds of individuals. That's the case here. There are two major tests of readiness for college, the ACT and the SAT. Most states have a strong preference for one or the other. In some states, many students take the ACT exam and few take the SAT—these states form the peak on the left. In other states, many students take the SAT and few choose the ACT—these states form the broader peak at the right.

Giving the center and spread of this distribution is not very useful. The midpoint falls in the 20% to 40% class, between the two peaks. The story told by the histogram is in the two peaks corresponding to ACT states and SAT states. ■

The overall shape of a distribution is important information about a variable. Many biological measurements on specimens from the same species and sex—lengths of bird bills, heights of young women—have symmetric distributions. On the other hand, data on people's incomes are usually strongly skewed to the right. There are many moderate incomes, some large incomes, and a few enormous incomes. Many distributions have irregular shapes that are neither symmetric nor skewed. Some data show other patterns, such as the two peaks in Figure 1.8. Use your eyes, describe the pattern you see, and then try to explain the pattern.

APPLY YOUR KNOWLEDGE

1.7 Traveling to work. In Exercise 1.6, you made a histogram of the average travel times to work in Table 1.2. The shape of the distribution is a bit irregular. Is it closer to symmetric or skewed? About where is the center (midpoint) of the data? What is the spread in terms of the smallest and largest values?

1.8 Unmarried women. Figure 1.9 shows the distribution of the state percents of women aged 15 and over who have never been married.

(a) The main body of the distribution is slightly skewed to the right. There is one clear outlier, the District of Columbia. Why is it not surprising that the percent of never-married women is higher in D.C. than in the 50 states?

FIGURE 1.9

Histogram of the state percents of women aged 15 and over who have never been married, for Exercise 1.8.

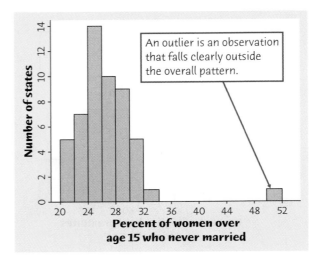

(b) The midpoint of the distribution is the 26th state in order of percent of never-married women. In which class does the midpoint fall? About what is the spread (smallest to largest) of the distribution?

Quantitative variables: stemplots

Histograms are not the only graphical display of distributions. For small data sets, a *stemplot* is quicker to make and presents more detailed information.

> **STEMPLOT**
>
> To make a **stemplot:**
>
> 1. Separate each observation into a **stem,** consisting of all but the final (rightmost) digit, and a **leaf,** the final digit. Stems may have as many digits as needed, but each leaf contains only a single digit.
> 2. Write the stems in a vertical column with the smallest at the top, and draw a vertical line at the right of this column. Be sure to include all the stems needed to span the data, even when some will have no leaves.
> 3. Write each leaf in the row to the right of its stem, in increasing order out from the stem.

EXAMPLE 1.8 **Making a stemplot**

Table 1.1 (page 10) presents the percents of state residents who were born outside the United States. To make a stemplot of these data, take the whole-number part of the percent as the stem and the final digit (tenths) as the leaf. Write stems from 1 for Mississippi, Montana, and West Virginia to 27 for California. Now add leaves. Arizona, 15.1%, has leaf 1 on the 15 stem. Texas, at 15.9%, places leaf 9 on the same stem. These are the only observations on this stem. Arrange the leaves in order, so that 15 | 19 is one row in the stemplot. Figure 1.10 is the complete stemplot for the data in Table 1.1. ■

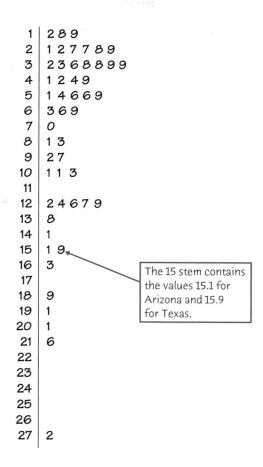

```
 1 | 2 8 9
 2 | 1 2 7 7 8 9
 3 | 2 3 6 8 8 9 9
 4 | 1 2 4 9
 5 | 1 4 6 6 9
 6 | 3 6 9
 7 | 0
 8 | 1 3
 9 | 2 7
10 | 1 1 3
11 |
12 | 2 4 6 7 9
13 | 8
14 | 1
15 | 1 9
16 | 3
17 |
18 | 9
19 | 1
20 | 1
21 | 6
22 |
23 |
24 |
25 |
26 |
27 | 2
```

The 15 stem contains the values 15.1 for Arizona and 15.9 for Texas.

FIGURE 1.10
Stemplot of the percents of foreign-born residents in the states, for Example 1.8. Each stem is a percent and leaves are tenths of a percent.

A stemplot looks like a histogram turned on end. Compare the stemplot in Figure 1.10 with the histograms of the same data in Figures 1.5 and 1.6. All three graphs show a distribution that has one peak and is right-skewed. Figures 1.6 and 1.10 have enough classes to show that California (27.2%) stands slightly apart from the long right tail of the skewed distribution. You can choose the classes in a histogram. The classes (the stems) of a stemplot are given to you. But the stemplot, unlike the histogram, preserves the actual value of each observation. Stemplots do not work well for large data sets, where each stem must hold a large number of leaves. Don't try to make a stemplot of a large data set, such as the 947 Iowa Test scores in Figure 1.7.

EXAMPLE 1.9   Pulling wood apart

Although handbooks give the strength of a material as a single number, in fact the strength varies from piece to piece. Here are data from a typical student laboratory exercise: the load in pounds needed to pull apart pieces of Douglas fir.

33,190	31,860	32,590	26,520	33,280
32,320	33,020	32,030	30,460	32,700
23,040	30,930	32,720	33,650	32,340
24,050	30,170	31,300	28,730	31,920

rounding

A stemplot of these data would have very many stems and either no leaves or just one leaf on most stems. So we first **round** the data to the nearest hundred pounds and then drop the two 0s from the end of each rounded number. The rounded data are

| 332 | 319 | 326 | 265 | 333 | 323 | 330 | 320 | 305 | 327 |
| 230 | 309 | 327 | 337 | 323 | 241 | 302 | 313 | 287 | 319 |

Now we can make a stemplot with the first two digits (thousands of pounds) as stems and the third digit (hundreds of pounds) as leaves. Figure 1.11 is the stemplot. The distribution is *skewed to the left*. The *midpoint* is around 320 (32,000 pounds) and the *spread* is from 230 to 337. Because of the strong skew, we are reluctant to call the smallest observations outliers. They appear to be part of the long left tail of the distribution. Before using wood like this in construction, we should ask why some pieces are much weaker than the rest. ■

FIGURE 1.11

Stemplot of the breaking strength of pieces of wood, rounded to the nearest hundred pounds, for Example 1.9. Stems are thousands of pounds and leaves are hundreds of pounds.

```
23 | 0
24 | 1
25 |
26 | 5
27 |
28 | 7
29 |
30 | 2 5 9
31 | 3 9 9
32 | 0 3 3 6 7 7
33 | 0 2 3 7
```

splitting stems

Comparing Figures 1.10 (right-skewed) and 1.11 (left-skewed) reminds us that *the direction of skewness is the direction of the long tail, not the direction where most observations are clustered.*

You can also **split stems** in a stemplot to double the number of stems when all the leaves would otherwise fall on just a few stems. Each stem then appears twice. Leaves 0 to 4 go on the upper stem, and leaves 5 to 9 go on the lower stem. If you split the stems in the stemplot of Figure 1.11, for example, the 32 and 33 stems become

```
32 | 0 3 3
32 | 6 7 7
33 | 0 2 3
33 | 7
```

Rounding and splitting stems are matters for judgment, like choosing the classes in a histogram. The wood strength data require rounding but don't require splitting stems.

1.9 Traveling to work. Make a stemplot of the average travel times to work in Table 1.2 (page 12). Use whole minutes as your stems. Because the stemplot preserves the actual values of the observations, it is easy to find the midpoint (26th of the 51 observations in order) and the spread. What are they?

1.10 Health care spending. Table 1.3 shows the annual spending per person on health care in the world's richer countries.[11] Make a stemplot of the data after rounding to the nearest $100 (so that stems are thousands of dollars and leaves are hundreds of dollars). Split the stems, placing leaves 0 to 4 on the first stem and leaves 5 to 9 on the second stem of the same value. Describe the shape, center, and spread of the distribution. Which country is the high outlier?

TABLE 1.3 Annual spending per person on health care (in U.S. dollars)

COUNTRY	DOLLARS	COUNTRY	DOLLARS	COUNTRY	DOLLARS
Argentina	1067	Hungary	1269	Poland	745
Australia	2874	Iceland	3110	Portugal	1791
Austria	2306	Ireland	2496	Saudi Arabia	578
Belgium	2828	Israel	1911	Singapore	1156
Canada	2989	Italy	2266	Slovakia	777
Croatia	838	Japan	2244	Slovenia	1669
Czech Republic	1302	Korea	1074	South Africa	669
Denmark	2762	Kuwait	567	Spain	1853
Estonia	682	Lithuania	754	Sweden	2704
Finland	2108	Netherlands	2987	Switzerland	3776
France	2902	New Zealand	1893	United Kingdom	2389
Germany	3001	Norway	3809	United States	5711
Greece	1997	Oman	419		

Time plots

Many variables are measured at intervals over time. We might, for example, measure the height of a growing child or the price of a stock at the end of each month. In these examples, our main interest is change over time. To display change over time, make a *time plot*.

TIME PLOT

A **time plot** of a variable plots each observation against the time at which it was measured. Always put time on the horizontal scale of your plot and the variable you are measuring on the vertical scale. Connecting the data points by lines helps emphasize any change over time.

EXAMPLE 1.10   **Water levels in the Everglades**

Water levels in Everglades National Park are critical to the survival of this unique region. The photo shows a water-monitoring station in Shark River Slough, the main path for surface water moving through the "river of grass" that is the Everglades. Figure 1.12 is a time plot of water levels at this station from mid-August 2000 to mid-June 2003.[12] ■

cycles

When you examine a time plot, look once again for an overall pattern and for strong deviations from the pattern. Figure 1.12 shows strong **cycles,** regular up-and-down movements in water level. The cycles show the effects of Florida's wet season (roughly June to November) and dry season (roughly December to May). Water levels are highest in late fall. In April and May of 2001 and 2002, water levels were less than zero—the water table was below ground level and the surface was dry.

trend

Another common overall pattern in a time plot is a **trend,** a long-term upward or downward movement over time. Many economic variables show an upward trend. Incomes, house prices, and (alas) college tuitions tend to move generally upward over time.

Courtesy U.S. Geological Survey

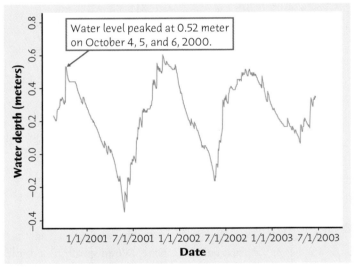

FIGURE 1.12

Time plot of water depth at a monitoring station in Everglades National Park over a period of almost three years, for Example 1.10. The yearly cycles reflect Florida's wet and dry seasons.

APPLY YOUR KNOWLEDGE

1.11 The cost of college. The chart gives data on the average tuition and fees charged to in-state students by public four-year colleges and universities for the 1976 to 2007 academic years. Because almost any variable measured in dollars increases over time due to inflation (the falling buying power of a dollar), the values are given in "constant dollars," adjusted to have the same buying power that a dollar had in 2007.[13]

Year	Tuition	Year	Tuition	Year	Tuition	Year	Tuition
1976	$2,197	1984	$2,426	1992	$3,444	2000	$4,221
1977	$2,225	1985	$2,532	1993	$3,623	2001	$4,411
1978	$1,986	1986	$2,656	1994	$3,758	2002	$4,715
1979	$1,986	1987	$2,699	1995	$3,802	2003	$5,231
1980	$1,939	1988	$2,721	1996	$3,913	2004	$5,624
1981	$2,018	1989	$2,792	1997	$4,022	2005	$5,814
1982	$2,194	1990	$2,977	1998	$4,131	2006	$5,918
1983	$2,358	1991	$3,187	1999	$4,183	2007	$6,185

(a) Make a time plot of average tuition and fees.

(b) What overall pattern does your plot show?

(c) Some possible deviations from the overall pattern are outliers, periods when charges went down (in 2007 dollars), and periods of particularly rapid increase. Which are present in your plot, and during which years?

CHAPTER 1 SUMMARY

- A data set contains information on a number of **individuals.** Individuals may be people, animals, or things. For each individual, the data give values for one or more **variables.** A variable describes some characteristic of an individual, such as a person's height, sex, or salary.

- Some variables are **categorical** and others are **quantitative.** A categorical variable places each individual into a category, such as male or female. A quantitative variable has numerical values that measure some characteristic of each individual, such as height in centimeters or salary in dollars.

- **Exploratory data analysis** uses graphs and numerical summaries to describe the variables in a data set and the relations among them.

- After you understand the background of your data (individuals, variables, units of measurement), the first thing to do is almost always **plot your data.**

- The **distribution** of a variable describes what values the variable takes and how often it takes these values. **Pie charts** and **bar graphs** display the distribution of a categorical variable. Bar graphs can also compare any set of quantities measured in the same units. **Histograms** and **stemplots** graph the distribution of a quantitative variable.

- When examining any graph, look for an **overall pattern** and for notable **deviations** from the pattern.

- **Shape, center, and spread** describe the overall pattern of the distribution of a quantitative variable. Some distributions have simple shapes, such as **symmetric** or **skewed.** Not all distributions have a simple overall shape, especially when there are few observations.

- **Outliers** are observations that lie outside the overall pattern of a distribution. Always look for outliers and try to explain them.

- When observations on a variable are taken over time, make a **time plot** that graphs time horizontally and the values of the variable vertically. A time plot can reveal **trends, cycles,** or other changes over time.

The multiple-choice exercises in "Check Your Skills" ask straightforward questions about basic facts from the chapter. Answers to all of these exercises appear in the back of the book. You should expect all of your answers to be correct.

1.12 A study of recent college graduates records the sex and total college debt in dollars for 10,000 people a year after they graduate from college.
(a) Sex and college debt are both categorical variables.
(b) Sex and college debt are both quantitative variables.
(c) Sex is a categorical variable and college debt is a quantitative variable.

1.13 To display the distribution of grades (A, B, C, D, F) among students in a course, it would be correct to use
(a) a pie chart but not a bar graph.
(b) a bar graph but not a pie chart.
(c) either a pie chart or a bar graph.

1.14 Figure 1.9 (page 16) is a histogram of the percent of women in each state aged 15 and over who have never been married. The leftmost bar in the histogram covers percents of never-married women ranging from about
(a) 20% to 24%.   (b) 20% to 22%.   (c) 0% to 20%.

1.15 Here are the amounts of money (cents) in coins carried by 10 students in a statistics class:
50   35   0   97   76   0   0   87   23   65
To make a stemplot of these data, you would use stems
(a) 0, 1, 2, 3, 4, 5, 6, 7, 8, 9.
(b) 0, 2, 3, 5, 6, 7, 8, 9.
(c) 00, 10, 20, 30, 40, 50, 60, 70, 80, 90.

1.16 Here is a stemplot of the percents of residents aged 65 and older in the 50 states and the District of Columbia. The stems are whole percents and the leaves are tenths of a percent.

```
 6 | 8
 7 |
 8 | 8
 9 | 79
10 | 08
11 | 15566
12 | 012223444457888999
13 | 0123333444899
14 | 02666
15 | 23
16 | 8
```

The low outlier is Alaska. What percent of Alaska residents are 65 or older?
(a) 6.8%   (b) 16.8%   (c) 68%

1.17 Ignoring the outlier, the shape of the distribution in Exercise 1.16 is
(a) clearly skewed to the right.
(b) roughly symmetric.
(c) clearly skewed to the left.

1.18 You look at real estate ads for houses in Naples, Florida. There are many houses ranging from $200,000 to $500,000 in price. The few houses on the water, however, have prices up to $15 million. The distribution of house prices will be
(a) skewed to the left.
(b) roughly symmetric.
(c) skewed to the right.

CHAPTER 1 EXERCISES

1.19 Medical students. Students who have finished medical school are assigned to residencies in hospitals to receive further training in a medical specialty. Here is part of a hypothetical database of students seeking residency positions. USMLE is the student's score on Step 1 of the national medical licensing examination.

Name	Medical school	Sex	Age	USMLE	Specialty sought
Abrams, Laurie	Florida	F	28	238	Family medicine
Brown, Gordon	Meharry	M	25	205	Radiology
Cabrera, Maria	Tufts	F	26	191	Pediatrics
Ismael, Miranda	Indiana	F	32	245	Internal medicine

(a) What individuals does this data set describe?
(b) In addition to the student's name, how many variables does the data set contain? Which of these variables are categorical and which are quantitative?

1.20 Protecting wood. How can we help wood surfaces resist weathering, especially when restoring historic wooden buildings? In a study of this question, researchers prepared wooden panels and then exposed them to the weather. Here are some of the variables recorded. Which of these variables are categorical and which are quantitative?
(a) Type of wood (yellow poplar, pine, cedar)
(b) Type of water repellent (solvent-based, water-based)
(c) Paint thickness (millimeters)
(d) Paint color (white, gray, light blue)
(e) Weathering time (months)

1.21 What color is your car? The most popular colors for cars and light trucks change over time. Silver passed green in 2000 to become the most popular color worldwide, then gave way to shades of white in 2007. Here is the distribution of colors for vehicles sold in North America in 2007:[14]

Color	Popularity
White	19%
Silver	18%
Black	16%
Red	13%
Gray	12%
Blue	12%
Beige, brown	5%
Other colors	

Fill in the percent of vehicles that are in other colors. Make a graph to display the distribution of color popularity.

1.22 Buying music online. Young people are more likely than older folk to buy music online. Here are the percents of people in several age groups who bought music online in 2006:[15]

Age group	Bought music online
12 to 17 years	24%
18 to 24 years	21%
25 to 34 years	20%
35 to 44 years	16%
45 to 54 years	10%
55 to 64 years	3%
65 years and over	1%

(a) Explain why it is *not* correct to use a pie chart to display these data.

(b) Make a bar graph of the data.

1.23 Deaths among young people. Among persons aged 15 to 24 years in the United States, the leading causes of death and number of deaths in 2005 were: accidents, 15,567; homicide, 5359; suicide, 4139; cancer, 1717; heart disease, 1067; congenital defects, 483.[16]

(a) Make a bar graph to display these data.

(b) To make a pie chart, you need one additional piece of information. What is it?

1.24 Spam. Email spam is the curse of the Internet. Here is a compilation of the most common types of spam:[17]

Type of spam	Percent
Adult	19
Financial	20
Health	7
Internet	7
Leisure	6
Products	25
Scams	9

Make two bar graphs of these percents, one with bars ordered as in the table (alphabetically) and the other with bars in order from tallest to shortest. Comparisons are easier if you order the bars by height.

1.25 Do adolescent girls eat fruit? We all know that fruit is good for us. Figure 1.13 is a histogram of the number of servings of fruit per day claimed by 74 seventeen-year-old girls in a study in Pennsylvania.[18] Describe the shape, center, and spread of this distribution. What percent of these girls ate fewer than two servings per day?

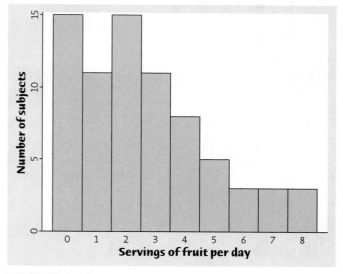

FIGURE 1.13

The distribution of fruit consumption in a sample of 74 seventeen-year-old girls, for Exercise 1.25.

1.26 IQ test scores. Figure 1.14 (see page 24) is a stemplot of the IQ test scores of 78 seventh-grade students in a rural midwestern school.[19]

(a) Four students had low scores that might be considered outliers. Ignoring these, describe the shape, center, and spread of the distribution. (Notice that it looks roughly bell-shaped.)

(b) We often read that IQ scores for large populations are centered at 100. What percent of these 78 students have scores above 100?

1.27 Name that variable. A survey of a large college class asked the following questions:

1. Are you female or male? (In the data, male = 0, female = 1.)

2. Are you right-handed or left-handed? (In the data, right = 0, left = 1.)

```
 7 | 2 4
 7 | 7 9
 8 |
 8 | 6 9
 9 | 0 1 3 3
 9 | 6 7 7 8
10 | 0 0 2 2 3 3 3 3 4 4
10 | 5 5 5 6 6 6 7 7 7 7 8 9
11 | 0 0 0 0 1 1 1 1 2 2 2 2 3 3 3 4 4 4 4
11 | 5 5 6 8 8 9 9 9
12 | 0 0 3 3 4 4
12 | 6 7 7 8 8 8
13 | 0 2
13 | 6
```

FIGURE 1.14

The distribution of IQ scores for 78 seventh-grade students, for Exercise 1.26.

3. What is your height in inches?

4. How many minutes do you study on a typical weeknight? Figure 1.15 shows histograms of the student responses, in scrambled order and without scale markings. Which histogram goes with each variable? Explain your reasoning.

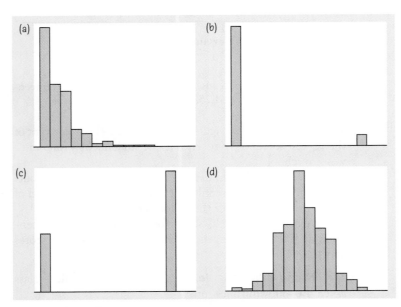

FIGURE 1.15

Histograms of four distributions, for Exercise 1.27.

1.28 Food oils and health. Fatty acids are necessary for human health. Two types of essential fatty acids, called omega-3

and omega-6, are not produced by our bodies and so must be obtained from our food. Food oils, widely used in food processing and cooking, are major sources of these compounds. There is some evidence that a healthy diet should have more omega-3 than omega-6. Table 1.4 gives the ratio of omega-3 to omega-6 in some common food oils.[20] Values greater than 1 show that an oil has more omega-3 than omega-6.

(a) Make a histogram of these data, using classes bounded by the whole numbers from 0 to 6.

(b) What is the shape of the distribution? How many of the 30 food oils have more omega-3 than omega-6? What does this distribution suggest about the possible health effects of modern food oils?

(c) Table 1.4 contains entries for several fish oils (cod, herring, menhaden, salmon, sardine). How do these values support the idea that eating fish is healthy?

1.29 Where are the doctors? Table 1.5 gives the number of active medical doctors per 100,000 people in each state.[21]

(a) Why is the number of doctors per 100,000 people a better measure of the availability of health care than a simple count of the number of doctors in a state?

(b) Make a histogram that displays the distribution of doctors per 100,000 people. Write a brief description of the distribution. Are there any outliers? If so, can you explain them?

1.30 Carbon dioxide emissions. Burning fuels in power plants or motor vehicles emits carbon dioxide (CO_2), which contributes to global warming. Table 1.6 displays CO_2 emissions per person from countries with populations of at least 20 million.[22]

(a) Why do you think we choose to measure emissions per person rather than total CO_2 emissions for each country?

(b) Make a stemplot to display the data of Table 1.6. Describe the shape, center, and spread of the distribution. Which countries are outliers?

1.31 Rock sole in the Bering Sea. "Recruitment," the addition of new members to a fish population, is

Sarkis Images/Alamy

TABLE 1.4 Omega-3 fatty acids as a fraction of omega-6 fatty acids in food oils

OIL	RATIO	OIL	RATIO
Perilla	5.33	Flaxseed	3.56
Walnut	0.20	Canola	0.46
Wheat germ	0.13	Soybean	0.13
Mustard	0.38	Grape seed	0.00
Sardine	2.16	Menhaden	1.96
Salmon	2.50	Herring	2.67
Mayonnaise	0.06	Soybean, hydrogenated	0.07
Cod liver	2.00	Rice bran	0.05
Shortening (household)	0.11	Butter	0.64
Shortening (industrial)	0.06	Sunflower	0.03
Margarine	0.05	Corn	0.01
Olive	0.08	Sesame	0.01
Shea nut	0.06	Cottonseed	0.00
Sunflower (oleic)	0.05	Palm	0.02
Sunflower (linoleic)	0.00	Cocoa butter	0.04

TABLE 1.5 Medical doctors per 100,000 people, by state

STATE	DOCTORS	STATE	DOCTORS	STATE	DOCTORS
Alabama	213	Louisiana	264	Ohio	261
Alaska	222	Maine	267	Oklahoma	171
Arizona	208	Maryland	411	Oregon	263
Arkansas	203	Massachusetts	450	Pennsylvania	294
California	259	Michigan	240	Rhode Island	351
Colorado	258	Minnesota	281	South Carolina	230
Connecticut	363	Mississippi	181	South Dakota	219
Delaware	248	Missouri	239	Tennessee	261
Florida	245	Montana	221	Texas	212
Georgia	220	Nebraska	239	Utah	209
Hawaii	310	Nevada	186	Vermont	362
Idaho	169	New Hampshire	260	Virginia	270
Illinois	272	New Jersey	306	Washington	265
Indiana	213	New Mexico	240	West Virginia	229
Iowa	187	New York	389	Wisconsin	254
Kansas	220	North Carolina	253	Wyoming	188
Kentucky	230	North Dakota	242	Dist. of Columbia	798

an important measure of the health of ocean ecosystems. Table 1.7 contains data on the recruitment of rock sole in the Bering Sea from 1973 to 2000.[23]

Make a stemplot to display the distribution of yearly rock sole recruitment. (Round to the nearest hundred and split the stems.) Describe the shape, center, and spread of the distribution and any striking deviations that you see.

TABLE 1.6 Carbon dioxide emissions (metric tons per person)

COUNTRY	CO$_2$	COUNTRY	CO$_2$	COUNTRY	CO$_2$
Algeria	2.6	Iran	6.0	Poland	7.8
Argentina	3.6	Iraq	2.9	Romania	4.2
Australia	18.4	Italy	7.8	Russia	10.8
Bangladesh	0.3	Japan	9.5	Saudi Arabia	13.8
Brazil	1.8	Kenya	0.3	South Africa	7.0
Canada	17.0	Korea, North	3.3	Spain	7.9
China	3.9	Korea, South	9.3	Sudan	0.3
Colombia	1.3	Malaysia	5.5	Tanzania	0.1
Congo	0.2	Mexico	3.7	Thailand	3.3
Egypt	2.0	Morocco	1.4	Turkey	3.0
Ethiopia	0.1	Myanmar	0.2	Ukraine	6.3
France	6.2	Nepal	0.1	United Kingdom	8.8
Germany	9.9	Nigeria	0.4	United States	19.6
Ghana	0.3	Pakistan	0.8	Uzbekistan	4.2
India	1.1	Peru	1.0	Venezuela	5.4
Indonesia	1.6	Philippines	0.9	Vietnam	1.0

TABLE 1.7 Recruitment of rock sole (millions) in the Bering Sea

YEAR	RECRUITMENT	YEAR	RECRUITMENT	YEAR	RECRUITMENT	YEAR	RECRUITMENT
1973	173	1980	1411	1987	4700	1994	505
1974	234	1981	1431	1988	1702	1995	304
1975	616	1982	1250	1989	1119	1996	425
1976	344	1983	2246	1990	2407	1997	214
1977	515	1984	1793	1991	1049	1998	385
1978	576	1985	1793	1992	505	1999	445
1979	727	1986	2809	1993	998	2000	676

1.32 Do women study more than men? We asked the students in a large first-year college class how many minutes they studied on a typical weeknight. Here are the responses of random samples of 30 women and 30 men from the class:

Women					Men				
180	120	180	360	240	90	120	30	90	200
120	180	120	240	170	90	45	30	120	75
150	120	180	180	150	150	120	60	240	300
200	150	180	150	180	240	60	120	60	30
120	60	120	180	180	30	230	120	95	150
90	240	180	115	120	0	200	120	120	180

(a) Examine the data. Why are you not surprised that most responses are multiples of 10 minutes? We eliminated one student who claimed to study 30,000 minutes per night. Are there any other responses you consider suspicious?

(b) Make a **back-to-back stemplot** to compare the two samples. That is, use one set of stems with two sets of leaves, one to the right and one to the left of the stems. (Draw a line on either side of the stems to separate stems and leaves.) Order both sets of leaves from smallest at the stem to largest away from the stem. Report the approximate midpoints of both groups. Does it appear that women study more than men (or at least claim that they do)?

1.33 Rock sole in the Bering sea. Make a time plot of the rock sole recruitment data in Exercise 1.31. What does the time plot show that your stemplot in Exercise 1.31 did not show? When you have time series data, a time plot is often needed to understand what is happening.

1.34 Marijuana and traffic accidents. Researchers in New Zealand interviewed 907 drivers at age 21. They had data on traffic accidents and they asked the drivers about marijuana use. Here are data on the numbers of accidents caused by these drivers at age 19, broken down by marijuana use at the same age:[24]

	Marijuana Use per Year			
	Never	1–10 times	11–50 times	51+ times
Drivers	452	229	70	156
Accidents caused	59	36	15	50

(a) Explain carefully why a useful graph must compare *rates* (accidents per driver) rather than *counts* of accidents in the four marijuana use classes.

(b) Make a graph that displays the accident rate for each class. What do you conclude? (You can't conclude that marijuana use *causes* accidents, because risk takers are more likely both to drive aggressively and to use marijuana.)

1.35 Dates on coins. Sketch a histogram for a distribution that is skewed to the left. Suppose that you and your friends emptied your pockets of coins and recorded the year marked on each coin. The distribution of dates would be skewed to the left. Explain why.

1.36 El Niño and the monsoon. It appears that El Niño, the periodic warming of the Pacific Ocean west of South America, affects the monsoon rains that are essential for agriculture in India. Here are the monsoon rains (in millimeters) for the 23 strong El Niño years between 1871 and 2004:[25]

628 669 740 651 710 736 717 698 653 604 781 784
790 811 830 858 858 896 806 790 792 957 872

(a) To make a stemplot of these rainfall amounts, round the data to the nearest 10, so that stems are hundreds of millimeters and leaves are tens of millimeters. Make two stemplots, with and without splitting the stems. Which plot do you prefer?

(b) Describe the shape, center, and spread of the distribution.

(c) The average monsoon rainfall for all years from 1871 to 2004 is about 850 millimeters. What effect does El Niño appear to have on monsoon rains?

1.37 Watch those scales! The impression that a time plot gives depends on the scales you use on the two axes. If you stretch the vertical axis and compress the time axis, change appears to be more rapid. Compressing the vertical axis and stretching the time axis make change appear slower. Make two more time plots of the college tuition data in Exercise 1.11 (page 20), one that makes tuition appear to increase very rapidly and one that shows only a gentle increase. The moral of this exercise is: pay close attention to the scales when you look at a time plot.

1.38 Housing starts. Figure 1.16 is a time plot of the number of single-family homes started by builders each month from January 1990 to July 2008.[26] The counts are in thousands of homes.

(a) The most notable pattern in this time plot is yearly up-and-down cycles. At what season of the year are housing starts highest? Lowest? The cycles are explained by the weather in the northern part of the country.

(b) Is there a longer-term trend visible in addition to the cycles? If so, describe it.

(c) The big economic news of 2007 and 2008 was a severe downturn in housing that began in mid-2006. How is this downturn visible in the time plot?

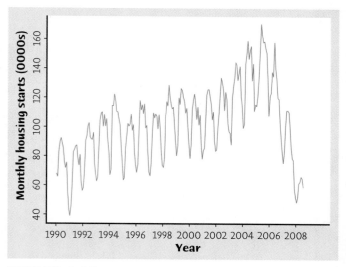

FIGURE 1.16

Time plot of the monthly count of new single-family houses started (in thousands) between January 1990 and July 2008, for Exercise 1.38.

1.39 Alligator bites. Here are data on the number of people bitten by alligators in Florida over 36 years:[27]

Year	Number bitten	Year	Number bitten	Year	Number bitten	Year	Number bitten
1972	4	1981	10	1990	17	1999	16
1973	3	1982	7	1991	20	2000	23
1974	4	1983	9	1992	15	2001	25
1975	5	1984	9	1993	19	2002	17
1976	2	1985	7	1994	20	2003	12
1977	14	1986	23	1995	22	2004	13
1978	7	1987	13	1996	13	2005	15
1979	2	1988	18	1997	8	2006	18
1980	5	1989	13	1998	9	2007	18

Make two graphs of these data to illustrate why you should always make a time plot for data collected over time.

(a) Make a histogram of the counts of people bitten by alligators. The distribution has an irregular shape. What is the midpoint of the yearly counts of people bitten?

(b) Make a time plot. There is great variation from year to year, but also an increasing trend. How many of the 22 years from 1986 to 2007 had more people bitten by alligators than your midpoint from (a)? The trend reflects Florida's growing population, which brings more people close to alligators.

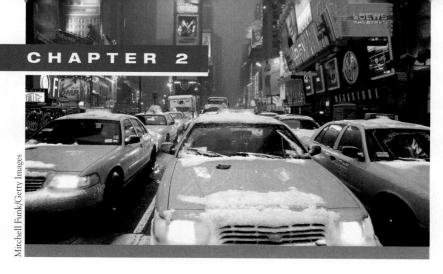

Mitchell Funk/Getty Images

New York City traffic. Travel times to work in New York State are longer than in most other states (Example 2.3).

Describing Distributions with Numbers

Here are the travel times in minutes for 15 workers in North Carolina, chosen at random by the Census Bureau:[1]

30   20   10   40   25   20   10   60   15   40   5   30   12   10   10

We aren't surprised that most people estimate their travel time in multiples of 5 minutes. Here is a stemplot of these data:

```
0 | 5
1 | 000025
2 | 005
3 | 00
4 | 00
5 |
6 | 0
```

The distribution is single-peaked and right-skewed. The longest travel time (60 minutes) may be an outlier. Our goal in this chapter is to describe with numbers the center and spread of this and other distributions.

Measuring center: the mean

The most common measure of center is the ordinary arithmetic average, or *mean*.

IN THIS CHAPTER WE COVER...

- Measuring center: the mean
- Measuring center: the median
- Comparing the mean and the median
- Measuring spread: the quartiles
- The five-number summary and boxplots
- Measuring spread: the standard deviation
- Choosing measures of center and spread
- Using technology
- Organizing a statistical problem

> **THE MEAN $\bar{x}$**
>
> To find the **mean** of a set of observations, add their values and divide by the number of observations. If the n observations are $x_1, x_2, \ldots, x_n$, their mean is
>
> $$\bar{x} = \frac{x_1 + x_2 + \cdots + x_n}{n}$$
>
> or, in more compact notation,
>
> $$\bar{x} = \frac{1}{n}\sum x_i$$

The $\sum$ (capital Greek sigma) in the formula for the mean is short for "add them all up." The subscripts on the observations x_i are just a way of keeping the n observations distinct. They do not necessarily indicate order or any other special facts about the data. The bar over the x indicates the mean of all the x-values. Pronounce the mean $\bar{x}$ as "x-bar." This notation is very common. When writers who are discussing data use $\bar{x}$ or $\bar{y}$, they are talking about a mean.

EXAMPLE 2.1 Travel times to work

The mean travel time of our 15 North Carolina workers is

$$\bar{x} = \frac{x_1 + x_2 + \cdots + x_n}{n}$$
$$= \frac{30 + 20 + \cdots + 10}{15}$$
$$= \frac{337}{15} = 22.5 \text{ minutes}$$

In practice, you can enter the data into your calculator and ask for the mean. You don't have to actually add and divide. But you should know that this is what the calculator is doing. ■

If we leave out the longest single travel time, 60 minutes, the mean for the remaining 14 people drops from 22.5 minutes to 19.8 minutes. One large observation raises the mean by 2.7 minutes. This is an important fact about the mean as a measure of center: it is sensitive to the influence of a few extreme observations. These may be outliers, but a skewed distribution that has no outliers will also pull the mean toward its long tail. Because the mean cannot resist the influence of extreme observations, we say that it is not a **resistant measure** of center.

resistant measure

APPLY YOUR KNOWLEDGE

2.1 **Pulling wood apart.** Example 1.9 (page 17) gives the breaking strength in pounds of 20 pieces of Douglas fir. Find the mean breaking strength. How many of the pieces of wood have strengths less than the mean? What feature of the stemplot (Figure 1.11, page 18) explains the fact that the mean is smaller than most of the observations?

2.2 Health care spending. Table 1.3 (page 19) gives the annual health care spending per person in 38 richer nations. The United States, at $5711 per person, is a high outlier. Find the mean health care spending in these nations with and without the United States. How much does the one outlier increase the mean?

Measuring center: the median

In Chapter 1, we used the midpoint of a distribution as an informal measure of center. The *median* is the formal version of the midpoint, with a specific rule for calculation.

THE MEDIAN *M*

The **median M** is the midpoint of a distribution, the number such that half the observations are smaller and the other half are larger. To find the median of a distribution:

1. Arrange all observations in order of size, from smallest to largest.
2. If the number of observations n is odd, the median M is the center observation in the ordered list. If the number of observations n is even, the median M is midway between the two center observations in the ordered list.
3. You can always locate the median in the ordered list of observations by counting up $(n + 1)/2$ observations from the start of the list.

EXAMPLE 2.2 Finding the median: odd *n*

What is the median travel time for our 15 North Carolina workers? Here are the data arranged in order:

   5   10   10   10   10   12   15   **20**   20   25   30   30   40   40   60

The count of observations $n = 15$ is odd. The bold **20** is the center observation in the ordered list, with 7 observations to its left and 7 to its right. This is the median, $M = 20$ minutes.

Because $n = 15$, our rule for the location of the median gives

$$\text{location of M} = \frac{n + 1}{2} = \frac{16}{2} = 8$$

That is, the median is the 8th observation in the ordered list. Pay attention: the formula $(n + 1)/2$ does *not* give the median, just the location of the median in the ordered list. ■

EXAMPLE 2.3 Finding the median: even *n*

Travel times to work in New York State are (on the average) longer than in North Carolina. Here are the travel times in minutes of 20 randomly chosen New York workers:

10   30   5   25   40   20   10   15   30   20   15   20   85   15   65   15   60   60   40   45

A stemplot not only displays the distribution but makes finding the median easy because it arranges the observations in order:

```
0 | 5
1 | 005555
2 | 0005
3 | 00
4 | 005
5 |
6 | 005
7 |
8 | 5
```

The distribution is single-peaked and right-skewed, with several travel times of an hour or more. There is no center observation, but there is a center pair. These are the red 20 and 25 in the stemplot, which have 9 observations before them in the ordered list and 9 after them. The median is midway between these two observations:

$$M = \frac{20 + 25}{2} = 22.5 \text{ minutes}$$

With $n = 20$, the rule for locating the median in the list gives

$$\text{location of } M = \frac{n + 1}{2} = \frac{21}{2} = 10.5$$

The location 10.5 means "halfway between the 10th and 11th observations in the ordered list." That agrees with what we found by eye. ■

Comparing the mean and the median

Examples 2.1 and 2.2 illustrate an important difference between the mean and the median. The median travel time (the midpoint of the distribution) in North Carolina is 20 minutes. The mean travel time is higher, 22.5 minutes. The mean is pulled toward the right tail of this right-skewed distribution. The median, unlike the mean, is *resistant*. If the longest travel time were 600 minutes rather than 60 minutes, the mean would increase to more than 58 minutes but the median would not change at all.

COMPARING THE MEAN AND THE MEDIAN

The mean and median of a roughly symmetric distribution are close together. If the distribution is exactly symmetric, the mean and median are exactly the same. In a skewed distribution, the mean is usually farther out in the long tail than is the median.[2]

Many economic variables have distributions that are skewed to the right. For example, the median endowment of colleges and universities in 2007 was about $91 million—but the mean endowment was almost $524 million. Most institutions have modest endowments, but a few are very wealthy. Harvard's endowment was almost $35 billion.[3] The few wealthy institutions pull the mean up but do not affect the median. Reports about incomes and other strongly skewed distributions usually give the median ("midpoint") rather than the mean ("arithmetic average").

2.3 New York travel times. Find the mean of the travel times to work for the 20 New York workers in Example 2.3. Compare the mean and median for these data. What general fact does your comparison illustrate?

2.4 House prices. The mean and median selling prices of existing single-family homes sold in 2007 were $217,900 and $266,200.[4] Which of these numbers is the mean and which is the median? Explain how you know.

2.5 Food oils. Table 1.4 (page 25) gives the ratio of two essential fatty acids in 30 food oils. Find the mean and the median for these data. Make a histogram of the data. What feature of the distribution explains why the mean is more than 10 times as large as the median?

Measuring spread: the quartiles

The mean and median provide two different measures of the center of a distribution. A measure of center alone can be misleading. In 2007, the median income of American households was $50,233. Half of all households had incomes below $50,233, and half had higher incomes. The mean was much higher, $67,609, because the distribution of incomes is skewed to the right. But the median and mean don't tell the whole story. The bottom 10% of households had incomes less than $12,162, and households in the top 5% took in more than $177,000.[5] We are interested in the *spread* or *variability* of incomes as well as their center. *The simplest useful numerical description of a distribution requires both a measure of center and a measure of spread.*

The full spread of the data runs from the smallest to the largest observation. Because the smallest and largest observations may be outliers, we can improve our description of spread by also looking at the spread of the middle half of the data. The *quartiles* mark out the middle half. Count up the ordered list of observations, starting from the smallest. The *first quartile* lies one-quarter of the way up the list. The *third quartile* lies three-quarters of the way up the list. The second quartile is the median, which is halfway up the list. That's the idea of quartiles. We need a rule to make the idea exact. The rule for calculating the quartiles uses the rule for the median.

THE QUARTILES Q_1 AND Q_3

To calculate the **quartiles:**

1. Arrange the observations in increasing order and locate the median M in the ordered list of observations.

2. The **first quartile Q_1** is the median of the observations whose position in the ordered list is to the left of the location of the overall median.

3. The **third quartile Q_3** is the median of the observations whose position in the ordered list is to the right of the location of the overall median.

Here are examples that show how the rules for the quartiles work for both odd and even numbers of observations.

EXAMPLE 2.4 **Finding the quartiles: odd *n***

Our North Carolina sample of 15 workers' travel times, arranged in increasing order, is

5 10 10 10 10 12 15 **20** 20 25 30 30 40 40 60

There is an odd number of observations, so the median is the middle one, the bold **20** in the list. The first quartile is the median of the 7 observations to the left of the median. This is the 4th of these 7 observations, so $Q_1 = 10$ minutes. If you want, you can use the rule for the location of the median with $n = 7$:

$$\text{location of } Q_1 = \frac{n+1}{2} = \frac{7+1}{2} = 4$$

The third quartile is the median of the 7 observations to the right of the median, $Q_3 = 30$ minutes. *When there is an odd number of observations, leave out the overall median when you locate the quartiles in the ordered list.*

The quartiles are *resistant* because they are not affected by a few extreme observations. For example, Q_3 would still be 30 if the outlier were 600 rather than 60. ■

EXAMPLE 2.5 **Finding the quartiles: even *n***

Here are the travel times to work of the 20 New Yorkers from Example 2.3, arranged in increasing order:

5 10 10 15 15 15 15 20 20 20 | 25 30 30 40 40 45 60 60 65 85

There is an even number of observations, so the median lies midway between the middle pair, the 10th and 11th in the list. Its value is $M = 22.5$ minutes. We have marked the location of the median by |. The first quartile is the median of the first 10 observations, because these are the observations to the left of the location of the median. Check that $Q_1 = 15$ minutes and $Q_3 = 42.5$ minutes. *When the number of observations is even, include all the observations when you locate the quartiles.* ■

Mitchell Funk/Getty Images

Be careful when, as in these examples, several observations take the same numerical value. Write down all of the observations, arrange them in order, and apply the rules just as if they all had distinct values.

The five-number summary and boxplots

The smallest and largest observations tell us little about the distribution as a whole, but they give information about the tails of the distribution that is missing if we know only the median and the quartiles. To get a quick summary of both center and spread, combine all five numbers.

THE FIVE-NUMBER SUMMARY

The **five-number summary** of a distribution consists of the smallest observation, the first quartile, the median, the third quartile, and the largest observation, written in order from smallest to largest. In symbols, the five-number summary is

Minimum Q_1 M Q_3 Maximum

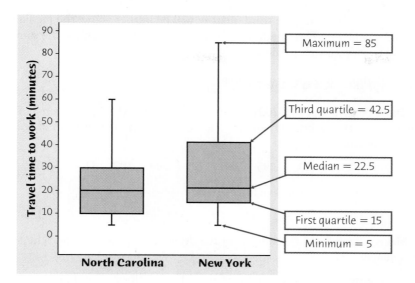

FIGURE 2.1
Boxplots comparing the travel times to work of samples of workers in North Carolina and New York.

These five numbers offer a reasonably complete description of center and spread. The five-number summaries of travel times to work from Examples 2.4 and 2.5 are

North Carolina	5	10	20	30	60
New York	5	15	22.5	42.5	85

The five-number summary of a distribution leads to a new graph, the *boxplot*. Figure 2.1 shows boxplots comparing travel times to work in North Carolina and New York.

BOXPLOT

A **boxplot** is a graph of the five-number summary.

- A central box spans the quartiles Q_1 and Q_3.
- A line in the box marks the median M.
- Lines extend from the box out to the smallest and largest observations.

Boxplots show less detail than histograms or stemplots, so they are best used for side-by-side comparison of more than one distribution, as in Figure 2.1. When you look at a boxplot, first find the median, which marks the center of the distribution. Then look at the spread. The span of the central box shows the spread of the middle half of the data, and the smallest and largest observations show the spread of the entire data set. We see from Figure 2.1 that travel times to work are in general a bit longer in New York than in North Carolina. The median, both quartiles, and the maximum are all larger in New York. New York travel times are also more variable, as shown by the span of the box and the spread from smallest to largest time.

Finally, the New York data are more strongly right-skewed. In a symmetric distribution, the first and third quartiles are equally distant from the median. In most distributions that are skewed to the right, the third quartile will be farther above the median than the first quartile is below it. The smallest and largest observations behave the same way, but remember that they may be outliers.

APPLY YOUR KNOWLEDGE

2.6 The Dallas Cowboys. The 2007 roster of the Dallas Cowboys professional football team included 9 defensive linemen and 10 offensive linemen. The weights in pounds of the defensive linemen were

300   300   295   255   298   298   300   310   300

and the weights of the offensive linemen were

312   305   340   320   366   324   309   315   305   305

(a) Make a stemplot of the weights of the defensive linemen and find the five-number summary.

(b) Make a stemplot of the weights of the offensive linemen and find the five-number summary.

(c) Does either group contain one or more clear outliers? Which group of players tends to be heavier?

2.7 Comparing investments. Should you put your money into a fund that buys stocks or a fund that invests in real estate? The boxplots in Figure 2.2 compare the daily returns (in percent) on a "total stock market" fund and a real estate fund over a year ending in November 2007.[6]

(a) Read the graph: about what were the highest and lowest daily returns on the stock fund?

(b) Read the graph: the median return was about the same on both investments. About what was the median return?

(c) What is the most important difference between the two distributions?

FIGURE 2.2

Boxplots comparing the distributions of daily returns on two kinds of investment, for Exercise 2.7.

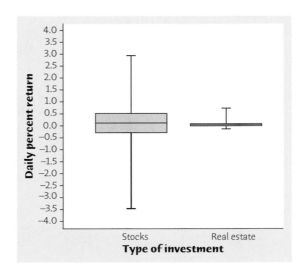

Measuring spread: the standard deviation

The five-number summary is not the most common numerical description of a distribution. That distinction belongs to the combination of the mean to measure center and the *standard deviation* to measure spread. The standard deviation and its close relative, the *variance*, measure spread by looking at how far the observations are from their mean.

THE STANDARD DEVIATION s

The **variance** s^2 of a set of observations is an average of the squares of the deviations of the observations from their mean. In symbols, the variance of n observations $x_1, x_2, \ldots, x_n$ is

$$s^2 = \frac{(x_1 - \overline{x})^2 + (x_2 - \overline{x})^2 + \cdots + (x_n - \overline{x})^2}{n-1}$$

or, more compactly,

$$s^2 = \frac{1}{n-1}\sum(x_i - \overline{x})^2$$

The **standard deviation** s is the square root of the variance s^2:

$$s = \sqrt{\frac{1}{n-1}\sum(x_i - \overline{x})^2}$$

In practice, use software or your calculator to obtain the standard deviation from keyed-in data. Doing an example step-by-step will help you understand how the variance and standard deviation work, however.

EXAMPLE 2.6   **Calculating the standard deviation**

A person's metabolic rate is the rate at which the body consumes energy. Metabolic rate is important in studies of weight gain, dieting, and exercise. Here are the metabolic rates of 7 men who took part in a study of dieting. The units are calories per 24 hours. These are the same calories used to describe the energy content of foods.

    1792   1666   1362   1614   1460   1867   1439

The researchers reported $\overline{x}$ and s for these men. First find the mean:

$$\overline{x} = \frac{1792 + 1666 + 1362 + 1614 + 1460 + 1867 + 1439}{7}$$

$$= \frac{11,200}{7} = 1600 \text{ calories}$$

FIGURE 2.3
Metabolic rates for 7 men, with
their mean (∗) and the
deviations of two observations
from the mean, for Example 2.6.

Figure 2.3 displays the data as points above the number line, with their mean marked by an asterisk (∗). The arrows mark two of the deviations from the mean. The deviations show how spread out the data are about their mean. They are the starting point for calculating the variance and the standard deviation.

Observations x_i	Deviations $x_i - \bar{x}$	Squared deviations $(x_i - \bar{x})^2$
1792	$1792 - 1600 = 192$	$192^2 = 36{,}864$
1666	$1666 - 1600 = 66$	$66^2 = 4{,}356$
1362	$1362 - 1600 = -238$	$(-238)^2 = 56{,}644$
1614	$1614 - 1600 = 14$	$14^2 = 196$
1460	$1460 - 1600 = -140$	$(-140)^2 = 19{,}600$
1867	$1867 - 1600 = 267$	$267^2 = 71{,}289$
1439	$1439 - 1600 = -161$	$(-161)^2 = 25{,}921$
	sum = 0	sum = 214,870

The variance is the sum of the squared deviations divided by one less than the number of observations:

$$s^2 = \frac{1}{n-1}\sum(x_i - \bar{x})^2 = \frac{214{,}870}{6} = 35{,}811.67$$

The standard deviation is the square root of the variance:

$$s = \sqrt{35{,}811.67} = 189.24 \text{ calories} \quad \blacksquare$$

Notice that the "average" in the variance s^2 divides the sum by one fewer than the number of observations, $n-1$ rather than n. The reason is that the n deviations $x_i - \bar{x}$ always sum to exactly 0, so that knowing $n-1$ of them determines the last one. The number $n-1$ is called the **degrees of freedom** of the variance or standard deviation. Here are the most important properties of the standard deviation:

degrees of freedom

- s measures *spread about the mean* and should be used only when the mean is chosen as the measure of center.
- s is *always zero or greater than zero*. $s = 0$ only when there is no spread. This happens only when all observations have the same value. Otherwise, $s > 0$. As the observations become more spread out about their mean, s gets larger.
- s has the *same units of measurement as the original observations*. For example, if you measure metabolic rates in calories, both the mean $\bar{x}$ and the standard deviation s are also in calories. This is one reason to prefer s to the variance s^2, which is in squared calories.
- Like the mean $\bar{x}$, s is *not resistant*. A few outliers can make s very large.

Choosing measures of center and spread

We now have a choice between two descriptions of the center and spread of a distribution: the five-number summary, or $\bar{x}$ and s. Because $\bar{x}$ and s are sensitive to extreme observations, they can be misleading when a distribution is strongly skewed or has outliers. In fact, because the two sides of a skewed distribution have different spreads, no single number such as s describes the spread well. The five-number summary, with its two quartiles and two extremes, does a better job.

CHOOSING A SUMMARY

The five-number summary is usually better than the mean and standard deviation for describing a skewed distribution or a distribution with strong outliers. Use $\bar{x}$ and s only for reasonably symmetric distributions that are free of outliers.

Outliers can greatly affect the values of the mean $\bar{x}$ and the standard deviation s, the most common measures of center and spread. Many more elaborate statistical procedures also can't be trusted when outliers are present. *Whenever you find outliers in your data, try to find an explanation for them.* Sometimes the explanation is as simple as a typing error, such as typing 10.1 as 101. In such cases you can simply correct or remove the outlier. When outliers are "real data," like the long travel times of some New York workers, you should choose statistical methods that are not greatly disturbed by the outliers. For example, use the five-number summary rather than $\bar{x}$ and s to describe a distribution with extreme outliers.

Remember that a graph gives the best overall picture of a distribution. Numerical measures of center and spread report specific facts about a distribution, but they do not describe its entire shape. Numerical summaries do not disclose the presence of multiple peaks or clusters, for example. Exercise 2.9 shows how misleading numerical summaries can be.

APPLY YOUR KNOWLEDGE

2.8 $\bar{x}$ and s by hand. The air in poultry-processing plants often contains high concentrations of fungus spores, especially during the summer. To measure the presence of spores, air samples are pumped to an agar plate and "colony-forming units (CFUs)" are counted after an incubation period. The CFUs per cubic meter of air in one location for four summer days were 3175, 2526, 1763, and 1090.[7] A graph of only 4 observations gives little information, so we proceed to compute the mean and standard deviation.

(a) Find the mean step-by-step. That is, find the sum of the 4 observations and divide by 4.

(b) Find the standard deviation step-by-step. That is, find the deviations of each observation from the mean, square the deviations, then obtain the variance and the standard deviation. Example 2.6 shows the method.

(c) Now enter the data into your calculator and use the mean and standard deviation buttons to obtain $\bar{x}$ and s. Do the results agree with your hand calculations?

2.9 $\bar{x}$ and s are not enough. Data sets with different shapes can have the same mean and standard deviation. To demonstrate this fact, use your calculator to find $\bar{x}$ and s for these two small data sets. Then make a stemplot of each and comment on the shape of each distribution.

Data A	9.14	8.14	8.74	8.77	9.26	8.10	6.13	3.10	9.13	7.26	4.74
Data B	6.58	5.76	7.71	8.84	8.47	7.04	5.25	5.56	7.91	6.89	12.50

2.10 Choose a summary. The shape of a distribution is a rough guide to whether the mean and standard deviation are a helpful summary of center and spread. For which of the following distributions would $\bar{x}$ and s be useful? In each case, give a reason for your decision.

(a) Percents of foreign-born residents in the states, Figure 1.5 (page 11).

(b) Iowa Test scores, Figure 1.7 (page 14).

(c) Breaking strength of wood, Figure 1.11 (page 18).

Using technology

Computer software or a graphing calculator will do calculations and make graphs as you command, freeing you to concentrate on choosing the right methods and interpreting your results. Figure 2.4 displays output describing the travel times to work of 20 people in New York State (Example 2.3). Can you find $\bar{x}$, s, and the five-number summary in each output? The big message of this section is: *once you know what to look for, you can read output from any technological tool.*

The displays in Figure 2.4 come from a Texas Instruments graphing calculator, the Minitab statistical program, and the Microsoft Excel spreadsheet program. Minitab allows you to choose what descriptive measures you want. Excel and the calculator give some things we don't need. Just ignore the extras. Excel's "Descriptive Statistics" menu item doesn't give the quartiles. We used the spreadsheet's separate quartile function to get Q_1 and Q_3.

EXAMPLE 2.7 **What is the third quartile?**

In Example 2.5, we saw that the quartiles of the New York travel times are $Q_1 = 15$ and $Q_3 = 42.5$. Look at the output displays in Figure 2.4. The calculator and Excel agree with our work. Minitab says that $Q_3 = 43.75$. What happened? *There are several rules for finding the quartiles. Some calculators and software use rules that give results different from ours for some sets of data.* This is true of Minitab and also of Excel, though Excel agrees with our work in this example. Results from the various rules are always close to each other, so that the differences are never important in practice. Our rule is the simplest for hand calculation. ■

Organizing a statistical problem

Making graphs and calculations isn't all there is to doing statistics—we need to use data to draw conclusions about real-world settings. For example, water depth in the Everglades has a yearly cycle that reflects Florida's wet and dry seasons, and travel times to work are generally longer in New York than in North Carolina.

Texas Instruments Graphing Calculator

Minitab

Descriptive Statistics: NYtime

| | | Total | | | | | | | |
variable	Count	Mean	StDev	Variance	Minimum	Q1	Median	Q3	Maximum
NYtime	20	31.25	21.88	478.62	5.00	15.00	22.50	43.75	85.00

Microsoft Excel

	A	B	C	D
1	*minutes*			
2				
3	Mean	31.25		
4	Standard Error	4.891924064		
5	Median	22.5	QUARTILE(A2:A21,1)	15
6	Mode	15	QUARTILE(A2:A21,3)	42.5
7	Standard Deviation	21.8773495		
8	Sample Variance	478.6184211		
9	Kurtosis	0.329884126		
10	Skewness	1.040110836		
11	Range	80		
12	Minimum	5		
13	Maximum	85		
14	Sum	625		
15	Count	20		

Sheet4 / Sheet1 / Sheet2 / Sheet

FIGURE 2.4

Output from a graphing calculator, a statistical software package, and a spreadsheet program describing the data on travel times to work in New York State.

As you learn more statistical tools and principles, you will face more complex statistical problems. Although no framework accommodates all the varied issues that arise in applying statistics to real settings, the following four-step thought process gives useful guidance. In particular, the first and last steps emphasize that statistical problems are tied to specific real-world settings.

> ### ORGANIZING A STATISTICAL PROBLEM: A FOUR-STEP PROCESS
>
> **STATE:** What is the practical question, in the context of the real-world setting?
>
> **PLAN:** What specific statistical operations does this problem call for?
>
> **SOLVE:** Make the graphs and carry out the calculations needed for this problem.
>
> **CONCLUDE:** Give your practical conclusion in the setting of the real-world problem.

To help you master the basics, many exercises will continue to tell you what to do—make a histogram, find the five-number summary, and so on. Real statistical problems don't come with detailed instructions. From now on, especially in the later chapters of the book, you will meet some exercises that are more realistic. Use the four-step process as a guide to solving and reporting these problems. They are marked with the four-step icon, as the following example illustrates.

EXAMPLE 2.8 Comparing tropical flowers

STATE: Ethan Temeles and W. John Kress of Amherst College studied the relationship between varieties of the tropical flower *Heliconia* and the hummingbirds that fertilize the flowers.[8] The researchers conjecture that flower varieties fertilized by different hummingbird species should have distinct distributions of length.

Table 2.1 gives length measurements (in millimeters) for samples of three varieties of *Heliconia*, each fertilized by a different species of hummingbird. Do the three varieties display distinct distributions of length? How do the mean lengths compare?

TABLE 2.1 Flower lengths (millimeters) for three *Heliconia* varieties

			H. bihai				
47.12	46.75	46.81	47.12	46.67	47.43	46.44	46.64
48.07	48.34	48.15	50.26	50.12	46.34	46.94	48.36
			H. caribaea red				
41.90	42.01	41.93	43.09	41.47	41.69	39.78	40.57
39.63	42.18	40.66	37.87	39.16	37.40	38.20	38.07
38.10	37.97	38.79	38.23	38.87	37.78	38.01	
			H. caribaea yellow				
36.78	37.02	36.52	36.11	36.03	35.45	38.13	37.10
35.17	36.82	36.66	35.68	36.03	34.57	34.63	

PLAN: Use graphs and numerical descriptions to describe and compare these three distributions of flower length.

SOLVE: We might use boxplots to compare the distributions, but stemplots preserve more detail and work well for data sets of these sizes. Figure 2.5 displays stemplots with the stems lined up for easy comparison. The lengths have been rounded to the nearest tenth of a millimeter. The *bihai* and red varieties have somewhat skewed distributions, so we might

Art Wolfe/Getty Images

```
    bihai                        red                          yellow
    34 |                         34 |                          34 | 6 6
    35 |                         35 |                          35 | 2 5 7
    36 |                         36 |                          36 | 0 0 1 5 7 8 8
    37 |                         37 | 4 8 9                     37 | 0 1
    38 |                         38 | 0 0 1 1 2 2 8 9           38 | 1
    39 |                         39 | 2 6 8                     39 |
    40 |                         40 | 6 7                       40 |
    41 |                         41 | 5 7 9 9                   41 |
    42 |                         42 | 0 2                       42 |
    43 |                         43 | 1                         43 |
    44 |                         44 |                           44 |
    45 |                         45 |                           45 |
    46 | 3 4 6 7 8 8 9           46 |                           46 |
    47 | 1 1 4                   47 |                           47 |
    48 | 1 2 3 4                 48 |                           48 |
    49 |                         49 |                           49 |
    50 | 1 3                     50 |                           50 |
```

FIGURE 2.5
Stemplots comparing the distributions of flower lengths from Table 2.1, for Example 2.8. The stems are whole millimeters and the leaves are tenths of a millimeter.

choose to compare the five-number summaries. But because the researchers plan to use $\bar{x}$ and s for further analysis, we instead calculate these measures:

Variety	Mean length	Standard deviation
bihai	47.60	1.213
red	39.71	1.799
yellow	36.18	0.975

CONCLUDE: The three varieties differ so much in flower length that there is little overlap among them. In particular, the flowers of *bihai* are longer than either red or yellow. The mean lengths are 47.6 mm for *H. bihai*, 39.7 mm for *H. caribaea* red, and 36.2 mm for *H. caribaea* yellow. ■

APPLY YOUR KNOWLEDGE

2.11 **Logging in the rain forest.** "Conservationists have despaired over destruction of tropical rain forest by logging, clearing, and burning." These words begin a report on a statistical study of the effects of logging in Borneo.[9] Charles Cannon of Duke University and his coworkers compared forest plots that had never been logged (Group 1) with similar plots nearby that had been logged 1 year earlier (Group 2) and 8 years earlier (Group 3). All plots were 0.1 hectare in area. Here are the counts of trees for plots in each group:

```
Group 1:   27   22   29   21   19   33   16   20   24   27   28   19
Group 2:   12   12   15    9   20   18   17   14   14    2   17   19
Group 3:   18    4   22   15   18   19   22   12   12
```

To what extent has logging affected the count of trees? Follow the four-step process in reporting your work.

2.12 Diplomatic scofflaws. Until Congress allowed some enforcement in 2002, foreign diplomats in New York City could freely violate parking laws. Two economists looked at the number of unpaid parking tickets per diplomat over a five-year period ending when enforcement reduced the problem.[10] They concluded that large numbers of unpaid tickets lined up well with measures of the degree of corruption in various countries. The data file *ex02-12.dat* on the text Web site and CD contains data for 145 countries. The first 32 countries in the list (Australia to Trinidad and Tobago) are classified by the World Bank as "developed" based on their national income. The remaining countries (Albania to Zimbabwe) are "developing."

Give a full description of the distribution of unpaid tickets for both groups of countries and identify any high outliers. Compare the two groups. Does national income alone do a good job of distinguishing countries whose diplomats do and do not obey parking laws?

CHAPTER 2 SUMMARY

- A numerical summary of a distribution should report at least its **center** and its **spread** or **variability.**

- The **mean** $\bar{x}$ and the **median M** describe the center of a distribution in different ways. The mean is the arithmetic average of the observations, and the median is the midpoint of the values.

- When you use the median to indicate the center of the distribution, describe its spread by giving the **quartiles.** The **first quartile** Q_1 has one-fourth of the observations below it, and the **third quartile** Q_3 has three-fourths of the observations below it.

- The **five-number summary** consists of the median, the quartiles, and the smallest and largest individual observations. The median describes the center, and the quartiles and extremes show the spread.

- **Boxplots** based on the five-number summary are useful for comparing several distributions. The box spans the quartiles and shows the spread of the central half of the distribution. The median is marked within the box. Lines extend from the box to the smallest and largest observations to show the full spread of the data.

- The **variance** s^2 and especially its square root, the **standard deviation** s, measure spread about the mean as center. The standard deviation s is zero when there is no spread and gets larger as the spread increases.

- A **resistant measure** of any aspect of a distribution is relatively unaffected by changes in the numerical value of a small proportion of the total number of observations, no matter how large these changes are. The median and quartiles are resistant, but the mean and the standard deviation are not.

- The mean and standard deviation are good descriptions for symmetric distributions without outliers. The five-number summary is a better description for skewed distributions.

- Numerical summaries do not fully describe the shape of a distribution. Always plot your data.

- A statistical problem has a real-world setting. You can organize many problems using the four steps **state, plan, solve,** and **conclude.**

CHECK YOUR SKILLS

2.13 Here are the amounts of money (cents) in coins carried by 10 students in a statistics class:

    50   35   0   97   76   0   0   87   23   65

The mean of these data is
(a) 37.2.   (b) 42.5.   (c) 43.3.

2.14 The standard deviation of the 10 amounts of money in Exercise 2.13 (use your calculator) is about
(a) 35.3.   (b) 37.2.   (c) 43.3.

2.15 The five-number summary of the data in Exercise 2.13 is
(a) 0, 0, 42.5, 76, 97.
(b) 0, 29, 57.5, 81.5, 97.
(c) 0, 29, 42.5, 75, 97.

2.16 If a distribution is skewed to the right,
(a) the mean is less than the median.
(b) the mean and median are equal.
(c) the mean is greater than the median.

2.17 What percent of the observations in a distribution lie between the first quartile and the third quartile?
(a) 25%   (b) 50%   (c) 75%

2.18 You have data on the weights in grams of 5 baby pythons. The mean weight is 31.8 and the standard deviation of the weights is 2.39. The correct units for the standard deviation are
(a) no units—it's just a number.
(b) grams.
(c) grams squared.

2.19 Which of the following is least affected if an extreme high outlier is added to your data?
(a) The median
(b) The mean
(c) The standard deviation

CHAPTER 2 EXERCISES

2.20 Incomes of college grads. According to the Census Bureau, the mean and median 2007 income of people at least 25 years old who had a bachelor's degree but no higher degree were $47,240 and $59,365. Which of these numbers is the mean and which is the median? Explain your reasoning.

2.21 Saving for retirement. Retirement seems a long way off and we need money now, so saving for retirement is hard. Among households with an employed person aged 21 to 64, only 63% own a retirement account. The mean value in these accounts is $112,300, but the median value is just $31,600. For people 55 or older, the mean is $222,100 and the median

is $64,400.[11] What explains the differences between the two measures of center?

2.22 University endowments. The National Association of College and University Business Officers collects data on college endowments. In 2007, 785 colleges and universities reported the value of their endowments. When the endowment values are arranged in order, what are the positions of the median and the quartiles in this ordered list?

2.23 Pulling wood apart. Example 1.9 (page 17) gives the breaking strengths of 20 pieces of Douglas fir.
(a) Give the five-number summary of the distribution of breaking strengths. (The stemplot, Figure 1.11, helps you arrange the data in order, but you should use the unrounded values in numerical work.)
(b) The stemplot shows that the distribution is skewed to the left. Does the five-number summary show the skew? Remember that only a graph gives a clear picture of the shape of a distribution.

2.24 Comparing tropical flowers. An alternative presentation of the flower length data in Table 2.1 reports the five-number summary and uses boxplots to display the distributions. Do this. Do the boxplots fail to reveal any important information visible in the stemplots in Figure 2.5?

2.25 How much fruit do adolescent girls eat? Figure 1.13 (page 23) is a histogram of the number of servings of fruit per day claimed by 74 seventeen-year-old girls. With a little care, you can find the median and the quartiles from the histogram. What are these numbers? How did you find them?

2.26 Weight of newborns. Here is the distribution of the weight at birth for all babies born in the United States in 2005:[12]

Weight (grams)	Count	Weight (grams)	Count
Less than 500	6,599	3,000 to 3,499	1,596,944
500 to 999	23,864	3,500 to 3,999	1,114,887
1,000 to 1,499	31,325	4,000 to 4,499	289,098
1,500 to 1,999	66,453	4,500 to 4,999	42,119
2,000 to 2,499	210,324	5,000 to 5,499	4,715
2,500 to 2,999	748,042		

(a) For comparison with other years and with other countries, we prefer a histogram of the *percents* in each weight class rather than the counts. Explain why.
(b) How many babies were there? Make a histogram of the distribution, using percents on the vertical scale.
(c) What are the positions of the median and quartiles in the ordered list of all birth weights? In which weight classes do the median and quartiles fall?

2.27 More on study times. In Exercise 1.32 (page 26) you examined the nightly study time claimed by first-year college men and women. The most common methods for formal comparison of two groups use $\bar{x}$ and s to summarize the data.
(a) What kinds of distributions are best summarized by $\bar{x}$ and s?
(b) One student in each group claimed to study at least 300 minutes (five hours) per night. How much does removing these observations change $\bar{x}$ and s for each group?

2.28 Guinea pig survival times. Here are the survival times in days of 72 guinea pigs after they were injected with infectious bacteria in a medical experiment.[13] Survival times, whether of machines under stress or cancer patients after treatment, usually have distributions that are skewed to the right.

43	45	53	56	56	57	58	66	67	73	74	79
80	80	81	81	81	82	83	83	84	88	89	91
91	92	92	97	99	99	100	100	101	102	102	102
103	104	107	108	109	113	114	118	121	123	126	128
137	138	139	144	145	147	156	162	174	178	179	184
191	198	211	214	243	249	329	380	403	511	522	598

Dorling Kindersley/Getty Images

(a) Graph the distribution and describe its main features. Does it show the expected right skew?
(b) Which numerical summary would you choose for these data? Calculate your chosen summary. How does it reflect the skewness of the distribution?

2.29 Never on Sunday: also in Canada? Exercise 1.5 (page 9) gives the number of births in the United States on each day of the week during an entire year. The boxplots in Figure 2.6 are based on more detailed data from Toronto, Canada: the number of births on each of the 365 days in a year, grouped by day of the week.[14] Based on these plots, give a more detailed description of how births depend on the day of the week.

2.30 Thinking about means. Table 1.1 (page 10) gives the percent of foreign-born residents in each of the states. For the nation as a whole, 12.5% of residents are foreign-born. Find the mean of the 51 entries in Table 1.1. It is *not* 12.5%. Explain carefully why this happens. (*Hint:* The states with the largest populations are California, Texas, New York, and Florida. Look at their entries in Table 1.1.)

2.31 Thinking about medians. A report says that "the median credit card debt of American households is zero." We know

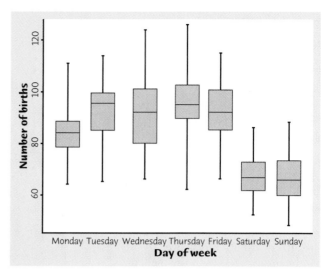

FIGURE 2.6
Boxplots of the distributions of numbers of births in Toronto, Canada, on each day of the week during a year, for Exercise 2.29.

that many households have large amounts of credit card debt. Explain how the median debt can nonetheless be zero.

2.32 A standard deviation contest. This is a standard deviation contest. You must choose four numbers from the whole numbers 0 to 10, with repeats allowed.
(a) Choose four numbers that have the smallest possible standard deviation.
(b) Choose four numbers that have the largest possible standard deviation.
(c) Is more than one choice possible in either (a) or (b)? Explain.

2.33 Test your technology. This exercise requires a calculator with a standard deviation button or software with a standard deviation function. The observations

$$10,001 \qquad 10,002 \qquad 10,003$$

have mean $\bar{x} = 10,002$ and standard deviation $s = 1$. Adding a 0 in the center of each number, the next set becomes

$$100,001 \qquad 100,002 \qquad 100,003$$

The standard deviation remains $s = 1$ as more 0s are added. Use your calculator or software to find the standard deviation of these numbers, adding extra 0s until you get an incorrect answer. How soon did you go wrong? This demonstrates that calculators and software cannot handle an arbitrary number of digits correctly.

2.34 You create the data. Create a set of 5 positive numbers (repeats allowed) that have median 10 and mean 7. What thought process did you use to create your numbers?

2.35 You create the data. Give an example of a small set of data for which the mean is larger than the third quartile.

Exercises 2.36 to 2.41 ask you to analyze data without having the details outlined for you. The exercise statements give you the **State** *step of the four-step process. In your work, follow the* **Plan, Solve,** *and* **Conclude** *steps as illustrated in Example 2.8.*

2.36 Athletes' salaries. In 2007, the Boston Red Sox won the World Series for the second time in 4 years. Table 2.2 gives the salaries of the 25 players on the Red Sox World Series roster. Provide the team owner with a full description of the distribution of salaries and a brief summary of its most important features.

2.37 Returns on stocks. How well have stocks done over the past generation? The Wilshire 5000 index describes the average performance of all U.S. stocks. The average is weighted by the total market value of each company's stock, so think of the index as measuring the performance of the average investor. Here are the percent returns on the Wilshire 5000 index for the years 1971 to 2008:

Year	Return	Year	Return	Year	Return
1971	16.19	1984	3.27	1997	31.48
1972	17.34	1985	31.46	1998	24.31
1973	−18.78	1986	15.61	1999	24.23
1974	−27.87	1987	1.75	2000	−10.89
1975	37.38	1988	17.59	2001	−10.97
1976	26.77	1989	28.53	2002	−20.86
1977	−2.97	1990	−6.03	2003	31.64
1978	8.54	1991	33.58	2004	12.48
1979	24.40	1992	9.02	2005	6.38
1980	33.21	1993	10.67	2006	15.77
1981	−3.98	1994	0.06	2007	5.62
1982	20.43	1995	36.41	2008	−37.23
1983	22.71	1996	21.56		

What can you say about the distribution of yearly returns on stocks?

2.38 Do good smells bring good business? Businesses know that customers often respond to background music. Do they also respond to odors? Nicolas Guéguen and his colleagues studied this question in a small pizza restaurant in France on Saturday evenings in May. On one evening, a relaxing lavender odor was spread through the restaurant; on another evening, a stimulating lemon odor; a third evening served as a control, with no odor. Table 2.3 (page 48) shows the amounts (in euros) that customers spent on each of these evenings.[15] Compare the three distributions. What effect did the two odors have on customer spending?

2.39 Daily activity and obesity. People gain weight when they take in more energy from food than they expend. Table 2.4 (page 48) compares volunteer subjects who were lean with others who were mildly obese. None of the subjects followed an exercise program. The subjects wore sensors that recorded every move for 10 days. The table shows the average minutes per day spent in activity (standing and walking) and in lying down.[16] Compare the distributions of time spent actively for lean and obese subjects and also the distributions of time spent lying down. How does the behavior of lean and mildly obese people differ?

2.40 Compressing soil. Farmers know that driving heavy equipment on wet soil compresses the soil and hinders the growth of crops. Table 2.5 (page 48) gives data on the "penetrability" of the same soil at three levels of compression.[17] Penetrability is a measure of the resistance plant roots meet when they grow through the soil. Low penetrability means high resistance. How does increasing compression affect penetrability?

2.41 Does breast-feeding weaken bones? Breast-feeding mothers secrete calcium into their milk. Some of

(*Text continues on page 49.*)

TABLE 2.2 Salaries for the 2007 Boston Red Sox World Series team

PLAYER	SALARY	PLAYER	SALARY	PLAYER	SALARY
Josh Beckett	$6,666,667	Jon Lester	$384,000	Jonathan Papelbon	$425,000
Alex Cora	$2,000,000	Javier López	$402,000	Dustin Pedroia	$380,000
Coco Crisp	$3,833,333	Mike Lowell	$9,000,000	Manny Ramirez	$17,016,381
Manny Delcarmen	$380,000	Julio Lugo	$8,250,000	Curt Schilling	$13,000,000
J. D. Drew	$14,400,000	Daisuke Matsuzaka	$6,333,333	Kyle Snyder	$535,000
Jacoby Ellsbury	$380,000	Doug Mirabelli	$750,000	Mike Timlin	$2,800,000
Eric Gagné	$6,000,000	Hideki Okajimi	$1,225,000	Jason Varitek	$11,000,000
Eric Hinske	$5,725,000	David Ortiz	$13,250,000	Kevin Youkilis	$424,000
Bobby Kielty	$2,100,000				

TABLE 2.3 Amount spent (euros) by customers in a restaurant when exposed to odors

No odor

15.9	18.5	15.9	18.5	18.5	21.9	15.9	15.9	15.9	15.9
15.9	18.5	18.5	18.5	20.5	18.5	18.5	15.9	15.9	15.9
18.5	18.5	15.9	18.5	15.9	18.5	15.9	25.5	12.9	15.9

Lemon odor

18.5	15.9	18.5	18.5	18.5	15.9	18.5	15.9	18.5	18.5
15.9	18.5	21.5	15.9	21.9	15.9	18.5	18.5	18.5	18.5
25.9	15.9	15.9	15.9	18.5	18.5	18.5	18.5		

Lavender odor

21.9	18.5	22.3	21.9	18.5	24.9	18.5	22.5	21.5	21.9
21.5	18.5	25.5	18.5	18.5	21.9	18.5	18.5	24.9	21.9
25.9	21.9	18.5	18.5	22.8	18.5	21.9	20.7	21.9	22.5

TABLE 2.4 Time (minutes per day) active and lying down by lean and obese subjects

LEAN SUBJECTS			OBESE SUBJECTS		
SUBJECT	STAND/WALK	LIE	SUBJECT	STAND/WALK	LIE
1	511.100	555.500	11	260.244	521.044
2	607.925	450.650	12	464.756	514.931
3	319.212	537.362	13	367.138	563.300
4	584.644	489.269	14	413.667	532.208
5	578.869	514.081	15	347.375	504.931
6	543.388	506.500	16	416.531	448.856
7	677.188	467.700	17	358.650	460.550
8	555.656	567.006	18	267.344	509.981
9	374.831	531.431	19	410.631	448.706
10	504.700	396.962	20	426.356	412.919

TABLE 2.5 Penetrability of soil at three compression levels

COMPRESSED		INTERMEDIATE		LOOSE	
2.86	3.08	3.14	3.54	3.99	4.11
2.68	2.82	3.38	3.36	4.20	4.30
2.92	2.78	3.10	3.18	3.94	3.96
2.82	2.98	3.40	3.12	4.16	4.03
2.76	3.00	3.38	3.86	4.29	4.89
2.81	2.78	3.14	2.92	4.19	4.12
2.78	2.96	3.18	3.46	4.13	4.00
3.08	2.90	3.26	3.44	4.41	4.34
2.94	3.18	2.96	3.62	3.98	4.27
2.86	3.16	3.02	4.26	4.41	4.91

the calcium may come from their bones, so mothers may lose bone mineral. Researchers compared 47 breast-feeding women with 22 women of similar age who were neither pregnant nor lactating. They measured the percent change in the mineral content of the women's spines over three months. The chart gives the data.[18]

Breast-feeding women						Other women					
−4.7	−2.5	−4.9	−2.7	−0.8	−5.3	2.4	0.0	0.9	−0.2	1.0	1.7
−8.3	−2.1	−6.8	−4.3	2.2	−7.8	2.9	−0.6	1.1	−0.1	−0.4	0.3
−3.1	−1.0	−6.5	−1.8	−5.2	−5.7	1.2	−1.6	−0.1	−1.5	0.7	−0.4
−7.0	−2.2	−6.5	−1.0	−3.0	−3.6	2.2	−0.4	−2.2	−0.1		
−5.2	−2.0	−2.1	−5.6	−4.4	−3.3						
−4.0	−4.9	−4.7	−3.8	−5.9	−2.5						
−0.3	−6.2	−6.8	1.7	0.3	−2.3						
0.4	−5.3	0.2	−2.2	−5.1							

Do the data show distinctly greater bone mineral loss among the breast-feeding women?

2.42 Canadians' earnings in 1901. Table 2.6 presents the "earnings from occupation or trade" in the year 1901 of a random sample of those Canadians who did have earnings in that year. The amounts are in Canadian dollars. If they seem low, remember that a loaf of bread cost 4 cents and a pound of beef 14 cents.[19] Of course, Canadians today have much higher incomes, even after adjusting for inflation. Give a complete graphical and numerical description of these data, and briefly describe your findings.

TABLE 2.6 Earnings (dollars) of a sample of 200 Canadians in 1901

400	360	400	200	150	175	60	96	600	100
125	525	500	200	175	360	50	300	175	480
300	500	160	960	300	96	500	170	380	600
300	10	250	200	124	350	150	225	600	100
250	250	220	100	200	250	100	256	399	125
100	360	250	600	400	450	150	550	250	240
100	970	240	300	100	400	450	125	250	225
480	350	300	100	144	500	200	150	225	240
250	300	250	150	100	225	96	200	500	20
250	500	100	165	350	200	200	500	300	57
1000	200	800	415	450	190	360	180	1200	100
320	240	100	208	8	142	420	300	700	600
205	150	75	205	300	300	350	150	450	350
450	462	350	1500	120	200	300	225	475	2000
150	325	300	150	720	140	350	150	85	400
184	125	300	500	340	150	160	480	300	376
220	1000	300	2200	350	290	700	120	700	600
375	150	450	360	500	575	500	400	350	180
600	300	1000	600	300	80	1000	300	390	499
210	500	550	450	520	200	300	200	540	1200

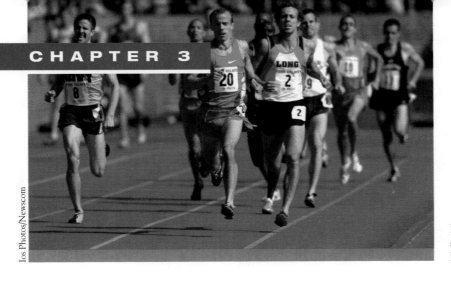

Ios Photos/Newscom

How fast can male college students run a mile? Exercise 3.5 has some information.

CHAPTER 3

The Normal Distributions

IN THIS CHAPTER
WE COVER...

- Density curves
- Describing density curves
- Normal distributions
- The 68–95–99.7 rule
- The standard Normal distribution
- Finding Normal proportions
- Using the standard Normal table
- Finding a value given a proportion

We now have a kit of graphical and numerical tools for describing distributions. What is more, we have a clear strategy for exploring data on a single quantitative variable.

EXPLORING A DISTRIBUTION

1. Plot your data: make a graph, usually a histogram or a stemplot.
2. Look for the overall pattern (shape, center, spread) and for striking deviations such as outliers.
3. Calculate a numerical summary to briefly describe center and spread.

In this chapter, we add one more step to this strategy:

4. Sometimes the overall pattern of a large number of observations is so regular that we can describe it by a smooth curve.

Density curves

Figure 3.1 is a histogram of the scores of all 947 seventh-grade students in Gary, Indiana, on the vocabulary part of the Iowa Test of Basic Skills.[1] Scores of many students on this national test have a quite regular distribution. The histogram is symmetric, and both tails fall off smoothly from a single center peak. There are no large gaps or obvious outliers.

FIGURE 3.1

Histogram of the Iowa Test vocabulary scores of all seventh-grade students in Gary, Indiana. The smooth curve shows the overall shape of the distribution.

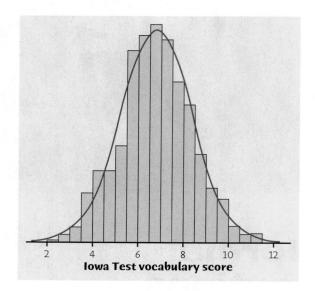

Iowa Test vocabulary score

EXAMPLE 3.1 **From histogram to density curve**

Our eyes respond to the *areas* of the bars in a histogram. The bar areas represent proportions of the observations. Figure 3.2(a) is a copy of Figure 3.1 with the leftmost bars shaded. The area of the shaded bars in Figure 3.2(a) represents the students with vocabulary scores 6.0 or lower. There are 287 such students, who make up the proportion $287/947 = 0.303$ of all Gary seventh-graders.

Now look at the curve drawn through the bars. In Figure 3.2(b), the area under the curve to the left of 6.0 is shaded. We can draw histogram bars taller or shorter by adjusting the vertical scale. In moving from histogram bars to a smooth curve, we make a specific choice: adjust the scale of the graph so that *the total area under the curve is exactly 1*. The total area represents the proportion 1, that is, all the observations. We can then interpret areas under the curve as proportions of the observations. The curve is now a *density curve*. The shaded area under the density curve in Figure 3.2(b) represents the proportion of students with score 6.0 or lower. This area is 0.293, only 0.010 away from the actual proportion 0.303. Areas under the density curve give quite good approximations to the actual distribution of the 947 test scores. ■

DENSITY CURVE

A **density curve** is a curve that

■ is always on or above the horizontal axis, and

■ has area exactly 1 underneath it.

A density curve describes the overall pattern of a distribution. The area under the curve and above any range of values is the proportion of all observations that fall in that range.

Density curves, like distributions, come in many shapes. A density curve is often a good description of the overall pattern of a distribution. Outliers, which are deviations from the

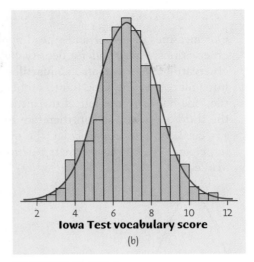

FIGURE 3.2(a)

The proportion of scores less than or equal to 6.0 in the actual data is 0.303.

FIGURE 3.2(b)

The proportion of scores less than or equal to 6.0 from the density curve is 0.293. The density curve is a good approximation to the distribution of the data.

overall pattern, are not described by the curve. *No set of real data is exactly described by a density curve. The curve is an idealized description that is easy to use and accurate enough for practical use.*

APPLY YOUR KNOWLEDGE

3.1 Sketch density curves. Sketch density curves that describe distributions with the following shapes:

   (a) Symmetric, but with two peaks (that is, two strong clusters of observations)

   (b) Single peak and skewed to the left

3.2 Accidents on a bike path. Accidents on a level, 3-mile bike path occur uniformly along the length of the path. Figure 3.3 displays the density curve that describes the distribution of accidents.

   (a) Explain why this curve satisfies the two requirements for a density curve.

   (b) The proportion of accidents that occur in the first mile of the path is the area under the density curve between 0 miles and 1 mile. What is this area?

   (c) Sue's property adjoins the bike path between the 0.8 mile mark and the 1.1 mile mark. What proportion of accidents happen in front of Sue's property?

FIGURE 3.3

The density curve for the location of accidents along a 3-mile bike path, for Exercise 3.2.

Describing density curves

Our measures of center and spread apply to density curves as well as to actual sets of observations. Areas under a density curve represent proportions of the total number of observations. The **median** and **quartiles** of a density curve divide the area under the curve into four equal parts. One-fourth of the area under the curve is to the left of the first quartile, one-half is to the left of the median, and three-fourths of the area is to the left of the third quartile. You can therefore roughly locate the median and quartiles of a density curve by eye. In particular, the median of a symmetric density curve is at its center. Figure 3.4 shows a symmetric density curve and a skewed curve with their medians marked.

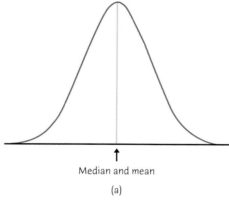

↑
Median and mean

(a)

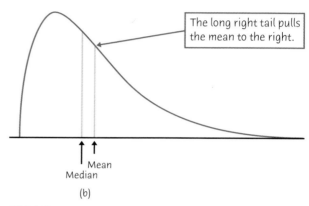

The long right tail pulls the mean to the right.

↑ ↑
Mean
Median

(b)

FIGURE 3.4(a)

The median and mean of a symmetric density curve both lie at the center of the curve.

FIGURE 3.4(b)

The median and mean of a right-skewed density curve. The mean is pulled away from the median toward the long tail.

The **mean** of a set of observations is their arithmetic average. If we think of the observations as weights strung out along a thin rod, the mean is the point at which the rod would balance. This fact is also true of density curves. The mean is the point at which the curve would balance if made of solid material. A symmetric curve balances at its center because the two sides are identical. *The mean and median of a symmetric density curve are equal,* as in Figure 3.4(a). We know that the mean of a skewed distribution is pulled toward the long tail. Figure 3.4(b) shows how the mean of a skewed density curve is pulled toward the long tail more than is the median. It's hard to locate the balance point by eye on a skewed curve.

MEDIAN AND MEAN OF A DENSITY CURVE

The **median** of a density curve is the equal-areas point, the point that divides the area under the curve in half.

The **mean** of a density curve is the balance point, at which the curve would balance if made of solid material.

The median and mean are the same for a symmetric density curve. They both lie at the center of the curve. The mean of a skewed curve is pulled away from the median in the direction of the long tail.

Because a density curve is an idealized description of a distribution of data, we need to distinguish between the mean and standard deviation of the density curve and the mean $\bar{x}$ and standard deviation s computed from the actual observations. We write the **mean of a density curve** as μ (the Greek letter mu). We write the **standard deviation of a density curve** as σ (the Greek letter sigma). You can roughly locate the mean μ of any density curve by eye, as the balance point. There is no easy way to locate the standard deviation σ by eye for density curves in general.

mean μ

standard deviation σ

APPLY YOUR KNOWLEDGE

3.3 Mean and median. What is the mean μ of the density curve pictured in Figure 3.3? (That is, where would the curve balance?) What is the median? (That is, where is the point with area 0.5 on either side?)

3.4 Mean and median. Figure 3.5 displays three density curves, each with three points marked on them. At which of these points on each curve do the mean and the median fall?

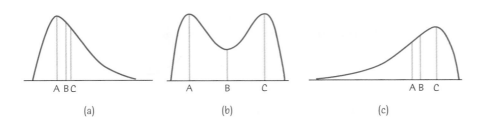

(a) (b) (c)

FIGURE 3.5
Three density curves, for Exercise 3.4.

Normal distributions

One particularly important class of density curves has already appeared in Figures 3.1 and 3.2. They are called **Normal curves.** The distributions they describe are called **Normal distributions.** Normal distributions play a large role in statistics, but they are rather special and not at all "normal" in the sense of being usual or average. We capitalize Normal to remind you that these curves are special. Look at the two Normal curves in Figure 3.6. They illustrate several important facts:

Normal curve

Normal distribution

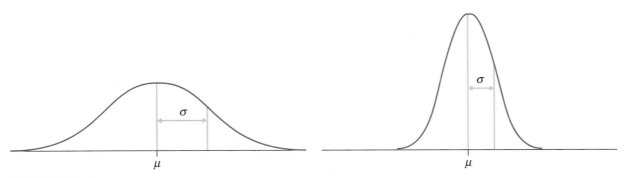

FIGURE 3.6
Two Normal curves, showing the mean μ and standard deviation σ.

- All Normal curves have the same overall shape: symmetric, single-peaked, bell-shaped.
- Any specific Normal curve is completely described by giving its mean μ and its standard deviation σ.
- The mean is located at the center of the symmetric curve and is the same as the median. Changing μ without changing σ moves the Normal curve along the horizontal axis without changing its spread.
- The standard deviation σ controls the spread of a Normal curve. Curves with larger standard deviation are more spread out.

The standard deviation σ is the natural measure of spread for Normal distributions. Not only do μ and σ completely determine the shape of a Normal curve, but we can locate σ by eye on a Normal curve. Here's how. Imagine that you are skiing down a mountain that has the shape of a Normal curve. At first, you descend at an ever-steeper angle as you go out from the peak:

Fortunately, before you find yourself going straight down, the slope begins to grow flatter rather than steeper as you go out and down:

The points at which this change of curvature takes place are located at distance σ on either side of the mean μ. You can feel the change as you run a pencil along a Normal curve, and so find the standard deviation. Remember that *μ and σ alone do not specify the shape of most distributions,* and that the shape of density curves in general does not reveal σ. These are special properties of Normal distributions.

NORMAL DISTRIBUTIONS

A **Normal distribution** is described by a Normal density curve. Any particular Normal distribution is completely specified by two numbers, its mean μ and standard deviation σ.

The mean of a Normal distribution is at the center of the symmetric Normal curve. The standard deviation is the distance from the center to the change-of-curvature points on either side.

Normal distributions are good descriptions for some distributions of real data. Distributions that are often close to Normal include scores on tests taken by many people (such as Iowa Tests and SAT exams), repeated careful measurements of the same quantity, and characteristics of biological populations (such as lengths of crickets and yields of corn). However, many sets of data do not follow a Normal distribution. Most income distributions, for example, are skewed to the right and so are not Normal.

The 68–95–99.7 rule

Although there are many Normal curves, they all have common properties. In particular, all Normal distributions obey the following rule.

THE 68–95–99.7 RULE

In the Normal distribution with mean μ and standard deviation σ:

- Approximately **68%** of the observations fall within σ of the mean μ.
- Approximately **95%** of the observations fall within 2σ of μ.
- Approximately **99.7%** of the observations fall within 3σ of μ.

Figure 3.7 illustrates the 68–95–99.7 rule. By remembering these three numbers, you can think about Normal distributions without constantly making detailed calculations.

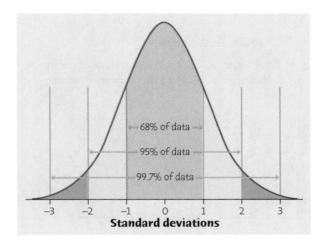

FIGURE 3.7
The 68–95–99.7 rule for Normal distributions.

EXAMPLE 3.2   Iowa Test scores

Figures 3.1 and 3.2 show that the distribution of Iowa Test vocabulary scores for seventh-grade students in Gary, Indiana, is close to Normal. Suppose that the distribution is exactly Normal with mean $\mu = 6.84$ and standard deviation $\sigma = 1.55$. (These are the mean and standard deviation of the 947 actual scores.)

Figure 3.8 applies the 68–95–99.7 rule to the Iowa Test scores. The 95 part of the rule says that 95% of all scores are between

$$\mu - 2\sigma = 6.84 - (2)(1.55) = 6.84 - 3.10 = 3.74$$

and

$$\mu + 2\sigma = 6.84 + (2)(1.55) = 6.84 + 3.10 = 9.94$$

The other 5% of scores are outside this range. Because Normal distributions are symmetric, half of these scores are lower than 3.74 and half are higher than 9.94. That is, 2.5% of the scores are below 3.74 and 2.5% are above 9.94. ■

FIGURE 3.8
The 68–95–99.7 rule applied to the distribution of Iowa Test scores for seventh-grade students in Gary, Indiana, for Example 3.2. The mean and standard deviation are $\mu = 6.84$ and $\sigma = 1.55$.

One standard deviation is 1.55.

68% of data

95% of data

99.7% of data

2.5% of scores are below 3.74.

2.19 3.74 5.29 6.84 8.39 9.94 11.49

Iowa Test score

EXAMPLE 3.3 **Iowa Test scores**

Look again at Figure 3.8. A score of 5.29 is one standard deviation below the mean. What percent of scores are higher than 5.29? Find the answer by adding areas in the figure. Here is the calculation in pictures:

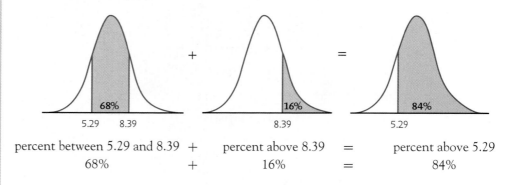

68%	16%	84%
5.29 8.39	8.39	5.29

percent between 5.29 and 8.39 + percent above 8.39 = percent above 5.29

68% + 16% = 84%

Be sure you see where the 16% came from. We know that 68% of scores are between 5.29 and 8.39, so 32% of scores are outside that range. Because the curve is symmetric, these are equally split between the two tails, 16% below 5.29 and 16% above 8.39. ∎

Because we will mention Normal distributions often, a short notation is helpful. We abbreviate the Normal distribution with mean μ and standard deviation σ as $N(\mu, \sigma)$. For example, the distribution of Gary Iowa Test scores is approximately $N(6.84, 1.55)$.

APPLY YOUR KNOWLEDGE

3.5 Running a mile. During World War II, physical training was required for male students in many colleges, as preparation for military service. That provided an opportunity to collect data on physical performance on a large scale. A study of 12,000 able-bodied male students at the University of Illinois found that their times for the mile run were approximately Normal with mean 7.11 minutes and standard deviation 0.74 minute.[2] Draw a Normal curve on which this mean and standard deviation are correctly located. (*Hint:* Draw an unlabeled Normal curve, locate the points where the curvature changes, then add number labels on the horizontal axis.)

3.6 Running a mile. The times for the mile run of a large group of male college students are approximately Normal with mean 7.11 minutes and standard deviation 0.74 minute. Use the 68–95–99.7 rule to answer the following questions. (Start by making a sketch like Figure 3.8.)

(a) What range of times covers almost all (99.7%) of this distribution?

(b) What percent of these men run a mile in less than 6.37 minutes?

3.7 Monsoon rains. The summer monsoon brings 80% of India's rainfall and is essential for the country's agriculture. Records going back more than a century show that the amount of monsoon rainfall varies from year to year according to a distribution that is approximately Normal with mean 852 millimeters (mm) and standard deviation 82 mm.[3] Use the 68–95–99.7 rule to answer the following questions.

(a) Between what values do the monsoon rains fall in 95% of all years?

(b) How small are the monsoon rains in the driest 2.5% of all years?

The standard Normal distribution

As the 68–95–99.7 rule suggests, all Normal distributions share many properties. In fact, all Normal distributions are the same if we measure in units of size σ about the mean μ as center. Changing to these units is called *standardizing*. To standardize a value, subtract the mean of the distribution and then divide by the standard deviation.

STANDARDIZING AND z-SCORES

If x is an observation from a distribution that has mean μ and standard deviation σ, the **standardized value** of x is

$$z = \frac{x - \mu}{\sigma}$$

A standardized value is often called a **z-score**.

A z-score tells us how many standard deviations the original observation falls away from the mean, and in which direction. Observations larger than the mean are positive when standardized, and observations smaller than the mean are negative.

EXAMPLE 3.4 **Standardizing women's heights**

The heights of women aged 20 to 29 are approximately Normal with $\mu = 64$ inches and $\sigma = 2.7$ inches.[4] The standardized height is

$$z = \frac{\text{height} - 64}{2.7}$$

A woman's standardized height is the number of standard deviations by which her height differs from the mean height of all young women. A woman 70 inches tall, for example, has standardized height

$$z = \frac{70 - 64}{2.7} = 2.22$$

or 2.22 standard deviations above the mean. Similarly, a woman 5 feet (60 inches) tall has standardized height

$$z = \frac{60 - 64}{2.7} = -1.48$$

or 1.48 standard deviations less than the mean height. ■

We often standardize observations from symmetric distributions to express them in a common scale. We might, for example, compare the heights of two children of different ages by calculating their z-scores. The standardized heights tell us where each child stands in the distribution for his or her age group.

If the variable we standardize has a Normal distribution, standardizing does more than give a common scale. It makes all Normal distributions into a single distribution, and this distribution is still Normal. Standardizing a variable that has any Normal distribution produces a new variable that has the *standard Normal distribution.*

STANDARD NORMAL DISTRIBUTION

The **standard Normal distribution** is the Normal distribution $N(0, 1)$ with mean 0 and standard deviation 1.

If a variable x has any Normal distribution $N(\mu, \sigma)$ with mean μ and standard deviation σ, then the standardized variable

$$z = \frac{x - \mu}{\sigma}$$

has the standard Normal distribution.

APPLY YOUR KNOWLEDGE

3.8 SAT versus ACT. In 2007, when she was a high school senior, Eleanor scored 680 on the mathematics part of the SAT. The distribution of SAT math scores in 2007 was Normal with mean 515 and standard deviation 114. Gerald took the ACT mathematics test and scored 27. ACT math scores for 2007 were Normally distributed with mean 21.0 and standard deviation 5.1. Find the standardized scores for both students. Assuming that both tests measure the same kind of ability, who had the higher score?

3.9 Men's and women's heights. The heights of women aged 20 to 29 are approximately Normal with mean 64 inches and standard deviation 2.7 inches. Men the same age have mean height 69.3 inches with standard deviation 2.8 inches. What are the z-scores for a woman 6 feet tall and a man 6 feet tall? Say in simple language what information the z-scores give that the actual heights do not.

Finding Normal proportions

Areas under a Normal curve represent proportions of observations from that Normal distribution. There is no formula for areas under a Normal curve. Calculations use either software that calculates areas or a table of areas. Most tables and software calculate one kind of area, *cumulative proportions*. The idea of "cumulative" is "everything that came before." Here is the exact statement.

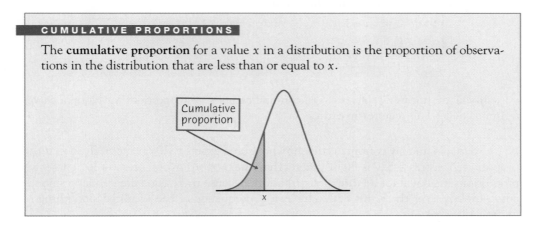

CUMULATIVE PROPORTIONS

The **cumulative proportion** for a value x in a distribution is the proportion of observations in the distribution that are less than or equal to x.

The key to calculating Normal proportions is to match the area you want with areas that represent cumulative proportions. If you make a sketch of the area you want, you will almost never go wrong. Find areas for cumulative proportions either from software or (with an extra step) from a table. The following example shows the method in a picture.

EXAMPLE 3.5 Who qualifies for college sports?

The National Collegiate Athletic Association (NCAA) requires Division II athletes to score at least 820 on the combined mathematics and reading parts of the SAT in order to compete in their first college year. The scores of the 1.5 million high school seniors taking the SAT this year are approximately Normal with mean 1026 and standard deviation 209. What percent of high school seniors qualify for Division II college sports?

Here is the calculation in a picture: the proportion of scores above 820 is the area under the curve to the right of 820. That's the total area under the curve (which is always 1) minus the cumulative proportion up to 820.

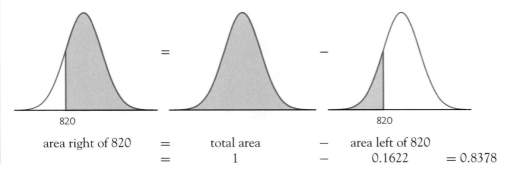

area right of 820	=	total area	−	area left of 820	
	=	1	−	0.1622	= 0.8378

About 84% of all high school seniors meet the NCAA requirement to compete in Division II college sports.

To find the numerical value 0.1622 of the cumulative proportion using software, plug in mean 1026 and standard deviation 209 and ask for the cumulative proportion for 820. Here, for example, is Minitab's output:

```
Session                                         [_][□][×]

Cumulative Distribution Function

Normal with mean = 1026 and standard deviation = 209

   x    P ( X <= x )
  820      0.162153
```

If you are not using software, you can find cumulative proportions for Normal curves from a table. This requires an extra step. ■

The actual data may contain a student who scored exactly 820 on the SAT, so that the proportion of scores ≥ 820 is slightly larger than the proportion of scores > 820. These two proportions are equal for a Normal distribution, because there is no area under a smooth curve exactly over the point 820. This is a consequence of the idealized smoothing of Normal distributions.

Using the standard Normal table

The extra step in finding cumulative proportions from a table is that we must first standardize to express the problem in the standard scale of z-scores. This allows us to get by with just one table, a table of *standard Normal cumulative proportions*. Table A in the back of the book gives cumulative proportions for the standard Normal distribution. The pictures at the top of the table remind us that the entries are cumulative proportions, areas under the curve to the left of a value z.

EXAMPLE 3.6   **The standard Normal table**

What proportion of observations on a standard Normal variable z take values less than 1.47?

Solution: To find the area to the left of 1.47, locate 1.4 in the left-hand column of Table A, then locate the remaining digit 7 as .07 in the top row. The entry opposite 1.4 and under .07 is 0.9292. This is the cumulative proportion we seek. Figure 3.9 illustrates this area. ■

FIGURE 3.9

The area under a standard Normal curve to the left of the point $z = 1.47$ is 0.9292. Table A gives cumulative proportions for the standard Normal curve.

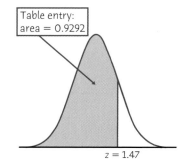

Table entry: area = 0.9292

$z = 1.47$

Now that you see how Table A works, let's redo Example 3.5 using the table. We can break Normal calculations using the table into three steps.

EXAMPLE 3.7 **Who qualifies for college sports?**

Scores of high school seniors on the SAT follow the Normal distribution with mean $\mu = 1026$ and standard deviation $\sigma = 209$. What percent of seniors score at least 820?

Step 1. Draw a picture. The picture is exactly as in Example 3.5. It shows that

$$\text{area to the right of } 820 = 1 - \text{area to the left of } 820$$

Step 2. Standardize. Call the SAT score x. Subtract the mean, then divide by the standard deviation, to transform the problem about x into a problem about a standard Normal z:

$$x \geq 820$$

$$\frac{x - 1026}{209} \geq \frac{820 - 1026}{209}$$

$$z \geq -0.99$$

Step 3. Use the table. The picture shows that we need the cumulative proportion for $x = 820$. Step 2 says this is the same as the cumulative proportion for $z = -0.99$. The Table A entry for $z = -0.99$ says that this cumulative proportion is 0.1611. The area to the right of -0.99 is therefore $1 - 0.1611 = 0.8389$. ∎

The area from the table in Example 3.7 (0.8389) is slightly less accurate than the area from software in Example 3.5 (0.8378) because we must round z to two decimal places when we use Table A. The difference is rarely important in practice. Here's the method in outline form.

USING TABLE A TO FIND NORMAL PROPORTIONS

Step 1. State the problem in terms of the observed variable x. **Draw a picture** that shows the proportion you want in terms of cumulative proportions.

Step 2. Standardize x to restate the problem in terms of a standard Normal variable z.

Step 3. Use Table A and the fact that the total area under the curve is 1 to find the required area under the standard Normal curve.

EXAMPLE 3.8 **Who qualifies for an athletic scholarship?**

The NCAA considers a student a "partial qualifier" for Division II athletics if high school grades are satisfactory and the combined SAT score is at least 720. Partial qualifiers can receive athletic scholarships and practice with the team, but they can't compete during their first college year. What proportion of all students who take the SAT would be partial qualifiers?

Step 1. State the problem and draw a picture. Call the SAT score x. The variable x has the $N(1026, 209)$ distribution. What proportion of SAT scores fall between 720 and 820? Here is the picture:

Step 2. Standardize. Subtract the mean, then divide by the standard deviation, to turn x into a standard Normal z:

$$720 \leq x < 820$$

$$\frac{720 - 1026}{209} \leq \frac{x - 1026}{209} < \frac{820 - 1026}{209}$$

$$-1.46 \leq z < -0.99$$

Step 3. Use the table. Follow the picture (we added the z-scores to the picture label to help you):

area between -1.46 and $-0.99 = $ (area left of -0.99) $-$ (area left of -1.46)

$$= 0.1611 - 0.0721 = 0.0890$$

About 9% of high school seniors would be partial qualifiers. ∎

Sometimes we encounter a value of z more extreme than those appearing in Table A. For example, the area to the left of $z = -4$ is not given directly in the table. The z-values in Table A leave only area 0.0002 in each tail unaccounted for. For practical purposes, we can act as if there is zero area outside the range of Table A.

APPLY YOUR KNOWLEDGE

3.10 Use the Normal table. Use Table A to find the proportion of observations from a standard Normal distribution that satisfies each of the following statements. In each case, sketch a standard Normal curve and shade the area under the curve that is the answer to the question.
(a) $z < 2.85$ (b) $z > 2.85$ (c) $z > -1.66$ (d) $-1.66 < z < 2.85$

3.11 Monsoon rains. The summer monsoon rains in India follow approximately a Normal distribution with mean 852 millimeters (mm) of rainfall and standard deviation 82 mm.

(a) In the drought year 1987, 697 mm of rain fell. In what percent of all years will India have 697 mm or less of monsoon rain?

(b) "Normal rainfall" means within 20% of the long-term average, or between 683 and 1022 mm. In what percent of all years is the rainfall normal?

3.12 Fruit flies. The common fruit fly *Drosophila melanogaster* is the most studied organism in genetic research because it is small, easy to grow, and reproduces rapidly. The length of the thorax (where the wings and legs attach) in a population of male fruit flies is approximately Normal with mean 0.800 millimeters (mm) and standard deviation 0.078 mm.

(a) What proportion of flies have thorax length 0.9 mm or longer?

(b) What proportion have thorax length between 0.9 and 1 mm?

Herman Eisenbeiss/Photo Researchers

Finding a value given a proportion

Examples 3.5 to 3.8 illustrate the use of software or Table A to find what proportion of the observations satisfies some condition, such as "SAT score above 820." We may instead want to find the observed value with a given proportion of the observations above or below it. Statistical software will do this directly.

EXAMPLE 3.9 **Find the top 10% using software**

Scores on the SAT reading test in recent years follow approximately the $N(504, 111)$ distribution. How high must a student score in order to place in the top 10% of all students taking the SAT?

We want to find the SAT score x with area 0.1 to its *right* under the Normal curve with mean $\mu = 504$ and standard deviation $\sigma = 111$. That's the same as finding the SAT score x with area 0.9 to its *left*. Figure 3.10 poses the question in graphical form. Most software will tell you x when you plug in mean 504, standard deviation 111, and cumulative proportion 0.9. Here is Minitab's output:

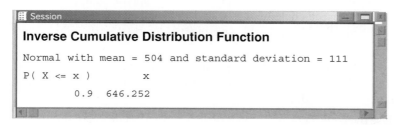

```
Session

Inverse Cumulative Distribution Function

Normal with mean = 504 and standard deviation = 111

P( X <= x )          x
        0.9   646.252
```

Minitab gives $x = 646.252$. So scores 647 or above are in the top 10%. (Round up because SAT scores can only be whole numbers.) ■

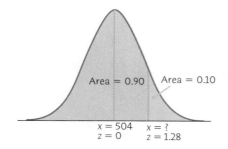

Area = 0.90   Area = 0.10

$x = 504$ $x = ?$
$z = 0$ $z = 1.28$

FIGURE 3.10

Locating the point on a Normal curve with area 0.10 to its right, for Examples 3.9 and 3.10.

Without software, use Table A backward. Find the given proportion in the body of the table and then read the corresponding z from the left column and top row. There are again three steps.

EXAMPLE 3.10 **Find the top 10% using Table A**

Scores on the SAT reading test in recent years follow approximately the $N(504, 111)$ distribution. How high must a student score in order to place in the top 10% of all students taking the SAT?

Step 1. State the problem and draw a picture. This step is exactly as in Example 3.9. The picture is Figure 3.10.

Step 2. Use the table. Look in the body of Table A for the entry closest to 0.9. It is 0.8997. This is the entry corresponding to $z = 1.28$. So $z = 1.28$ is the standardized value with area 0.9 to its left.

Step 3. Unstandardize to transform z back to the original x scale. We know that the standardized value of the unknown x is $z = 1.28$. This means that x itself lies 1.28 standard deviations above the mean on this particular Normal curve. That is,

$$x = \text{mean} + (1.28)(\text{standard deviation})$$
$$= 504 + (1.28)(111) = 646.1$$

A student must score at least 647 to place in the highest 10%. ■

EXAMPLE 3.11 **Find the first quartile**

High levels of cholesterol in the blood increase the risk of heart disease. For 14-year-old boys, the distribution of blood cholesterol is approximately Normal with mean $\mu = 170$ milligrams of cholesterol per deciliter of blood (mg/dl) and standard deviation $\sigma = 30$ mg/dl.[5] What is the first quartile of the distribution of blood cholesterol?

Step 1. State the problem and draw a picture. Call the cholesterol level x. The variable x has the $N(170, 30)$ distribution. The first quartile is the value with 25% of the distribution to its left. Figure 3.11 is the picture.

Step 2. Use the table. Look in the body of Table A for the entry closest to 0.25. It is 0.2514. This is the entry corresponding to $z = -0.67$. So $z = -0.67$ is the standardized value with area 0.25 to its left.

FIGURE 3.11

Locating the first quartile of a Normal curve, for Example 3.11.

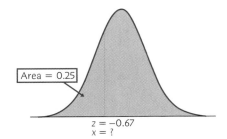

Step 3. Unstandardize. The cholesterol level corresponding to $z = -0.67$ lies 0.67 standard deviations below the mean, so

$$x = \text{mean} - (0.67)(\text{standard deviation})$$

$$= 170 - (0.67)(30) = 149.9$$

The first quartile of blood cholesterol levels in 14-year-old boys is about 150 mg/dl. ■

APPLY YOUR KNOWLEDGE

3.13 Table A. Use Table A to find the value z of a standard Normal variable that satisfies each of the following conditions. (Use the value of z from Table A that comes closest to satisfying the condition.) In each case, sketch a standard Normal curve with your value of z marked on the axis.

(a) The point z with 20% of the observations falling below it

(b) The point z with 40% of the observations falling above it

3.14 Fruit flies. The thorax lengths in a population of male fruit flies follow a Normal distribution with mean 0.800 millimeters (mm) and standard deviation 0.078 mm. What are the median and the first and third quartiles of thorax length?

CHAPTER 3 SUMMARY

■ We can sometimes describe the overall pattern of a distribution by a **density curve.** A density curve has total area 1 underneath it. An area under a density curve gives the proportion of observations that fall in a range of values.

■ A density curve is an idealized description of the overall pattern of a distribution that smooths out the irregularities in the actual data. We write the **mean of a density curve** as μ and the **standard deviation of a density curve** as σ to distinguish them from the mean $\bar{x}$ and standard deviation s of the actual data.

■ The mean, the median, and the quartiles of a density curve can be located by eye. The **mean** μ is the balance point of the curve. The **median** divides the area under the curve in half. The **quartiles** and the median divide the area under the curve into quarters. The **standard deviation** σ cannot be located by eye on most density curves.

■ The mean and median are equal for symmetric density curves. The mean of a skewed curve is located farther toward the long tail than is the median.

■ The **Normal distributions** are described by a special family of bell-shaped, symmetric density curves, called **Normal curves.** The mean μ and standard deviation σ completely specify a Normal distribution $N(\mu, \sigma)$. The mean is the center of the curve, and σ is the distance from μ to the change-of-curvature points on either side.

■ To **standardize** any observation x, subtract the mean of the distribution and then divide by the standard deviation. The resulting **z-score**

$$z = \frac{x - \mu}{\sigma}$$

says how many standard deviations x lies from the distribution mean.

■ All Normal distributions are the same when measurements are transformed to the standardized scale. In particular, all Normal distributions satisfy the **68–95–99.7** rule, which describes what percent of observations lie within one, two, and three standard deviations of the mean.

■ If x has the $N(\mu, \sigma)$ distribution, then the **standardized variable** $z = (x - \mu)/\sigma$ has the **standard Normal distribution** $N(0, 1)$ with mean 0 and standard deviation 1. Table A gives the **cumulative proportions** of standard Normal observations that are less than z for many values of z. By standardizing, we can use Table A for any Normal distribution.

CHECK YOUR SKILLS

3.15 Which of these variables is least likely to have a Normal distribution?
(a) Income per person for 150 different countries
(b) Lengths of 50 newly hatched pythons
(c) Heights of 100 white pine trees in a forest

3.16 Figure 3.12 shows a Normal curve. The mean of this distribution is
(a) 0.   (b) 2.   (c) 3.

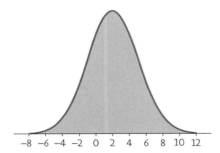

FIGURE 3.12
A Normal curve, for Exercises 3.16 and 3.17.

3.17 The standard deviation of the Normal distribution in Figure 3.12 is
(a) 2.   (b) 3.   (c) 5.

3.18 The length of human pregnancies from conception to birth varies according to a distribution that is approximately Normal with mean 266 days and standard deviation 16 days. 95% of all pregnancies last between
(a) 250 and 282 days.   (b) 234 and 298 days.
(c) 218 and 314 days.

3.19 The scores of adults on an IQ test are approximately Normal with mean 100 and standard deviation 15. The organization MENSA, which calls itself "the high IQ society," requires an IQ score of 130 or higher for membership. What percent of adults would qualify for membership?
(a) 95%   (b) 5%   (c) 2.5%

3.20 The scores of adults on an IQ test are approximately Normal with mean 100 and standard deviation 15. Corinne scores 118 on such a test. Her z-score is about
(a) 1.2.   (b) 7.87.   (c) 18.

3.21 The scores of adults on an IQ test are approximately Normal with mean 100 and standard deviation 15. Corinne scores 118 on such a test. She scores higher than what percent of all adults?
(a) About 12%   (b) About 88%   (c) About 98%

CHAPTER 3 EXERCISES

3.22 Daily activity. It appears that people who are mildly obese are less active than leaner people. One study looked at the average number of minutes per day that people spend standing or walking.[6] Among mildly obese people, minutes of activity varied according to the $N(373, 67)$ distribution. Minutes of activity for lean people had the $N(526, 107)$ distribution. Within what limits do the active minutes for 95% of the people in each group fall? Use the 68–95–99.7 rule.

3.23 Low IQ test scores. Scores on the Wechsler Adult Intelligence Scale (WAIS) are approximately Normal with mean 100 and standard deviation 15. People with WAIS scores below 70 are considered mentally retarded when, for example, applying for Social Security disability benefits. According to the 68–95–99.7 rule, about what percent of adults are retarded by this criterion?

3.24 Standard Normal drill. Use Table A to find the proportion of observations from a standard Normal distribution that falls in each of the following regions. In each case, sketch a standard Normal curve and shade the area representing the region.
(a) $z \leq -2.25$ (b) $z \geq -2.25$ (c) $z > 1.77$
(d) $-2.25 < z < 1.77$

3.25 Standard Normal drill.
(a) Find the number z such that the proportion of observations that are less than z in a standard Normal distribution is 0.8.

(b) Find the number z such that 35% of all observations from a standard Normal distribution are greater than z.

3.26 Running a mile. After the physical training required during World War II, the distribution of mile run times for male students at the University of Illinois was approximately Normal with mean 7.11 minutes and standard deviation 0.74 minute. What proportion of these students could run a mile in 5 minutes or less?

3.27 Acid rain? Emissions of sulfur dioxide by industry set off chemical changes in the atmosphere that result in "acid rain." The acidity of liquids is measured by pH on a scale of 0 to 14. Distilled water has pH 7.0, and lower pH values indicate acidity. Normal rain is somewhat acidic, so acid rain is sometimes defined as rainfall with a pH below 5.0. The pH of rain at one location varies among rainy days according to a Normal distribution with mean 5.4 and standard deviation 0.54. What proportion of rainy days have rainfall with pH below 5.0?

3.28 Runners. In a study of exercise, a large group of male runners walk on a treadmill for 6 minutes. Their heart rates in beats per minute at the end vary from runner to runner according to the $N(104, 12.5)$ distribution. The heart rates for male nonrunners after the same exercise have the $N(130, 17)$ distribution.
(a) What percent of the runners have heart rates above 130?
(b) What percent of the nonrunners have heart rates above 130?

3.29 A milling machine. Automated manufacturing operations are quite precise but still vary, often with distributions that are close to Normal. The width in inches of slots cut by a milling machine follows approximately the $N(0.8750, 0.0012)$ distribution. The specifications allow slot widths between 0.8720 and 0.8780 inch. What proportion of slots meet these specifications?

3.30 Making tablets. A pharmaceutical manufacturer forms tablets by compressing a granular material that contains the active ingredient and various fillers. The force in kilograms (kg) applied to the tablets varies a bit, with the $N(11.5, 0.2)$ distribution. The process specifications call for applying a force between 11.2 and 12.2 kg.
(a) What percent of tablets are subject to a force that meets the specifications?
(b) The manufacturer adjusts the process so that the mean force is at the center of the specifications, $\mu = 11.7$ kg. The standard deviation remains 0.2 kg. What percent now meet the specifications?

Miles per gallon. *In its* Fuel Economy Guide *for 2008 model vehicles, the Environmental Protection Agency gives data on 1152*

vehicles. There are a number of outliers, mainly vehicles with very poor gas mileage. If we ignore the outliers, however, the combined city and highway gas mileage of the other 1120 or so vehicles is approximately Normal with mean 18.7 miles per gallon (mpg) and standard deviation 4.3 mpg. Exercises 3.31 to 3.34 concern this distribution.

3.31 In my Chevrolet. The 2008 Chevrolet Malibu with a four-cylinder engine has combined gas mileage 25 mpg. What percent of all vehicles have worse gas mileage than the Malibu?

3.32 The top 10%. How high must a 2008 vehicle's gas mileage be in order to fall in the top 10% of all vehicles? (The distribution omits a few high outliers, mainly hybrid gas-electric vehicles.)

3.33 The middle half. The quartiles of any distribution are the values with cumulative proportions 0.25 and 0.75. They span the middle half of the distribution. What are the quartiles of the distribution of gas mileage?

3.34 Quintiles. The quintiles of any distribution are the values with cumulative proportions 0.20, 0.40, 0.60, and 0.80. What are the quintiles of the distribution of gas mileage?

3.35 What's your percentile? Reports on a student's ACT or SAT usually give the percentile as well as the actual score. The percentile is just the cumulative proportion stated as a percent: the percent of all scores that were lower than this one. In 2007, composite ACT scores were close to Normal with mean 21.2 and standard deviation 5.0.[7] Jacob scored 16. What was his percentile?

3.36 Perfect SAT scores. It is possible to score higher than 1600 on the SAT, but scores 1600 and above are reported as 1600. In 2007 the distribution of SAT scores (combining mathematics and reading) was close to Normal with mean 1021 and standard deviation 211.[8] What proportion of 2007 SAT scores were reported as 1600?

3.37 Heights of men and women. The heights of women aged 20 to 29 follow approximately the $N(64, 2.7)$ distribution. Men the same age have heights distributed as $N(69.3, 2.8)$. What percent of young women are taller than the mean height of young men?

3.38 Heights of men and women. The heights of women aged 20 to 29 follow approximately the $N(64, 2.7)$ distribution. Men the same age have heights distributed as $N(69.3, 2.8)$. What percent of young men are shorter than the mean height of young women?

3.39 Grading managers. Some companies "grade on a bell curve" to compare the performance of their managers and professional workers. This forces the use of some low performance ratings so that not all workers are listed as "above average." Ford Motor Company's "performance management process" for a time assigned 10% A grades, 80% B grades, and 10% C grades to the company's managers. Suppose that Ford's performance scores really are Normally distributed. This year, managers with scores less than 25 received C's and those with scores above 475 received A's. What are the mean and standard deviation of the scores?

3.40 Osteoporosis. Osteoporosis is a condition in which the bones become brittle due to loss of minerals. To diagnose osteoporosis, measure bone mineral density (BMD). BMD is usually reported in standardized form. The standardization is based on a population of healthy young adults. The World Health Organization (WHO) criterion for osteoporosis is a BMD 2.5 standard deviations below the mean for young adults. BMD measurements in a population of people similar in age and sex roughly follow a Normal distribution.

Solid bone matrix   Weakened bone matrix

(a) What percent of healthy young adults have osteoporosis by the WHO criterion?
(b) Women aged 70 to 79 are of course not young adults. The mean BMD in this age is about −2 on the standard scale for young adults. Suppose that the standard deviation is the same as for young adults. What percent of this older population have osteoporosis?

In later chapters we will meet many statistical procedures that work well when the data are "close enough to Normal." Exercises 3.41 to 3.46 concern data that are mostly close enough to Normal for statistical work. These exercises ask you to do data analysis and Normal calculations to investigate how close to Normal real data are.

3.41 Normal is only approximate: IQ test scores. The following lists give the IQ test scores of 31 seventh-grade girls in a Midwest school district.[9]

114	100	104	89	102	91	114	114	103	105
108	130	120	132	111	128	118	119	86	72
111	103	74	112	107	103	98	96	112	112	93

(a) We expect IQ scores to be approximately Normal. Make a stemplot to check that there are no major departures from Normality.
(b) Nonetheless, proportions calculated from a Normal distribution are not always very accurate for small numbers of observations. Find the mean $\bar{x}$ and standard deviation s for these IQ scores. What proportions of the scores are within one standard deviation and within two standard deviations of the mean? What would these proportions be in an exactly Normal distribution?

3.42 Normal is only approximate: ACT scores. Scores on the ACT test for the 2007 high school graduating class had mean 21.2 and standard deviation 5.0. In all, 1,300,599 students in this class took the test. Of these, 149,164 had scores higher than 27 and another 50,310 had scores exactly 27. ACT scores are always whole numbers. The exactly Normal $N(21.2, 5.0)$ distribution can include any value, not just whole numbers. What is more, there is *no* area exactly above 27 under the smooth Normal curve. So ACT scores can be only approximately Normal. To illustrate this fact, find
(a) the percent of 2007 ACT scores greater than 27.
(b) the percent of 2007 ACT scores greater than or equal to 27.
(c) the percent of observations from the $N(21.2, 5.0)$ distribution that are greater than 27. (The percent greater than or equal to 27 is the same, because there is no area exactly over 27.)

3.43 Are the data Normal? Acidity of rainfall. Exercise 3.27 concerns the acidity (measured by pH) of rainfall. A sample of 105 rainwater specimens had mean pH 5.43, standard deviation 0.54, and five-number summary 4.33, 5.05, 5.44, 5.79, 6.81.[10]
(a) Compare the mean and median and also the distances of the two quartiles from the median. Does it appear that the distribution is quite symmetric? Why?
(b) If the distribution is really $N(5.43, 0.54)$, what proportion of observations would be less than 5.05? Less than 5.79? Do these proportions suggest that the distribution is close to Normal? Why?

3.44 Are the data Normal? Fruit fly thorax lengths. Here are the lengths in millimeters of the thorax for 49 male fruit flies:[11]

0.64	0.64	0.64	0.68	0.68	0.68	0.72	0.72	0.72	0.72
0.74	0.76	0.76	0.76	0.76	0.76	0.76	0.76	0.76	0.78
0.80	0.80	0.80	0.80	0.80	0.82	0.82	0.84	0.84	0.84
0.84	0.84	0.84	0.84	0.84	0.84	0.84	0.88	0.88	0.88
0.88	0.88	0.88	0.88	0.88	0.92	0.92	0.92	0.94	

(a) Make a histogram of the distribution. Although the result depends a bit on your choice of classes, the distribution appears roughly symmetric with no outliers.

(b) Find the mean, median, standard deviation, and quartiles for these data. Comparing the mean and the median and comparing the distances of the two quartiles from the median suggest that the distribution is quite symmetric. Why?

(c) If the distribution were exactly Normal with the mean and standard deviation you found in (b), what proportion of observations would lie between the two quartiles you found in (b)? What proportion of the actual observations lie between the quartiles (include observations equal to either quartile value)? Despite the discrepancy, this distribution is "close enough to Normal" for statistical work in later chapters.

3.45 Are the data Normal? Monsoon rains. Here are the amounts of summer monsoon rainfall (millimeters) for India in the 100 years 1901 to 2000:[12]

722.4	792.2	861.3	750.6	716.8	885.5	777.9	897.5	889.6	935.4
736.8	806.4	784.8	898.5	781.0	951.1	1004.7	651.2	885.0	719.4
866.2	869.4	823.5	863.0	804.0	903.1	853.5	768.2	821.5	804.9
877.6	803.8	976.2	913.8	843.9	908.7	842.4	908.6	789.9	853.6
728.7	958.1	868.6	920.8	911.3	904.0	945.9	874.3	904.2	877.3
739.2	793.3	923.4	885.8	930.5	983.6	789.0	889.6	944.3	839.9
1020.5	810.0	858.1	922.8	709.6	740.2	860.3	754.8	831.3	940.0
887.0	653.1	913.6	748.3	963.0	857.0	883.4	909.5	708.0	882.9
852.4	735.6	955.9	836.9	760.0	743.2	697.4	961.7	866.9	908.8
784.7	785.0	896.6	938.4	826.4	857.3	870.5	873.8	827.0	770.2

(a) Make a histogram of these rainfall amounts. Find the mean and the median.

(b) Although the distribution is reasonably Normal, your work shows some departure from Normality. In what way are the data not Normal?

3.46 Are the data Normal? Soil penetrability. Table 2.5 (page 48) gives data on the penetrability of soil at each of three levels of compression. We might expect the penetrability of specimens of the same soil at the same level of compression to follow a Normal distribution. Make stemplots of the data for loose and for intermediate compression. Does either sample seem roughly Normal? Does either appear distinctly non-Normal? If so, what kind of departure from Normality does your stemplot show?

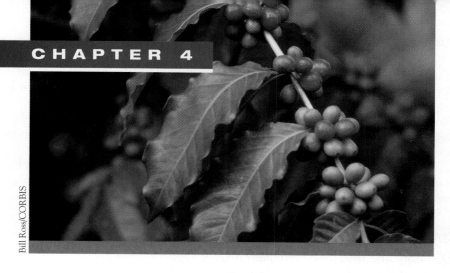

A coffee plant. Exercise 4.22 has data on an unexpected effect of growing coffee in Indonesia.

CHAPTER 4

Scatterplots and Correlation

IN THIS CHAPTER
WE COVER...

- Explanatory and response variables
- Displaying relationships: scatterplots
- Interpreting scatterplots
- Measuring linear association: correlation
- Facts about correlation

A medical study finds that short women are more likely to have heart attacks than women of average height, while tall women have the fewest heart attacks. An insurance group reports that heavier cars have fewer deaths per 10,000 vehicles registered than do lighter cars. These and many other statistical studies look at the *relationship between two variables*. To understand a statistical relationship between two variables, we measure both variables on the same individuals. Then we apply our basic principles: plot the data, look for the overall pattern and striking deviations, then add numerical summaries.

Explanatory and response variables

We think that car weight helps explain accident deaths and that smoking influences life expectancy. In each of these relationships, the two variables play different roles: one explains or influences the other.

> **RESPONSE VARIABLE, EXPLANATORY VARIABLE**
>
> A **response variable** measures an outcome of a study. An **explanatory variable** may explain or influence changes in a response variable.

EXAMPLE 4.1 Explanatory and response variables

How does drinking beer affect the level of alcohol in our blood? Student volunteers at Ohio State University drank different numbers of cans of beer. Thirty minutes later, a police officer measured their blood alcohol content. Number of beers consumed is the explanatory variable, and percent of alcohol in the blood is the response variable.

Record the SAT scores of high school students and then their first-year grades in college. We think that SAT score (explanatory variable) helps to predict college grades (response variable).

More beers *cause* higher blood alcohol. But high SAT scores don't *cause* high college grades. A cause-and-effect relationship is not necessary for the distinction between explanatory and response variables. ■

APPLY YOUR KNOWLEDGE

4.1 Explanatory and response variables? You have data on a large group of college students. Here are four pairs of variables measured on these students. For each pair, is it more reasonable to simply explore the relationship between the two variables or to view one of the variables as an explanatory variable and the other as a response variable? In the latter case, which is the explanatory variable and which is the response variable?

(a) Amount of time spent studying for a statistics exam and grade on the exam.

(b) Weight in kilograms and height in centimeters.

(c) Hours per week of extracurricular activities and grade point average.

(d) Score on the SAT Mathematics exam and score on the SAT Critical Reading exam.

4.2 Coral reefs. How sensitive to changes in water temperature are coral reefs? To find out, measure the growth of corals in aquariums where the water temperature is controlled at different levels. Growth is measured by weighing the coral before and after the experiment. What are the explanatory and response variables? Are they categorical or quantitative?

Displaying relationships: scatterplots

The most useful graph for displaying the relationship between two quantitative variables is a *scatterplot*.

EXAMPLE 4.2   State SAT mathematics scores

In some states most high school graduates take the SAT test of readiness for college, and in other states most take the ACT. Who takes a test may influence the average score. Let's follow our four-step process (page 42) to examine this influence.[1]

STATE: The percent of high school students who take the SAT varies from state to state. Does this fact help explain differences among the states in average SAT mathematics score?

PLAN: Examine the relationship between percent taking the SAT and state mean score on the mathematics part of the SAT. Choose the explanatory and response variables (if any). Make a *scatterplot* to display the relationship between the variables. Interpret the plot to understand the relationship.

SOLVE (make the plot): We suspect that "percent taking" will help explain "mean score." So "percent taking" is the explanatory variable and "mean score" is the response variable. We

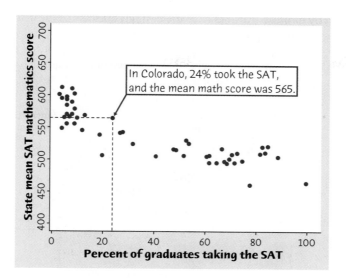

FIGURE 4.1
Scatterplot of the mean SAT mathematics score in each state against the percent of that state's high school graduates who take the SAT, for Example 4.2. The dotted lines intersect at the point (24, 565), the data for Colorado.

want to see how mean score changes when percent taking changes, so we put percent taking (the explanatory variable) on the horizontal axis. Figure 4.1 is the scatterplot. Each point represents a single state. In Colorado, for example, 24% took the SAT, and their mean SAT math score was 565. Find 24 on the x (horizontal) axis and 565 on the y (vertical) axis. Colorado appears as the point above 24 and to the right of 565. ■

SCATTERPLOT

A **scatterplot** shows the relationship between two quantitative variables measured on the same individuals. The values of one variable appear on the horizontal axis, and the values of the other variable appear on the vertical axis. Each individual in the data appears as the point in the plot fixed by the values of both variables for that individual.

Always plot the explanatory variable, if there is one, on the horizontal axis (the x axis) of a scatterplot. As a reminder, we usually call the explanatory variable x and the response variable y. If there is no explanatory-response distinction, either variable can go on the horizontal axis.

APPLY YOUR KNOWLEDGE

4.3 Do heavier people burn more energy? Metabolic rate, the rate at which the body consumes energy, is important in studies of weight gain, dieting, and exercise. We have data on the lean body mass and resting metabolic rate for 12 women who are subjects in a study of dieting. Lean body mass, given in kilograms, is a person's weight leaving out all fat. Metabolic rate is measured in calories burned per 24 hours.

Mass	36.1	54.6	48.5	42.0	50.6	42.0	40.3	33.1	42.4	34.5	51.1	41.2
Rate	995	1425	1396	1418	1502	1256	1189	913	1124	1052	1347	1204

The researchers believe that lean body mass is an important influence on metabolic rate. Make a scatterplot to examine this belief.

4.4 Outsourcing by airlines. Airlines have increasingly outsourced the maintenance of their planes to other companies. Critics say that the maintenance may be less carefully done, so that outsourcing creates a safety hazard. As evidence, they point to government data on percent of major maintenance outsourced and percent of flight delays blamed on the airline (often due to maintenance problems):[2]

Airline	Outsource percent	Delay percent	Airline	Outsource percent	Delay percent
AirTran	66	14	Frontier	65	31
Alaska	92	42	Hawaiian	80	70
American	46	26	JetBlue	68	18
America West	76	39	Northwest	76	43
ATA	18	19	Southwest	68	20
Continental	69	20	United	63	27
Delta	48	26	US Airways	77	24

Make a scatterplot that shows how delays depend on outsourcing.

Interpreting scatterplots

To interpret a scatterplot, adapt the strategies of data analysis learned in Chapters 1 and 2 to the new two-variable setting.

EXAMINING A SCATTERPLOT

In any graph of data, look for the **overall pattern** and for striking **deviations** from that pattern.

You can describe the overall pattern of a scatterplot by the **direction, form**, and **strength** of the relationship.

An important kind of deviation is an **outlier**, an individual value that falls outside the overall pattern of the relationship.

---

clusters

EXAMPLE 4.3   Understanding state SAT scores

SOLVE (interpret the plot): Figure 4.1 shows a clear *direction*: the overall pattern moves from upper left to lower right. That is, states in which higher percents of high school graduates take the SAT tend to have lower mean SAT mathematics scores. We call this a *negative association* between the two variables.

The *form* of the relationship is roughly a straight line with a slight curve to the right as it moves down. What is more, most states fall into two distinct **clusters**. The ACT states cluster at the left and the SAT states at the right. In 22 states, fewer than 20% of seniors took the SAT; in another 22 states, more than 50% took the SAT.

The *strength* of a relationship in a scatterplot is determined by how closely the points follow a clear form. The overall relationship in Figure 4.1 is moderately strong: states with similar percents taking the SAT tend to have roughly similar mean SAT math scores.

CONCLUDE: Percent taking explains much of the variation among states in average SAT mathematics score. States in which a higher percent of students take the SAT tend to have lower mean scores because the mean includes a broader group of students. SAT states as a group have lower mean SAT scores than ACT states. ■

POSITIVE ASSOCIATION, NEGATIVE ASSOCIATION

Two variables are **positively associated** when above-average values of one tend to accompany above-average values of the other, and below-average values also tend to occur together.

Two variables are **negatively associated** when above-average values of one tend to accompany below-average values of the other, and vice versa.

Douglas Faulkner/Photo Researchers

Not all relationships have a clear direction that we can describe as positive association or negative association. Exercise 4.11 gives an example that does not have a single direction. Here is an example of a strong positive association with a simple and important form.

EXAMPLE 4.4   The endangered manatee

STATE: Manatees are large, gentle, slow-moving creatures found along the coast of Florida. Many manatees are injured or killed by boats. Table 4.1 contains data on the number of boats registered in Florida (in thousands) and the number of manatees killed by boats for the years 1977 to 2007.[3] Examine the relationship. Is it plausible that restricting the number of boats would help protect manatees?

TABLE 4.1 Florida boat registrations (thousands) and manatees killed by boats

YEAR	BOATS	MANATEES	YEAR	BOATS	MANATEES	YEAR	BOATS	MANATEES
1977	447	13	1988	675	43	1999	830	82
1978	460	21	1989	711	50	2000	880	78
1979	481	24	1990	719	47	2001	944	81
1980	498	16	1991	681	53	2002	962	95
1981	513	24	1992	679	38	2003	978	73
1982	512	20	1993	678	35	2004	983	69
1983	526	15	1994	696	49	2005	1010	79
1984	559	34	1995	713	42	2006	1024	92
1985	585	33	1996	732	60	2007	1027	73
1986	614	33	1997	755	54			
1987	645	39	1998	809	66			

PLAN: Make a scatterplot with "boats registered" as the explanatory variable and "manatees killed" as the response variable. Describe the direction, form, and strength of the relationship.

FIGURE 4.2

Scatterplot of the number of Florida manatees killed by boats in the years 1977 to 2007 against the number of boats registered in Florida that year, for Example 4.4. There is a strong linear (straight-line) pattern.

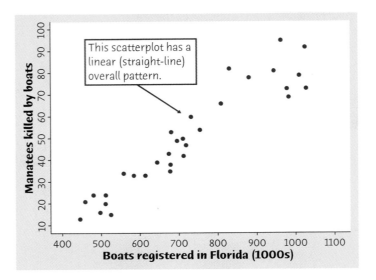

This scatterplot has a linear (straight-line) overall pattern.

SOLVE: Figure 4.2 is the scatterplot. There is a positive association—more boats goes with more manatees killed. The form of the relationship is **linear.** That is, the overall pattern follows a straight line from lower left to upper right. The relationship is strong because the points don't deviate greatly from a line.

linear relation

CONCLUDE: As more boats are registered, the number of manatees killed by boats goes up linearly. The Florida Wildlife Commission says that in recent years boats accounted for 24% of manatee deaths and 42% of deaths whose causes could be determined. Although many manatees die from other causes, it appears that fewer boats would mean fewer manatee deaths. ■

APPLY YOUR KNOWLEDGE

4.5 Do heavier people burn more energy? Describe the direction, form, and strength of the relationship between lean body mass and metabolic rate, as displayed in your plot for Exercise 4.3.

4.6 Outsourcing by airlines. Does your plot for Exercise 4.4 show a positive association between maintenance outsourcing and delays caused by the airline? One airline is a high outlier in delay percent. Which airline is this? Aside from the outlier, does the plot show a roughly linear form? Is the relationship very strong?

4.7 Do heavier people burn more energy? The study of dieting described in Exercise 4.3 collected data on the lean body mass (in kilograms) and metabolic rate (in calories) for both female and male subjects:

Sex	F	F	F	F	F	F	F	F	F	F
Mass	36.1	54.6	48.5	42.0	50.6	42.0	40.3	33.1	42.4	34.5
Rate	995	1425	1396	1418	1502	1256	1189	913	1124	1052

Sex	F	F	M	M	M	M	M	M	M
Mass	51.1	41.2	51.9	46.9	62.0	62.9	47.4	48.7	51.9
Rate	1347	1204	1867	1439	1792	1666	1362	1614	1460

(a) Make a scatterplot of metabolic rate versus lean body mass for all 19 subjects. Use separate symbols to distinguish women and men. (*This is a common method to compare two groups of individuals in a scatterplot.*)

(b) Does the same overall pattern hold for both women and men? What is the most important difference between women and men?

Measuring linear association: correlation

A scatterplot displays the direction, form, and strength of the relationship between two quantitative variables. Linear (straight-line) relations are particularly important because a straight line is a simple pattern that is quite common. A linear relation is strong if the points lie close to a straight line, and weak if they are widely scattered about a line. *Correlation* is a numerical measure of the strength of a linear relationship.

> **CORRELATION**
>
> The **correlation** measures the direction and strength of the linear relationship between two quantitative variables. Correlation is usually written as r.
>
> Suppose that we have data on variables x and y for n individuals. The values for the first individual are x_1 and y_1, the values for the second individual are x_2 and y_2, and so on. The means and standard deviations of the two variables are $\bar{x}$ and s_x for the x-values, and $\bar{y}$ and s_y for the y-values. The correlation r between x and y is
>
> $$r = \frac{1}{n-1}\left[\left(\frac{x_1 - \bar{x}}{s_x}\right)\left(\frac{y_1 - \bar{y}}{s_y}\right) + \left(\frac{x_2 - \bar{x}}{s_x}\right)\left(\frac{y_2 - \bar{y}}{s_y}\right)\right.$$
> $$\left. + \cdots + \left(\frac{x_n - \bar{x}}{s_x}\right)\left(\frac{y_n - \bar{y}}{s_y}\right)\right]$$
>
> or, more compactly,
>
> $$r = \frac{1}{n-1}\sum\left(\frac{x_i - \bar{x}}{s_x}\right)\left(\frac{y_i - \bar{y}}{s_y}\right)$$

Correlation uses *standardized observations*. Suppose that x is height in centimeters and y is weight in kilograms. Then $\bar{x}$ and s_x are the mean and standard deviation in centimeters of all the heights in our data. The value

$$\frac{x_i - \bar{x}}{s_x}$$

that appears in the formula for r is the standardized height of the ith person. Standardized height has no units—it just says how many standard deviations above or below the mean this person's height lies. The correlation r is an average of the products of the standardized height and the standardized weight for all the individuals. Just as in the case of the standard deviation s, the "average" here divides by one fewer than the number of individuals. The formula helps us see what correlation is, but in practice you should use software or a calculator that finds r from keyed-in values of two variables x and y.

Millard H. Sharp/Photo Researchers

4.8 Ebola and gorillas. An outbreak of the deadly Ebola virus in 2002 and 2003 killed 91 of the 95 gorillas in 7 home ranges in the Congo. To study the spread of the virus, measure "distance" by the number of home ranges separating a group of gorillas from the first group infected. Here are data on distance and number of days until deaths began in each later group:[4]

Distance	1	3	4	4	4	5
Days	4	21	33	41	43	46

(a) Make a scatterplot. Which is the explanatory variable? The plot shows a positive linear pattern.

(b) Find the correlation r step-by-step. First find the mean and standard deviation of each variable. Then find the six standardized values for each variable. Finally, use the formula for r. Explain how your value for r matches your graph in (a).

(c) Enter these data into your calculator or software and use the correlation function to find r. Check that you get the same result as in (b), up to roundoff error.

Facts about correlation

How correlation behaves is more important than the details of the formula. Here is what you need to know in order to interpret correlation.

1. *Correlation makes no distinction between explanatory and response variables.* It makes no difference which variable you call x and which you call y in calculating the correlation.

2. Because r uses the standardized values of the observations, r *does not change when we change the units of measurement of x, y, or both.* Measuring height in inches rather than centimeters and weight in pounds rather than kilograms does not change the correlation between height and weight. The correlation r itself has no unit of measurement; it is just a number.

3. *Positive r indicates positive association between the variables, and negative r indicates negative association.*

4. *The correlation r is always a number between -1 and 1.* Values of r near 0 indicate a very weak linear relationship. The strength of the linear relationship increases as r moves away from 0 toward either -1 or 1. Values of r close to -1 or 1 indicate that the points in a scatterplot lie close to a straight line. The extreme values $r = -1$ and $r = 1$ occur only in the case of a perfect linear relationship, when the points lie exactly along a straight line.

EXAMPLE 4.5 **From scatterplot to correlation**

The scatterplots in Figure 4.3 illustrate how values of r closer to 1 or -1 correspond to stronger linear relationships. To make the meaning of r clearer, the standard deviations of both variables in these plots are equal, and the horizontal and vertical scales are the same.

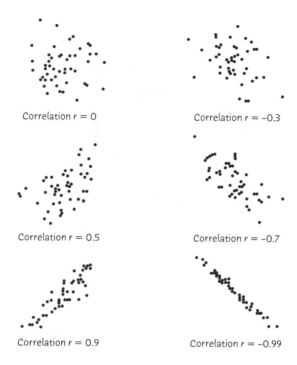

FIGURE 4.3
How correlation measures the strength of a linear relationship, for Example 4.5. Patterns closer to a straight line have correlations closer to 1 or −1.

Correlation r = 0

Correlation r = -0.3

Correlation r = 0.5

Correlation r = -0.7

Correlation r = 0.9

Correlation r = -0.99

The scatterplots in Figure 4.4 show four sets of real data. The patterns are less regular than those in Figure 4.3, but they also illustrate how correlation measures the strength of linear relationships.[5]

(a) This repeats the manatee plot in Figure 4.2. There is a strong positive linear relationship, $r = 0.947$.

(b) Here are the number of named tropical storms each year between 1984 and 2007 plotted against the number predicted before the start of hurricane season by William Gray of Colorado State University. There is a moderate linear relationship, $r = 0.529$.

(c) These data come from an experiment that studied how quickly cuts in the limbs of newts heal. Each point represents the healing rate in micrometers (millionths of a meter) per hour for the two front limbs of the same newt. This relationship is weaker than those in (a) and (b), with $r = 0.358$.

(d) Does last year's stock market performance help predict how stocks will do this year? No. The correlation between last year's percent return and this year's percent return over 56 years is only $r = -0.081$. The scatterplot shows a cloud of points with no visible linear pattern. ■

Describing the relationship between two variables is a more complex task than describing the distribution of one variable. Here are some cautions to keep in mind when you use correlation.

1. *Correlation requires that both variables be quantitative, so that it makes sense to do the arithmetic indicated by the formula for r*. We cannot calculate a correlation between the incomes of a group of people and what city they live in, because city is a categorical variable.

FIGURE 4.4
How correlation measures the strength of a linear relationship, for Example 4.5. Four sets of real data with (a) $r = 0.947$, (b) $r = 0.529$, (c) $r = 0.358$, and (d) $r = -0.081$.

(a)

(b)

(c)

(d)

2. Correlation measures the strength of only the linear relationship between two variables. *Correlation does not describe curved relationships between variables, no matter how strong they are.* Exercise 4.11 illustrates this important fact.

3. *Like the mean and standard deviation, the correlation is not resistant: r is strongly affected by a few outlying observations.* Use r with caution when outliers appear in the scatterplot. Figure 4.4(b) contains an outlier, the disastrous 2005 season, whose 27 named storms included Hurricane Katrina. Adding this one point to the other 23 increases the correlation from 0.475 to 0.529. Because the outlier extends the linear pattern, it increases the correlation.

4. *Correlation is not a complete summary of two-variable data,* even when the relationship between the variables is linear. You should give the means and standard deviations of both x and y along with the correlation.

Because the formula for correlation uses the means and standard deviations, these measures are the proper choice to accompany a correlation. Of course, even giving means, standard deviations, and the correlation for state SAT scores and percent taking will not point out the clusters in Figure 4.1. Numerical summaries complement plots of data, but they don't replace them.

4.9 Changing the units. The healing rates plotted in Figure 4.4(c) are measured in micrometers (millionths of a meter) per hour. The correlation between healing rates for the two front limbs of newts is $r = 0.358$. If the measurements were made in inches per day, would the correlation change? Explain your answer.

4.10 Changing the correlation. Use your calculator or software to demonstrate how outliers can affect correlation.

(a) What is the correlation between lean body mass and metabolic rate for the 12 women in Exercise 4.3?

(b) Make a scatterplot of the data with two new points added. Point A: mass 65 kilograms, metabolic rate 1761 calories. Point B: mass 35 kilograms, metabolic rate 1400 calories. Find two new correlations: one for the original data plus Point A, and another for the original data plus Point B.

(c) By looking at your plot, explain why adding Point A makes the correlation stronger (closer to 1) and adding Point B makes the correlation weaker (closer to 0).

4.11 Strong association but no correlation. The gas mileage of an automobile first increases and then decreases as the speed increases. Suppose that this relationship is very regular, as shown by the following data on speed (miles per hour) and mileage (miles per gallon):

Speed	20	30	40	50	60
Mileage	24	28	30	28	24

Make a scatterplot of mileage versus speed. Show that the correlation between speed and mileage is $r = 0$. Explain why the correlation is 0 even though there is a strong relationship between speed and mileage.

CHAPTER 4 SUMMARY

- To study relationships between variables, we measure the variables on the same group of individuals. If we think that a variable x may explain or even cause changes in another variable y, we call x an **explanatory variable** and y a **response variable.**

- A **scatterplot** displays the relationship between two quantitative variables measured on the same individuals. Mark values of one variable on the horizontal axis (x axis) and values of the other variable on the vertical axis (y axis). Plot each individual's data as a point on the graph. Always plot the explanatory variable, if there is one, on the x axis of a scatterplot.

- In examining a scatterplot, look for an overall pattern showing the **direction, form,** and **strength** of the relationship, and then for **outliers** or other deviations from this pattern.

- **Direction:** If the relationship has a clear direction, we speak of either **positive association** (high values of the two variables tend to occur together) or **negative association** (high values of one variable tend to occur with low values of the other variable).

■ **Form: Linear relationships,** where the points show a straight-line pattern, are an important form of relationship between two variables. Curved relationships and **clusters** are other forms to watch for.

■ **Strength:** The **strength** of a relationship is determined by how close the points in the scatterplot lie to a simple form such as a line.

■ The **correlation r** measures the direction and strength of the linear association between two quantitative variables x and y. Although you can calculate a correlation for any scatterplot, r measures only straight-line relationships.

■ Correlation indicates the direction of a linear relationship by its sign: $r > 0$ for a positive association and $r < 0$ for a negative association. Correlation always takes values between -1 and 1, and indicates the strength of a relationship by how close it is to -1 or 1. Perfect correlation, $r = 1$ or $r = -1$, occurs only when the points on a scatterplot lie exactly on a straight line.

■ Correlation ignores the distinction between explanatory and response variables. The value of r is not affected by changes in the unit of measurement of either variable. Correlation is not resistant, so outliers can greatly change the value of r.

CHECK YOUR SKILLS

4.12 In a scatterplot of the average price of a barrel of oil and the average retail price of a gallon of gasoline, you expect to see
(a) a positive association.
(b) very little association.
(c) a negative association.

4.13 Figure 4.5 is a scatterplot of reading test scores against IQ test scores for 14 fifth-grade children. There is one low outlier in the plot. The IQ and reading scores for this child are
(a) IQ = 10, reading = 124.
(b) IQ = 124, reading = 72.
(c) IQ = 124, reading = 10.

4.14 If we leave out the low outlier, the correlation for the remaining 13 points in Figure 4.5 is closest to
(a) 0.5.   (b) −0.5.   (c) 0.95.

4.15 If the correlation between two variables is close to 0, you can conclude that a scatterplot would show
(a) a strong straight-line pattern.
(b) a cloud of points with no visible pattern.
(c) no straight-line pattern, but there might be a strong pattern of another form.

4.16 The points on a scatterplot lie very close to the line whose equation is $y = 4 - 3x$. The correlation between x and y is close to
(a) −3.   (b) −1.   (c) 1.

4.17 For a biology project, you measure the weight in grams and the tail length in millimeters of a group of mice. The

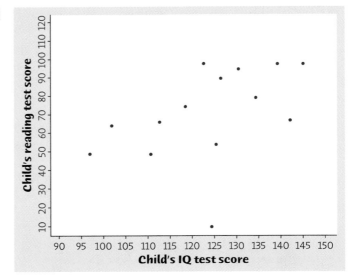

FIGURE 4.5

Scatterplot of reading test score against IQ test score for fifth-grade children, for Exercises 4.13 and 4.14.

correlation is $r = 0.7$. If you had measured tail length in centimeters instead of millimeters, what would be the correlation? (There are 10 millimeters in a centimeter.)
(a) 0.7/10 = 0.07   (b) 0.7   (c) (0.7)(10) = 7

4.18 Because elderly people may have difficulty standing to have their heights measured, a study looked at predicting overall height from height to the knee. Following are data (in centimeters) for five elderly men.

Knee height x	57.7	47.4	43.5	44.8	55.2
Height y	192.1	153.3	146.4	162.7	169.1

Use your calculator or software: the correlation between knee height and overall height is about
(a) $r = 0.88$.   (b) $r = 0.09$.   (c) $r = 0.77$.

CHAPTER 4 EXERCISES

4.19 Scores at the Masters. The Masters is one of the four major golf tournaments. Figure 4.6 is a scatterplot of the scores for the first two rounds of the 2007 Masters for all of the golfers entered. Only the 60 golfers with the lowest two-round total advance to the final two rounds. The plot has a grid pattern because golf scores must be whole numbers.[6]

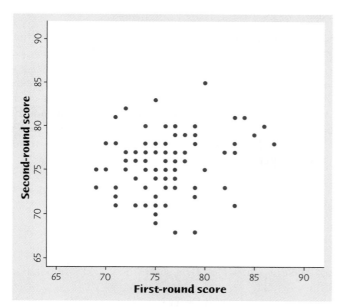

FIGURE 4.6

Scatterplot of the scores in the first two rounds of the 2007 Masters Tournament, for Exercise 4.19.

(a) What was the lowest score in the first round of play? How many golfers had this low score? What were their scores in the second round?
(b) Camilo Villegas had the highest score in the second round. What was this score? What was Villegas's score in the first round?
(c) Is the correlation between first-round scores and second-round scores closest to $r = 0.2$, $r = 0.6$, or $r = 0.9$? Explain your choice. Does the graph suggest that knowing a professional golfer's score for one round is much help in predicting his score for another round on the same course?

4.20 Can children estimate their own reading ability? To study this question, investigators asked 60 fifth-grade children to estimate their own reading ability, on a scale from 1 (low) to 5 (high). Figure 4.7 is a scatterplot of the children's estimates (response) against their scores on a reading test (explanatory).[7] Both scores take only whole-number values.

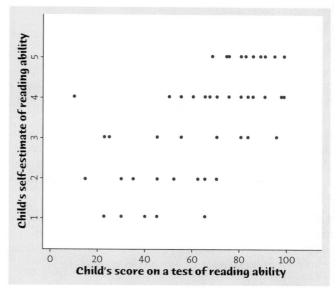

FIGURE 4.7

Scatterplot of children's estimates of their reading ability (on a scale of 1 to 5) against their score on a reading test, for Exercise 4.20.

(a) Is there an overall positive association between reading score and self-estimate?
(b) There is one clear outlier. What is this child's self-estimated reading level? Does this over- or underestimate the level as measured by the test?

4.21 Data on dating. A student wonders if tall women tend to date taller men than do short women. She measures herself, her dormitory roommate, and the women in the adjoining rooms; then she measures the next man each woman dates. Here are the data (heights in inches):

Women (x)	66	64	66	65	70	65
Men (y)	72	68	70	68	71	65

(a) Make a scatterplot of these data. Based on the scatterplot, do you expect the correlation to be positive or negative? Near ± 1 or not?
(b) Find the correlation r between the heights of the men and women. Do the data show that taller women tend to date taller men?

4.22 Coffee and deforestation. Coffee is a leading export from several developing countries. When coffee prices are high, farmers often clear forest to plant more coffee trees. Here are five years of data on prices paid to coffee growers in Indonesia and the percent of forest area lost in a national park that lies in a coffee-producing region:[8]

Price (cents per pound)	29	40	54	55	72
Forest lost (percent)	0.49	1.59	1.69	1.82	3.10

(a) Make a scatterplot. Which is the explanatory variable? What kind of pattern does your plot show?

(b) Find the correlation r between coffee price and forest loss. Do your scatterplot and correlation support the idea that higher coffee prices increase the loss of forest?

(c) The price of coffee in international trade is given in dollars and cents. If the prices in the data were translated into the equivalent prices in euros, would the correlation between coffee price and percent of forest loss change? Explain your answer.

4.23 Sparrowhawk colonies. One of nature's patterns connects the percent of adult birds in a colony that return from the previous year and the number of new adults that join the colony. Here are data for 13 colonies of sparrowhawks:[9]

Percent return	74	66	81	52	73	62	52	45	62	46	60	46	38
New adults	5	6	8	11	12	15	16	17	18	18	19	20	20

(a) Plot the count of new adults (response) against the percent of returning birds (explanatory). Describe the direction and form of the relationship. Is the correlation r an appropriate measure of the strength of this relationship? If so, find r.

(b) For short-lived birds, the association between these variables is positive: changes in weather and food supply drive the populations of new and returning birds up or down together. For long-lived territorial birds, on the other hand, the association is negative because returning birds claim their territories in the colony and don't leave room for new recruits. Which type of species is the sparrowhawk?

4.24 Our brains don't like losses. Most people dislike losses more than they like gains. In money terms, people are about as sensitive to a loss of $10 as to a gain of $20. To discover what parts of the brain are active in decisions about gain and loss, psychologists presented subjects with a series of gambles with different odds and different amounts of winnings and losses. From a subject's choices, they constructed a measure of "behavioral loss aversion." Higher scores show greater sensitivity to losses. Observing brain activity while subjects made their decisions pointed to specific brain regions. Here are data for 16 subjects on behavioral loss aversion and "neural loss aversion," a measure of activity in one region of the brain:[10]

Neural	−50.0	−39.1	−25.9	−26.7	−28.6	−19.8	−17.6	5.5
Behavioral	0.08	0.81	0.01	0.12	0.68	0.11	0.36	0.34

Neural	2.6	20.7	12.1	15.5	28.8	41.7	55.3	155.2
Behavioral	0.53	0.68	0.99	1.04	0.66	0.86	1.29	1.94

(a) Make a scatterplot that shows how behavior responds to brain activity.

(b) Describe the overall pattern of the data. There is one clear outlier.

(c) Find the correlation r between neural and behavioral loss aversion both with and without the outlier. Does the outlier have a strong influence on the value of r? By looking at your plot, explain why adding the outlier to the other data points causes r to increase.

4.25 Sulfur, the ocean, and the sun. Sulfur in the atmosphere affects climate by influencing formation of clouds. The main natural source of sulfur is dimethyl sulfide (DMS) produced by small organisms in the upper layers of the oceans. DMS production is in turn influenced by the amount of energy the upper ocean receives from sunlight. Here are monthly data on solar radiation dose (SRD, in watts per square meter) and surface DMS concentration (in nanomolars) for a region in the Mediterranean:[11]

SRD	12.55	12.91	14.34	19.72	21.52	22.41	37.65	48.41
DMS	0.796	0.692	1.744	1.062	0.682	1.517	0.736	0.720

SRD	74.41	94.14	109.38	157.79	262.67	268.96	289.23
DMS	1.820	1.099	2.692	5.134	8.038	7.280	8.872

(a) Make a scatterplot that shows how DMS responds to SRD.

(b) Describe the overall pattern of the data. Find the correlation r between DMS and SRD. Because SRD changes with the seasons of the year, the close relationship between SRD and DMS helps explain other seasonal patterns.

4.26 How fast do icicles grow? Japanese researchers measured the growth of icicles in a cold chamber under various conditions of temperature, wind, and water flow.[12] Table 4.2 contains data produced under two sets of conditions. In both cases, there was no wind and the temperature was set at −11°C. Water flowed over the icicle at a higher rate (29.6 milligrams per second) in Run 8905 and at a slower rate (11.9 mg/s) in Run 8903.

(a) Make a scatterplot of the length of the icicle in centimeters versus time in minutes, using separate symbols for the two runs.

TABLE 4.2 Growth of icicles over time

	RUN 8903				RUN 8905		
TIME (MIN)	LENGTH (CM)	TIME (MIN)	LENGTH (CM)	TIME (MIN)	LENGTH (CM)	TIME (MIN)	LENGTH (CM)
10	0.6	130	18.1	10	0.3	130	10.4
20	1.8	140	19.9	20	0.6	140	11.0
30	2.9	150	21.0	30	1.0	150	11.9
40	4.0	160	23.4	40	1.3	160	12.7
50	5.0	170	24.7	50	3.2	170	13.9
60	6.1	180	27.8	60	4.0	180	14.6
70	7.9			70	5.3	190	15.8
80	10.1			80	6.0	200	16.2
90	10.9			90	6.9	210	17.9
100	12.7			100	7.8	220	18.8
110	14.4			110	8.3	230	19.9
120	16.6			120	9.6	240	21.1

(b) What does your plot show about the pattern of growth of icicles? What does it show about the effect of changing the rate of water flow on icicle growth?

4.27 How many corn plants are too many? How much corn per acre should a farmer plant to obtain the highest yield? Too few plants will give a low yield. On the other hand, if there are too many plants, they will compete with each other and yields will fall. To find the best planting rate, plant at different rates on several plots of ground and measure the harvest. (Be sure to treat all the plots the same except for the planting rate.) Here are data from such an experiment:[13]

Plants per acre (thousands)	Yield (bushels per acre)			
12	150.1	113.0	118.4	142.6
16	166.9	120.7	135.2	149.8
20	165.3	130.1	139.6	149.9
24	134.7	138.4	156.1	
28	119.0	150.5		

(a) Make a scatterplot that shows how yield responds to planting rate. Use a scale of yields from 100 to 200 bushels per acre so that the pattern will be clear.
(b) Describe the overall pattern of the relationship. Is it linear? Is there a positive or negative association, or neither? Find the correlation r. Is r a helpful description of this relationship?
(c) Find the mean yield for each of the five planting rates. Plot each mean yield against its planting rate on your scatterplot and connect these five points with lines. This combination of numerical description and graphing makes the relationship clearer. What planting rate would you recommend to a farmer whose conditions were similar to those in the experiment?

4.28 Attracting beetles. To detect the presence of harmful insects in farm fields, we can put up boards covered with a sticky material and examine the insects trapped on the boards. Which colors attract insects best? Experimenters placed six boards of each of four colors at random locations in a field of oats and measured the number of cereal leaf beetles trapped. Here are the data:[14]

Board color	Beetles trapped					
Blue	16	11	20	21	14	7
Green	37	32	20	29	37	32
White	21	12	14	17	13	20
Yellow	45	59	48	46	38	47

(a) Make a plot of beetles trapped against color (space the four colors equally on the horizontal axis). Which color appears best at attracting beetles?
(b) Does it make sense to speak of a positive or negative association between board color and beetles trapped? Why? Is correlation r a helpful description of the relationship? Why?

4.29 Thinking about correlation. Exercise 4.21 presents data on the heights of women and of the men they date.
(a) If heights were measured in centimeters rather than inches, how would the correlation change? (There are 2.54 centimeters in an inch.)
(b) How would r change if all the men were 6 inches shorter than the heights given in the table? Does the correlation tell us whether women tend to date men taller than themselves?
(c) If every woman dated a man exactly 3 inches taller than herself, what would be the correlation between male and female heights?

4.30 The effect of changing units. Changing the units of measurement can dramatically alter the appearance of a scatterplot. Return to the data on knee height and overall height in Exercise 4.18:

Knee height x	57.7	47.4	43.5	44.8	55.2
Height y	192.1	153.3	146.4	162.7	169.1

Both heights are measured in centimeters. A mad scientist decides to measure knee height in millimeters and height in meters. The same data in these units are

Knee height x	577	474	435	448	552
Height y	1.921	1.533	1.464	1.627	1.691

(a) Make a plot with the x axis extending from 0 to 600 and the y axis from 0 to 250. Plot the original data on these axes. Then plot the new data using a different color or symbol. The two plots look very different.

(b) Nonetheless, the correlation is exactly the same for the two sets of measurements. Why do you know that this is true without doing any calculations? Find the two correlations to verify that they are the same.

4.31 Statistics for investing. A mutual funds company's newsletter says, "A well-diversified portfolio includes assets with low correlations." The newsletter includes a table of correlations between the returns on various classes of investments. For example, the correlation between municipal bonds and large-cap stocks is 0.50, and the correlation between municipal bonds and small-cap stocks is 0.21.

(a) Rachel invests heavily in municipal bonds. She wants to diversify by adding an investment whose returns do not closely follow the returns on her bonds. Should she choose large-cap stocks or small-cap stocks for this purpose? Explain your answer.

(b) If Rachel wants an investment that tends to increase when the return on her bonds drops, what kind of correlation should she look for?

4.32 Teaching and research. A college newspaper interviews a psychologist about student ratings of the teaching of faculty members. The psychologist says, "The evidence indicates that the correlation between the research productivity and teaching rating of faculty members is close to zero." The paper reports this as "Professor McDaniel said that good researchers tend to be poor teachers, and vice versa." Explain why the paper's report is wrong. Write a statement in plain language (don't use the word "correlation") to explain the psychologist's meaning.

4.33 Sloppy writing about correlation. Each of the following statements contains a blunder. Explain in each case what is wrong.

(a) "There is a high correlation between the gender of American workers and their income."

(b) "We found a high correlation ($r = 1.09$) between students' ratings of faculty teaching and ratings made by other faculty members."

(c) "The correlation between height and weight of the subjects was $r = 0.63$ centimeter."

*The following exercises ask you to answer questions from data without having the details outlined for you. The exercise statements give you the **State** step of the four-step process. In your work, follow the **Plan, Solve,** and **Conclude** steps of the process, described on page 42.*

4.34 Brighter sunlight? The brightness of sunlight at the earth's surface changes over time depending on whether the earth's atmosphere is more or less clear. Sunlight dimmed between 1960 and 1990. After 1990, air pollution dropped in industrial countries. Did sunlight brighten? Here are data from Boulder, Colorado, averaging over only clear days each year. (Other locations show similar trends.) The response variable is solar radiation in watts per square meter.[15]

Year	1992	1993	1994	1995	1996	1997	1998
Sun	243.2	246.0	248.0	250.3	250.9	250.9	250.0

Year	1999	2000	2001	2002
Sun	248.9	251.7	251.4	250.9

4.35 Saving energy with solar panels. We have data from a house in the Midwest that uses natural gas for heating. Will installing solar panels reduce the amount of gas consumed? Gas consumption is higher in cold weather, so the relationship between outside temperature and gas consumption is important. Here are data for 16 consecutive months:[16]

	Nov.	Dec.	Jan.	Feb.	Mar.	Apr.	May	June
Degree-days per day	24	51	43	33	26	13	4	0
Gas used per day	6.3	10.9	8.9	7.5	5.3	4.0	1.7	1.2

	July	Aug.	Sept.	Oct.	Nov.	Dec.	Jan.	Feb.
Degree-days per day	0	1	6	12	30	32	52	30
Gas used per day	1.2	1.2	2.1	3.1	6.4	7.2	11.0	6.9

Outside temperature is recorded in degree-days, a common measure of demand for heating. A day's degree-days are the number of degrees its average temperature falls below 65°F. Gas used is recorded in hundreds of cubic feet. The chart gives data for 23 more months after installing solar panels.

Degree-days	19	3	3	0	0	0	8	11
Gas used	3.2	2.0	1.6	1.0	0.7	0.7	1.6	3.1
Degree-days	27	46	38	34	16	9	2	1
Gas used	5.1	7.7	7.0	6.1	3.0	2.1	1.3	1.0
Degree-days	0	2	3	18	32	34	40	
Gas used	1.0	1.0	1.2	3.4	6.1	6.5	7.5	

What do the before-and-after data show about the effect of solar panels? (Start by plotting both sets of data on the same plot, using two different plotting symbols.)

4.36 Merlins breeding. The percent of an animal species in the wild that survive to breed again is often lower following a successful breeding season. A study of merlins (small falcons) in northern Sweden observed the number of breeding pairs in an isolated area and the percent of males (banded for identification) who returned the next breeding season. Here are data for nine years:[17]

Breeding pairs	28	29	29	29	30	32	33	38	38
Percent return	82	83	70	61	69	58	43	50	47

Investigate the relationship between breeding pairs and percent return.

4.37 Does social rejection hurt? We often describe our emotional reaction to social rejection as "pain." Does social rejection cause activity in areas of the brain that are known to be activated by physical pain? If it does, we really do experience social and physical pain in similar ways. Psychologists first included and then deliberately excluded individuals from a social activity while they measured changes in brain activity. After each activity, the subjects filled out questionnaires that assessed how excluded they felt. Here are data for 13 subjects:[18]

Subject	Social distress	Brain activity	Subject	Social distress	Brain activity
1	1.26	−0.055	8	2.18	0.025
2	1.85	−0.040	9	2.58	0.027
3	1.10	−0.026	10	2.75	0.033
4	2.50	−0.017	11	2.75	0.064
5	2.17	−0.017	12	3.33	0.077
6	2.67	0.017	13	3.65	0.124
7	2.01	0.021			

The explanatory variable is "social distress" measured by each subject's questionnaire score after exclusion relative to the score after inclusion. (So values greater than 1 show the degree of distress caused by exclusion.) The response variable is change in activity in a region of the brain that is activated by physical pain. Discuss what the data show.

NASA/GSFC

Can scientists predict in advance
how many hurricanes the
coming season will bring?
Exercise 5.44 has some data.

CHAPTER 5

Regression

**IN THIS CHAPTER
WE COVER...**

■ Regression lines

■ The least-squares regression line

■ Using technology

■ Facts about least-squares
regression

■ Residuals

■ Influential observations

■ Cautions about correlation and
regression

■ Association does not imply
causation

Linear (straight-line) relationships between two quantitative variables are easy to understand and quite common. In Chapter 4, we found linear relationships in settings as varied as Florida manatee deaths, icicle growth, and predicting tropical storms. Correlation measures the direction and strength of these relationships. When a scatterplot shows a linear relationship, we would like to summarize the overall pattern by drawing a line on the scatterplot.

Regression lines

A *regression line* summarizes the relationship between two variables, but only in a specific setting: one of the variables helps explain or predict the other. That is, regression describes a relationship between an explanatory variable and a response variable.

> **REGRESSION LINE**
>
> A **regression line** is a straight line that describes how a response variable y changes as an explanatory variable x changes. We often use a regression line to predict the value of y for a given value of x.

EXAMPLE 5.1 Does fidgeting keep you slim?

Here, following our four-step process (page 42), is an account of a study that sheds some light on gaining weight.

STATE: Some people don't gain weight even when they overeat. Perhaps fidgeting and other "nonexercise activity" (NEA) explains why. These people may spontaneously increase nonexercise activity when fed more. Researchers deliberately overfed 16 healthy young adults for 8 weeks. They measured fat gain (in kilograms) and, as an explanatory variable, change in energy use (in calories) from activity other than deliberate exercise—fidgeting, daily living, and the like. Here are the data:[1]

NEA change (cal)	−94	−57	−29	135	143	151	245	355
Fat gain (kg)	4.2	3.0	3.7	2.7	3.2	3.6	2.4	1.3
NEA change (cal)	392	473	486	535	571	580	620	690
Fat gain (kg)	3.8	1.7	1.6	2.2	1.0	0.4	2.3	1.1

Do people with larger increases in NEA tend to gain less fat?

PLAN: Make a scatterplot of the data and examine the pattern. If it is linear, use correlation to measure its strength and draw a regression line on the scatterplot to predict fat gain from change in NEA.

SOLVE: Figure 5.1 is a scatterplot of these data. The plot shows a moderately strong negative linear association with no outliers. The correlation is $r = -0.7786$. The line on the plot is a regression line for predicting fat gain from change in NEA.

CONCLUDE: People with larger increases in nonexercise activity do indeed gain less fat. To add to this conclusion, we must study regression lines in more detail. ■

FIGURE 5.1

Weight gain after 8 weeks of overeating, plotted against increase in nonexercise activity over the same period, for Example 5.1.

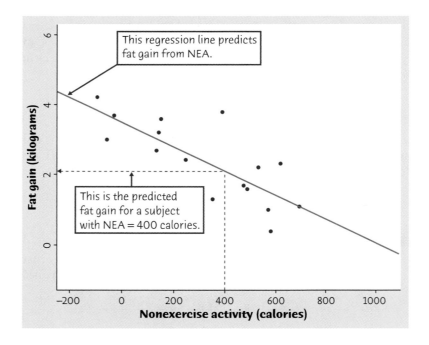

Many calculators and software programs will give you the equation of a regression line from keyed-in data. Understanding and using the line are more important than the details of where the equation comes from.

REVIEW OF STRAIGHT LINES

Suppose that y is a response variable (plotted on the vertical axis) and x is an explanatory variable (plotted on the horizontal axis). A straight line relating y to x has an equation of the form

$$y = a + bx$$

In this equation, b is the **slope,** the amount by which y changes when x increases by one unit. The number a is the **intercept,** the value of y when $x = 0$.

EXAMPLE 5.2 **Using a regression line**

Any straight line describing the NEA data has the form

$$\text{fat gain} = a + (b \times \text{NEA change})$$

The line in Figure 5.1 is the regression line with the equation

$$\text{fat gain} = 3.505 - 0.00344 \times \text{NEA change}$$

Be sure you understand the role of the two numbers in this equation:

- The slope $b = -0.00344$ tells us that fat gained goes down by 0.00344 kilogram for each added calorie of NEA. The slope of a regression line is the *rate of change* in the response as the explanatory variable changes.
- The intercept, $a = 3.505$ kilograms, is the estimated fat gain if NEA does not change when a person overeats.

The equation of the regression line makes it easy to predict fat gain. If a person's NEA increases by 400 calories when she overeats, substitute $x = 400$ in the equation. The predicted fat gain is

$$\text{fat gain} = 3.505 - (0.00344 \times 400) = 2.13 \text{ kilograms}$$

Figure 5.1 shows the prediction graphically: go "up and over" from $x = 400$.

To **plot the line** on the scatterplot, use the equation to find the predicted y for two values of x, one near each end of the range of x in the data. Plot each y above its x-value and draw the line through the two points. ∎

plotting a line

The slope $b = -0.00344$ in Example 5.2 looks small. This does *not* mean that change in NEA has little effect on fat gain. The size of the slope depends on the units in which we measure the two variables. In this example, the slope is the change in fat gain in kilograms when NEA increases by one calorie. There are 1000 grams in a kilogram. If we measured fat gain in grams, the slope would be 1000 times larger, $b = 3.44$. *You can't say how important a relationship is by looking at the size of the slope of the regression line.*

APPLY YOUR KNOWLEDGE

5.1 City mileage, highway mileage. We expect a car's highway gas mileage to be related to its city gas mileage. Data for all 1198 vehicles in the government's *2008 Fuel Economy Guide* give the regression line

$$\text{highway mpg} = 4.62 + (1.109 \times \text{city mpg})$$

for predicting highway mileage from city mileage.

(a) What is the slope of this line? Say in words what the numerical value of the slope tells you.

(b) What is the intercept? (Because no car has city mileage close to $x = 0$, the intercept is not of practical interest.)

(c) Find the predicted highway mileage for a car that gets 16 miles per gallon in the city. Do the same for a car with city mileage 28 mpg.

5.2 What's the line? You use the same bar of soap to shower each morning. The bar weighs 80 grams when it is new. Its weight goes down by 6 grams per day on the average. What is the equation of the regression line for predicting weight from days of use?

The least-squares regression line

How should we draw a regression line on a scatterplot? Because we use the line to predict y from x, the prediction errors we make are errors in y, the vertical direction in the scatterplot. *A good regression line makes the vertical distances of the points from the line as small as possible.* The most common way to make the collection of vertical distances "as small as possible" is the *least-squares* method.

LEAST-SQUARES REGRESSION LINE

The **least-squares regression line** of y on x is the line that makes the sum of the squares of the vertical distances of the data points from the line as small as possible.

We can give the equation for the least-squares line in terms of the means and standard deviations of the two variables and the correlation between them.

EQUATION OF THE LEAST-SQUARES REGRESSION LINE

We have data on an explanatory variable x and a response variable y for n individuals. From the data, calculate the means $\overline{x}$ and $\overline{y}$ and the standard deviations s_x and s_y of the two variables, and their correlation r. The least-squares regression line is the line

$$\hat{y} = a + bx$$

with **slope**

$$b = r\frac{s_y}{s_x}$$

and **intercept**

$$a = \overline{y} - b\overline{x}$$

We write $\hat{y}$ (read "y hat") in the equation of the regression line to emphasize that the line gives a *predicted* response $\hat{y}$ for any x. Because of the scatter of points about the line, the predicted response will usually not be exactly the same as the actually *observed* response y. In practice, you don't need to calculate the means, standard deviations, and correlation first. Software or your calculator will give the slope b and intercept a of the least-squares line from the values of the variables x and y. You can then concentrate on understanding and using the regression line.

Using technology

Least-squares regression is one of the most common statistical procedures. Any technology for statistical calculations will give you the least-squares line and related information. Figure 5.2 displays the regression output for the data of Examples 5.1 and 5.2 from a graphing calculator, a statistical program, and a spreadsheet program. Each output records the slope and intercept of the least-squares line. The software also provides information that we do not yet need, although we will use much of it later. (In fact, we left out part of the Minitab and Excel outputs.) Be sure that you can locate the slope and intercept on all three outputs. *Once you understand the statistical ideas, you can read and work with almost any software output.*

APPLY YOUR KNOWLEDGE

5.3 Ebola and gorillas. In Exercise 4.8 (page 80), you looked at the spread of an outbreak of the deadly Ebola virus among gorillas in the Congo. The data give a measure of the distance of each group of gorillas from the first group infected and the number of days until deaths began in each later group:[2]

Distance x	1	3	4	4	4	5
Days y	4	21	33	41	43	46

There is a strong linear relationship between distance x and days y.

(a) Use your calculator to find the mean and standard deviation of both x and y and the correlation r between x and y. Use these basic measures to find the equation of the least-squares line for predicting y from x.

(b) Enter the data into your software or calculator and use the regression function to find the least-squares line. The result should agree with your work in (a) up to roundoff error.

5.4 Do heavier people burn more energy? We have data on the lean body mass and resting metabolic rate for 12 women who are subjects in a study of dieting. Lean body mass, given in kilograms, is a person's weight leaving out all fat. Metabolic rate, in calories burned per 24 hours, is the rate at which the body consumes energy.

Mass	36.1	54.6	48.5	42.0	50.6	42.0	40.3	33.1	42.4	34.5	51.1	41.2
Rate	995	1425	1396	1418	1502	1256	1189	913	1124	1052	1347	1204

(a) Make a scatterplot that shows how metabolic rate depends on body mass. There is a quite strong linear relationship, with correlation $r = 0.876$.

FIGURE 5.2

Least-squares regression for the nonexercise activity data: output from a graphing calculator, a statistical program, and a spreadsheet program.

Texas Instruments Graphing Calculator

```
LinReg
  y=a+bx
  a=3.505122916
  b=-.003441487
  r²=.6061492049
  r=-.7785558457
```

Minitab

Regression Analysis: fat versus nea

The regression equation is
fat = 3.51 - 0.00344 nea

Predictor	Coef	SE Coef	T	P
Constant	3.5051	0.3036	11.54	0.000
nea	-0.0034415	0.0007414	-4.64	0.000

S = 0.739853   R-Sq = 60.6%   R-Sq (adj) = 57.8%

Microsoft Excel

Book1

	A	B	C	D	E	F
1	SUMMARY OUTPUT					
2						
3	*Regression statistics*					
4	Multiple R	0.778555846				
5	R Square	0.606149205				
6	Adjusted R Square	0.578017005				
7	Standard Error	0.739852874				
8	Observations	16				
9						
10		Coefficients	Standard Error	t Stat	P-value	
11	Intercept	3.505122916	0.303616403	11.54458	1.53E-08	
12	nea	-0.003441487	0.00074141	-4.64182	0.000381	
13						

Output / nea data

(b) Find the least-squares regression line for predicting metabolic rate from body mass. Add this line to your scatterplot.

(c) Explain in words what the slope of the regression line tells us.

(d) Another woman has lean body mass 45 kilograms. What is her predicted metabolic rate?

Facts about least-squares regression

One reason for the popularity of least-squares regression lines is that they have many convenient properties. Here are some facts about least-squares regression lines.

Fact 1. The distinction between explanatory and response variables is essential in regression. Least-squares regression makes the distances of the data points from the line small only in the y direction. If we reverse the roles of the two variables, we get a different least-squares regression line.

Fact 2. The least-squares regression line always passes through the point $(\overline{x}, \overline{y})$ on the graph of y against x.

Fact 3. The correlation r describes the strength of a straight-line relationship. In the regression setting, this description takes a specific form: **the square of the correlation, r^2, is the fraction of the variation in the values of y that is explained by the least-squares regression of y on x.**

The idea is that when there is a linear relationship, some of the variation in y is accounted for by the fact that as x changes it pulls y along with it. More exactly, the predicted response $\hat{y}$ moves along the regression line as we move x from one end of its scale to the other. This is the variation in y that is explained by regression. Unless all of the data points lie exactly on a line, there is additional variation in the actual response y that appears as the scatter of points above and below the line. Although we will skip the algebra, it's possible to write

$$r^2 = \frac{\text{variation in } \hat{y} \text{ as } x \text{ pulls it along the line}}{\text{total variation in observed values of } y}$$

EXAMPLE 5.3 Using r^2

For the NEA data, $r = -0.7786$ and $r^2 = (-0.7786)^2 = 0.6062$. About 61% of the variation in fat gained is accounted for by the linear relationship with change in NEA. The other 39% is individual variation among subjects that is not explained by the linear relationship.

Figure 4.2 (page 78) shows a stronger linear relationship between boat registrations in Florida and manatees killed by boats. The correlation is $r = 0.947$ and $r^2 = (0.947)^2 = 0.897$. Almost 90% of the year-to-year variation in number of manatees killed by boats is explained by regression on number of boats registered. Only about 10% is variation among years with similar numbers of boats registered. ■

You can find a regression line for any relationship between two quantitative variables, but the usefulness of the line for prediction depends on the strength of the linear relationship. So r^2 is almost as important as the equation of the line in reporting a regression. All of the outputs in Figure 5.2 include r^2, either in decimal form or as a percent.

Facts 2 and 3 are special properties of least-squares regression. They are not true for other methods of fitting a line to data.

APPLY YOUR KNOWLEDGE

5.5 How useful is regression? Figure 4.6 (page 85) displays the relationship between golfers' scores on the first and second rounds of the 2007 Masters Tournament. The correlation is $r = 0.192$. Exercise 4.25 gives data on solar radiation dose (SRD) and concentration of dimethyl sulfide (DMS) over a region of the Mediterranean. The correlation is $r = 0.969$. Explain in simple language why knowing only these correlations enables you to say that prediction of DMS from SRD by a regression line will be much more accurate than prediction of a professional golfer's second-round score from his first-round score.

5.6 Growing corn. Exercise 4.27 (page 85) gives data from an agricultural experiment. The purpose of the study was to see how the yield of corn changes as we change the planting rate (plants per acre).

(a) Make a scatterplot of the data. (Use a scale of yields from 100 to 200 bushels per acre.) Find the least-squares regression line for predicting yield from planting rate and add this line to your plot. Why should we *not* use the regression line for prediction in this setting?

(b) What is r^2? What does this value say about the success of the regression line in predicting yield?

Residuals

One of the principles of data analysis is to look for an overall pattern and also for striking deviations from the pattern. A regression line describes the overall pattern of a linear relationship between an explanatory variable and a response variable. Deviations from this pattern appear in the scatter of the data points above and below the regression line. Because the vertical distances from the points to the line represent "left-over" variation in the response after fitting the regression line, we call these distances *residuals*.

> **RESIDUALS**
>
> A **residual** is the difference between an observed value of the response variable and the value predicted by the regression line. That is, a residual is the prediction error that remains after we have chosen the regression line:
>
> $$\text{residual} = \text{observed } y - \text{predicted } y$$
> $$= y - \hat{y}$$

Photodisc Green/Getty Images

EXAMPLE 5.4 **I feel your pain**

"Empathy" means being able to understand what others feel. To see how the brain expresses empathy, researchers recruited 16 couples in their midtwenties who were married or had been dating for at least two years. They zapped the man's hand with an electrode while the woman watched, and measured the activity in several parts of the woman's brain that would respond to her own pain. Brain activity was recorded as a fraction of the activity observed when the woman herself was zapped with the electrode. The women also completed a psychological test that measures empathy. Will women who score higher in empathy respond more strongly when their partner has a painful experience? Here are data for one brain region:[3]

Subject	1	2	3	4	5	6	7	8
Empathy score	38	53	41	55	56	61	62	48
Brain activity	−0.120	0.392	0.005	0.369	0.016	0.415	0.107	0.506

Subject	9	10	11	12	13	14	15	16
Empathy score	43	47	56	65	19	61	32	105
Brain activity	0.153	0.745	0.255	0.574	0.210	0.722	0.358	0.779

Figure 5.3 is a scatterplot, with empathy score as the explanatory variable x and brain activity as the response variable y. The plot shows a positive association. That is, women who score higher in empathy do indeed react more strongly to their partner's pain. The overall pattern is moderately linear, correlation $r = 0.515$.

The line on the plot is the least-squares regression line of brain activity on empathy score. Its equation is

$$\hat{y} = -0.0578 + 0.00761x$$

For Subject 1, with empathy score 38, we predict

$$\hat{y} = -0.0578 + (0.00761)(38) = 0.231$$

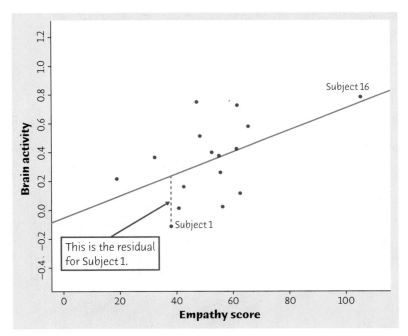

FIGURE 5.3

Scatterplot of activity in a region of the brain that responds to pain versus score on a test of empathy, for Example 5.4. Brain activity is measured as the subject watches her partner experience pain. The line is the least-squares regression line.

This subject's actual brain activity level was −0.120. The residual is

$$\text{residual} = \text{observed } y - \text{predicted } y$$

$$= -0.120 - 0.231 = -0.351$$

The residual is negative because the data point lies below the regression line. The dashed line segment in Figure 5.3 shows the size of the residual. ∎

There is a residual for each data point. Finding the residuals is a bit unpleasant because you must first find the predicted response for every x. Software or a graphing calculator gives you the residuals all at once. Here are the 16 residuals for the empathy study data, from software:

```
residuals:
-0.3515  -0.2494  -0.3526  -0.3072  -0.1166  -0.1136  0.1231  0.1721
 0.0463   0.0080   0.0084   0.1983   0.4449   0.1369  0.3154  0.0374
```

Because the residuals show how far the data fall from our regression line, examining the residuals helps assess how well the line describes the data. Although residuals can be calculated from any curve fitted to the data, the residuals from the least-squares line have a special property: **the mean of the least-squares residuals is always zero.**

Compare the scatterplot in Figure 5.3 with the *residual plot* for the same data in Figure 5.4. The horizontal line at zero in Figure 5.4 helps orient us. This "residual = 0" line corresponds to the regression line in Figure 5.3. A residual plot in effect turns the regression line horizontal and magnifies the deviations of the points from the line. This makes it easier to see unusual observations and patterns.

FIGURE 5.4

Residual plot for the data shown in Figure 5.3. The horizontal line at zero residual corresponds to the regression line in Figure 5.3.

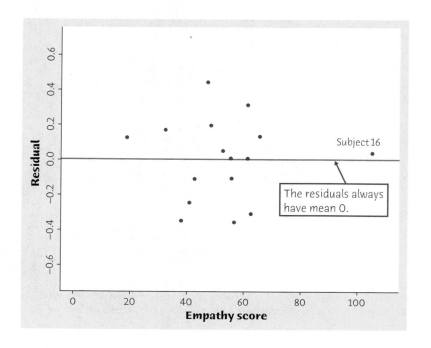

> ### RESIDUAL PLOTS
>
> A **residual plot** is a scatterplot of the regression residuals against the explanatory variable. Residual plots help us assess how well a regression line fits the data.

APPLY YOUR KNOWLEDGE

5.7 Residuals by hand. In Exercise 5.3 you found the equation of the least-squares line for predicting the number of days y until gorillas in a social group begin to die in an Ebola virus epidemic from the "distance" x from the first group infected.

(a) Use the equation to obtain the 6 residuals step-by-step. That is, find the prediction $\hat{y}$ for each observation and then find the residual $y - \hat{y}$.

(b) Check that (up to roundoff error) the residuals add to 0.

(c) The residuals are the part of the response y left over after the straight-line tie between y and x is removed. Show that the correlation between the residuals and x is 0 (up to roundoff error). That this correlation is always 0 is another special property of least-squares regression.

Influential observations

Figures 5.3 and 5.4 show one unusual observation. Subject 16 is an outlier in the x direction, with empathy score 40 points higher than any other subject. Because of its extreme position on the empathy scale, this point has a strong influence on the correlation. Dropping Subject 16 reduces the correlation from $r = 0.515$ to $r = 0.331$. You can see that this point extends the linear pattern in Figure 5.3 and so increases the correlation. We say that Subject 16 is *influential* for calculating the correlation.

> ### INFLUENTIAL OBSERVATIONS
>
> An observation is **influential** for a statistical calculation if removing it would markedly change the result of the calculation.
>
> The result of a statistical calculation may be of little practical use if it depends strongly on a few influential observations.
>
> Points that are outliers in either the x or y direction of a scatterplot are often influential for the correlation. Points that are outliers in the x direction are often influential for the least-squares regression line.

EXAMPLE 5.5 An influential observation?

Subject 16 in Example 5.4 is influential for the correlation between empathy score and brain activity because removing it reduces r from 0.515 to 0.331. Is this observation also

Subject 16 is an outlier in the *x* direction. The outlier is not influential for least-squares regression, because removing it moves the regression line only a little.

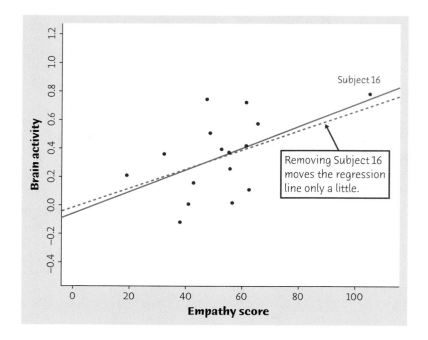

influential for the least-squares line? Figure 5.5 shows that it is not. The regression line calculated without Subject 16 (dashed) differs little from the line that uses all of the observations (solid). The reason that the outlier has little influence on the regression line is that it lies close to the dashed regression line calculated from the other observations. ■

To see why points that are outliers in the *x* direction are often influential for regression, let's try an experiment. Suppose that Subject 16's point in the scatterplot moves straight down. What happens to the regression line? Figure 5.6 gives the answer. The dashed line is the regression line with the outlier in its new, lower position. Because there are no other points with similar *x*-values, the line chases the outlier. *An outlier in x pulls the least-squares line toward itself. If the outlier does not lie close to the line calculated from the other observations, it will be influential.*

APPLY YOUR KNOWLEDGE

5.8 Do heavier people burn more energy? Return to the data of Exercise 5.4 (page 95) on lean body mass and metabolic rate. We will use these data to illustrate influence.

(a) Make a scatterplot of the data that is suitable for predicting metabolic rate from body mass, with two new points added. Point A: mass 42 kilograms, metabolic rate 1500 calories. Point B: mass 70 kilograms, metabolic rate 1400 calories. In which direction is each of these points an outlier?

(b) Add three least-squares regression lines to your plot: for the original 12 women, for the original women plus Point A, and for the original women plus Point B. Which new point is more influential for the regression line? Explain in simple language why each new point moves the line in the way your graph shows.

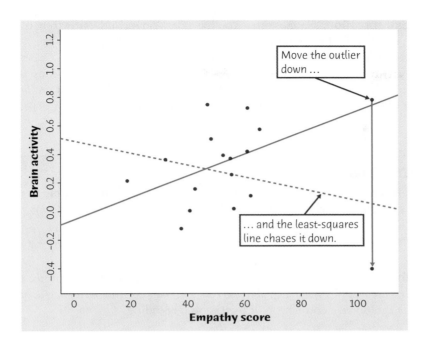

Move the outlier down ...

... and the least-squares line chases it down.

FIGURE 5.6
An outlier in the x direction pulls the least-squares line to itself because there are no other observations with similar values of x to hold the line in place. When the outlier moves down, the regression line chases it down. The original regression line is solid, and the final position of the regression line is dashed.

5.9 Outsourcing by airlines. Exercise 4.4 (page 76) gives data for 14 airlines on the percent of major maintenance outsourced and the percent of flight delays blamed on the airline.

(a) Make a scatterplot with outsourcing percent as x and delay percent as y. Hawaiian Airlines is a high outlier in the y direction. Because several other airlines have similar values of x, the influence of this outlier is unclear without actual calculation.

(b) Find the correlation r with and without Hawaiian Airlines. How influential is the outlier for correlation?

(c) Find the least-squares line for predicting y from x with and without Hawaiian Airlines. Draw both lines on your scatterplot. Use both lines to predict the percent of delays blamed on an airline that has outsourced 76% of its major maintenance. How influential is the outlier for the least-squares line?

Cautions about correlation and regression

Correlation and regression are powerful tools for describing the relationship between two variables. When you use these tools, you must be aware of their limitations. You already know that

■ *Correlation and regression lines describe only linear relationships.* You can do the calculations for any relationship between two quantitative variables, but the results are useful only if the scatterplot shows a linear pattern.

■ *Correlation and least-squares regression lines are not resistant.* Always plot your data and look for observations that may be influential.

Here are two more things to keep in mind when you use correlation and regression.

Beware extrapolation. Suppose that you have data on a child's growth between 3 and 8 years of age. You find a strong linear relationship between age x and height y. If you fit a regression line to these data and use it to predict height at age 25 years, you will predict that the child will be 8 feet tall. Growth slows down and then stops at maturity, so extending the straight line to adult ages is foolish. *Few relationships are linear for all values of x. Don't make predictions far outside the range of x that actually appears in your data.*

EXTRAPOLATION

Extrapolation is the use of a regression line for prediction far outside the range of values of the explanatory variable x that you used to obtain the line. Such predictions are often not accurate.

Beware the lurking variable Another caution is even more important: *the relationship between two variables can often be understood only by taking other variables into account. Lurking variables* can make a correlation or regression misleading.

LURKING VARIABLE

A **lurking variable** is a variable that is not among the explanatory or response variables in a study and yet may influence the interpretation of relationships among those variables.

You should always think about possible lurking variables before you draw conclusions based on correlation or regression.

EXAMPLE 5.6 Magic Mozart?

The Kalamazoo (Michigan) Symphony once advertised a "Mozart for Minors" program with this statement: "Question: Which students scored 51 points higher in verbal skills and 39 points higher in math? Answer: Students who had experience in music."[4]

We could as well answer "Students who played soccer." Why? Children with prosperous and well-educated parents are more likely than poorer children to have experience with music and also to play soccer. They are also likely to attend good schools, get good health care, and be encouraged to study hard. These advantages lead to high test scores. Family background is a lurking variable that explains why test scores are related to experience with music. ■

APPLY YOUR KNOWLEDGE

5.10 The endangered manatee. Table 4.1 (page 77) gives 31 years' data on boats registered in Florida and manatees killed by boats. Figure 4.2 (page 78) shows a strong positive linear relationship. The correlation is $r = 0.947$.

(a) Find the equation of the least-squares line for predicting manatees killed from thousands of boats registered. Because the linear pattern is so strong, we expect predictions from this line to be quite accurate—but only if conditions in Florida remain similar to those of the past 31 years.

(b) In a future year, there are 1,100,000 boats registered in Florida. Predict the number of manatees killed by boats in this year.

(c) Predict manatee deaths if there were *no* boats registered in Florida. Explain why the predicted count of deaths is impossible. (We use $x = 0$ to find the intercept of the regression line, but unless the explanatory variable x actually takes values near 0, prediction for $x = 0$ is an example of extrapolation.)

5.11 Is math the key to success in college? A College Board study of 15,941 high school graduates found a strong correlation between how much math minority students took in high school and their later success in college. News articles quoted the head of the College Board as saying that "math is the gatekeeper for success in college."[5] Maybe so, but we should also think about lurking variables. What might lead minority students to take more or fewer high school math courses? Would these same factors influence success in college?

Association does not imply causation

Thinking about lurking variables leads to the most important caution about correlation and regression. When we study the relationship between two variables, we often hope to show that changes in the explanatory variable *cause* changes in the response variable. A *strong association between two variables is not enough to draw conclusions about cause and effect.* Sometimes an observed association really does reflect cause and effect. A household that heats with natural gas uses more gas in colder months because cold weather requires burning more gas to stay warm. In other cases, an association is explained by lurking variables, and the conclusion that x causes y is either wrong or not proved.

EXAMPLE 5.7 **Does having more cars make you live longer?**

A serious study once found that people with two cars live longer than people who own only one car.[6] Owning three cars is even better, and so on. There is a substantial positive correlation between number of cars x and length of life y.

The basic meaning of causation is that by changing x we can bring about a change in y. Could we lengthen our lives by buying more cars? No. The study used number of cars as a quick indicator of affluence. Well-off people tend to have more cars. They also tend to live longer, probably because they are better educated, take better care of themselves, and get better medical care. The cars have nothing to do with it. There is no cause-and-effect tie between number of cars and length of life. ■

Colin Young-Wolff/Alamy

Correlations such as that in Example 5.7 are sometimes called "nonsense correlations." The correlation is real. What is nonsense is the conclusion that changing one of the variables causes changes in the other. A lurking variable—such as personal affluence in Example 5.7—that influences both x and y can create a high correlation even though there is no direct connection between x and y.

> ### ASSOCIATION DOES NOT IMPLY CAUSATION
>
> An association between an explanatory variable x and a response variable y, even if it is very strong, is not by itself good evidence that changes in x actually cause changes in y.

EXAMPLE 5.8   Overweight mothers, overweight daughters

Overweight parents tend to have overweight children. The results of a study of Mexican American girls aged 9 to 12 years are typical. The investigators measured body mass index (BMI), a measure of weight relative to height, for both the girls and their mothers. People with high BMI are overweight. The correlation between the BMI of daughters and the BMI of their mothers was $r = 0.506$.[7]

Body type is in part determined by heredity. Daughters inherit half their genes from their mothers. There is therefore a direct cause-and-effect link between the BMI of mothers and daughters. But perhaps mothers who are overweight also set an example of little exercise, poor eating habits, and lots of television. Their daughters may pick up these habits, so the influence of heredity is mixed up with influences from the girls' environment. Both contribute to the mother-daughter correlation. ■

experiment

The lesson of Example 5.8 is that *even when direct causation is present, it may not be the whole explanation for a correlation.* You must still worry about lurking variables. The best way to get good evidence that x causes y is to do an **experiment** in which we change x and keep lurking variables under control. We will discuss experiments in Chapter 8.

James Leynse/CORBIS

EXAMPLE 5.9   Does smoking cause lung cancer?

Despite the difficulties, it is sometimes possible to build a strong case for causation in the absence of experiments. The evidence that smoking causes lung cancer is about as strong as nonexperimental evidence can be.

Doctors had long observed that most lung cancer patients were smokers. Comparison of smokers and "similar" nonsmokers showed a very strong association between smoking and death from lung cancer. Could the association be explained by lurking variables? Might there be, for example, a genetic factor that predisposes people both to nicotine addiction and to lung cancer? Smoking and lung cancer would then be positively associated even if smoking had no direct effect on the lungs. How were these objections overcome? ■

Let's answer this question in general terms: what are the criteria for establishing causation when we cannot do an experiment?

- *The association is strong.* The association between smoking and lung cancer is very strong.
- *The association is consistent.* Many studies of different kinds of people in many countries link smoking to lung cancer. That reduces the chance that a lurking variable specific to one group or one study explains the association.
- *Higher doses are associated with stronger responses.* People who smoke more cigarettes per day or who smoke over a longer period get lung cancer more often. People who stop smoking reduce their risk.

- *The alleged cause precedes the effect in time.* Lung cancer develops after years of smoking. The number of men dying of lung cancer rose as smoking became more common, with a lag of about 30 years. Lung cancer kills more men than any other form of cancer. Lung cancer was rare among women until women began to smoke. Lung cancer in women rose along with smoking, again with a lag of about 30 years, and has now passed breast cancer as the leading cause of cancer death among women.

- *The alleged cause is plausible.* Experiments with animals show that tars from cigarette smoke do cause cancer.

Medical authorities do not hesitate to say that smoking causes lung cancer. The U.S. surgeon general has long stated that cigarette smoking is "the largest avoidable cause of death and disability in the United States."[8] The evidence for causation is overwhelming—but it is not as strong as the evidence provided by well-designed experiments.

APPLY YOUR KNOWLEDGE

5.12 Another reason not to smoke? A stop-smoking booklet says, "Children of mothers who smoked during pregnancy scored nine points lower on intelligence tests at ages three and four than children of nonsmokers." Suggest some lurking variables that may help explain the association between smoking during pregnancy and children's later test scores. The association by itself is not good evidence that mothers' smoking *causes* lower scores.

5.13 Education and income. There is a strong positive association between workers' education and their income. For example, the Census Bureau reports that the median income of young adults (ages 25 to 34) who work full-time increases from $20,641 for those with less than a ninth-grade education to $29,698 for high school graduates, to $45,358 for holders of a bachelor's degree, and on up for yet more education. In part, this association reflects causation—education helps people qualify for better jobs. Suggest several lurking variables that also contribute. (Ask yourself what kinds of people tend to get more education.)

5.14 To earn more, get married? Data show that men who are married, and also divorced or widowed men, earn quite a bit more than men the same age who have never been married. This does not mean that a man can raise his income by getting married, because men who have never been married are different from married men in many ways other than marital status. Suggest several lurking variables that might help explain the association between marital status and income.

CHAPTER 5 SUMMARY

- A **regression line** is a straight line that describes how a response variable y changes as an explanatory variable x changes. You can use a regression line to **predict** the value of y for any value of x by substituting this x into the equation of the line.

- The **slope** b of a regression line $\hat{y} = a + bx$ is the rate at which the predicted response $\hat{y}$ changes along the line as the explanatory variable x changes. Specifically, b is the change in $\hat{y}$ when x increases by 1 unit.

■ The **intercept** a of a regression line $\hat{y} = a + bx$ is the predicted response $\hat{y}$ when the explanatory variable $x = 0$. This prediction is of no practical interest unless x can actually take values near 0.

■ The most common method of fitting a line to a scatterplot is least squares. The **least-squares regression line** is the straight line $\hat{y} = a + bx$ that minimizes the sum of the squares of the vertical distances of the observed points from the line.

■ The least-squares regression line of y on x is the line with slope $b = r s_y / s_x$ and intercept $a = \overline{y} - b\overline{x}$. This line always passes through the point $(\overline{x}, \overline{y})$.

■ **Correlation and regression** are closely connected. The correlation r and the regression slope b always have the same sign. The **square of the correlation** r^2 is the fraction of the variation in one variable that is explained by least-squares regression on the other variable.

■ Correlation and regression must be **interpreted with caution. Plot the data** to be sure the relationship is roughly linear and to detect outliers and influential observations. A plot of the **residuals** makes these effects easier to see.

■ Look for **influential observations,** individual points that substantially change the correlation or the regression line. Outliers in either x or y can influence correlation. Outliers in the x direction are often influential for the regression line.

■ Avoid **extrapolation,** the use of a regression line for prediction for values of the explanatory variable far outside the range of the data from which the line was calculated.

■ **Lurking variables** may explain the relationship between the explanatory and response variables. Correlation and regression can be misleading if you ignore important lurking variables.

■ Most of all, be careful not to conclude that there is a cause-and-effect relationship between two variables just because they are strongly associated. **High correlation does not imply causation.** The best evidence that an association is due to causation comes from an **experiment** in which the explanatory variable is directly changed and other influences on the response are controlled.

CHECK YOUR SKILLS

5.15 Figure 5.7 is a scatterplot of reading test scores against IQ test scores for 14 fifth-grade children. The line is the least-squares regression line for predicting reading score from IQ score. If another child in this class has IQ score 110, you predict the reading score to be close to

(a) 50.   (b) 60.   (c) 70.

5.16 The slope of the line in Figure 5.7 is closest to

(a) −1.   (b) 0.   (c) 1.

5.17 Smokers don't live as long (on the average) as nonsmokers, and heavy smokers don't live as long as light smokers. You regress the age at death of a group of male smokers on the number of packs per day they smoked. The slope of your regression line

(a) will be greater than 0.
(b) will be less than 0.
(c) Can't tell without seeing the data.

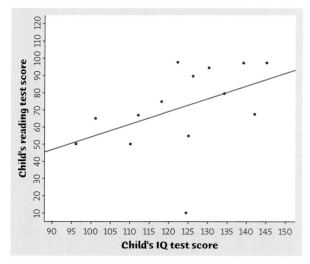

FIGURE 5.7

IQ test scores and reading test scores for 14 children, for Exercises 5.15 and 5.16.

5.18 Measurements on young children in Mumbai, India, found this least-squares line for predicting height y from armspan x:[9]

$$\hat{y} = 6.4 + 0.93x$$

Measurements are in centimeters (cm). How much on the average does height increase for each additional centimeter of armspan?
(a) 0.93 cm.   (b) 6.4 cm.   (c) 7.33 cm.

5.19 According to the regression line in Exercise 5.18, the predicted height of a child with armspan 100 cm is about
(a) 106.4 cm.   (b) 99.4 cm.   (c) 93 cm.

5.20 By looking at the equation of the least-squares regression line in Exercise 5.18, you can see that the correlation between height and armspan is
(a) greater than zero.
(b) less than zero.
(c) Can't tell without seeing the data.

5.21 In addition to the regression line in Exercise 5.18, the report on the Mumbai measurements says that $r^2 = 0.95$. This suggests that
(a) although armspan and height are correlated, armspan does not predict height very accurately.
(b) height increases by $\sqrt{0.95} = 0.97$ cm for each additional centimeter of armspan.
(c) prediction of height from armspan will be quite accurate.

5.22 Because elderly people may have difficulty standing to have their heights measured, a study looked at predicting overall height from height to the knee. Here are data (in centimeters) for five elderly men:

Knee height x	57.7	47.4	43.5	44.8	55.2
Height y	192.1	153.3	146.4	162.7	169.1

Use your calculator or software: what is the equation of the least-squares regression line for predicting height from knee height?
(a) $\hat{y} = 2.4 + 44.1x$ (b) $\hat{y} = 44.1 + 2.4x$
(c) $\hat{y} = -2.5 + 0.32x$

CHAPTER 5 EXERCISES

5.23 Penguins diving. A study of king penguins looked for a relationship between how deep the penguins dive to seek food and how long they stay underwater.[10] There is a linear relationship that is different for different penguins. The study report gives a scatterplot for one penguin titled "The relation of dive duration (DD) to depth (D)." Duration DD is measured in minutes and depth D is in meters. The report then says, "The regression equation for this bird is: DD = 2.69 + 0.0138D."

(a) What is the slope of the regression line? Explain in specific language what this slope says about this penguin's dives.
(b) According to the regression line, how long does a typical dive to a depth of 200 meters last?
(c) The dives varied from 40 meters to 300 meters in depth. Plot the regression line from $x = 40$ to $x = 300$.

5.24 Measuring water quality. Biochemical oxygen demand (BOD) measures organic pollutants in water by measuring the amount of oxygen consumed by microorganisms that break down these compounds. BOD is hard to measure accurately. Total organic carbon (TOC) is easy to measure, so it is common to measure TOC and use regression to predict BOD. A typical regression equation for water entering a municipal treatment plant is[11]

$$BOD = -55.43 + 1.507\ TOC$$

Both BOD and TOC are measured in milligrams per liter of water.
(a) What does the slope of this line say about the relationship between BOD and TOC?
(b) What is the predicted BOD when TOC = 0? Values of BOD less than 0 are impossible. Why do you think the prediction gives an impossible value?

5.25 Does social rejection hurt? Exercise 4.37 (page 89) gives data from a study that shows that social exclusion causes "real pain." That is, activity in an area of the brain that responds to physical pain goes up as distress from social exclusion goes up. A scatterplot shows a moderately strong linear relationship. Figure 5.8 shows Minitab regression output for these data.

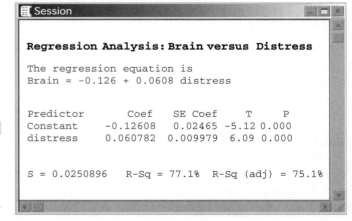

FIGURE 5.8

Minitab regression output for a study of the effects of social rejection on brain activity, for Exercise 5.25.

(a) What is the equation of the least-squares regression line for predicting brain activity from social distress score? Use the equation to predict brain activity for social distress score 2.0.
(b) What percent of the variation in brain activity among these subjects is explained by the straight-line relationship with social distress score?
(c) Use the information in Figure 5.8 to find the correlation r between social distress score and brain activity. How do you know whether the sign of r is $+$ or $-$?

5.26 Merlins breeding. Exercise 4.36 (page 89) gives data on the number of breeding pairs of merlins in an isolated area in each of nine years and the percent of males who returned the next year. The data show that the percent returning is lower after successful breeding seasons and that the relationship is roughly linear. Figure 5.9 shows Minitab regression output for these data.

FIGURE 5.9
Minitab regression output for a study of how breeding success affects survival in birds, for Exercise 5.26.

(a) What is the equation of the least-squares regression line for predicting the percent of males that return from the number of breeding pairs? Use the equation to predict the percent of returning males after a season with 30 breeding pairs.
(b) What percent of the year-to-year variation in percent of returning males is explained by the straight-line relationship with number of breeding pairs the previous year?
(c) Use the information in Figure 5.9 to find the correlation r between percent of males that return and number of breeding pairs. How do you know whether the sign of r is $+$ or $-$?

5.27 Husbands and wives. The mean height of American women in their twenties is about 64 inches, and the standard deviation is about 2.7 inches. The mean height of men the same age is about 69.3 inches, with standard deviation about 2.8 inches. Suppose that the correlation between the heights of husbands and wives is about $r = 0.5$.
(a) What are the slope and intercept of the regression line of the husband's height on the wife's height in young couples?
(b) Draw a graph of this regression line for heights of wives between 56 and 72 inches. Predict the height of the husband of a woman who is 67 inches tall and plot the wife's height and predicted husband's height on your graph.
(c) You don't expect this prediction for a single couple to be very accurate. Why not?

5.28 What's my grade? In Professor Friedman's economics course the correlation between the students' total scores prior to the final examination and their final examination scores is $r = 0.6$. The pre-exam totals for all students in the course have mean 280 and standard deviation 30. The final-exam scores have mean 75 and standard deviation 8. Professor Friedman has lost Julie's final exam but knows that her total before the exam was 300. He decides to predict her final-exam score from her pre-exam total.
(a) What is the slope of the least-squares regression line of final-exam scores on pre-exam total scores in this course? What is the intercept?
(b) Use the regression line to predict Julie's final-exam score.
(c) Julie doesn't think this method accurately predicts how well she did on the final exam. Use r^2 to argue that her actual score could have been much higher (or much lower) than the predicted value.

5.29 Going to class. A study of class attendance and grades among first-year students at a state university showed that in general students who attended a higher percent of their classes earned higher grades. Class attendance explained 16% of the variation in grade index among the students. What is the numerical value of the correlation between percent of classes attended and grade index?

5.30 Sisters and brothers. How strongly do physical characteristics of sisters and brothers correlate? Here are data on the heights (in inches) of 11 adult pairs:[12]

Brother	71	68	66	67	70	71	70	73	72	65	66
Sister	69	64	65	63	65	62	65	64	66	59	62

(a) Use your calculator or software to find the correlation and the equation of the least-squares line for predicting sister's height from brother's height. Make a scatterplot of the data and add the regression line to your plot.
(b) Damien is 70 inches tall. Predict the height of his sister Tonya. Based on the scatterplot and the correlation r, do you expect your prediction to be very accurate? Why or why not?

5.31 Sparrowhawk colonies. One of nature's patterns connects the percent of adult birds in a colony that return from the previous year and the number of new adults that join the colony. Here are data for 13 colonies of sparrowhawks:[13]

Percent return x	74	66	81	52	73	62	52
New adults y	5	6	8	11	12	15	16
Percent return x	45	62	46	60	46	38	
New adults y	17	18	18	19	20	20	

You saw in Exercise 4.23 that there is a moderately strong linear relationship, correlation $r = -0.748$.
(a) Find the least-squares regression line for predicting y from x. Make a scatterplot and draw your line on the plot.
(b) Explain in words what the slope of the regression line tells us.
(c) An ecologist uses the line, based on 13 colonies, to predict how many new birds will join another colony, to which 60% of the adults from the previous year return. What is the prediction?

5.32 Our brains don't like losses. Exercise 4.24 (page 86) describes an experiment that showed a linear relationship between how sensitive people are to monetary losses ("behavioral loss aversion") and activity in one part of their brains ("neural loss aversion").
(a) Make a scatterplot with neural loss aversion as x and behavioral loss aversion as y. One point is a high outlier in both the x and y directions.
(b) Find the least-squares line for predicting y from x, *leaving out the outlier*, and add the line to your plot.
(c) The outlier lies very close to your regression line. Looking at the plot, you now expect that adding the outlier will increase the correlation but will have little effect on the least-squares line. Explain why.
(d) Find the correlation and the equation of the least-squares line with and without the outlier. Your results verify the expectations from part (c).

5.33 Keeping water clean. Keeping water supplies clean requires regular measurement of levels of pollutants. The measurements are indirect—a typical analysis involves forming a dye by a chemical reaction with the dissolved pollutant, then passing light through the solution and measuring its "absorbence." To calibrate such measurements, the laboratory measures known standard solutions and uses regression to relate absorbence and pollutant concentration. This is usually done every day. Here is one series of data on the absorbence for different levels of nitrates. Nitrates are measured in milligrams per liter of water.[14]

Nitrates	50	50	100	200	400
Absorbence	7.0	7.5	12.8	24.0	47.0
Nitrates	800	1200	1600	2000	2000
Absorbence	93.0	138.0	183.0	230.0	226.0

(a) Chemical theory says that these data should lie on a straight line. If the correlation is not at least 0.997, something went wrong and the calibration procedure is repeated. Plot the data and find the correlation. Must the calibration be done again?
(b) The calibration process sets nitrate level and measures absorbence. The linear relationship that results is used to estimate the nitrate level in water from a measurement of absorbence. What is the equation of the line used to estimate nitrate level? What is the estimated nitrate level in a water specimen with absorbence 40?
(c) Do you expect estimates of nitrate level from absorbence to be quite accurate? Why?

5.34 Always plot your data! Table 5.1 presents four sets of data prepared by the statistician Frank Anscombe to illustrate the dangers of calculating without first plotting the data.[15]
(a) Without making scatterplots, find the correlation and the least-squares regression line for all four data sets. What do you notice? Use the regression line to predict y for $x = 10$.
(b) Make a scatterplot for each of the data sets and add the regression line to each plot.
(c) In which of the four cases would you be willing to use the regression line to describe the dependence of y on x? Explain your answer in each case.

5.35 Managing diabetes. People with diabetes measure their fasting plasma glucose (FPG) after fasting for at least 8 hours. Another measurement, made at regular medical checkups, is called HbA. This is roughly the percent of red blood cells that have a glucose molecule attached. It measures average exposure to glucose over a period of several months. Table 5.2 gives data on both HbA and FPG for 18 diabetics five months after they had completed a diabetes education class.[16]
(a) Make a scatterplot with HbA as the explanatory variable. There is a positive linear relationship, but it is surprisingly weak.
(b) Subject 15 is an outlier in the y direction. Subject 18 is an outlier in the x direction. Find the correlation for all 18 subjects, for all except Subject 15, and for all except Subject 18. Are either or both of these subjects influential for the correlation? Explain in simple language why r changes in opposite directions when we remove each of these points.

5.36 The effect of changing units. The equation of a regression line, unlike the correlation, depends on the units we use to measure the explanatory and response variables. Here

TABLE 5.1 Four data sets for exploring correlation and regression

Data Set A

x	10	8	13	9	11	14	6	4	12	7	5
y	8.04	6.95	7.58	8.81	8.33	9.96	7.24	4.26	10.84	4.82	5.68

Data Set B

x	10	8	13	9	11	14	6	4	12	7	5
y	9.14	8.14	8.74	8.77	9.26	8.10	6.13	3.10	9.13	7.26	4.74

Data Set C

x	10	8	13	9	11	14	6	4	12	7	5
y	7.46	6.77	12.74	7.11	7.81	8.84	6.08	5.39	8.15	6.42	5.73

Data Set D

x	8	8	8	8	8	8	8	8	8	8	19
y	6.58	5.76	7.71	8.84	8.47	7.04	5.25	5.56	7.91	6.89	12.50

TABLE 5.2 Two measures of glucose level in diabetics

SUBJECT	HBA (%)	FPG (MG/ML)	SUBJECT	HBA (%)	FPG (MG/ML)	SUBJECT	HBA (%)	FPG (MG/ML)
1	6.1	141	7	7.5	96	13	10.6	103
2	6.3	158	8	7.7	78	14	10.7	172
3	6.4	112	9	7.9	148	15	10.7	359
4	6.8	153	10	8.7	172	16	11.2	145
5	7.0	134	11	9.4	200	17	13.7	147
6	7.1	95	12	10.4	271	18	19.3	255

are data on knee height and overall height (in centimeters) for five elderly men:

Knee height x	57.7	47.4	43.5	44.8	55.2
Height y	192.1	153.3	146.4	162.7	169.1

(a) Find the equation of the regression line for predicting overall height in centimeters from knee height in centimeters.
(b) A mad scientist decides to measure knee height in millimeters and height in meters. The same data in these units are

Knee height x	577	474	435	448	552
Height y	1.921	1.533	1.464	1.627	1.691

Find the equation of the regression line for predicting overall height in meters from knee height in millimeters.
(c) Use both lines to predict the overall height of a man whose knee height is 50 centimeters, which is the same as 500 mil-

limeters. Use the fact that there are 100 centimeters in a meter to show that the two predictions are the same (up to roundoff error).

5.37 Managing diabetes, continued. Add three regression lines for predicting FPG from HbA to your scatterplot from Exercise 5.35: for all 18 subjects, for all except Subject 15, and for all except Subject 18. Is either Subject 15 or Subject 18 strongly influential for the least-squares line? Explain in simple language what features of the scatterplot explain the degree of influence.

5.38 Do artificial sweeteners cause weight gain? People who use artificial sweeteners in place of sugar tend to be heavier than people who use sugar. Does this mean that artificial sweeteners cause weight gain? Give a more plausible explanation for this association.

5.39 Learning online. Many colleges offer online versions of courses that are also taught in the classroom. It often happens that the students who enroll in the online version do better than the classroom students on the course exams. This does not show that online instruction is more effective than classroom teaching, because the people who sign up for online courses are often quite different from the classroom students. Suggest some differences between online and classroom students that might explain why online students do better.

5.40 Some regression math. Use the equation of the least-squares regression line (box on page 94) to show that the regression line for predicting y from x always passes through the point $(\bar{x}, \bar{y})$. That is, when $x = \bar{x}$, the equation gives $\hat{y} = \bar{y}$.

5.41 Regression to the mean. Figure 4.6 (page 85) displays the relationship between golfers' scores on the first and second rounds of the 2007 Masters Tournament. The least-squares line for predicting second-round scores from first-round scores has equation $\hat{y} = 61.93 + 0.180x$. Find the predicted second-round scores for a player who shot 80 in the first round and for a player who shot 70. The mean second-round score for all players was 75.63. So a player who does well in the first round is predicted to do less well, but still better than average, in the second round. And a player who does poorly in the first is predicted to do better, but still worse than average, in the second.

(*Comment:* This is **regression to the mean.** If you select individuals with extreme scores on some measure, they tend to have less extreme scores when measured again. That's because their extreme position is partly merit and partly luck. The luck will be different next time. Regression to the mean contributes to lots of "effects." The rookie of the year often doesn't do as well the next year; a student who feels she needs coaching after the SAT often does better on the next try without coaching.)

The following exercises ask you to answer questions from data without having the details outlined for you. The exercise statements give you the **State** *step of the four-step process. In your work, follow the* **Plan, Solve,** *and* **Conclude** *steps of the process, described on page 42.*

5.42 Beavers and beetles. Do beavers benefit beetles? Researchers laid out 23 circular plots, each 4 meters in diameter, in an area where beavers were cutting down cottonwood trees. In each plot, they counted the number of stumps from trees cut by beavers and the number of clusters of beetle larvae. Ecologists think that the new sprouts from stumps are more tender than other cottonwood growth, so that beetles prefer them. If so, more stumps should produce more beetle larvae. Here are the data:[17]

Stumps	2	2	1	3	3	4	3	1	2	5	1	3
Beetle larvae	10	30	12	24	36	40	43	11	27	56	18	40

Stumps	2	1	2	2	1	1	4	1	2	1	4
Beetle larvae	25	8	21	14	16	6	54	9	13	14	50

Analyze these data to see if they support the "beavers benefit beetles" idea.

5.43 A computer game. A multimedia statistics learning system includes a test of skill in using the computer's mouse. The software displays a circle at a random location on the computer screen. The subject clicks in the circle with the mouse as quickly as possible. A new circle appears as soon as the subject clicks the old one. Table 5.3 gives data for one subject's trials, 20 with each hand. Distance is the distance from the cursor location to the center of the new circle, in units whose actual size depends on the size of the screen. Time is the time required to click in the new circle, in milliseconds.[18] We suspect that time depends on distance. We also suspect that performance will not be the same with the right and left hands. Analyze the data with a view to predicting performance separately for the two hands.

5.44 Predicting tropical storms. William Gray heads the Tropical Meteorology Project at Colorado State University. His forecasts before each year's hurricane season attract lots of attention. Here are data on the number of named Atlantic tropical storms predicted by Dr. Gray and the actual number of storms for the years 1984 to 2008:[19]

Year	Forecast	Actual	Year	Forecast	Actual	Year	Forecast	Actual
1984	10	12	1992	8	6	2000	12	14
1985	11	11	1993	11	8	2001	12	15
1986	8	6	1994	9	7	2002	11	12
1987	8	7	1995	12	19	2003	14	16
1988	11	12	1996	10	13	2004	14	14
1989	7	11	1997	11	7	2005	15	27
1990	11	14	1998	10	14	2006	17	9
1991	8	8	1999	14	12	2007	17	14
						2008	15	16

Analyze these data. How accurate are Dr. Gray's forecasts? How many tropical storms would you expect in a year when his preseason forecast calls for 16 storms? What is the effect of the disastrous 2005 season on your answers?

5.45 Climate change. Global warming has many indirect effects on climate. For example, the summer monsoon winds in the Arabian Sea bring rain to India and are critical for agriculture. As the climate warms and winter snow cover in the vast landmass of Europe and Asia decreases, the land heats

TABLE 5.3 Reaction times in a computer game

TIME	DISTANCE	HAND	TIME	DISTANCE	HAND
115	190.70	right	240	190.70	left
96	138.52	right	190	138.52	left
110	165.08	right	170	165.08	left
100	126.19	right	125	126.19	left
111	163.19	right	315	163.19	left
101	305.66	right	240	305.66	left
111	176.15	right	141	176.15	left
106	162.78	right	210	162.78	left
96	147.87	right	200	147.87	left
96	271.46	right	401	271.46	left
95	40.25	right	320	40.25	left
96	24.76	right	113	24.76	left
96	104.80	right	176	104.80	left
106	136.80	right	211	136.80	left
100	308.60	right	238	308.60	left
113	279.80	right	316	279.80	left
123	125.51	right	176	125.51	left
111	329.80	right	173	329.80	left
95	51.66	right	210	51.66	left
108	201.95	right	170	201.95	left

more rapidly in the summer. This may increase the strength of the monsoon. Here are data on snow cover (in millions of square kilometers) and summer wind stress (in newtons per square meter):[20]

Snow cover	Wind stress	Snow cover	Wind stress	Snow cover	Wind stress
6.6	0.125	16.6	0.111	26.6	0.062
5.9	0.160	18.2	0.106	27.1	0.051
6.8	0.158	15.2	0.143	27.5	0.068
7.7	0.155	16.2	0.153	28.4	0.055
7.9	0.169	17.1	0.155	28.6	0.033
7.8	0.173	17.3	0.133	29.6	0.029
8.1	0.196	18.1	0.130	29.4	0.024

Analyze these data to uncover the nature and strength of the effect of decreasing snow cover on wind stress.

5.46 Saving energy with solar panels. Exercise 4.35 (page 88) gives monthly data on outside temperature (in degree-days per day) and natural gas consumed for a house in the Midwest both before and after installing solar panels. A cold win- ter month in this location may average 45 degree-days per day (temperature 20°F). Use before-and-after regression lines to estimate the savings in gas consumption due to solar panels.

5.47 Effects of health care spending. Table 1.3 (page 19) gives United Nations data on annual health care spending per person in 38 richer nations. The United States, at $5711 per person, is a high outlier. The data file *ex05-47.dat* on the text CD and Web site adds more information about these countries: female life expectancy at birth (in years) and infant mortality per 1000 live births.[21] Use these data to investigate the extent to which higher spending on health care increases life expectancy and reduces infant mortality. Would you use regression to predict either outcome from spending? (Two comments to help explain what you find: In addition to the United States, South Africa is an outlier in scatterplots. South Africa is out of place in this group of richer nations, although it does meet the criteria that the United Nations used to make up the list. If the effects of health care spending on overall health seem small, that is in part because the data include only richer nations, most of which spend enough to ensure basic good health for their citizens.)

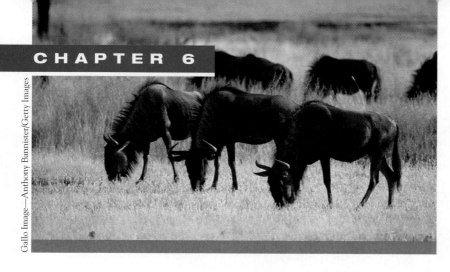

Wildebeest graze in Tanzania's Serengeti National Park. Exercise 6.42 describes a relationship between Wildebeest and grass fires.

Exploring Data: Part I Review

IN THIS CHAPTER
WE COVER...

- Part I Summary
- Review Exercises
- Supplementary Exercises

Part I Summary

Data analysis is the art of describing data using graphs and numerical summaries. The purpose of data analysis is to help us see and understand the most important features of a set of data. Chapter 1 commented on graphs to display distributions: pie charts and bar graphs for categorical variables, histograms and stemplots for quantitative variables. In addition, time plots show how a quantitative variable changes over time. Chapter 2 presented numerical tools for describing the center and spread of the distribution of one variable. Chapter 3 discussed density curves for describing the overall pattern of a distribution, with emphasis on the Normal distributions.

The first STATISTICS IN SUMMARY figure on the next page organizes the big ideas for exploring a quantitative variable. Plot your data, then describe their center and spread using either the mean and standard deviation or the five-number summary. The last step, which makes sense only for some data, is to summarize the data in compact form by using a Normal curve as a description of the overall pattern. The question marks at the last two stages remind us that the usefulness of numerical summaries and Normal distributions depends on what we find when we examine graphs of our data. No short summary does justice to irregular shapes or to data with several distinct clusters.

Chapters 4 and 5 applied the same ideas to relationships between two quantitative variables. The second STATISTICS IN SUMMARY figure retraces the big ideas, with details that fit the new setting. Begin by making graphs of your data. In the case of a scatterplot, we have learned a numerical summary only for data that show a roughly linear pattern on the scatterplot. The summary is then the means and standard deviations of the two variables and their correlation. A regression line drawn on the plot gives a compact description of the overall pattern that we can use for prediction. Once

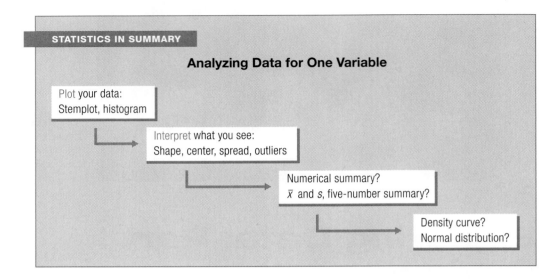

again there are question marks at the last two stages to remind us that correlation and regression describe only straight-line relationships.

You can organize your work in any open-ended data analysis setting by following the four-step STATE, PLAN, SOLVE, and CONCLUDE process first introduced in Chapter 2. After we have mastered the extra background needed for statistical inference, this process will also guide practical work on inference later in the book.

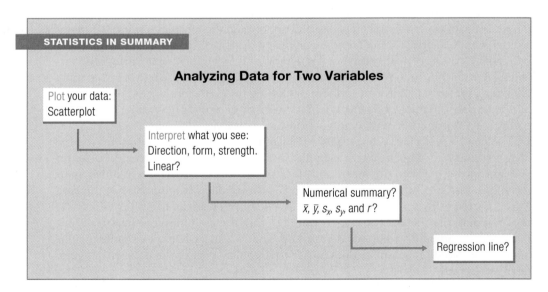

REVIEW EXERCISES

Review exercises help you solidify the basic ideas and skills in Chapters 1 to 5.

6.1 Describing colleges. Popular magazines rank colleges and universities on their academic quality in serving under-

graduate students. Below are several variables that might contribute to ranking colleges. Which of these are categorical and which are quantitative?

(a) Percent of freshmen who eventually graduate.

(b) College type: liberal arts college, national university, etc.

(c) Require SAT or ACT for admission (required, recommended, not used)?
(d) Mean faculty salary.

6.2 Data on mice. For a biology project, you measure the tail length in centimeters and weight in grams of 12 mice of the same variety. What units of measurement do each of the following have?
(a) The mean length of the tails.
(b) The first quartile of the tail lengths.
(c) The standard deviation of the tail lengths.
(d) The correlation between tail length and weight.

6.3 What do you think of Microsoft? The Pew Research Center asked a random sample of adults whether they had favorable or unfavorable opinions of a number of major companies. Answers to such questions depend a lot on recent news. Here are the percents with favorable opinions for several of the companies:[1]

Company	Percent favorable
Apple	71
Ben and Jerry's	59
Coors	53
Exxon/Mobil	44
Google	73
Halliburton	25
McDonald's	71
Microsoft	78
Starbucks	64
Wal-Mart	68

Make a graph that displays these data.

6.4 The state of the country. The Pew Research Center reports the following percents of American adults who said "satisfied" when asked, "All in all, are you satisfied or dissatisfied with the way things are going in this country today?"[2]

Year	Percent	Year	Percent	Year	Percent
1988	55	1996	29	2004	38
1990	47	1998	52	2005	36
1992	28	2000	52	2006	30
1994	24	2002	45	2007	30

Make a graph that displays the trend over time for these data.

6.5 How heavy are diamonds? Here are the weights (in milligrams) of 58 diamonds from a nodule carried up to the earth's surface in surrounding rock. This represents a single population of diamonds formed in a single event deep in the earth.[3]

13.8	3.7	33.8	11.8	27.0	18.9	19.3	20.8	25.4
23.1	7.8	10.9	9.0	9.0	14.4	6.5	7.3	5.6
18.5	1.1	11.2	7.0	7.6	9.0	9.5	7.7	7.6
3.2	6.5	5.4	7.2	7.8	3.5	5.4	5.1	5.3
3.8	2.1	2.1	4.7	3.7	3.8	4.9	2.4	1.4
0.1	4.7	1.5	2.0	0.1	0.1	1.6	3.5	3.7
2.6	4.0	2.3	4.5					

Make a graph that shows the distribution of weights of diamonds. Describe the shape of the distribution and any outliers. Use numerical measures appropriate for the shape to describe the center and spread.

6.6 Garbage. The formal name for garbage is "municipal solid waste." Here is a breakdown of the materials that make up American municipal solid waste, in millions of tons:[4]

Material	Weight
Food	31.3
Glass	13.2
Metals	19.1
Paper, paperboard	85.3
Plastics	29.5
Rubber, leather, textiles	18.3
Wood	13.9
Yard trimmings	32.4
Other	8.3
Total	251.3

(a) Make a bar graph, ordering the bars from highest to lowest weight.
(b) If you use software, make a pie chart as well. In which graph is it easier to see small differences, such as between glass and wood?

6.7 Recycling. Of the municipal solid waste described in the previous exercise, about 55% is discarded, 32.5% is recovered through recycling or composting, and 12.5% is burned to produce energy. Here are the percents of several materials in solid waste that are recycled:

Material	Percent recycled
Aluminum cans	45.1
Auto batteries	99.0
Glass containers	25.3
Paper, paperboard	51.6
Plastic bottles	31.0
Steel cans	62.9
Tires	34.9
Yard trimmings	62.0

(a) Make a bar graph, ordering the bars from highest to lowest percent.

(b) Could you also use a pie chart to display these data? Why or why not?

6.8 Nitrogen in diamonds. Scientists made detailed chemical analyses of 24 of the diamonds from Exercise 6.5. The abundances of various elements give clues to how the diamonds were formed. Here are the data on nitrogen content, in parts per million:

487	1430	60	244	196	274	41	54	473	30	98	41
273	94	69	262	120	302	75	242	115	65	311	61

(a) Make a stemplot. What is the overall shape of the distribution?

(b) There is one extreme high outlier. Find the median, mean, and standard deviation with and without this outlier. Which of these measures is least changed when the outlier is removed? (If you recall Chapter 2's discussion of resistant measures, the result is not a surprise.)

6.9 Two species of pine trees. The Aleppo pine and the Torrey pine are widely planted as ornamental trees in Southern California. Here are the lengths (centimeters) of 15 Aleppo pine needles:[5]

10.2 7.2 7.6 9.3 12.1 10.9 9.4 11.3 8.5 8.5 12.8 8.7 9.0 9.0 9.4

Here are the lengths of 18 needles from Torrey pines:

33.7	21.2	26.8	29.7	21.6	21.7	33.7	32.5	23.1
23.7	30.2	29.0	24.2	24.2	25.5	26.6	28.9	29.7

Use five-number summaries and boxplots to compare the two distributions. Given only the length of a needle, do you think you could say which pine species it comes from?

6.10 Genetic engineering for cancer treatment. Here's a new idea for treating advanced melanoma, the most serious kind of skin cancer. Genetically engineer white blood cells to better recognize and destroy cancer cells, then infuse these cells into patients. The subjects in a small initial study were 11 patients whose melanoma had not responded to existing treatments. One question was how rapidly the new cells would multiply after infusion, as measured by the doubling time in days. Here are the doubling times:[6]

1.4　1.0　1.3　1.0　1.3　2.0　0.6　0.8　0.7　0.9　1.9

Another outcome was the increase in the presence of cells that trigger an immune response in the body and so may help fight cancer. Here are the increases, in counts of active cells per 100,000 cells:

27　7　0　215　20　700　13　510　34　86　108

Make stemplots of both distributions (use split stems and leave out any extreme outliers). Describe the overall shapes and any

outliers. Then give the five-number summary for both. (We can't compare the summaries because the two variables have different scales.)

6.11 Distribution shapes. Biologists commonly act as if measurements on many individuals from the same species follow a Normal distribution. They therefore use the mean $\bar{x}$ and standard deviation s as numerical summaries.

(a) Make stemplots of the lengths of needles of Aleppo pines and of Torrey pines from Exercise 6.9. Which distribution appears "more Normal" and why? (The distribution of a small number of observations often has an irregular shape even when, as here, more data would show that the overall distribution is close to Normal.)

(b) Find the mean and median length for both species. What fact about the distributions explains why the mean and median are close together for both species?

6.12 Weights aren't Normal. The heights of people of the same sex and similar ages follow a Normal distribution reasonably closely. Weights, on the other hand, are not Normally distributed. The weights of women aged 20 to 29 have mean 141.7 pounds and median 133.2 pounds. The first and third quartiles are 118.3 pounds and 157.3 pounds. What can you say about the shape of the weight distribution? Why?

6.13 Pine needles. The lengths of needles from Aleppo pines follow approximately the Normal distribution with mean 9.6 centimeters (cm) and standard deviation 1.6 cm. According to the 68–95–99.7 rule, what range of lengths covers the center 95% of Aleppo pine needles? What percent of needles are less than 6.4 cm long?

6.14 Body mass index. Your body mass index (BMI) is your weight in kilograms divided by the square of your height in meters. Online BMI calculators allow you to enter weight in pounds and height in inches. High BMI is a common but controversial indicator of overweight or obesity. A study by the National Center for Health Statistics found that the BMI of American young women (ages 20 to 29) is approximately Normal with mean 26.8 and standard deviation 7.4.[7]

(a) People with BMI less than 18.5 are often classed as "underweight." What percent of young women are underweight by this criterion?

(b) People with BMI over 30 are often classed as "obese." What percent of young women are obese by this criterion?

6.15 The Medical College Admission Test. Almost all medical schools in the United States and Canada require applicants to take the Medical College Admission Test (MCAT). The scores of applicants on the biological sciences part of the MCAT in 2007 were approximately Normal with mean 9.6 and standard deviation 2.2. For applicants who actually entered medical school, the mean score was 10.6 and the standard deviation was 1.7.[8]

(a) What percent of all applicants had scores higher than 13?

(b) What percent of those who entered medical school had scores between 8 and 12?

6.16 Breaking bolts. Mechanical measurements on supposedly identical objects usually vary. The variation often follows a Normal distribution. The stress required to break a type of bolt varies Normally with mean 75 kilopounds per square inch (ksi) and standard deviation 8.3 ksi.

(a) What percent of these bolts will withstand a stress of 90 ksi without breaking?

(b) What range covers the middle 50% of breaking strengths for these bolts?

Soap in the shower. *From Rex Boggs in Australia comes an unusual data set: before showering in the morning, he weighed the bar of soap in his shower stall. The weight goes down as the soap is used. The data appear below (weights in grams). Notice that Mr. Boggs forgot to weigh the soap on some days. Exercises 6.17 to 6.19 are based on the soap data set.*

Day	Weight	Day	Weight	Day	Weight
1	124	8	84	16	27
2	121	9	78	18	16
5	103	10	71	19	12
6	96	12	58	20	8
7	90	13	50	21	6

6.17 Scatterplot and correlation. Plot the weight of the bar of soap against day. Is the overall pattern roughly linear? Based on your scatterplot, is the correlation between day and weight close to 1, positive but not close to 1, close to 0, negative but not close to -1, or close to -1? Explain your answer. Then find the correlation r to verify what you concluded from the graph.

6.18 Regression. Find the equation of the least-squares regression line for predicting soap weight from day.

(a) What is the equation? Explain what it tells us about the rate at which the soap lost weight.

(b) Mr. Boggs did not measure the weight of the soap on Day 4. Use the regression equation to predict that weight.

(c) Add the regression line to your scatterplot from the previous exercise.

6.19 Prediction? Use the regression equation in the previous exercise to predict the weight of the soap after 30 days. Why is it clear that your answer makes no sense? What's wrong with using the regression line to predict weight after 30 days?

6.20 Growing icicles. Table 4.2 (page 87) gives data on the growth of icicles over time. Let's look again at Run

8903, for which a slower flow of water produces faster growth.

(a) How can you tell from a calculation, without drawing a scatterplot, that the pattern of growth is very close to a straight line?

(b) What is the equation of the least-squares regression line for predicting an icicle's length from time in minutes under these conditions?

(c) Predict the length of an icicle after one full day. This prediction can't be trusted. Why not?

6.21 Thin monkeys, fat monkeys. Animals and people that take in more energy than they expend will get fatter. Here are data on 12 rhesus monkeys: 6 lean monkeys (4% to 9% body fat) and 6 obese monkeys (13% to 44% body fat). The data report the energy expended in 24 hours (kilojoules per minute) and the lean body mass (kilograms, leaving out fat) for each monkey.[9]

Lean		Obese	
Mass	**Energy**	**Mass**	**Energy**
6.6	1.17	7.9	0.93
7.8	1.02	9.4	1.39
8.9	1.46	10.7	1.19
9.8	1.68	12.2	1.49
9.7	1.06	12.1	1.29
9.3	1.16	10.8	1.31

(a) What is the mean lean body mass of the lean monkeys? Of the obese monkeys? Because animals with higher lean mass usually expend more energy, we can't directly compare energy expended.

(b) Instead, look at how energy expended is related to body mass. Make a scatterplot of energy versus mass, using different plot symbols for lean and obese monkeys. Then add to the plot two regression lines, one for lean monkeys and one for obese monkeys. What do these lines suggest about the monkeys?

6.22 The end of smoking? The number of adult Americans who smoke continues to drop. Here are estimates of the percent of adults (aged 18 and over) who were smokers in the years between 1965 and 2006:[10]

Year	1965	1974	1979	1983	1987	1990
Smokers	41.9	37.0	33.3	31.9	28.6	25.3
Year	1993	1997	2000	2002	2006	
Smokers	24.8	24.6	23.1	22.5	20.8	

(a) Make a scatterplot of these data. There is a strong negative linear association. Find the least-squares regression line for predicting percent of smokers from year and add the line to your plot.

TABLE 6.1 Neuron response to tones and monkey calls

NEURON	TONE	CALL	NEURON	TONE	CALL	NEURON	TONE	CALL
1	474	500	14	145	42	26	71	134
2	256	138	15	141	241	27	68	65
3	241	485	16	129	194	28	59	182
4	226	338	17	113	123	29	59	97
5	185	194	18	112	182	30	57	318
6	174	159	19	102	141	31	56	201
7	176	341	20	100	118	32	47	279
8	168	85	21	74	62	33	46	62
9	161	303	22	72	112	34	41	84
10	150	208	23	20	193	35	26	203
11	19	66	24	21	129	36	28	192
12	20	54	25	26	135	37	31	70
13	35	103						

(b) According to your regression line, how much did smoking decline per year during this period, on the average? What percent of the observed variation in percent of adults who smoke can be explained by linear change over time?

(c) One of the government's national health objectives was to reduce smoking to no more than 12% of adults by 2010. Use your regression line to predict the percent of adults who smoke in 2010. Did it appear that this health objective would be met?

6.23 Squirrels and their food supply. Animal species produce more offspring when their supply of food goes up. Some animals appear able to anticipate unusual food abundance. Red squirrels eat seeds from pine cones, a food source that occasionally has very large crops. Here are data on an index of the abundance of pine cones and the average number of offspring per female over 16 years:[11]

Cone index x	0.00	2.02	0.25	3.22	4.68	0.31	3.37	3.09
Offspring y	1.49	1.10	1.29	2.71	4.07	1.29	3.36	2.41
Cone index x	2.44	4.81	1.88	0.31	1.61	1.88	0.91	1.04
Offspring y	1.97	3.41	1.49	2.02	3.34	2.41	2.15	2.12

Describe the relationship with both a graph and numerical measures, then summarize in words. What is striking is that the offspring are conceived in the spring, *before* the cones mature in the fall to feed the new young squirrels through the winter.

6.24 The end of smoking, continued. Use your regression line from Exercise 6.22 to predict the percent of adults who will smoke in 2050. Why is your result impossible? Why was it foolish to use the regression line for this prediction?

6.25 Monkey calls. The usual way to study the brain's response to sounds is to have subjects listen to "pure tones." The response to recognizable sounds may differ. To compare responses, researchers anesthetized macaque monkeys. They fed pure tones and also monkey calls directly to their brains by inserting electrodes. Response to the stimulus was measured by the firing rate (electrical spikes per second) of neurons in various areas of the brain. Table 6.1 contains the responses for 37 neurons.[12]

(a) One important finding is that responses to monkey calls are generally stronger than responses to pure tones. For how many of the 37 neurons is this true?

(b) We might expect some neurons to have strong responses to any stimulus and others to have consistently weak responses. There would then be a strong relationship between tone response and call response. Make a scatterplot of monkey call response against pure tone response (explanatory variable). Find the correlation r between tone and call responses. How strong is the linear relationship?

6.26 Remember what you ate. How well do people remember their past diet? Data are available for 91 people who were asked about their diet when they were 18 years old. Researchers asked them at about age 55 to describe their eating habits at age 18. For each subject, the researchers calculated the correlation between actual intakes of many foods at age 18 and the intakes the subjects now remember. The median of the 91 correlations was $r = 0.217$. The authors say, "We conclude that memory of food intake in the distant past is fair to poor."[13] Explain why $r = 0.217$ points to this conclusion.

6.27 Statistics for investing. Joe's retirement plan invests in stocks through an "index fund" that follows the behavior of the

stock market as a whole, as measured by the S&P 500 stock index. Joe wants to buy a mutual fund that does not track the index closely. He reads that monthly returns from Fidelity Technology Fund have correlation $r = 0.77$ with the S&P 500 index and that Fidelity Real Estate Fund has correlation $r = 0.37$ with the index.
(a) Which of these funds has the closer relationship to returns from the stock market as a whole? How do you know?
(b) Does the information given tell Joe anything about which fund has had higher returns?

6.28 Moving in step? One reason to invest abroad is that markets in different countries don't move in step. When American stocks go down, foreign stocks may go up. So an investor who holds both bears less risk. That's the theory. Now we read: "The correlation between changes in American and European share prices has risen from 0.4 in the mid-1990s to 0.8 in 2000."[14] Explain to an investor who knows no statistics why this fact reduces the protection provided by buying European stocks.

6.29 Interpreting correlation. The same article that claims that the correlation between changes in stock prices in Europe and the United States is 0.8 goes on to say: "Crudely, that means that movements on Wall Street can explain 80% of price movements in Europe." Is this true? What is the correct percent explained if $r = 0.8$?

6.30 Weeds among the corn. Lamb's-quarter is a common weed that interferes with the growth of corn. An agriculture researcher planted corn at the same rate in 16 small plots of ground, then weeded the plots by hand to allow a fixed number of lamb's-quarter plants to grow in each meter of corn row. No other weeds were allowed to grow. Here are the yields of corn (bushels per acre) in each of the plots:[15]

Weeds per meter	Corn yield	Weeds per meter	Corn yield	Weeds per meter	Corn yield	Weeds per meter	Corn yield
0	166.7	1	166.2	3	158.6	9	162.8
0	172.2	1	157.3	3	176.4	9	142.4
0	165.0	1	166.7	3	153.1	9	162.8
0	176.9	1	161.1	3	156.0	9	162.4

(a) What are the explanatory and response variables in this experiment?
(b) Make side-by-side stemplots of the yields, after rounding to the nearest bushel. Give the mean yield for each group (using the unrounded data). What do you conclude about the effect of this weed on corn yield?

(c) With only 4 observations in each group, it isn't surprising that the "3 weeds" and "9 weeds" groups each have a possible outlier. Find the median yield for each group. How does switching from means to medians affect your conclusion?

6.31 Weeds among the corn, continued. We can also use regression to analyze the data on weeds and corn yield. The advantage of regression over the side-by-side comparison in the previous exercise is that we can use the fitted line to draw conclusions for counts of weeds other than the ones the researcher actually used.
(a) Make a scatterplot of corn yield against weeds per meter. Find the least-squares regression line and add it to your plot. What does the slope of the fitted line tell us about the effect of lamb's-quarter on corn yield?
(b) Predict the yield for corn grown under these conditions with 6 lamb's-quarter plants per meter of row. (The small number of observations and possible outliers make this prediction unreliable.)

SUPPLEMENTARY EXERCISES

*Supplementary exercises apply the skills you have learned in ways that require more thought or more elaborate use of technology. Some of these exercises ask you to follow the **Plan, Solve,** and **Conclude** steps of the four-step process introduced on page 42.*

6.32 The Mississippi River. Table 6.2 gives the volume of water discharged by the Mississippi River into the Gulf of Mexico for each year from 1954 to 2001.[16] The units are cubic kilometers of water.
(a) Make a graph of the distribution of water volume. Describe the overall shape of the distribution and any outliers.
(b) Based on the shape of the distribution, do you expect the mean to be close to the median, clearly less than the median, or clearly greater than the median? Why? Find the mean and the median to check your answer.
(c) Based on the shape of the distribution, does it seem reasonable to use $\bar{x}$ and s to describe the center and spread of this distribution? Why? Find $\bar{x}$ and s if you think they are a good choice. Otherwise, find the five-number summary.

6.33 More on the Mississippi River. The data in Table 6.2 are a time series. Make a time plot that shows how the volume of water in the Mississippi changed between 1954 and 2001. What does the time plot reveal that the histogram from the previous exercise does not? It is a good idea to always make a time plot of time series data because a histogram cannot show changes over time.

Falling through the ice. *The Nenana Ice Classic is an annual contest to guess the exact time in the spring when a tripod erected on*

TABLE 6.2 Yearly discharge (cubic kilometers of water) of the Mississippi River

YEAR	DISCHARGE	YEAR	DISCHARGE	YEAR	DISCHARGE	YEAR	DISCHARGE
1954	290	1966	410	1978	560	1990	680
1955	420	1967	460	1979	800	1991	700
1956	390	1968	510	1980	500	1992	510
1957	610	1969	560	1981	420	1993	900
1958	550	1970	540	1982	640	1994	640
1959	440	1971	480	1983	770	1995	590
1960	470	1972	600	1984	710	1996	670
1961	600	1973	880	1985	680	1997	680
1962	550	1974	710	1986	600	1998	690
1963	360	1975	670	1987	450	1999	580
1964	390	1976	420	1988	420	2000	390
1965	500	1977	430	1989	630	2001	580

TABLE 6.3 Days from April 20 for the Tanana River tripod to fall

YEAR	DAY	YEAR	DAY	YEAR	DAY	YEAR	DAY	YEAR	DAY	YEAR	DAY
1917	11	1933	19	1949	25	1965	18	1981	11	1997	11
1918	22	1934	11	1950	17	1966	19	1982	21	1998	1
1919	14	1935	26	1951	11	1967	15	1983	10	1999	10
1920	22	1936	11	1952	23	1968	19	1984	20	2000	12
1921	22	1937	23	1953	10	1969	9	1985	23	2001	19
1922	23	1938	17	1954	17	1970	15	1986	19	2002	18
1923	20	1939	10	1955	20	1971	19	1987	16	2003	10
1924	22	1940	1	1956	12	1972	21	1988	8	2004	5
1925	16	1941	14	1957	16	1973	15	1989	12	2005	9
1926	7	1942	11	1958	10	1974	17	1990	5	2006	13
1927	23	1943	9	1959	19	1975	21	1991	12	2007	8
1928	17	1944	15	1960	13	1976	13	1992	25	2008	17
1929	16	1945	27	1961	16	1977	17	1993	4		
1930	19	1946	16	1962	23	1978	11	1994	10		
1931	21	1947	14	1963	16	1979	11	1995	7		
1932	12	1948	24	1964	31	1980	10	1996	16		

the frozen Tanana River near Nenana, Alaska, will fall through the ice. The 2008 jackpot prize was $303,985. The contest has been run since 1917. Table 6.3 gives simplified data that record only the date on which the tripod fell each year. The earliest date so far is April 20. To make the data easier to use, the table gives the date each year in days starting with April 20. That is, April 20 is 1, April 21 is 2, and so on. Exercises 6.34 to 6.36 concern these data.[17]

6.34 When does the ice break up? We have 92 years of data on the date of ice breakup on the Tanana River. Describe the distribution of the breakup date with both a graph or graphs and appropriate numerical summaries. What is the median date (month and day) for ice breakup?

2006 Bill Watkins/AlaskaStock.com

6.35 Global warming? Because of the high stakes, the falling of the tripod has been carefully observed for many years. If the date the tripod falls has been getting earlier, that may be evidence for the effects of global warming.
(a) Make a time plot of the date the tripod falls against year.
(b) There is a great deal of year-to-year variation. Fitting a regression line to the data may help us see the trend. Fit the least-squares line and add it to your time plot. What do you conclude?
(c) There is much variation about the line. Give a numerical description of how much of the year-to-year variation in ice breakup time is accounted for by the time trend represented by the regression line. (This simple example is typical of more complex evidence for the effects of global warming: large year-to-year variation requires many years of data to see a trend.)

6.36 More on global warming. Side-by-side boxplots offer a different look at the data. Group the data into periods of roughly equal length: 1917 to 1939, 1940 to 1962, 1963 to 1985, and 1986 to 2008. Make boxplots to compare ice breakup dates in these four time periods. Write a brief description of what the plots show.

6.37 Big government? The data file *ex06-37.dat* on the text CD and Web site contains the percent of gross domestic product (GDP, the total value of all goods and services a country produces) taken by the government in 82 countries. For example, the government share of GDP is 12.28% in Canada and 10.54% in the United States.[18]
(a) Make a stemplot or a histogram to display the distribution of government share of GDP.
(b) There are several high outliers. What countries are these? (In the most extreme case, the government took more than the total annual GDP!) What is the overall shape of the distribution if you ignore the outliers?
(c) Based on your work in (b), give a numerical summary of the center and spread of the distribution, omitting the outliers.
(d) Some Americans complain about big government and heavy taxes. Where does the United States (10.54%) stand in this international comparison?

6.38 Cicadas as fertilizer? Periodically, swarms of cicadas emerge from the ground in the eastern United States, live for about six weeks, then die. There are so many cicadas that their dead bodies can serve as fertilizer and increase plant growth. In an experiment, a researcher added 10 cicadas under some plants in a natural plot of bellflowers in a forest, leaving other plants undisturbed. One of the response variables was the size of seeds produced by the plants. Here are data (seed mass in milligrams) for 39 cicada plants and 33 undisturbed (control) plants:[19]

Cicada plants				Control plants			
0.237	0.277	0.241	0.142	0.212	0.188	0.263	0.253
0.109	0.209	0.238	0.277	0.261	0.265	0.135	0.170
0.261	0.227	0.171	0.235	0.203	0.241	0.257	0.155
0.276	0.234	0.255	0.296	0.215	0.285	0.198	0.266
0.239	0.266	0.296	0.217	0.178	0.244	0.190	0.212
0.238	0.210	0.295	0.193	0.290	0.253	0.249	0.253
0.218	0.263	0.305	0.257	0.268	0.190	0.196	0.220
0.351	0.245	0.226	0.276	0.246	0.145	0.247	0.140
0.317	0.310	0.223	0.229	0.241			
0.192	0.201	0.211					

Describe and compare the two distributions. Do the data support the idea that dead cicadas can serve as fertilizer?

6.39 A big toe problem. Hallux abducto valgus (call it HAV) is a deformation of the big toe that is not common in youth and often requires surgery. Doctors used X-rays to measure the angle (in degrees) of deformity in 38 consecutive patients under the age of 21 who came to a medical center for surgery to correct HAV.[20] The angle is a measure of the seriousness of the deformity. The data appear in Table 6.4 as "HAV angle." Describe the distribution of the angle of deformity among young patients needing surgery for this condition.

6.40 Prey attract predators. Here is one way in which nature regulates the size of animal populations: high population density attracts predators, who remove a higher proportion of the population than when the density of the prey is low. One study looked at kelp perch and their common predator, the kelp bass. The researcher set up four large circular pens on sandy ocean bottom in Southern California. He chose young perch at random from a large group and placed 10, 20, 40, and 60 perch in the four pens. Then he dropped the nets protecting the pens, allowing bass to swarm in, and counted the perch left after 2 hours. Here are data on the proportions of perch eaten in four repetitions of this setup:[21]

Perch	Proportion killed			
10	0.0	0.1	0.3	0.3
20	0.2	0.3	0.3	0.6
40	0.075	0.3	0.6	0.725
60	0.517	0.55	0.7	0.817

Do the data support the principle that "more prey attract more predators, who drive down the number of prey"?

6.41 Predicting foot problems. Metatarsus adductus (call it MA) is a turning in of the front part of the foot that is common in adolescents and usually corrects itself.

TABLE 6.4 Angle of deformity (degrees) for two types of foot deformity

HAV ANGLE	MA ANGLE	HAV ANGLE	MA ANGLE	HAV ANGLE	MA ANGLE
28	18	21	15	16	10
32	16	17	16	30	12
25	22	16	10	30	10
34	17	21	7	20	10
38	33	23	11	50	12
26	10	14	15	25	25
25	18	32	12	26	30
18	13	25	16	28	22
30	19	21	16	31	24
26	10	22	18	38	20
28	17	20	10	32	37
13	14	18	15	21	23
20	20	26	16		

Table 6.4 gives the severity of MA ("MA angle") as well. Doctors speculate that the severity of MA can help predict the severity of HAV. Describe the relationship between MA and HAV. Do you think the data confirm the doctors' speculation? Why or why not?

6.41 Change in the Serengeti. Long-term records from the Serengeti National Park in Tanzania show interesting ecological relationships. When wildebeest are more abundant, they graze the grass more heavily, so there are fewer fires and more trees grow. Lions feed more successfully when there are more trees, so the lion population increases. Here are data on one part of this cycle, wildebeest abundance (in thousands of animals) and the percent of the grass area that burned in the same year:[22]

Wildebeest (1000s)	Percent burned	Wildebeest (1000s)	Percent burned	Wildebeest (1000s)	Percent burned
396	56	360	88	1147	32
476	50	444	88	1173	31
698	25	524	75	1178	24
1049	16	622	60	1253	24
1178	7	600	56	1249	53
1200	5	902	45		
1302	7	1440	21		

To what extent do these data support the claim that more wildebeest reduce the percent of grasslands that burn? How rapidly does burned area decrease as the number of wildebeest increases? Include a graph and suitable calculations.

6.42 Casting aluminum. In casting metal parts, molten metal flows through a "gate" into a die that shapes the part. The gate velocity (the speed at which metal is forced through the gate) plays a critical role in die casting. A firm that casts cylindrical aluminum pistons examined 12 types formed from the same alloy. How does the piston wall thickness (inches) influence the gate velocity (feet per second) chosen by the skilled workers who do the casting? If there is a clear pattern, it can be used to direct new workers or to automate the process. Analyze these data and report your findings.[23]

Thickness	Velocity	Thickness	Velocity	Thickness	Velocity
0.248	123.8	0.524	228.6	0.697	145.2
0.359	223.9	0.552	223.8	0.752	263.1
0.366	180.9	0.628	326.2	0.806	302.4
0.400	104.8	0.697	302.4	0.821	302.4

6.43 Influence: hot mutual funds? Investment advertisements always warn that "past performance does not guarantee future results." Here is an example that shows why you should pay attention to this warning. Stocks fell sharply in 2002, then rose sharply in 2003. The table below gives the percent returns from 23 Fidelity Investments "sector funds" in these two years. Sector funds invest in narrow segments of the stock market. They often rise and fall faster than the market as a whole.

2002 return	2003 return	2002 return	2003 return	2002 return	2003 return
−17.1	23.9	−0.7	36.9	−37.8	59.4
−6.7	14.1	−5.6	27.5	−11.5	22.9
−21.1	41.8	−26.9	26.1	−0.7	36.9
−12.8	43.9	−42.0	62.7	64.3	32.1
−18.9	31.1	−47.8	68.1	−9.6	28.7
−7.7	32.3	−50.5	71.9	−11.7	29.5
−17.2	36.5	−49.5	57.0	−2.3	19.1
−11.4	30.6	−23.4	35.0		

(a) Make a scatterplot of 2003 return (response) against 2002 return (explanatory). The funds with the best performance in 2002 tend to have the worst performance in 2003. Fidelity Gold Fund, the only fund with a positive return in both years, is an extreme outlier.

(b) To demonstrate that correlation is not resistant, find r for all 23 funds and then find r for the 22 funds other than Gold. Explain from Gold's position in your plot why omitting this point makes r more negative.

(c) Find the equations of two least-squares lines for predicting 2003 return from 2002 return, one for all 23 funds and one omitting Fidelity Gold Fund. Add both lines to your scatterplot. Starting with the least-squares idea, explain why adding Fidelity Gold Fund to the other 22 funds moves the line in the direction that your graph shows.

6.44 Influence: monkey calls. Table 6.1 contains data on the response of 37 monkey neurons to pure tones and to monkey calls. You made a scatterplot of these data in Exercise 6.25.

(a) Find the least-squares line for predicting a neuron's call response from its pure tone response. Add the line to your scatterplot. Mark on your plot the point (call it A) with the largest residual (either positive or negative) and also the point (call it B) that is an outlier in the x direction.

(b) How influential are each of these points for the correlation r?

(c) How influential are each of these points for the regression line?

6.45 Canadian students gambling. Here are the percents of students at four universities in Ontario who engage in several types of gambling:[24]

Type of gambling	Percent of males	Percent of females
Instant game tickets	38.8	52.6
LOTTO 6/49 or similar	27.8	19.1
Pro-Line	27.8	2.2
Bingo	7.0	14.7
Casino slots	30.7	41.1
Casino blackjack	16.4	6.4
Card games for money	23.5	7.3
Raffles or fundraising tickets	34.2	46.5
Sports pools	29.1	4.1
Horse races	8.9	7.1

(LOTTO 6/49 is a nationwide Canadian lottery. Pro-Line is a sports betting game offered by the Ontario provincial government.) Make a graph that compares the gambling behaviors of male and female students and briefly discuss what the data show.

From Exploration to Inference

PART II

PRODUCING DATA

CHAPTER 7 Producing Data: Sampling

CHAPTER 8 Producing Data: Experiments

PROBABILITY AND SAMPLING DISTRIBUTIONS

CHAPTER 9 Introducing Probability

CHAPTER 10 Sampling Distributions

CHAPTER 11 General Rules of Probability*

CHAPTER 12 Binomial Distributions*

FOUNDATIONS OF INFERENCE

CHAPTER 13 Introduction to Inference

CHAPTER 14 Thinking about Inference

CHAPTER 15 Part II Review

The purpose of statistics is to gain understanding from data. We can seek understanding in different ways, depending on the circumstances. We have studied one approach to data, *exploratory data analysis*, in some detail. Now we move from data analysis toward *statistical inference*. Both types of reasoning are essential to effective work with data. Here is a brief sketch of the differences between them.

EXPLORATORY DATA ANALYSIS	STATISTICAL INFERENCE
Purpose is unrestricted exploration of the data, searching for interesting patterns.	Purpose is to answer specific questions, posed before the data were produced.
Conclusions apply only to the individuals and circumstances for which we have data in hand.	Conclusions apply to a larger group of individuals or a broader class of circumstances.
Conclusions are informal, based on what we see in the data.	Conclusions are formal, backed by a statement of our confidence in them.

Our journey toward inference begins in Chapters 7 and 8, which describe statistical designs for *producing data* by samples and experiments. The conclusions of inference use the language of *probability*, the mathematics of chance. Chapters 9 and 10 present the ideas we need, and the optional Chapters 11 and 12 add more detail. Armed with designs for producing trustworthy data, data analysis to examine the data, and the language of probability, we are prepared to understand the big ideas of inference in Chapters 13 and 14. These chapters are the foundation for the discussion of inference in practice that occupies the rest of the book.

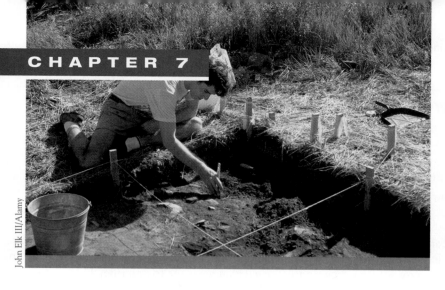

John Elk III/Alamy

A student works at an archaeological dig. Archaeologists use sampling to check the work of their student helpers (Exercise 7.2).

Producing Data: Sampling

IN THIS CHAPTER
WE COVER...

- Population versus sample
- How to sample badly
- Simple random samples
- Inference about the population
- Cautions about sample surveys

Exploratory data analysis helps us understand data that describe some group of individuals. But sometimes we have specific questions and no data to answer them. To get answers, we must *produce data*.

Suppose our question is "What percent of college students think that people should not obey laws that violate their personal values?" To answer the question, we interview undergraduate college students. We can't afford to ask all students, so we put the question to a *sample* chosen to represent the entire student *population*. How shall we choose a sample that truly represents the opinions of the entire population? Statistical designs for choosing samples are the topic of this chapter. We will see that

- a sound statistical design is necessary if we are to trust data from a sample;
- in sampling from large human populations, however, "practical problems" can overwhelm even sound designs.

Population versus sample

A political scientist wants to know what percent of college-age adults consider themselves conservatives. An automaker hires a market research firm to learn what percent of adults aged 18 to 35 recall seeing television advertisements for a new gas-electric hybrid car. Government economists inquire about average household income. In all these cases, we want information about a large group of individuals. In practice, we can afford to contact only part of the group in order to draw conclusions about the whole.

POPULATION, SAMPLE, SAMPLING DESIGN

The **population** in a statistical study is the entire group of individuals about which we want information.

A **sample** is a part of the population from which we actually collect information. We use a sample to draw conclusions about the entire population.

A **sampling design** describes exactly how to choose a sample from the population.

---

sample survey

Pay careful attention to the details of the definitions of "population" and "sample." Look at Exercise 7.1 right now to check your understanding. The first step in planning a **sample survey** is to say exactly *what population* we want to describe. The second step is to say exactly *what we want to measure*, that is, to give exact definitions of our variables.

EXAMPLE 7.1 The Current Population Survey

The government's Current Population Survey (CPS) contacts about 60,000 households each month. It produces the monthly unemployment rate and much other economic and social information. (See Figure 7.1.) To measure unemployment, we must first specify the *population* we want to describe. The CPS defines its population as all U.S. residents (including illegal immigrants) 16 years of age and over who are civilians and are not in an institution such as a prison. The unemployment rate announced in the news refers to this specific population.

To define the unemployment rate carefully, the CPS must say what it means to be "unemployed." Someone who is not looking for work—for example, a full-time student—should not be called unemployed just because she is not working for pay. If you are chosen for the CPS sample, the interviewer first asks whether you are available to work and whether you actually looked for work in the past four weeks. If not, you are neither employed nor unemployed—you are not in the labor force.

If you are in the labor force, the interviewer goes on to ask about employment. If you did any work for pay or in your own business during the week of the survey, you are employed. If you worked at least 15 hours in a family business without pay, you are employed. You are also employed if you have a job but didn't work because of vacation, being on strike, or other good reason. An unemployment rate of 5.7% means that 5.7% of the sample was unemployed, using the exact CPS definitions of both "labor force" and "unemployed." ■

FIGURE 7.1

The home page of the Current Population Survey at the Bureau of Labor Statistics.

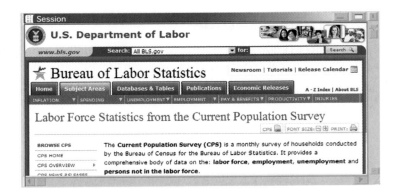

APPLY YOUR KNOWLEDGE

7.1 Sampling students. A political scientist wants to know how college students feel about the Social Security system. She obtains a list of the 3456 undergraduates at her college and mails a questionnaire to 250 students selected at random. Only 104 questionnaires are returned.

(a) What is the population in this study? Be careful: what group does she *want information about?*

(b) What is the sample? Be careful: from what group does she *actually obtain information?*

7.2 Student archaeologists. An archaeological dig turns up large numbers of pottery shards, broken stone implements, and other artifacts. Students working on the project classify each artifact and assign it a number. The counts in different categories are important for understanding the site, so the project director chooses 2% of the artifacts at random and checks the students' work. What are the population and the sample here?

John Elk III/Alamy

7.3 Customer satisfaction. A department store mails a customer satisfaction survey to people who make credit card purchases at the store. This month, 45,000 people made credit card purchases. Surveys are mailed to 1000 of these people, chosen at random, and 137 people return the survey form. What is the population for this survey? What is the sample from which information was actually obtained?

How to sample badly

The final step in planning a sample survey is the sampling design.

A sampling design is a specific method for choosing a sample from the population. The easiest—but not the best—design just chooses individuals close at hand. A sample selected by taking the members of the population that are easiest to reach is called a **convenience sample.** Convenience samples often produce unrepresentative data.

convenience sample

EXAMPLE 7.2 Sampling at the mall

A sample of mall shoppers is fast and cheap. But people at shopping malls tend to be more prosperous than typical Americans. They are also more likely to be teenagers or retired. Moreover, unless interviewers are carefully trained, they tend to question well-dressed, respectable people and avoid poorly dressed or tough-looking individuals. In short, mall interviews will not contact a sample that is representative of the entire population. ■

Interviews at shopping malls will almost always overrepresent middle-class and retired people and underrepresent the poor. This is *bias:* the outcomes of mall surveys will repeatedly miss the truth about the population in the same ways. Bias isn't bad luck on one sample, but rather a systematic error caused by a bad sampling design.

BIAS

The design of a statistical study is **biased** if it systematically favors certain outcomes.

EXAMPLE 7.3   Online polls

The CNN evening commentator Lou Dobbs doesn't like illegal immigration. One of his broadcasts in 2007 was largely devoted to attacking a proposal by the governor of New York State to offer driver's licenses to illegal immigrants as a public safety measure. During the show, Mr. Dobbs invited his viewers to go to `loudobbs.com` to vote on the question "Would you be more or less likely to vote for a presidential candidate who supports giving drivers' licences to illegal aliens?" We aren't surprised that 97% of the 7350 people who voted by the end of the broadcast said "Less likely." ▪

The `loudobbs.com` poll was biased because people chose whether or not to participate. Most who voted were viewers of Lou Dobbs's program who had just heard him denounce the governor's idea. *People who take the trouble to respond to an open invitation are usually not representative of any clearly defined population.* That's true of the people who bother to respond to write-in, call-in, or online polls in general. Polls like these are examples of *voluntary response sampling.*

VOLUNTARY RESPONSE SAMPLE

A **voluntary response sample** consists of people who choose themselves by responding to a broad appeal. Voluntary response samples are biased because people with strong opinions are most likely to respond.

APPLY YOUR KNOWLEDGE

7.4 Sampling on campus. You see a woman student standing in front of the student center, now and then stopping other students to ask them questions. She says that she is collecting student opinions for a class assignment. Explain why this sampling method is almost certainly biased.

7.5 More sampling on campus. Your college wants to gather student opinion about parking for students on campus. It isn't practical to contact all students.

(a) Give an example of a way to choose a sample of students that is poor practice because it depends on voluntary response.

(b) Give another example of a bad way to choose a sample that doesn't use voluntary response.

Simple random samples

In a voluntary response sample, people choose whether to respond. In a convenience sample, the interviewer makes the choice. In both cases, personal choice produces bias. *Choosing a sample by chance* attacks bias by giving all individuals an equal chance to be chosen. Rich and poor, young and old, black and white, all have the same chance to be in the sample. The simplest way to use chance to select a sample is to place names in a hat (the population) and draw out a handful (the sample). This is the idea of *simple random sampling.*

An SRS not only gives each individual an equal chance to be chosen but also gives every possible sample an equal chance to be chosen. There are other random sampling designs that give each individual, but not each sample, an equal chance. Exercise 7.36 describes one such design.

When you think of an SRS, picture drawing names from a hat to remind yourself that an SRS doesn't favor any part of the population. That's why an SRS is a better method of choosing samples than convenience or voluntary response sampling. But writing names on slips of paper and drawing them from a hat is slow and inconvenient. In practice, samplers use software. If you don't use software, you can randomize by using a *table of random digits*. In fact, software for choosing samples starts by generating random digits, so using a table just does by hand what the software does more quickly.

RANDOM DIGITS

A **table of random digits** is a long string of the digits 0, 1, 2, 3, 4, 5, 6, 7, 8, 9 with these two properties:

1. Each entry in the table is equally likely to be any of the 10 digits 0 through 9.
2. The entries are independent of each other. That is, knowledge of one part of the table gives no information about any other part.

Table B at the back of the book is a table of random digits. Table B begins with the digits 19223950340575628713. To make the table easier to read, the digits appear in groups of five and in numbered rows. The groups and rows have no meaning—the table is just a long list of randomly chosen digits. There are two steps in using the table to choose a simple random sample.

USING TABLE B TO CHOOSE AN SRS

Label: Give each member of the population a numerical label of the *same length*.

Table: To choose an SRS, read from Table B successive groups of digits of the length you used as labels. Your sample contains the individuals whose labels you find in the table.

You can label up to 100 items with two digits: 01, 02, ..., 99, 00. Up to 1000 items can be labeled with three digits, and so on. Always use the shortest labels that will cover your population. We recommend that you begin with label 1 (or 01 or 001, as needed). Reading groups of digits from the table gives all individuals the same chance to be chosen because all labels of the same length have the same chance to be found in the table. For example, any pair of digits in the table is equally likely to be any of the 100 possible labels

01, 02, ... , 99, 00. Ignore any group of digits that was not used as a label or that duplicates a label already in the sample.

Robert Daly/Getty Images

EXAMPLE 7.4   **Sampling spring break resorts**

A campus newspaper plans a major article on spring break destinations. The authors intend to call 4 randomly chosen resorts at each destination to ask about their attitudes toward groups of students as guests. Here are the resorts listed in one city:

01	Aloha Kai	08	Captiva	15	Palm Tree	22	Sea Shell
02	Anchor Down	09	Casa del Mar	16	Radisson	23	Silver Beach
03	Banana Bay	10	Coconuts	17	Ramada	24	Sunset Beach
04	Banyan Tree	11	Diplomat	18	Sandpiper	25	Tradewinds
05	Beach Castle	12	Holiday Inn	19	Sea Castle	26	Tropical Breeze
06	Best Western	13	Lime Tree	20	Sea Club	27	Tropical Shores
07	Cabana	14	Outrigger	21	Sea Grape	28	Veranda

LABEL: Because two digits are needed to label the 28 resorts, all labels will have two digits. We have added labels 01 to 28 to the list of resorts. Always say how you labeled the members of the population. To sample from the 1240 resorts in a major vacation area, you would label the resorts 0001, 0002, ... , 1239, 1240.

TABLE: Read two-digit groups from Table B until you have chosen four resorts. Starting at line 130 (any line will do), we find

69051   64817   87174   09517   84534   06489   87201   97245

Because the labels are two digits long, read successive two-digit groups from the table. Ignore groups not used as labels, like the initial 69. Also ignore any repeated labels, like the second and third 17s in this row, because you can't choose the same resort twice. Your sample contains the resorts labeled 05, 16, 17, and 20. These are Beach Castle, Radisson, Ramada, and Sea Club. ■

random sampling   **Random sampling,** the use of impersonal chance to avoid bias, is the basic idea of sampling design. Online polls and mall interviews also produce samples, but these samples are chosen in ways that invite bias. *The first question to ask about any sample is whether it was chosen at random.*

EXAMPLE 7.5   **The future of the environment**

"Do you think the condition of the environment for the next generation will be better, worse, or about the same as it is now?" When the *New York Times* and CBS News asked this question of 1052 adults, 57% said "worse" and just 11% said "better." Can we trust the opinions of this sample to fairly represent the opinions of all adults? Here's part of the statement by the *Times* on "How the Poll Was Conducted":[1]

The latest New York Times/CBS News poll is based on telephone interviews conducted April 20 through April 24 with 1,052 adults throughout the United States.

The sample of telephone exchanges called was randomly selected by a computer from a complete list of more than 42,000 active residential exchanges across the country. The exchanges were chosen so as to ensure that each region of the country was represented in proportion to its population.

Within each exchange, random digits were added to form a complete telephone number, thus permitting access to listed and unlisted numbers alike. Within each household, one adult was designated by a random procedure to be the respondent for the survey.

This is a good description of the most common method for choosing national samples, called **random digit dialing.** This statement is a good start toward gaining our confidence. We know the size of the sample, when the poll was taken, and the comforting word "random" appears three times. ■

random digit dialing

Large-scale sample surveys often use random sampling designs more complicated than an SRS. For example, the opinion poll described in Example 7.5 uses a three-stage design: choose a random sample of telephone exchanges, then a random sample of household telephone numbers within each exchange, then a random adult in each household. Analysis of data from sampling designs more complex than an SRS takes us beyond basic statistics. But the SRS is the building block of more elaborate designs, and analysis of other designs differs more in complexity of detail than in fundamental concepts.

APPLY YOUR KNOWLEDGE

7.6 Apartment living. You are planning a report on apartment living in a college town. You decide to select three apartment complexes at random for in-depth interviews with residents. Use software or Table B to select a simple random sample of three of the following apartment complexes. If you use Table B, start at line 117.

Ashley Oaks	Country View	Mayfair Village
Bay Pointe	Country Villa	Nobb Hill
Beau Jardin	Crestview	Pemberly Courts
Bluffs	Del-Lynn	Peppermill
Brandon Place	Fairington	Pheasant Run
Briarwood	Fairway Knolls	River Walk
Brownstone	Fowler	Sagamore Ridge
Burberry Place	Franklin Park	Salem Courthouse
Cambridge	Georgetown	Village Square
Chauncey Village	Greenacres	Waterford Court
Country Squire	Lahr House	Williamsburg

7.7 Minority managers. A firm wants to understand the attitudes of its minority managers toward its system for assessing management performance. Below is a list of all the firm's managers who are members of minority groups. Use software or Table B at line 139 to choose six to be interviewed in detail about the performance appraisal system.

Abdulhamid	Duncan	Huang	Puri
Agarwal	Fernandez	Kim	Richards
Baxter	Fleming	Lumumba	Rodriguez
Bonds	Gates	Mourning	Santiago
Brown	Gomez	Nguyen	Shen
Castro	Gupta	Peters	Vargas
Chavez	Hernandez	Peña	Wang

7.8 Sampling gravestones. The local genealogical society in Coles County, Illinois, has compiled records on all 55,914 gravestones in cemeteries in the county for the years 1825 to 1985. Historians plan to use these records to learn about African Americans in Coles

© The Photo Works

County's history. They first choose an SRS of 395 records to check their accuracy by visiting the actual gravestones.[2]

(a) How would you label the 55,914 records?

(b) Use Table B, beginning at line 120, to choose the first five records for the SRS.

Inference about the population

inference

The purpose of a sample is to give us information about a larger population. The process of drawing conclusions about a population on the basis of sample data is called **inference** because we *infer* information about the population from what we *know* about the sample.

Inference from convenience samples or voluntary response samples would be misleading because these methods of choosing a sample are biased. We are almost certain that the sample does *not* fairly represent the population. *The first reason to rely on random sampling is to eliminate bias in selecting samples from the list of available individuals.*

Nonetheless, it is unlikely that results from a random sample are exactly the same as for the entire population. Sample results, like the unemployment rate obtained from the monthly Current Population Survey, are only estimates of the truth about the population. If we select two samples at random from the same population, we will almost certainly draw different individuals. So the sample results will differ somewhat, just by chance.

Why can we trust random samples? The big idea is that the results of random sampling don't change haphazardly from sample to sample. Because we deliberately use chance, the results obey the laws of probability that govern chance behavior. These laws allow us to say how likely it is that sample results are close to the truth about the population. *The second reason to use random sampling is that the laws of probability allow trustworthy inference about the population.* Results from random samples come with a margin of error that sets bounds on the size of the likely error. We will begin to learn the details in Chapter 13.

One point is worth making now: *larger random samples give more accurate results than smaller samples.* By taking a very large sample, you can be confident that the sample result is very close to the truth about the population. The Current Population Survey contacts about 60,000 households, so it estimates the national unemployment rate quite accurately. Opinion polls that contact 1000 or 1500 people give less accurate results. Of course, only samples chosen by chance carry this guarantee. Lou Dobbs's online sample tells us little about overall American public opinion even though 7350 people clicked a response.

APPLY YOUR KNOWLEDGE

7.9 Ask more people. Just before a presidential election, a national opinion-polling firm increases the size of its weekly sample from the usual 1500 people to 4000 people. Why do you think the firm does this?

7.10 Sampling Pentecostals. Pentecostals are among the fastest-growing Christian groups in many countries. The Pew Forum on Religion and Public Life surveyed Pentecostal Christians in 10 countries and compared their opinions with those of the general population. In South Korea, random samples by Gallup Korea had margins of error (more detail in later chapters) of ±4% for the general public and ±9% for Pentecostals.[3] What do you think explains the fact that estimates for Pentecostals were less accurate?

Cautions about sample surveys

Random selection eliminates bias in the choice of a sample from a list of the population. When the population consists of human beings, however, accurate information from a sample requires more than a good sampling design.

To begin, we need an accurate and complete list of the population. Because such a list is rarely available, most samples suffer from some degree of *undercoverage*. A sample survey of households, for example, will miss not only homeless people but prison inmates and students in dormitories. An opinion poll conducted by calling landline telephone numbers will miss households that have only cell phones as well as households without a phone. The results of national sample surveys therefore have some bias if the people not covered differ from the rest of the population.

A more serious source of bias in most sample surveys is *nonresponse*, which occurs when a selected individual cannot be contacted or refuses to cooperate. Nonresponse to sample surveys often exceeds 50%, even with careful planning and several callbacks. Because nonresponse is higher in urban areas, many sample surveys substitute other people in the same area to avoid favoring rural areas in the final sample. If the people contacted differ from those who are rarely at home or who refuse to answer questions, some bias remains.

UNDERCOVERAGE AND NONRESPONSE

Undercoverage occurs when some groups in the population are left out of the process of choosing the sample.

Nonresponse occurs when an individual chosen for the sample can't be contacted or refuses to participate.

EXAMPLE 7.6 **Cell phones and undercoverage**

A few national sample surveys, especially government surveys, interview some or all of their subjects in person. Most national surveys contact subjects by telephone using the random digit dialing (RDD) method described in Example 7.5. Technology, especially the spread of cell phones, is making traditional RDD methods outdated.

The number of cell-phone-only households is increasing rapidly. By 2008, 18% of American households had a cell phone but no landline phone. Even if the United States and Canada don't approach the 52% of households in Finland that have no landline phone, it's clear that RDD reaching only landline numbers suffers from undercoverage. Can surveys just add cell phone numbers? Not easily. Federal regulations require hand dialing of cell phone numbers, ruling out computerized RDD sampling and adding expense. A cell phone can be anywhere, so breaking down a sample by location becomes difficult. And a cell phone user may be driving or otherwise unable to talk safely.

People who screen calls and people who have only a cell phone tend to be younger than the general population. In fact, one projection claims that by the end of 2009 more than 40% of American adults under age 30 will have no landline phone. So RDD surveys may be biased. ∎

EXAMPLE 7.7 **How bad is nonresponse?**

The Census Bureau's American Community Survey (ACS) has the lowest nonresponse rate of any poll we know: only about 1% of the households in the sample refuse to respond;

the overall nonresponse rate, including "never at home" and other causes, is just 2.5%.[4] This monthly survey of about 250,000 households replaces the "long form" that in the past was sent to some households in the every-ten-years national census. Participation in the ACS is mandatory, and the Census Bureau follows up by telephone and then in person if a household fails to return the mail questionnaire.

The University of Chicago's General Social Survey (GSS) is the nation's most important social science survey. (See Figure 7.2.) The GSS contacts its sample in person, and it is run by a university. Despite these advantages, its most recent survey had a 30% rate of nonresponse.

What about opinion polls by news media and opinion-polling firms? Polls don't tell us how bad their nonresponse is. The Pew Research Center for the People and the Press imitated a careful random digit dialing survey and published the results: over 5 days, the survey reached 76% of the households in its chosen sample, but "because of busy schedules, skepticism and outright refusals, interviews were completed in just 38% of households that were reached." Combining households that could not be contacted with those who did not complete the interview gave a nonresponse rate of 73%.[5] ■

FIGURE 7.2

The home page of the General Social Survey at the University of Chicago's National Opinion Research Center. The GSS has tracked opinions about a wide variety of issues since 1972.

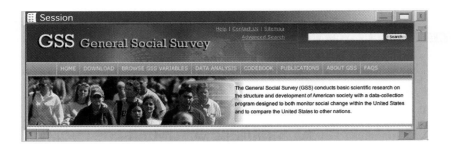

response bias   In addition, the behavior of the respondent or the interviewer can cause **response bias** in sample results. People know that they should take the trouble to vote, for example, so many who didn't vote in the last election will tell an interviewer that they did. Answers to questions that ask respondents to recall past events are often inaccurate because of faulty memory. For example, many people "telescope" events in the past, bringing them forward in memory to more recent time periods. "Have you visited a dentist in the last 6 months?" will often draw a "Yes" from someone who last visited a dentist 8 months ago.[6] Careful training of interviewers and careful supervision to avoid variation among the interviewers can reduce response bias. Good interviewing technique is another aspect of a well-done sample survey.

wording of effects   The **wording of questions** is the most important influence on the answers given to a sample survey. Confusing or leading questions can introduce strong bias, and changes in wording can greatly change a survey's outcome. Even the order in which questions are asked matters. Here are some examples.[7]

EXAMPLE 7.8   **What was that question?**

How do Americans feel about illegal immigrants? "Should illegal immigrants be prosecuted and deported for being in the U.S. illegally, or shouldn't they?" Asked this question in an opinion poll, 69% favored deportation. But when the very same sample was asked whether illegal immigrants who have worked in the United States for two years "should be given a chance to keep their jobs and eventually apply for legal status," 62% said that they should. Different questions give quite different impressions of attitudes toward illegal immigrants.

What about government help for the poor? Only 13% think we are spending too much on "assistance to the poor," but 44% think we are spending too much on "welfare." ■

EXAMPLE 7.9 Are you happy?

Ask a sample of college students these two questions:

"How happy are you with your life in general?" (Answers on a scale of 1 to 5)
"How many dates did you have last month?"

The correlation between answers is $r = -0.012$ when asked in this order. It appears that dating has little to do with happiness. Reverse the order of the questions, however, and $r = 0.66$. Asking a question that brings dating to mind makes dating success a big factor in happiness. ■

Don't trust the results of a sample survey until you have read the exact questions asked. The amount of nonresponse and the date of the survey are also important. Good statistical design is a part, but only a part, of a trustworthy survey.

APPLY YOUR KNOWLEDGE

7.11 Ring-no-answer. A common form of nonresponse in telephone surveys is "ring-no-answer." That is, a call is made to an active number but no one answers. The Italian National Statistical Institute looked at nonresponse to a government survey of households in Italy during the periods January 1 to Easter and July 1 to August 31. All calls were made between 7 and 10 P.M., but 21.4% gave "ring-no-answer" in one period versus 41.5% "ring-no-answer" in the other period.[8] Which period do you think had the higher rate of no answers? Why? Explain why a high rate of nonresponse makes sample results less reliable.

7.12 Question wording. In 2000, when the federal budget showed a large surplus, the Pew Research Center asked two questions of random samples of adults. Both questions stated that Social Security would be "fixed." Here are two questions about using the remaining surplus:

> Question A: *Should the money be used for a tax cut, or should it be used to fund new government programs?*
> Question B: *Should the money be used for a tax cut, or should it be spent on programs for education, the environment, health care, crime-fighting and military defense?*

One of these questions drew 60% favoring a tax cut. The other drew only 22%. Which wording pulls respondents toward a tax cut? Why?

CHAPTER 7 SUMMARY

■ A **sample survey** selects a **sample** from the **population** of all individuals about which we desire information. We base conclusions about the population on data from the sample. It is important to specify exactly what population you are interested in and what variables you will measure.

■ The **design** of a sample describes the method used to select the sample from the population. **Random sampling** designs use chance to select a sample.

■ The basic random sampling design is a **simple random sample (SRS).** An SRS gives every possible sample of a given size the same chance to be chosen.

■ Choose an SRS by labeling the members of the population and using **random digits** to select the sample. Software can automate this process.

■ Failure to use random sampling often results in **bias,** or systematic errors in the way the sample represents the population. **Voluntary response samples,** in which the respondents choose themselves, are particularly prone to large bias.

■ In human populations, even random samples can suffer from bias due to **undercoverage** or **nonresponse,** from **response bias,** or from misleading results due to **poorly worded questions.** Sample surveys must deal expertly with these potential problems in addition to using a random sampling design.

■ Most national sample surveys are carried out by telephone, using **random digit dialing** to choose residential telephone numbers at random. Call screening is increasing nonresponse to such surveys, and the rise of cell-phone-only households is increasing undercoverage.

CHECK YOUR SKILLS

7.13 An opinion poll contacts 1161 adults and asks them, "Which political party do you think has better ideas for leading the country in the twenty-first century?" In all, 696 of the 1161 say, "The Democrats." The sample in this setting is
(a) all 235 million adults in the United States.
(b) the 1161 people interviewed.
(c) the 696 people who chose the Democrats.

7.14 A committee on community relations in a college town plans to survey local businesses about the importance of students as customers. From telephone book listings, the committee chooses 150 businesses at random. Of these, 73 return the questionnaire mailed by the committee. The population for this study is
(a) all businesses in the college town.
(b) the 150 businesses chosen.
(c) the 73 businesses that returned the questionnaire.

7.15 The Web portal AOL places opinion poll questions next to many of its news stories. Simply click your response to join the sample. One of the questions in January 2008 was "Do you plan to diet this year?" More than 30,000 people responded, with 68% saying "Yes." You can conclude that

(a) about 68% of Americans planned to diet in 2008.
(b) the poll uses voluntary response, so the results tell us little about the population of all adults.
(c) the sample is too small to draw any conclusion.

7.16 You must choose an SRS of 10 of the 440 retail outlets in New York that sell your company's products. How would you label this population in order to use Table B?
(a) 001, 002, 003, …, 439, 440
(b) 000, 001, 002, …, 439, 440
(c) 1, 2, …, 439, 440

7.17 You are using the table of random digits to choose a simple random sample of 6 students from a class of 30 students. You label the students 01 to 30 in alphabetical order. Go to line 133 of Table B. Your sample contains the students labeled
(a) 45, 74, 04, 18, 07, 65.
(b) 04, 18, 07, 13, 02, 07.
(c) 04, 18, 07, 13, 02, 05.

7.18 You want to choose an SRS of 5 of the 7200 salaried employees of a corporation. You label the employees 0001 to 7200 in alphabetical order. Using line 111 of Table B, your sample contains the employees labeled

(a) 6694, 5130, 0041, 2712, 3827.
(b) 6694, 0513, 0929, 7004, 1271.
(c) 8148, 6694, 8760, 5130, 9297.

7.19 A sample of households in a community is selected at random from the telephone directory. In this community, 4% of households have no telephone, 10% have only cell phones, and another 25% have unlisted telephone numbers. The sample will certainly suffer from
(a) nonresponse.
(b) undercoverage.
(c) false responses.

CHAPTER 7 EXERCISES

In all exercises asking for an SRS, you may use either Table B or software.

7.20 Are you feeling stressed? A Gallup Poll asked, "In general, how often do you experience stress in your daily life—never, rarely, sometimes, or frequently?" Gallup's report said, "Results are based on telephone interviews with 1,027 national adults, aged 18 and older, conducted Dec. 6–9, 2007."[9] What is the population for this sample survey? What is the sample?

7.21 Sampling stuffed envelopes. A large retailer prepares its customers' monthly credit card bills using an automatic machine that folds the bills, stuffs them into envelopes, and seals the envelopes for mailing. Are the envelopes completely sealed? Inspectors choose 40 envelopes from the 1000 stuffed each hour for visual inspection. What is the population for this sample survey? What is the sample?

7.22 Do you trust the Internet? You want to ask a sample of college students the question "How much do you trust information about health that you find on the Internet—a great deal, somewhat, not much, or not at all?" You try out this and other questions on a pilot group of 10 students chosen from your class. The class members are

Anderson	Deng	Glaus	Nguyen	Samuels
Arroyo	De Ramos	Helling	Palmiero	Shen
Batista	Drasin	Husain	Percival	Tse
Bell	Eckstein	Johnson	Prince	Velasco
Burke	Fernandez	Kim	Puri	Wallace
Cabrera	Fullmer	Molina	Richards	Washburn
Calloway	Gandhi	Morgan	Rider	Zabidi
Delluci	Garcia	Murphy	Rodriguez	Zhao

Choose an SRS of 10 students. If you use Table B, start at line 117.

7.23 Sampling telephone area codes. There are approximately 341 active telephone area codes covering Canada, the United States, and some Caribbean areas. (More are created regularly.) Choose an SRS of 25 of these area codes for a study of available telephone numbers. (If you use Table B rather than software, start at line 129 and choose only the first 5 codes in the sample.)

7.24 Sampling the forest. To gather data on a 1200-acre pine forest in Louisiana, the U.S. Forest Service laid a grid of 1410 equally spaced circular plots over a map of the forest. A ground survey visited a sample of 10% of these plots.[10]
(a) How would you label the plots?
(b) Choose the first 5 plots in an SRS of 141 plots. (If you use Table B, start at line 105.)

7.25 Sampling pharmacists. All pharmacists in the Canadian province of Ontario are required to be members of the Ontario College of Pharmacists. The membership list contains 7500 names.
(a) How would you label the names in order to select an SRS?
(b) Use software or Table B, starting at line 142, to select an SRS of 10 Ontario pharmacists.

7.26 Random digits. In using Table B repeatedly to choose random samples, you should not always begin at the same place, such as line 101. Why not?

7.27 Random digits. Which of the following statements are true of a table of random digits, and which are false? Briefly explain your answers.
(a) There are exactly four 0s in each row of 40 digits.
(b) Each pair of digits has chance 1/100 of being 00.
(c) The digits 0000 can never appear as a group, because this pattern is not random.

7.28 Movie viewing. An opinion poll calls 2000 randomly chosen residential telephone numbers, then asks to speak with an adult member of the household. The interviewer asks, "How many movies have you watched in a movie theater in the past 12 months?"
(a) What population do you think the poll has in mind?
(b) In all, 831 people respond. What is the rate (percent) of nonresponse?
(c) What source of response error is likely for the question asked?

7.29 Online polls. Example 7.3 reports an online poll in which 97% of the respondents opposed issuing driver's licenses to illegal immigrants. National random samples taken at the same time showed about 70% of the respondents opposed to such licenses. Explain briefly to someone who knows no statistics why the random samples report public opinion more reliably than the online poll.

7.30 Nonresponse. Academic sample surveys, unlike commercial polls, often discuss nonresponse. In a survey of drivers, researchers called a random sample of all listed residential telephone numbers in the United States. Of 45,956 calls, 5029 were completed.[11] What was the rate of nonresponse for this sample? (Only one call was made to each number. Nonresponse would be lower if more calls were made.)

7.31 Running red lights. The sample described in the previous exercise produced a list of 5024 licensed drivers. The investigators then chose an SRS of 880 of these drivers to answer questions about their driving habits.
(a) How would you assign labels to the 5024 drivers? Use Table B, starting at line 104, to choose the first 5 drivers in the sample.
(b) One question asked was "Recalling the last ten traffic lights you drove through, how many of them were red when you entered the intersections?" Of the 880 respondents, 171 admitted that at least one light had been red. A practical problem with this survey is that people may not give truthful answers. What is the likely direction of the bias: do you think more or fewer than 171 of the 880 respondents really ran a red light? Why?

7.32 Seat belt use. A study in El Paso, Texas, looked at seat belt use by drivers. Drivers were observed at randomly chosen convenience stores. After they left their cars, they were invited to answer questions that included questions about seat belt use. In all, 75% said they always used seat belts, yet only 61.5% were wearing seat belts when they pulled into the store parking lots.[12] Explain the reason for the bias observed in responses to the survey. Do you expect bias in the same direction in most surveys about seat belt use?

7.33 Sampling at a party. At a party there are 30 students over age 21 and 20 students under age 21. You choose at random 3 of those over 21 and separately choose at random 2 of those under 21 to interview about attitudes toward alcohol. You have given every student at the party the same chance to be interviewed: what is that chance? Why is your sample not an SRS?

7.34 Stratified random samples. Cook County, Illinois, has the second-largest population of any county in the United States (after Los Angeles County, California). Cook County has 30 suburban townships and an additional 8 townships that make up the city of Chicago. The suburban townships are

Barrington	Hanover	Norwood Park	Riverside
Berwyn	Lemont	Oak Park	Schaumburg
Bloom	Leyden	Orland	Stickney
Bremen	Lyons	Palatine	Thornton
Calumet	Maine	Palos	Wheeling
Cicero	New Trier	Proviso	Worth
Elk Grove	Niles	Rich	
Evanston	Northfield	River Forest	

The Chicago townships are

Hyde Park	Lake	North Chicago	South Chicago
Jefferson	Lake View	Rogers Park	West Chicago

Because city and suburban areas may differ, the first stage of a multistage sample chooses an SRS of 6 suburban townships and a separate SRS of 4 of the more heavily populated Chicago townships. This is called a **stratified random sample:** divide the population into groups using information available in advance, then take separate SRSs in each group. Use Table B or software to choose this sample. (If you use Table B, assign labels in alphabetical order and start at line 101 for the suburbs and at line 110 for Chicago.)

7.35 Sampling at a party. At a large block party there are 290 men and 110 women. You want to ask for opinions about how to improve the next party. To be sure that women's opinions are adequately represented, you decide to choose a *stratified random sample* (see the previous exercise) of 20 men and 20 women. Explain how you will assign labels to the names of the people at the party. Give the labels of the first 3 men and the first 3 women in your sample. If you use Table B, start at line 130.

7.36 Systematic random samples. *Systematic random samples* go through a list of the population and choose individuals at fixed intervals from a randomly chosen starting point. For example, a study of dating among college students chose a systematic sample of 200 single male students at a university as follows.[13] Start with a list of all 9000 single male students. Because $9000/200 = 45$, choose one of the first 45 names on the list at random and then every 45th name after that. For example, if the first name chosen is at position 23, the systematic sample consists of the names at positions 23, 68, 113, 158, and so on up to 8978.
(a) Use Table B to choose a systematic random sample of 5 addresses from a list of 200. Enter the table at line 120.
(b) Like an SRS, a systematic sample gives all individuals the same chance to be chosen. Explain why this is true, then explain carefully why a systematic sample is nonetheless *not* an SRS.

7.37 Regulating guns. The National Gun Policy Survey asked respondents' opinions about government regulation of firearms. A report from the survey says, "Participating households were identified through random digit dialing; the respondent in each household was selected by the most-recent-birthday method."[14]
(a) What is random digit dialing? Why is it a practical method for obtaining (almost) an SRS of households with landline phones?
(b) The survey wants the opinion of an individual adult. Several adults may live in a household. In that case, the survey interviewed the adult with the most recent birthday. Why is this preferable to simply interviewing the person who answers the phone?

7.38 Wording survey questions. Comment on each of the following as a potential sample survey question. Is the question clear? Is it slanted toward a desired response?
(a) "Some cell phone users have developed brain cancer. Should all cell phones come with a warning label explaining the danger of using cell phones?"
(b) "Do you agree that a national system of health insurance should be favored because it would provide health insurance for everyone and would reduce administrative costs?"
(c) "In view of the negative externalities in parent labor force participation and pediatric evidence associating increased group size with morbidity of children in day care, do you support government subsidies for day care programs?"

7.39 Your own bad questions. Write your own examples of bad sample survey questions.
(a) Write a biased question designed to get one answer rather than another.
(b) Write a question to which many people may not give truthful answers.

7.40 Canada's national health care. The Ministry of Health in the Canadian province of Ontario wants to know whether the national health care system is achieving its goals in the province. Much information about health care comes from patient records, but that source doesn't allow us to compare people who use health services with those who don't. So the Ministry of Health conducted the Ontario Health Survey, which interviewed a random sample of 61,239 people who live in Ontario.[15]
(a) What is the population for this sample survey? What is the sample?
(b) The survey found that 76% of males and 86% of females in the sample had visited a general practitioner at least once in the past year. Do you think these estimates are close to the truth about the entire population? Why?

7.41 Polling Hispanics. A New York Times News Service article on a poll concerned with the opinions of Hispanics includes this paragraph:

> The poll was conducted by telephone from July 13 to 27, with 3,092 adults nationwide, 1,074 of whom described themselves as Hispanic. It has a margin of sampling error of plus or minus three percentage points for the entire poll and plus or minus four percentage points for Hispanics. Sample sizes for most Hispanic nationalities, like Cubans or Dominicans, were too small to break out the results separately.[16]

(a) Why is the "margin of sampling error" larger for Hispanics than for all 3092 respondents?
(b) Why would a very small sample size prevent a responsible news organization from breaking out results for Cubans separately?

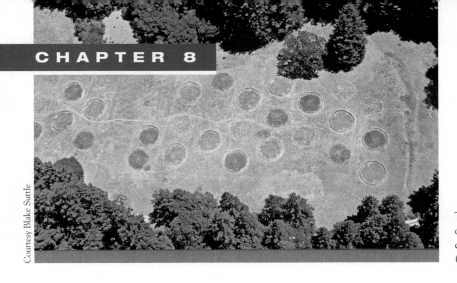

These circular plots are the site of an experiment on the effect of climate change in California (Exercise 8.9).

Courtesy Blake Suttle

Producing Data: Experiments

IN THIS CHAPTER WE COVER...

- Observation versus experiment
- Subjects, factors, treatments
- How to experiment badly
- Randomized comparative experiments
- The logic of randomized comparative experiments
- Cautions about experimentation
- Matched pairs designs

A sample survey aims to gather information about a population without disturbing the population in the process. Sample surveys are one kind of *observational study*. Other observational studies observe the behavior of animals in the wild or the interactions between teacher and students in the classroom. This chapter is about statistical designs for *experiments*, a quite different way to produce data.

Observation versus experiment

Experiments don't just observe individuals or ask them questions. They actively impose some treatment in order to observe the response. Experiments can answer questions such as "Does aspirin reduce the chance of a heart attack?" and "Do a majority of college students prefer Pepsi to Coke when they taste both without knowing which they are drinking?"

OBSERVATION VERSUS EXPERIMENT

An **observational study** observes individuals and measures variables of interest but does not attempt to influence the responses. The purpose of an observational study is to describe some group or situation.

An **experiment,** on the other hand, deliberately imposes some treatment on individuals in order to observe their responses. The purpose of an experiment is to study whether the treatment causes a change in the response.

An observational study, even one based on a statistical sample, is a poor way to gauge the effect of a treatment. To see the response to a change, we must actually impose the change. *When our goal is to understand cause and effect, experiments are the only source of fully convincing data.* For this reason, the distinction between observation and experiment is one of the most important in statistics.

EXAMPLE 8.1 **Drink a little, but not a lot**

Many observational studies show that people who drink a moderate amount of alcohol have less heart disease than people who drink no alcohol or who drink heavily.[1] ("Moderate" means one or two drinks a day for men and one drink a day for women.) Is this *association* good reason to think that moderate drinking actually *causes* less heart disease? People who choose to drink in moderation are, as a group, different from both heavy drinkers and abstainers. They are more likely to maintain a healthy weight, get enough sleep, and exercise regularly. Moderate drinkers may be healthier because of these healthy habits rather than because of the effect of alcohol on health.

It is easy to imagine an experiment that would settle the issue of whether moderate drinking really *causes* reduced heart disease. Choose half of a large group of adults at random to be the "treatment" group. The remaining half becomes the "control" group. Require the treatment group to have one alcoholic drink every day. Require the control group to abstain from alcohol. Follow both groups for a decade. This experiment isolates the effect of alcohol. Of course, it isn't practical to carry out such an experiment. ■

The point of Example 8.1 is the contrast between observing people who choose for themselves what to drink and an experiment that requires some people to drink and others to abstain. When we simply observe people's drinking choices, the effect of moderate drinking is *confounded* with (mixed up with) the characteristics of people who choose to drink in moderation. These characteristics are lurking variables (see page 104) that make it hard to see the true relationship between the explanatory and response variables. Figure 8.1 shows the confounding in picture form.

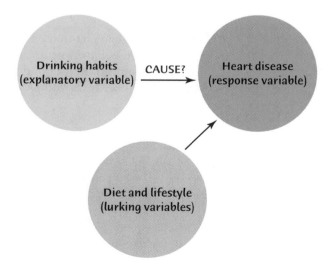

FIGURE 8.1

Confounding: We can't distinguish the effects of drinking habits from the effects of overall diet and lifestyle.

> **CONFOUNDING**
>
> Two variables (explanatory variables or lurking variables) are **confounded** when their effects on a response variable cannot be distinguished from each other.

Observational studies of the effect of one variable on another often fail because the explanatory variable is confounded with lurking variables. Well-designed experiments take steps to prevent confounding.

APPLY YOUR KNOWLEDGE

8.1 Cell phones and brain cancer. A study of cell phones and the risk of brain cancer looked at a group of 469 people who have brain cancer. The investigators matched each cancer patient with a person of the same sex, age, and race who did not have brain cancer, then asked about use of cell phones.[2] Result: "Our data suggest that use of handheld cellular telephones is not associated with risk of brain cancer." Is this an observational study or an experiment? Why? What are the explanatory and response variables?

8.2 Teaching economics. An educational software company wants to compare the effectiveness of its computer animation for teaching about supply and demand curves with that of a textbook presentation. The company tests the economic knowledge of a number of first-year college students, then divides them into two groups. One group uses the animation, and the other studies the text. The company retests all the students and compares the increase in economic understanding in the two groups. Is this an experiment? Why or why not? What are the explanatory and response variables?

8.3 Effects of binge drinking. A common definition of "binge drinking" is 5 or more drinks at one setting for men, and 4 or more for women. An observational study finds that students who binge have lower average GPA than those who don't. Suggest some lurking variables that may be confounded with binge drinking. The possibility of confounding means that we can't conclude that binge drinking *causes* lower GPA.

Subjects, factors, treatments

A study is an experiment when we actually do something to people, animals, or objects in order to observe the response. Because the purpose of an experiment is to reveal the response of one variable to changes in other variables, the distinction between explanatory and response variables is essential. Here is the basic vocabulary of experiments.

> **SUBJECTS, FACTORS, TREATMENTS**
>
> The **individuals** studied in an experiment are often called **subjects,** particularly when they are people.
>
> The explanatory variables in an experiment are often called **factors.**
>
> A **treatment** is any specific experimental condition applied to the subjects. If an experiment has more than one factor, a treatment is a combination of specific values of each factor.

EXAMPLE 8.2 **Foster care versus orphanages**

Do abandoned children placed in foster homes do better than similar children placed in an institution? The Bucharest Early Intervention Project found that the answer is a clear "Yes." The *subjects* were 136 young children abandoned at birth and living in orphanages in Bucharest, Romania. Half of the children, chosen at random, were placed in foster homes (paid for by the study). The other half remained in the orphanages. The experiment compared these two *treatments*. There is a single *factor* type of care, (foster versus institutional care). The *response variables* included measures of mental and physical development.[3] ▧

EXAMPLE 8.3 **Effects of TV advertising**

What are the effects of watching an ad on TV? The answer may depend both on the length of the ad and on how often it is repeated. An experiment investigated this question using undergraduate students as *subjects*. All subjects viewed a 40-minute television program that included ads for a digital camera. Some subjects saw a 30-second commercial; others, a 90-second version. The same commercial was shown either 1, 3, or 5 times during the program.

This experiment has two *factors*: length of the commercial, with 2 values, and repetitions, with 3 values. The 6 combinations of one value of each factor form 6 *treatments*. Figure 8.2 shows the layout of the treatments. After viewing, all of the subjects answered questions about their recall of the ad, their attitude toward the camera, and their intention to purchase it. These are the *response variables*. ▧

FIGURE 8.2

The treatments in the experimental design of Example 8.3. Combinations of values of the two factors form six treatments.

Examples 8.2 and 8.3 illustrate the advantages of experiments over observational studies. In an experiment, we can study the effects of the specific treatments we are interested in. By assigning subjects to treatments, we can avoid confounding. For example, observational studies of the effects of foster homes versus institutions on the development of children have often been biased because healthier or more alert children tend to be placed in homes. The random assignment in Example 8.2 eliminates bias in placing the children. Moreover, we can control the environment of the subjects to hold constant factors that are of no interest to us, such as the specific product advertised in Example 8.3.

APPLY YOUR KNOWLEDGE

For each of the following experiments, identify the subjects, the factors, the treatments, and the response variables.

8.4 Ginkgo extract and the post-lunch dip. The post-lunch dip is the drop in mental alertness after a midday meal. Does an extract of the leaves of the ginkgo tree reduce the post-lunch dip? Assign healthy people aged 18 to 40 to take either ginkgo extract or a placebo pill. After lunch, ask them to read seven pages of random letters and place an X over every *e*. Count the number of misses.

8.5 Growing in the shade. Ability to grow in shade may help pines in the dry forests of Arizona resist drought. How well do these pines grow in shade? Plant pine seedlings in a greenhouse in either full light, light reduced to 25% of normal by shade cloth, or light reduced to 5% of normal. At the end of the study, dry the young trees and weigh them.

8.6 Exercise and heart rate. A student project measured the increase in the heart rates of fellow students when they stepped up and down for three minutes to the beat of a metronome. The step was either 5.75 inches or 11.5 inches high and the metronome beat was either 14, 21, or 28 steps per minute. Five students stepped at each combination of height and speed. (Use a diagram like Figure 8.2 to display the factors and treatments.)

Howard Bjornson/Getty Images

How to experiment badly

Statistical designs are often essential for effective experiments. To see why, let's look at an example in which an experiment suffers from confounding.

EXAMPLE 8.4 An uncontrolled experiment

A college offers a review course to prepare candidates for the Graduate Management Admission Test (GMAT). This year, it offers only an online version of the course. The average GMAT score of students in the online course is 10% higher than the longtime average for those who took the classroom review course. Is the online course more effective?

This experiment has a very simple design. A group of subjects (the students) were exposed to a treatment (the online course), and the outcome (GMAT scores) was observed. Here is the design:

$$\text{Subjects} \longrightarrow \text{Online course} \longrightarrow \text{GMAT scores}$$

The students in the online review course were different from the students who in past years took the classroom course—they were older and more likely to be employed. We can't compare the performance of these mature students with that of the undergraduates who previously dominated the course. The online course might even be less effective than the classroom version. The effect of online versus in-class instruction is confounded with the effect of lurking variables. ∎

Most laboratory experiments use a design like that in Example 8.4:

$$\text{Subjects} \longrightarrow \text{Treatment} \longrightarrow \text{Measure response}$$

In the controlled environment of the laboratory, simple designs often work well. Field experiments and experiments with living subjects are exposed to more variable conditions and deal with more variable subjects. *Outside the laboratory, uncontrolled experiments often yield worthless results because of confounding with lurking variables.*

8.7 Reducing unemployment. Will cash bonuses speed the return to work of unemployed people? A state department of labor notes that last year 68% of people who filed claims for unemployment insurance found a new job within 15 weeks. As an experiment, the state offers $500 to people filing unemployment claims if they find a job within 15 weeks. The percent who do so increases to 77%. Suggest some conditions that might make it easier or harder to find a job this year as opposed to last year. Confounding with these lurking variables makes it impossible to say whether the bonus really caused the increase.

Randomized comparative experiments

control group

The remedy for the confounding in Example 8.4 is to do a *comparative experiment* in which some students are taught in the classroom and other, similar students take the course online. The first group is called a **control group.** Most well-designed experiments compare two or more treatments.

Comparison alone isn't enough to produce results we can trust. If the treatments are given to groups that differ markedly when the experiment begins, bias will result. For example, if we allow students to elect online or classroom instruction, students who are older and employed are likely to sign up for the online course. Personal choice will bias our results in the same way that volunteers bias the results of online opinion polls. The solution to the problem of bias in sampling is random selection, and the same is true in experiments. The subjects assigned to any treatment should be chosen at random from the available subjects.

> **RANDOMIZED COMPARATIVE EXPERIMENT**
>
> An experiment that uses both comparison of two or more treatments and random assignment of subjects to treatments is a **randomized comparative experiment.**

EXAMPLE 8.5 On-campus versus online

The college decides to compare the progress of 25 on-campus students taught in the classroom with that of 25 students taught the same material online. Select the students who will be taught online by taking a simple random sample of size 25 from the 50 available subjects. The remaining 25 students form the control group. They will receive classroom instruction. The result is a randomized comparative experiment with two groups. Figure 8.3 outlines the design in graphical form.

The selection procedure is exactly the same as it is for sampling. **Label:** Label the 50 students 01 to 50. **Table:** Go to the table of random digits and read successive two-digit groups. The first 25 labels encountered select the online group. As usual, ignore repeated

FIGURE 8.3
Outline of a randomized comparative experiment to compare online and classroom instruction, for Example 8.5.

labels and groups of digits not used as labels. For example, if you begin at line 125 in Table B, the first five students chosen are those labeled 21, 49, 37, 18, and 44. You can also use software to choose treatment groups at random. ■

The design in Example 8.5 is *comparative* because it compares two treatments (the two instructional settings). It is *randomized* because the subjects are assigned to the treatments by chance. This "flowchart" outline in Figure 8.3 presents all the essentials: randomization, the sizes of the groups and which treatment they receive, and the response variable. We call designs like that in Figure 8.3 *completely randomized*.

COMPLETELY RANDOMIZED DESIGN

In a **completely randomized** experimental design, all the subjects are allocated at random among all the treatments.

Completely randomized designs can compare any number of treatments. Here is an example that compares three treatments.

EXAMPLE 8.6 Conserving energy

How can an electric company encourage energy conservation among its customers? One approach places small digital displays in households that show what the cost would be if current electricity use continued for a month. Will the displays reduce electricity use? Would cheaper methods work almost as well? The company decides to conduct an experiment.

One cheaper approach is to give customers a chart and information about monitoring their electricity use from their outside meter. The experiment compares these two approaches (display, chart) and also a control. The control group of customers receives information about energy conservation but no help in monitoring electricity use. The response variable is total electricity used in a year. The company finds 60 single-family residences in the same city willing to participate, so it assigns 20 residences at random to each of the three treatments. Figure 8.4 outlines the design.

To use Table B, label the 60 households 01 to 60. Enter the table to select an SRS of 20 to receive the displays. Continue in Table B, selecting 20 more to receive charts. The remaining 20 form the control group. ■

Examples 8.5 and 8.6 describe completely randomized designs that compare values of a single factor. In Example 8.5, the factor is the type of instruction. In Example 8.6, it is

FIGURE 8.4

Outline of a completely randomized design comparing three energy-saving programs, for Example 8.6.

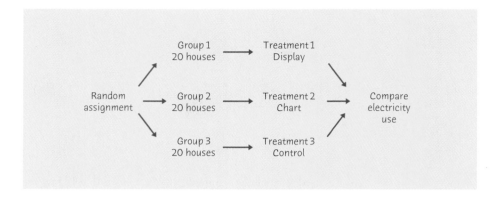

the method used to encourage energy conservation. Completely randomized designs can have more than one factor. The advertising experiment of Example 8.3 has two factors: the length and the number of repetitions of a television commercial. Their combinations form the six treatments outlined in Figure 8.2. A completely randomized design assigns subjects at random to these six treatments. Once the layout of treatments is set, the randomization needed for a completely randomized design is tedious but straightforward.

APPLY YOUR KNOWLEDGE

8.8 Evaluating your own performance. Undergraduate music students often don't evaluate their own performances accurately. Can small-group discussions help? The subjects were 29 students preparing for an end-of-semester performance. Assign 15 students to the treatment: videotape a practice performance, ask the student to evaluate it, then have the student discuss the tape with a small group of other students. The remaining 14 students form a control group who watch and evaluate their tapes alone. At the end of the semester, the discussion-group students evaluated their final performance more accurately.[4]

(a) Outline the design of this experiment, following the model of Figure 8.3.

(b) Carry out the random assignment of 15 students to the treatment group, using software or Table B, starting at line 132.

8.9 More rain for California? The changing climate will probably bring more rain to California, but we don't know whether the additional rain will come during the winter wet season or extend into the long dry season in spring and summer. Kenwyn Suttle of the University of California at Berkeley and his coworkers carried out a randomized controlled experiment to study the effects of more rain in either season. They randomly assigned plots of open grassland to 3 treatments: added water equal to 20% of annual rainfall either during January to March (winter) or during April to June (spring), and no added water (control). Thirty-six circular plots of area 70 square meters were available (see the photo), of which 18 were used for this study. One response variable was total plant biomass, in grams per square meter, produced in a plot over a year.[5]

(a) Outline the design of the experiment, following the model of Figure 8.4.

(b) Number all 36 plots and choose 6 at random for each of the 3 treatments. Be sure to explain how you did the random selection.

Courtesy Blake Suttle

8.10 Effects of TV advertising. Figure 8.2 (page 148) displays the 6 treatments for the two-factor experiment on TV advertising described in Example 8.3. The 36 students named below will serve as subjects. Outline the design and randomly assign the subjects to the 6 treatments. If you use Table B, start at line 130.

Alomar	Denman	Han	Liang	Padilla	Valasco
Asihiro	Durr	Howard	Maldonado	Plochman	Vaughn
Bennett	Edwards	Hruska	Marsden	Rosen	Wei
Bikalis	Farouk	Imrani	Montoya	Solomon	Wilder
Chao	Fleming	James	O'Brian	Trujillo	Willis
Clemente	George	Kaplan	Ogle	Tullock	Zhang

The logic of randomized comparative experiments

Randomized comparative experiments are designed to give good evidence that differences in the treatments actually *cause* the differences we see in the response. The logic is as follows:

- Random assignment of subjects forms groups that should be similar in all respects before the treatments are applied.
- Comparative design ensures that influences other than the experimental treatments operate equally on all groups.
- Therefore, differences in average response must be due either to the treatments or to the play of chance in the random assignment of subjects to the treatments.

Be careful about that "either-or." In Example 8.5, we cannot say that *any* difference between the average GMAT scores of students enrolled online and in the classroom must be caused by a difference in the effectiveness of the two types of instruction. There would be some difference even if both groups received the same instruction, because of variation among students in background and study habits. Chance assigns students to one group or the other, and this creates a chance difference between the groups. If we assign many subjects to each group, the effects of chance will average out and there will be little difference in the average responses in the two groups unless the treatments themselves cause a difference. "Use enough subjects to reduce chance variation" is the third big idea of statistical design of experiments.

PRINCIPLES OF EXPERIMENTAL DESIGN

The basic principles of statistical design of experiments are

1. **Control** the effects of lurking variables on the response, most simply by comparing two or more treatments.
2. **Randomize**—use chance to assign subjects to treatments.
3. **Use enough subjects** in each group to reduce chance variation in the results.

We hope to see a difference in the responses so large that it is unlikely to happen just because of chance variation. We can use the laws of probability, which describe chance behavior, to learn if the treatment effects are larger than we would expect to see if only chance were operating. If they are, we call them *statistically significant*.

STATISTICAL SIGNIFICANCE

An observed effect so large that it would rarely occur by chance is called **statistically significant.**

If we observe statistically significant differences among the groups in a randomized comparative experiment, we have good evidence that the treatments actually caused these differences. You will often see the phrase "statistically significant" in reports of investigations in many fields of study.

APPLY YOUR KNOWLEDGE

8.11 Prayer and meditation. You read in a magazine that "nonphysical treatments such as meditation and prayer have been shown to be effective in controlled scientific studies for such ailments as high blood pressure, insomnia, ulcers, and asthma." Explain in simple language what the article means by "controlled scientific studies." Why can such studies in principle provide good evidence that, for example, meditation is an effective treatment for high blood pressure?

8.12 Conserving energy. Example 8.6 describes an experiment to learn whether providing households with digital displays or charts will reduce their electricity consumption. An executive of the electric company objects to including a control group. He says: "It would be simpler to just compare electricity use last year (before the display or chart was provided) with consumption in the same period this year. If households use less electricity this year, the display or chart must be working." Explain clearly why this design is inferior to that in Example 8.6.

8.13 Arsenic and lung cancer. Arsenic is frequently found both in the natural environment and in food. A study of the relationship between arsenic in drinking water and deaths from lung cancer measured arsenic levels in drinking water in 138 villages in Taiwan and examined death certificates to identify lung cancer deaths. The study summary says that "arsenic levels above 0.64 mg/l were associated with a significant increase in the mortality of lung cancer in both genders, but no significant effect was observed at lower levels."[6]

(a) Explain why this is an observational study rather than an experiment.

(b) The word "significant" in the conclusion has its statistical meaning, not its everyday meaning. Restate the study conclusion without using the word "significant" in a way that is clear to readers who know no statistics.

Cautions about experimentation

The logic of a randomized comparative experiment depends on our ability to treat all the subjects identically in every way except for the actual treatments being compared. Good experiments therefore require careful attention to details to ensure that all subjects really are treated identically.

EXAMPLE 8.7 **Vitamin E and heart disease**

Will daily doses of vitamin E reduce the risk of heart disease? Divide the subjects at random into two groups. All of the subjects receive the same medical attention during the several years of the experiment. All of them take a pill every day, vitamin E in the treatment group and a dummy pill (called a *placebo*) in the control group. Many patients respond favorably to any treatment, even a placebo, perhaps because they trust the doctor. The response to a dummy treatment is called the *placebo effect*. If the control group did not take any pills, the effect of vitamin E in the treatment group would be confounded with the placebo effect, the effect of simply taking pills.

In addition, the experiment is *double-blind*. The subjects don't know whether they are taking vitamin E or a placebo. Neither do the medical personnel who work with them. The double-blind method avoids unconscious bias by, for example, a doctor who is convinced that a vitamin must be better than a placebo. ■

THE PLACEBO AND DOUBLE-BLIND METHODS

A **placebo** is a dummy treatment. Experiments in medicine and psychology often give a placebo to a control group because just being in an experiment can affect responses.

In a **double-blind** experiment, neither the subjects nor the people who interact with them know which treatment each subject is receiving.

Even well-designed experiments often face another problem: **lack of realism.** Practical constraints may mean that the subjects or treatments or setting of an experiment don't realistically duplicate the conditions we really want to study. Here are two examples.

lack of realism

EXAMPLE 8.8 **Response to advertising**

The study of television advertising in Example 8.3 showed a 40-minute video to students who knew an experiment was going on. We can't be sure that the results apply to everyday television viewers. Many behavioral science experiments use as subjects students or other volunteers who know they are subjects in an experiment. That's not a realistic setting. ■

EXAMPLE 8.9 **Center brake lights**

Do those high center brake lights, required on all cars sold in the United States since 1986, really reduce rear-end collisions? Randomized comparative experiments with fleets of rental and business cars, done before the lights were required, showed that the third brake light reduced rear-end collisions by as much as 50%. Alas, requiring the third light in all cars led to only a 5% drop.

What happened? Most cars did not have the extra brake light when the experiments were carried out, so it caught the eye of following drivers. Now that almost all cars have the third light, they no longer capture attention. ■

Lack of realism can limit our ability to apply the conclusions of an experiment to the settings of greatest interest. Most experimenters want to generalize their conclusions to some setting wider than that of the actual experiment. *Statistical analysis of an experiment cannot tell us how far the results will generalize*. Nonetheless, the randomized comparative experiment, because of its ability to give convincing evidence for causation, is one of the most important ideas in statistics.

8.14 Testosterone for older men. As men age, their testosterone levels gradually decrease. This may cause a reduction in lean body mass, an increase in fat, and other undesirable changes. Do testosterone supplements reverse some of these effects? A study in the Netherlands assigned 237 men aged 60 to 80 with low or low-normal testosterone levels to either a testosterone supplement or a placebo. The report in the *Journal of the American Medical Association* described the study as a "double-blind, randomized, placebo-controlled trial."[7] Explain each of these terms to someone who knows no statistics.

8.15 Does meditation reduce anxiety? An experiment that claimed to show that meditation reduces anxiety proceeded as follows. The experimenter interviewed the subjects and rated their level of anxiety. Then the subjects were randomly assigned to two groups. The experimenter taught one group how to meditate and they meditated daily for a month. The other group was simply told to relax more. At the end of the month, the experimenter interviewed all the subjects again and rated their anxiety level. The meditation group now had less anxiety. Psychologists said that the results were suspect because the ratings were not blind. Explain what this means and how lack of blindness could bias the reported results.

Matched pairs designs

Completely randomized designs are the simplest statistical designs for experiments. They illustrate clearly the principles of control, randomization, and adequate number of subjects. However, more elaborate designs are common. In particular, matching the subjects in various ways can produce more precise results than simple randomization. One common design that combines matching with randomization is the *matched pairs design*.

MATCHED PAIRS DESIGN

A **matched pairs design** compares two treatments. Choose pairs of subjects that are as closely matched as possible. Use chance to decide which subject in a pair gets the first treatment. The other subject in that pair gets the other treatment.

Sometimes each "pair" in a matched pairs design consists of just one subject, who gets both treatments one after the other. Use chance to decide the order in which subjects receive the treatments.

Royalty Free/CORBIS

EXAMPLE 8.10 **Cell phones and driving**

Does talking on a hands-free cell phone distract drivers? Undergraduate students "drove" in a high-fidelity driving simulator equipped with a hands-free cell phone. The car ahead brakes: how quickly does the subject react? Let's compare two designs for this experiment. There are 40 student subjects available.

In a *completely randomized design*, all 40 subjects are assigned at random, 20 to simply drive and the other 20 to talk on the cell phone while driving. In the *matched pairs design* that was actually used, all subjects drive both with and without using the cell phone. The two drives are on separate days to reduce carryover effects. The *order* of the two treatments is assigned at random: 20 subjects are chosen to drive first with the phone, and the remaining 20 drive first without the phone.[8]

Some subjects naturally react faster than others. The completely randomized design relies on chance to distribute the faster subjects roughly evenly between the two groups. The matched pairs design compares each subject's reaction time with and without the cell phone. This makes it easier to see the effects of using the phone. ▪

Matched pairs designs use the principles of comparison of treatments and randomization. However, the randomization is not complete—we do not randomly assign all the subjects at once to the two treatments. Instead, we randomize only within each matched pair. This allows matching to reduce the effect of variation among the subjects.

Like the design of samples, the design of complex experiments is a job for experts. Now that we have seen a bit of what is involved, we will concentrate for the most part on completely randomized experiments.

APPLY YOUR KNOWLEDGE

8.16 Comparing hand strength. Is the right hand generally stronger than the left in right-handed people? You can crudely measure hand strength by placing a bathroom scale on a shelf with the end protruding, then squeezing the scale between the thumb below and the four fingers above it. The reading of the scale shows the force exerted. Describe the design of a matched pairs experiment to compare the strength of the right and left hands, using 10 right-handed people as subjects. (You need not actually do the randomization.)

8.17 How long did I work? A psychologist wants to know if the difficulty of a task influences our estimate of how long we spend working at it. She designs two sets of mazes that subjects can work through on a computer. One set has easy mazes and the other has hard mazes. Subjects work until told to stop. They are then asked to estimate how long they worked. The psychologist has 30 students available to serve as subjects.

(a) Describe the design of a completely randomized experiment to learn the effect of difficulty on estimated time.

(b) Describe the design of a matched pairs experiment using the same 30 subjects.

CHAPTER 8 SUMMARY

▪ We can produce data intended to answer specific questions by **observational studies** or **experiments.** Sample surveys that select a part of a population to represent the whole are one type of observational study. **Experiments,** unlike observational studies, actively impose some treatment on the subjects of the experiment.

▪ Variables are **confounded** when their effects on a response can't be distinguished from each other. Observational studies and uncontrolled experiments often fail to show that changes in an explanatory variable actually cause changes in a response variable because the explanatory variable is confounded with lurking variables.

- In an experiment, we impose one or more **treatments** on individuals, often called **subjects.** Each treatment is a combination of values of the explanatory variables, which we call **factors.**

- The **design** of an experiment describes the choice of treatments and the manner in which the subjects are assigned to the treatments. The basic principles of statistical design of experiments are **control** and **randomization** to combat bias and **using enough subjects** to reduce chance variation.

- The simplest form of control is **comparison.** Experiments should compare two or more treatments in order to avoid confounding of the effect of a treatment with other influences, such as lurking variables.

- **Randomization** uses chance to assign subjects to the treatments. Randomization creates treatment groups that are similar (except for chance variation) before the treatments are applied. Randomization and comparison together prevent **bias,** or systematic favoritism, in experiments.

- You can carry out randomization by using software or by giving numerical labels to the subjects and using a **table of random digits** to choose treatment groups.

- Applying each treatment to many subjects reduces the role of chance variation and makes the experiment more sensitive to differences among the treatments.

- Good experiments require attention to detail as well as good statistical design. Many behavioral and medical experiments are **double-blind.** Some give a **placebo** to a control group. **Lack of realism** in an experiment can prevent us from generalizing its results.

- **A matched pairs design** compares just two treatments. In some matched pairs designs, each subject receives both treatments in a random order. In others, the subjects are matched in pairs as closely as possible, and each subject in a pair receives one of the treatments.

CHECK YOUR SKILLS

8.18 The Nurses' Health Study has interviewed a sample of more than 100,000 female registered nurses every two years since 1976. The study finds that "light-to-moderate drinkers had a significantly lower risk of death" than either nondrinkers or heavy drinkers. The Nurses' Health Study is
(a) an observational study.
(b) an experiment.
(c) Can't tell without more information.

8.19 Can changing diet reduce high blood pressure? Vegetarian diets and low-salt diets are both promising. Men with high blood pressure are assigned at random to four diets: (1) normal diet with unrestricted salt; (2) vegetarian with unrestricted salt; (3) normal with restricted salt; and (4) vegetarian with restricted salt. This experiment has
(a) one factor, the choice of diet.
(b) two factors, normal/vegetarian diet and unrestricted/restricted salt.
(c) four factors, the four diets being compared.

8.20 In the experiment of the previous exercise, the 240 subjects are labeled 001 to 240. Software assigns an SRS of 60 subjects to Diet 1, an SRS of 60 of the remaining 180 to Diet 2, and an SRS of 60 of the remaining 120 to Diet 3. The 60 who are left get Diet 4. This is a
(a) completely randomized design.
(b) a stratified random sample.
(c) matched pairs design.

8.21 A medical experiment compares an antidepression medicine with a placebo for relief of chronic headaches. There are 36 headache patients available to serve as subjects. To choose 18 patients to receive the medicine, you would
(a) assign labels 01 to 36 and use Table B to choose 18.
(b) assign labels 01 to 18, because only 18 need to be chosen.
(c) assign the first 18 who signed up to get the medicine.

8.22 The Community Intervention Trial for Smoking Cessation asked whether a community-wide advertising campaign would reduce smoking. The researchers located 11 pairs of communities, each pair similar in location, size, economic status,

and so on. One community in each pair participated in the advertising campaign and the other did not. This is
(a) an observational study.
(b) a matched pairs experiment.
(c) a completely randomized experiment.

8.23 To decide which community in each pair in the previous exercise should get the advertising campaign, it is best to
(a) toss a coin.
(b) choose the community that will help pay for the campaign.
(c) choose the community with a mayor who will participate.

8.24 A marketing class designs two videos advertising a Mercedes sports car. They test the videos by asking fellow students to view both (in random order) and say which makes them more likely to buy the car. Mercedes should be reluctant to agree that the video favored in this study will sell more cars because
(a) the study used a matched pairs design instead of a completely randomized design.
(b) results from students may not generalize to the older and richer customers who might buy a Mercedes.
(c) this is an observational study, not an experiment.

CHAPTER 8 EXERCISES

In all exercises that require randomization, you may use either Table B or software.

8.25 Alcohol and heart attacks. Many studies have found that people who drink alcohol in moderation have lower risk of heart attacks than either nondrinkers or heavy drinkers. Does alcohol consumption also improve survival after a heart attack? One study followed 1913 people who were hospitalized after severe heart attacks. In the year before their heart attacks, 47% of these people did not drink, 36% drank moderately, and 17% drank heavily. After four years, fewer of the moderate drinkers had died.[9]
(a) Is this an observational study or an experiment? Why? What are the explanatory and response variables?
(b) Suggest some lurking variables that may be confounded with the drinking habits of the subjects. The possible confounding makes it difficult to conclude that drinking habits explain death rates.

8.26 Reducing nonresponse. How can we reduce the rate of refusals in telephone surveys? Most people who answer at all listen to the interviewer's introductory remarks and then decide whether to continue. One study made telephone calls to randomly selected households to ask opinions about the next election. In some calls, the interviewer gave her name,

in others she identified the university she was representing, and in still others she identified both herself and the university. The study recorded what percent of each group of interviews was completed. Is this an observational study or an experiment? Why? What are the explanatory and response variables?

8.27 Samples versus experiments. Give an example of a question about college students, their behavior, or their opinions that would best be answered by
(a) a sample survey.
(b) an experiment.

8.28 Observation versus experiment. Observational studies had suggested that vitamin E reduces the risk of heart disease. Careful experiments, however, showed that vitamin E has no effect. According to a commentary in the *Journal of the American Medical Association*:

> Thus, vitamin E enters the category of therapies that were promising in epidemiologic and observational studies but failed to deliver in adequately powered randomized controlled trials. As in other studies, the "healthy user" bias must be considered, ie, the healthy lifestyle behaviors that characterize individuals who care enough about their health to take various supplements are actually responsible for the better health, but this is minimized with the rigorous trial design.[10]

A friend who knows no statistics asks you to explain this.
(a) What is the difference between observational studies and experiments?
(b) What is a "randomized controlled trial"?
(c) How does "healthy user bias" explain how people who take vitamin E supplements have better health in observational studies but not in controlled experiments?

8.29 Attitudes toward homeless people. Are attitudes toward poor people more negative when a person is homeless? To find out, read to subjects a description of a poor person. There are two versions. One begins

> Jim is a 30-year-old single man. He is currently living in a small single-room apartment.

The other description begins

> Jim is a 30-year-old single man. He is currently homeless and lives in a shelter for homeless people.

After reading the description, ask subjects what they believe about Jim and what they think should be done to help him. The subjects are 544 adults interviewed by telephone.[11] Outline the design of this experiment.

8.30 Getting teachers to come to school. Elementary schools in rural India are usually small, with a single teacher. The teachers often fail to show up for work. Here is an idea for improving attendance: give the teacher a digital camera with a tamper-proof time and date stamp and ask a student to take a photo of the teacher and class at the beginning and end of the day. Offer the teacher better pay for good attendance verified by the photos. Will this work? A randomized comparative experiment started with 120 rural schools in Rajasthan and assigned 60 to this treatment and 60 to a control group. Random checks for teacher attendance showed that 21% of teachers in the treatment group were absent, as opposed to 42% in the control group.[12]
(a) Outline the design of this experiment.
(b) Label the schools and choose the first 10 schools for the treatment group. If you use Table B, start at line 108.

8.31 Marijuana and work. How does smoking marijuana affect willingness to work? Canadian researchers persuaded young adult men who used marijuana to live for 98 days in a "planned environment." One group smoked two potent marijuana cigarettes every evening. The other group smoked two weak marijuana cigarettes. All subjects could buy more cigarettes but were given strong or weak cigarettes depending on their group. Did the weak and strong groups differ in work output?[13]
(a) Outline the design of this experiment.
(b) Here are the names of the 20 subjects. Use software or Table B at line 131 to carry out the randomization your design requires.

Abate	Dubois	Gutierrez	Lucero	Rosen
Afifi	Engel	Huang	McNeill	Thompson
Brown	Fluharty	Iselin	Morse	Travers
Cheng	Gerson	Kaplan	Quinones	Ullmann

8.32 The benefits of red wine. Some people think that red wine protects moderate drinkers from heart disease better than other alcoholic beverages. This calls for a randomized comparative experiment. The subjects were healthy men aged 35 to 65. They were randomly assigned to drink red wine (9 subjects), drink white wine (9 subjects), drink white wine and also take polyphenols from red wine (6 subjects), take polyphenols alone (9 subjects), or drink vodka and lemonade (6 subjects).[14] Outline the design of the experiment and randomly assign the 39 subjects to the 5 groups. If you use Table B, start at line 107.

8.33 Fabric finishing. A maker of fabric for clothing is setting up a new line to "finish" the raw fabric. The line will use either metal rollers or natural-bristle rollers to raise the surface of the fabric; a dyeing cycle time of either 30 minutes or 40 minutes; and a temperature of either 150°C or 175°C. An experiment will compare all combinations of these choices. Three specimens of fabric will be subjected to each treatment and scored for quality.
(a) What are the factors and the treatments? How many individuals (fabric specimens) does the experiment require?
(b) Outline a completely randomized design for this experiment. (You need not actually do the randomization.)

8.34 Relieving headaches. Can antidepressant medications or stress management training reduce the number and severity of chronic headaches? Are both together more effective than either alone?
(a) Use a diagram like Figure 8.2 to display the treatments in a design with two factors: "medication, yes or no" and "stress management, yes or no." Then outline the design of a completely randomized experiment to compare these treatments.
(b) The headache sufferers named below have agreed to participate in the study. Randomly assign the subjects to the treatments. If you use software, assign all the subjects. If you use Table B, start at line 130 and assign subjects to only the first treatment group.

Abbott	Decker	Herrera	Lucero	Richter
Abdalla	Devlin	Hersch	Masters	Riley
Alawi	Engel	Hurwitz	Morgan	Samuels
Broden	Fuentes	Irwin	Nelson	Smith
Chai	Garrett	Jiang	Nho	Suarez
Chuang	Gill	Kelley	Ortiz	Upasani
Cordoba	Glover	Kim	Ramdas	Wilson
Custer	Hammond	Landers	Reed	Xiang

Treating sinus infections. *Sinus infections are common, and doctors often treat them with antibiotics. Another treatment is to spray a steroid solution into the nose. A well-designed clinical trial found that these treatments, alone or in combination, do not reduce the severity or the length of sinus infections.[15] Exercises 8.35 to 8.37 concern this trial.*

8.35 Experimental design. The clinical trial was a completely randomized experiment that assigned 240 patients at random among 4 treatments as follows:

	Antibiotic pill	Placebo pill
Steroid spray	53	64
Placebo spray	60	63

(a) Outline the design of the experiment.
(b) How will you label the 240 subjects?
(c) Explain briefly how you would do the random assignment of patients to treatments. Assign the first 5 patients who will receive the first treatment.

8.36 Describing the design. The report of this study in the *Journal of the American Medical Association* describes it as a "double-blind, randomized, placebo-controlled factorial trial." "Factorial" means that the treatments are formed from more than one factor. What are the factors? What do "double-blind" and "placebo-controlled" mean?

8.37 Checking the randomization. If the random assignment of patients to treatments did a good job of eliminating bias, possible lurking variables such as smoking history, asthma, and hay fever should be similar in all 4 groups. After recording and comparing many such variables, the investigators said that "all showed no significant difference between groups." Explain to someone who knows no statistics what "no significant difference" means. Does it mean that the presence of all these variables was exactly the same in all four treatment groups?

8.38 Frappuccino light? Here's the opening of a Starbucks press release: "Starbucks Corp. on Monday said it would roll out a line of blended coffee drinks intended to tap into the growing popularity of reduced-calorie and reduced-fat menu choices for Americans." You wonder if Starbucks customers like the new "Mocha Frappuccino Light" as well as the regular mocha Frappuccino coffee.
(a) Describe a matched pairs design to answer this question. Be sure to include proper blinding of your subjects.
(b) You have 20 regular Starbucks customers on hand. Use software or Table B at line 141 to do the randomization that your design requires.

8.39 Growing trees faster. Carbon dioxide (CO_2) in the atmosphere is increasing due to our use of fossil fuels. Because green plants use CO_2 to fuel photosynthesis, more CO_2 may cause trees to grow faster. An elaborate apparatus allows researchers to pipe extra CO_2 to a 30-meter circle of forest. We want to compare the growth in base area of trees in treated and untreated areas to see if extra CO_2 does in fact increase growth. We can afford to treat three circular areas.[16]
(a) Describe the design of a completely randomized experiment using six well-separated 30-meter circular areas in a pine forest. Sketch the circles and carry out the randomization your design calls for.
(b) Areas within the forest may differ in soil fertility. Describe a matched pairs design using three pairs of circles that will reduce the extra variation due to different fertility. Sketch the circles and carry out the randomization your design calls for.

8.40 Athletes taking oxygen. We often see players on the sidelines of a football game inhaling oxygen. Their coaches think this will speed their recovery. We might measure recovery from intense exertion as follows: Have a football player run 100 yards three times in quick succession. Then allow three minutes to rest before running 100 yards again. Time the final run. Because players vary greatly in speed, you plan a matched pairs experiment using 25 football players as subjects. Discuss the design of such an experiment to investigate the effect of inhaling oxygen during the rest period.

8.41 Do antioxidants prevent cancer? People who eat lots of fruits and vegetables have lower rates of colon cancer than those who eat little of these foods. Fruits and vegetables are rich in "antioxidants" such as vitamins A, C, and E. Will taking antioxidants help prevent colon cancer? A medical experiment studied this question with 864 people who were at risk of colon cancer. The subjects were divided into four groups: daily beta-carotene, daily vitamins C and E, all three vitamins every day, or daily placebo. After four years, the researchers were surprised to find no significant difference in colon cancer among the groups.[17]
(a) What are the explanatory and response variables in this experiment?
(b) Outline the design of the experiment. Use your judgment in choosing the group sizes.
(c) The study was double-blind. What does this mean?
(d) What does "no significant difference" mean in describing the outcome of the study?
(e) Suggest some lurking variables that could explain why people who eat lots of fruits and vegetables have lower rates of colon cancer. The experiment suggests that these variables, rather than the antioxidants, may be responsible for the observed benefits of fruits and vegetables.

8.42 An herb for depression? Does the herb Saint-John's-wort relieve major depression? Here are some excerpts from the report of a study of this issue.[18] The study concluded that the herb is no more effective than a placebo.
(a) "Design: Randomized, double-blind, placebo-controlled clinical trial...." A clinical trial is a medical experiment using actual patients as subjects. Explain the meaning of each of the other terms in this description.
(b) "Participants ... were randomly assigned to receive either Saint-John's-wort extract ($n = 98$) or placebo ($n = 102$).... The primary outcome measure was the rate of change in the Hamilton Rating Scale for Depression over the treatment period." Based on this information, use a diagram to outline the design of this clinical trial.

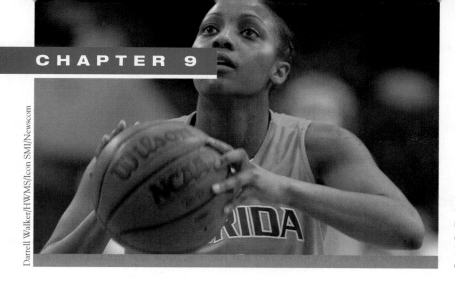

CHAPTER 9

A basketball player who makes 80% of her free throws over a season may not make exactly 8 of 10 in her next game. Probability describes patterns in chance behavior.

Introducing Probability

IN THIS CHAPTER
WE COVER...

- The idea of probability
- Probability models
- Probability rules
- Discrete probability models
- Continuous probability models
- Random variables

Why is probability, the mathematics of chance behavior, needed to understand statistics, the science of data? Let's look at a typical sample survey.

EXAMPLE 9.1 Do you lotto?

What proportion of all adults bought a lottery ticket in the past 12 months? We don't know, but we do have results from the Gallup Poll. Gallup took a random sample of 1523 adults. The poll found that 868 of the people in the sample bought tickets. The proportion who bought tickets was

$$\text{sample proportion} = \frac{868}{1523} = 0.57 \quad \text{(that is, 57\%)}$$

Because all adults had the same chance to be among the chosen 1523, it seems reasonable to use this 57% as an estimate of the unknown proportion in the population. It's a *fact* that 57% of the sample bought lottery tickets—we know because Gallup asked them. We don't know what percent of all adults bought tickets, but we *estimate* that about 57% did. This is a basic move in statistics: use a result from a sample to estimate something about a population. ■

What if Gallup took a second random sample of 1523 adults? The new sample would have different people in it. It is almost certain that there would not be exactly 868 positive responses. That is, Gallup's estimate of the proportion of adults who bought a lottery ticket will vary from sample to sample. *Random samples eliminate bias from the act of choosing a sample, but they can still be wrong because of the variability that results when we choose at random.*

This is why we need facts about probability to make progress in statistics. Because Gallup uses chance to choose its samples, the laws of probability govern the behavior of the samples. Gallup says that the probability is 0.95 that an estimate from one of their samples comes within ±3 percentage points of the truth about the population of all adults. The first step toward understanding this statement is to understand what "probability 0.95" means. Our purpose in this chapter is to understand the language of probability, but without going into the mathematics of probability theory.

The idea of probability

To understand why we can trust random samples and randomized comparative experiments, we must look closely at chance behavior. The big fact that emerges is this: **chance behavior is unpredictable in the short run but has a regular and predictable pattern in the long run.**

Toss a coin, or choose a random sample. The result can't be predicted in advance, because the result will vary when you toss the coin or choose the sample repeatedly. But there is still a regular pattern in the results, a pattern that emerges clearly only after many repetitions. This remarkable fact is the basis for the idea of probability.

EXAMPLE 9.2 **Coin tossing**

When you toss a coin, there are only two possible outcomes, heads or tails. Figure 9.1 shows the results of tossing a coin 5000 times twice. For each number of tosses from 1 to 5000, we have plotted the proportion of those tosses that gave a head. Trial A (solid red line) begins tail, head, tail, tail. You can see that the proportion of heads for Trial A starts at 0 on the first toss, rises to 0.5 when the second toss gives a head, then falls to 0.33 and 0.25 as we get two more tails. Trial B, on the other hand, starts with five straight heads, so the proportion of heads is 1 until the sixth toss.

SuperStock

FIGURE 9.1
The proportion of tosses of a coin that give a head changes as we make more tosses. Eventually, however, the proportion approaches 0.5, the probability of a head. This figure shows the results of two trials of 5000 tosses each.

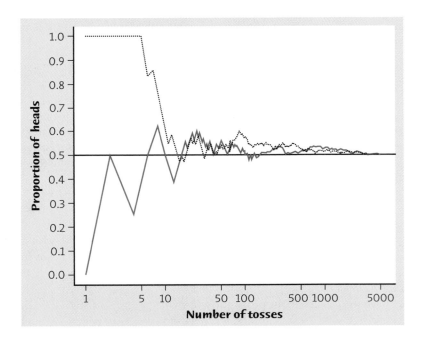

The proportion of tosses that produce heads is quite variable at first. Trial A starts low and Trial B starts high. As we make more and more tosses, however, the proportion of heads for both trials gets close to 0.5 and stays there. If we made yet a third trial at tossing the coin a great many times, the proportion of heads would again settle down to 0.5 in the long run. This is the intuitive idea of probability. Probability 0.5 means "occurs half the time in a very large number of trials." The probability 0.5 appears as a horizontal line on the graph. ■

RANDOMNESS AND PROBABILITY

We call a phenomenon **random** if individual outcomes are uncertain but there is none-theless a regular distribution of outcomes in a large number of repetitions.

The **probability** of any outcome of a random phenomenon is the proportion of times the outcome would occur in a very long series of repetitions.

We might suspect that a coin has probability 0.5 of coming up heads just because the coin has two sides. But we can't be sure. In fact, spinning a penny on a flat surface, rather than tossing the coin, gives heads probability about 0.45 rather than 0.5.[1] The best way to understand randomness is to observe random behavior, as in Figure 9.1. We are willing to say that most coins have probability 0.5 of giving a head when tossed because some people have actually made thousands of tosses. Experience shows that the proportion of heads gradually settles down close to 0.5. Equally important, experience shows that *the proportion in a small or moderate number of tosses can be far from the probability*. *Probability describes* only *what happens in the long run*. Of course, we can never observe a probability exactly. We could always continue tossing the coin, for example. Mathematical probability is an idealization based on imagining what would happen in an indefinitely long series of trials.

APPLY YOUR KNOWLEDGE

9.1 Texas hold 'em. In the popular Texas hold 'em variety of poker, players make their best five-card poker hand by combining the two cards they are dealt with three of five cards available to all players. You read in a book on poker that if you hold a pair (two cards of the same rank) in your hand, the probability of getting four of a kind is 88/1000. Explain carefully what this means. In particular, explain why it does *not* mean that if you play 1000 such hands, exactly 88 will be four of a kind.

9.2 Probability says... Probability is a measure of how likely an event is to occur. Match one of the probabilities that follow with each statement of likelihood given. (The probability is usually a more exact measure of likelihood than is the verbal statement.)

0   0.01   0.3   0.6   0.99   1

(a) This event is impossible. It can never occur.

(b) This event is certain. It will occur on every trial.

(c) This event is very unlikely, but it will occur once in a while in a long sequence of trials.

(d) This event will occur more often than not.

9.3 Random digits. The table of random digits (Table B) was produced by a random mechanism that gives each digit probability 0.1 of being a 0. So random digits can illustrate the idea of probability.

(a) Count the number of 0s in each of the first 5 rows of Table B. Each row has 40 digits. What are the proportions of 0s in each of the first 5 rows? You see that proportions in just 40 trials need not be very close to the probability 0.1.

(b) Combine your counts: how many 0s are there among the 200 digits in the first 5 rows of the table? Of course, 200 trials is not the long run, but already the proportion is coming closer to the probability 0.1.

Probability models

The idea of probability rests on the observed fact that the average result of many thousands of chance outcomes can be known with near certainty. How can we give a mathematical description of this long-run regularity?

Think first about a very simple random phenomenon, tossing a coin once. When we toss a coin, we cannot know the outcome in advance. What *do* we know? We are willing to say that the outcome will be either heads or tails. We believe that each of these outcomes has probability 1/2. This description of coin tossing has two parts:

- a list of possible outcomes
- a probability for each outcome

Such a description is the basis for all *probability models*. Here is the basic vocabulary we use.

PROBABILITY MODELS

The **sample space** *S* of a random phenomenon is the set of all possible outcomes.

An **event** is an outcome or a set of outcomes of a random phenomenon. That is, an event is a subset of the sample space.

A **probability model** is a mathematical description of a random phenomenon consisting of two parts: a sample space *S* and a way of assigning probabilities to events.

A sample space *S* can be very simple or very complex. When we toss a coin once, there are only two outcomes, heads and tails. The sample space is *S* = {H, T}. When Gallup draws a random sample of 1523 adults, the sample space contains all possible choices of 1523 of the 235 million adults in the country. This *S* is extremely large. Each member of *S* is a possible sample, which explains the term *sample space*.

EXAMPLE 9.3 **Rolling dice**

Rolling two dice is a common way to lose money in casinos. There are 36 possible outcomes when we roll two dice and record the up-faces in order (first die, second die). Figure 9.2

FIGURE 9.2

The 36 possible outcomes in rolling two dice, for Example 9.3. If the dice are carefully made, all of these outcomes have the same probability.

displays these outcomes. They make up the sample space S. "Roll a 5" is an event, call it A, that contains four of these 36 outcomes:

$$A = \{\blacksquare\ \blacksquare\qquad\blacksquare\ \blacksquare\qquad\blacksquare\ \blacksquare\qquad\blacksquare\ \blacksquare\}$$

What probabilities should we assign to this sample space? Different dice may be unbalanced in different ways, and so may have different probabilities. Let's assume that we have ideal, perfectly balanced dice. Carefully made casino dice are close to this ideal.

If the dice are perfectly balanced, all 36 outcomes in Figure 9.2 will be *equally likely*. That is, each of the 36 outcomes will come up on one thirty-sixth of all rolls in the long run. So each outcome has probability 1/36. There are 4 outcomes in the event A ("roll a 5"), so this event has probability 4/36. In this way we can assign a probability to any event. So we have a complete probability model. ■

EXAMPLE 9.4 **Rolling dice and counting the spots**

Gamblers care only about the total number of spots on the up-faces of the dice. The sample space for rolling two dice and counting the spots is

$$S = \{2, 3, 4, 5, 6, 7, 8, 9, 10, 11, 12\}$$

Comparing this S with Figure 9.2 reminds us that *we can change S by changing the detailed description of the random phenomenon we are describing.*

What are the probabilities for this new sample space? The 11 possible outcomes are *not* equally likely, because there are six ways to roll a 7 and only one way to roll a 2 or a 12. That's the key: each outcome in Figure 9.2 has probability 1/36. So "roll a 7" has probability 6/36 because this event contains 6 of the 36 outcomes. Similarly, "roll a 2" has probability 1/36, and "roll a 5" (4 outcomes from Figure 9.2) has probability 4/36. Here is the complete probability model:

Spots	2	3	4	5	6	7	8	9	10	11	12
Probability	1/36	2/36	3/36	4/36	5/36	6/36	5/36	4/36	3/36	2/36	1/36

■

APPLY YOUR KNOWLEDGE

9.4 Sample space. Choose a student at random from a large statistics class. Describe a sample space S for each of the following. (In some cases you may have some freedom in specifying S.)

(a) Is the student male or female?

(b) What is the student's height in inches?

(c) Ask how much money in coins (not bills) the student is carrying.

(d) Record the student's letter grade at the end of the course.

9.5 Role-playing games. Computer games in which the players take the roles of characters go back to earlier tabletop games such as Dungeons & Dragons. These games use many different types of dice. A four-sided die has faces with 1, 2, 3, and 4 spots.

(a) What is the sample space for rolling a four-sided die twice (spots on the first and second rolls)? Follow the example of Figure 9.2.

(b) What is the assignment of probabilities to outcomes in this sample space? Assume that the die is perfectly balanced, and follow the method of Example 9.3.

9.6 Role-playing games. The intelligence of a character in a game is determined by rolling the four-sided die twice and adding 1 to the sum of the spots. Start with your work in the previous exercise to give a probability model (sample space and probabilities of outcomes) for the character's intelligence. Follow the method of Example 9.4.

Probability rules

In Examples 9.3 and 9.4 we found probabilities for tossing perfectly balanced dice. As random phenomena go, dice are pretty simple. In most situations, it isn't easy to give a "correct" probability model. We can make progress by listing some facts that must be true for *any* assignment of probabilities. These facts follow from the idea of probability as "the long-run proportion of repetitions on which an event occurs."

1. **Any probability is a number between 0 and 1.** Any proportion is a number between 0 and 1, so any probability is also a number between 0 and 1. An event with probability 0 never occurs, and an event with probability 1 occurs on every trial. An event with probability 0.5 occurs in half the trials in the long run.

2. **All possible outcomes together must have probability 1.** Because some outcome must occur on every trial, the sum of the probabilities for all possible outcomes must be exactly 1.

3. **If two events have no outcomes in common, the probability that one or the other occurs is the sum of their individual probabilities.** If one event occurs in 40% of all trials, a different event occurs in 25% of all trials, and the two can never occur together, then one or the other occurs on 65% of all trials because 40% + 25% = 65%.

4. **The probability that an event does not occur is 1 minus the probability that the event does occur.** If an event occurs in 70% of all trials, it fails to occur in the other 30%. The probability that an event occurs and the probability that it does not occur always add to 100%, or 1.

We can use mathematical notation to state Facts 1 to 4 more concisely. Capital letters near the beginning of the alphabet denote events. If A is any event, we write its probability as $P(A)$. Here are our probability facts in formal language. As you apply these rules, remember that they are just another form of intuitively true facts about long-run proportions.

PROBABILITY RULES

Rule 1.   The probability $P(A)$ of any event A satisfies $0 \leq P(A) \leq 1$.

Rule 2.   If S is the sample space in a probability model, then $P(S) = 1$.

Rule 3.   Two events A and B are **disjoint** if they have no outcomes in common and so can never occur together. If A and B are disjoint,

$$P(A \text{ or } B) = P(A) + P(B)$$

This is the **addition rule for disjoint events.**

Rule 4.   For any event A,

$$P(A \text{ does not occur}) = 1 - P(A)$$

The addition rule extends to more than two events that are disjoint in the sense that no two have any outcomes in common. If events A, B, and C are disjoint, the probability that one of these events occurs is $P(A) + P(B) + P(C)$.

EXAMPLE 9.5   Using the probability rules

We already used the addition rule, without calling it by that name, to find the probabilities in Example 9.4. The event "roll a 5" contains the four disjoint outcomes displayed in Example 9.3, so the addition rule (Rule 3) says that its probability is

$$P(\text{roll a 5}) = P\left(\boxed{\cdot}\ \boxed{::}\right) + P\left(\boxed{::}\ \boxed{\cdot\cdot}\right) + P\left(\boxed{\cdot\cdot}\ \boxed{::}\right) + P\left(\boxed{::}\ \boxed{\cdot}\right)$$

$$= \frac{1}{36} + \frac{1}{36} + \frac{1}{36} + \frac{1}{36}$$

$$= \frac{4}{36} = 0.111$$

What is the probability of rolling anything other than a 5? By Rule 4,

$$P(\text{roll does not give a 5}) = 1 - P(\text{roll a 5})$$

$$= 1 - 0.111 = 0.889$$

Our model assigns probabilities to individual outcomes. To find the probability of an event, just add the probabilities of the outcomes that make up the event. For example: ·

$$P(\text{outcome is odd}) = P(3) + P(5) + P(7) + P(9) + P(11)$$

$$= \frac{2}{36} + \frac{4}{36} + \frac{6}{36} + \frac{4}{36} + \frac{2}{36}$$

$$= \frac{18}{36} = \frac{1}{2} \blacksquare$$

APPLY YOUR KNOWLEDGE

9.7 Preparing for the GMAT. In many settings, the "rules of probability" are just basic facts about percents. A company that offers courses to prepare students for the Graduate Management Admission Test (GMAT) has the following information about its customers: 20% are currently undergraduate students in business; 15% are undergraduate students in other fields of study; 60% are college graduates who are currently employed; and 5% are college graduates who are not employed.

(a) What percent of customers are currently undergraduates? Which rule of probability did you use to find the answer?

(b) What percent of customers are not undergraduate business students? Which rule of probability did you use to find the answer?

9.8 Overweight? Although the rules of probability are just basic facts about percents or proportions, we need to be able to use the language of events and their probabilities. Choose an American adult at random. Define two events:

A = the person chosen is obese

B = the person chosen is overweight, but not obese

According to the National Center for Health Statistics, $P(A) = 0.32$ and $P(B) = 0.34$.

(a) Explain why events A and B are disjoint.

(b) Say in plain language what the event "A or B" is. What is $P(A \text{ or } B)$?

(c) If C is the event that the person chosen has normal weight or less, what is $P(C)$?

9.9 Languages in Canada. Canada has two official languages, English and French. Choose a Canadian at random and ask, "What is your mother tongue?" Here is the distribution of responses, combining many separate languages from the broad Asia/Pacific region:[2]

Language	English	French	Asian/Pacific	Other
Probability	0.63	0.22	0.06	?

(a) What probability should replace "?" in the distribution?

(b) What is the probability that a Canadian's mother tongue is not English?

(c) What is the probability that a Canadian's mother tongue is a language other than English or French?

Discrete probability models

Examples 9.3, 9.4, and 9.5 illustrate one way to assign probabilities to events: assign a probability to every individual outcome, then add these probabilities to find the probability of any event. This idea works well when there are only a finite (fixed and limited) number of outcomes.

DISCRETE PROBABILITY MODEL

A probability model with a finite sample space is called **discrete.**

To assign probabilities in a discrete model, list the probabilities of all the individual outcomes. These probabilities must be numbers between 0 and 1 that add to exactly 1. The probability of any event is the sum of the probabilities of the outcomes making up the event.

EXAMPLE 9.6 Benford's law

Dishonest people try to fake numbers in tax returns, invoices, or expense account claims. It's hard to make up numbers that are fully realistic. One reason is that the first digits of numbers in legitimate records often follow a model known as Benford's law.[3] Call the first digit of a randomly chosen record X for short. Benford's law gives this probability model for X (note that a first digit can't be 0):

First digit X	1	2	3	4	5	6	7	8	9
Probability	0.301	0.176	0.125	0.097	0.079	0.067	0.058	0.051	0.046

Check that the probabilities of the outcomes sum to exactly 1. This is therefore a legitimate discrete probability model. Investigators can detect fraud by comparing the first digits in records such as invoices paid by a business with these probabilities.

The probability that a first digit is equal to or greater than 6 is

$$P(X \geq 6) = P(X=6) + P(X=7) + P(X=8) + P(X=9)$$
$$= 0.067 + 0.058 + 0.051 + 0.046 = 0.222$$

This is less than the probability that a record has first digit 1,

$$P(X=1) = 0.301$$

Fraudulent records tend to have too few 1s and too many higher first digits.

Note that the probability that a first digit is greater than or equal to 6 is not the same as the probability that a first digit is strictly greater than 6. The latter probability is

$$P(X > 6) = 0.058 + 0.051 + 0.046 = 0.155$$

The outcome $X = 6$ is included in "greater than or equal to" and is not included in "strictly greater than." ∎

APPLY YOUR KNOWLEDGE

9.10 Rolling a die. Figure 9.3 displays several discrete probability models for rolling a die. We can learn which model is actually *accurate* for a particular die only by rolling the die many times. However, some of the models are not *legitimate*. That is, they do not

FIGURE 9.3
Four assignments of probabilities
to the six faces of a die, for
Exercise 9.10.

	Probability			
Outcome	Model 1	Model 2	Model 3	Model 4
⚀	1/7	1/3	1/3	1
⚁	1/7	1/6	1/6	1
⚂	1/7	1/6	1/6	2
⚃	1/7	0	1/6	1
⚄	1/7	1/6	1/6	1
⚅	1/7	1/6	1/6	2

obey the rules. Which are legitimate and which are not? In the case of the illegitimate models, explain what is wrong.

9.11 Benford's law. The first digit of a randomly chosen expense account claim follows Benford's law (Example 9.6). Consider the events

$$A = \{\text{first digit is 7 or greater}\}$$
$$B = \{\text{first digit is odd}\}$$

(a) What outcomes make up the event A? What is $P(A)$?

(b) What outcomes make up the event B? What is $P(B)$?

(c) What outcomes make up the event "A or B"? What is $P(A \text{ or } B)$? Why is this probability not equal to $P(A) + P(B)$?

9.12 Working out. Choose a person aged 19 to 25 years at random and ask, "In the past seven days, how many times did you go to an exercise or fitness center or work out?" Call the response X for short. Based on a large sample survey, here is a probability model for the answer you will get:[4]

Days	0	1	2	3	4	5	6	7
Probability	0.68	0.05	0.07	0.08	0.05	0.04	0.01	0.02

(a) Verify that this is a legitimate discrete probability model.

(b) Describe the event $X < 7$ in words. What is $P(X < 7)$?

(c) Express the event "worked out at least once" in terms of X. What is the probability of this event?

Continuous probability models

When we use the table of random digits to select a digit between 0 and 9, the discrete probability model assigns probability 1/10 to each of the 10 possible outcomes. Suppose that we want to choose a number at random between 0 and 1, allowing *any* number between 0 and 1 as the outcome. Software random number generators will do this. The sample space is now an entire interval of numbers:

$$S = \{\text{all numbers between 0 and 1}\}$$

Call the outcome of the random number generator Y for short. How can we assign probabilities to such events as $\{0.3 \leq Y \leq 0.7\}$? As in the case of selecting a random digit, we would like all possible outcomes to be equally likely. But we cannot assign probabilities to each individual value of Y and then add them, because there are infinitely many possible values.

We use a new way of assigning probabilities directly to events—as *areas under a density curve*. Any density curve has area exactly 1 underneath it, corresponding to total probability 1. We met density curves as models for data in Chapter 3 (page 52).

CONTINUOUS PROBABILITY MODEL

A **continuous probability model** assigns probabilities as areas under a density curve. The area under the curve and above any range of values is the probability of an outcome in that range.

EXAMPLE 9.7 **Random numbers**

The random number generator will spread its output uniformly across the entire interval from 0 to 1 as we allow it to generate a long sequence of numbers. Figure 9.4 is a histogram of 10,000 random numbers. They are quite uniform, but not exactly so. The bar heights

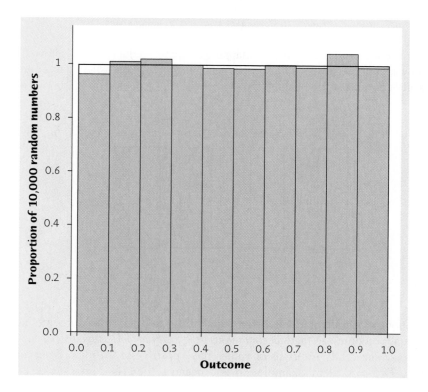

FIGURE 9.4

The probability model for the outcomes of a software random number generator, for Example 9.7. Compare the histogram of 10,000 actual outcomes with the uniform density curve that spreads probability evenly between 0 and 1.

uniform distribution

would all be exactly equal (1000 numbers for each bar) if the 10,000 numbers were exactly uniform. In fact, the counts vary from a low of 960 to a high of 1022.

As in Chapter 3, we have adjusted the histogram scale so that the total area of the bars is exactly 1. Now we can add the density curve that describes the distribution of perfectly random numbers. This density curve also appears in Figure 9.4. It has height 1 over the interval from 0 to 1. This is the density curve of a **uniform distribution.** It is the continuous probability model for the results of generating very many random numbers. Like the probability model for perfectly balanced dice, the density curve is an idealized description of the outcomes of a perfectly uniform random number generator. It is a good approximation for software outcomes, but even 10,000 tries isn't enough for actual outcomes to look exactly like the idealized model. ■

EXAMPLE 9.8 **Probabilities for random numbers**

The uniform density curve has height 1 over the interval from 0 to 1. The area under the curve is 1, and the probability of any event is the area under the curve and above the event in question. Figure 9.5 illustrates finding probabilities as areas under the density curve. The probability that the random number generator produces a number between 0.3 and 0.7 is

$$P(0.3 \leq Y \leq 0.7) = 0.4$$

because the area under the density curve and above the interval from 0.3 to 0.7 is 0.4 as Figure 9.5(a) shows. The height of the curve is 1 and the area of a rectangle is the product of height and length, so the probability of any interval of outcomes is just the length of the interval. Similarly,

$$P(Y \leq 0.5) = 0.5$$

$$P(Y > 0.8) = 0.2$$

$$P(Y \leq 0.5 \text{ or } Y > 0.8) = 0.7$$

The last event consists of two nonoverlapping intervals, so the total area above the event is found by adding two areas, as illustrated by Figure 9.5(b). This assignment of probabilities obeys all of our rules for probability. ■

FIGURE 9.5

Finding probabilities as areas under a density curve, for Example 9.8. The uniform density curve spreads probability evenly between 0 and 1.

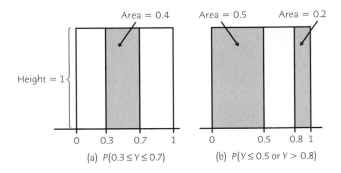

(a) $P(0.3 \leq Y \leq 0.7)$ (b) $P(Y \leq 0.5 \text{ or } Y > 0.8)$

Continuous probability models assign probabilities to intervals of outcomes rather than to individual outcomes. In fact, *all continuous probability models assign probability 0 to every individual outcome.* Only intervals of values have positive probability. For example, the probability $P(Y = 0.8)$ in Example 9.8 is 0 because there is 0 area under the density curve and exactly above 0.8. Put another way, $P(Y > 0.8)$ and $P(Y \geq 0.8)$ are both 0.2 because that is the area in Figure 9.5(b) between 0.8 and 1.

We can use any density curve to assign probabilities. The density curves that are most familiar to us are the Normal curves. **Normal distributions are continuous probability models** as well as descriptions of data. There is a close connection between a Normal distribution as an idealized description for data and a Normal probability model. If we look at the heights of all young women, we find that they closely follow the Normal distribution with mean $\mu = 64$ inches and standard deviation $\sigma = 2.7$ inches. This is a distribution for a large set of data. Now choose one young woman at random. Call her height X. If we repeat the random choice very many times, the distribution of values of X is the same Normal distribution that describes the heights of all young women.

EXAMPLE 9.9   **The heights of young women**

What is the probability that a randomly chosen young woman has height between 68 and 70 inches? The height X of the woman we choose has the $N(64, 2.7)$ distribution. We want $P(68 \leq X \leq 70)$. This is the area under the Normal curve in Figure 9.6. Software gives us the answer at once: $P(68 \leq X \leq 70) = 0.0561$.

Henrik Sorensen/Getty Images

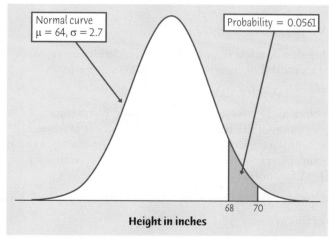

FIGURE 9.6

The probability in Example 9.9 as an area under a Normal curve.

We can also find the probability by standardizing and using Table A, the table of standard Normal probabilities. We will reserve capital Z for a standard Normal variable.

$$P(68 \leq X \leq 70) = P\left(\frac{68 - 64}{2.7} \leq \frac{X - 64}{2.7} \leq \frac{70 - 64}{2.7}\right)$$

$$= P(1.48 \leq Z \leq 2.22)$$

$$= 0.9868 - 0.9306 = 0.0562$$

(As usual, there is a small roundoff error.) The calculation is the same as those we did in Chapter 3. Only the language of probability is new. ■

9.13 Random numbers. Let Y be a random number between 0 and 1 produced by the idealized random number generator described in Example 9.7 and Figure 9.4. Find the following probabilities:

(a) $P(Y \leq 0.4)$

(b) $P(Y < 0.4)$

(c) $P(0.3 \leq Y \leq 0.5)$

9.14 Adding random numbers. Generate two random numbers between 0 and 1 and take X to be their sum. The sum X can take any value between 0 and 2. The density curve of X is the triangle shown in Figure 9.7.

FIGURE 9.7

The density curve for the sum of two random numbers, for Exercise 9.14. This density curve spreads probability between 0 and 2.

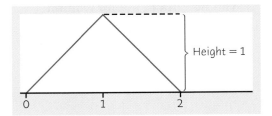

(a) Verify by geometry that the area under this curve is 1.

(b) What is the probability that X is less than 1? (Sketch the density curve, shade the area that represents the probability, then find that area. Do this for (c) also.)

(c) What is the probability that X is less than 0.5?

9.15 Iowa Test scores. The Normal distribution with mean $\mu = 6.8$ and standard deviation $\sigma = 1.6$ is a good description of the Iowa Test vocabulary scores of seventh-grade students in Gary, Indiana. This is a continuous probability model for the score of a randomly chosen student. Figure 3.1 (page xx) pictures the density curve. Call the score of a randomly chosen student X for short.

(a) Write the event "the student chosen has a score of 10 or higher" in terms of X.

(b) Find the probability of this event.

Random variables

Examples 9.6 to 9.9 use a convenient shorthand notation. In Example 9.9, we let X stand for the result of choosing a woman at random and measuring her height. We know that X would take a different value if we made another random choice. Because its value changes from one random choice to another, we call the height X a *random variable*.

RANDOM VARIABLE

A **random variable** is a variable whose value is a numerical outcome of a random phenomenon.

The **probability distribution** of a random variable X tells us what values X can take and how to assign probabilities to those values.

We usually denote random variables by capital letters near the end of the alphabet, such as X or Y. Of course, the random variables of greatest interest to us are outcomes such as the mean $\bar{x}$ of a random sample, for which we will keep the familiar notation. There are two main types of random variables, corresponding to two types of probability models: *discrete* and *continuous*.

EXAMPLE 9.10 **Discrete and continuous random variables**

The first digit X in Example 9.6 is a random variable whose possible values are the whole numbers $\{1, 2, 3, 4, 5, 6, 7, 8, 9\}$. The distribution of X assigns a probability to each of these outcomes. Random variables that have a finite list of possible outcomes are called **discrete**.

discrete random variable

Compare the output Y of the random number generator in Example 9.7. The values of Y fill the entire interval of numbers between 0 and 1. The probability distribution of Y is given by its density curve, shown in Figure 9.4. Random variables that can take on any value in an interval, with probabilities given as areas under a density curve, are called **continuous**. ■

continuous random variable

APPLY YOUR KNOWLEDGE

9.16 Grades in a statistics course. North Carolina State University posts the grade distributions for its courses online.[5] Students in Statistics 101 in the fall 2007 semester received 26% A's, 42% B's, 20% C's, 10% D's, and 2% F's. Choose a Statistics 101 student at random. To "choose at random" means to give every student the same chance to be chosen. The student's grade on a four-point scale (with A = 4) is a discrete random variable X with this probability distribution:

Value of X	0	1	2	3	4
Probability	0.02	0.10	0.20	0.42	0.26

(a) Say in words what the meaning of $P(X \geq 3)$ is. What is this probability?

(b) Write the event "the student got a grade poorer than C" in terms of values of the random variable X. What is the probability of this event?

9.17 Running a mile. A study of 12,000 able-bodied male students at the University of Illinois found that their times for the mile run were approximately Normal with mean 7.11 minutes and standard deviation 0.74 minute.[6] Choose a student at random from this group and call his time for the mile Y.

(a) Say in words what the meaning of $P(Y \geq 8)$ is. What is this probability?

(b) Write the event "the student could run a mile in less than 6 minutes" in terms of values of the random variable Y. What is the probability of this event?

CHAPTER 9 SUMMARY

■ A **random phenomenon** has outcomes that we cannot predict but that nonetheless have a regular distribution in very many repetitions.

■ The **probability** of an event is the proportion of times the event occurs in many repeated trials of a random phenomenon.

- A **probability model** for a random phenomenon consists of a sample space S and an assignment of probabilities P.

- The **sample space S** is the set of all possible outcomes of the random phenomenon. Sets of outcomes are called **events.** P assigns a number $P(A)$ to an event A as its probability.

- Any assignment of probability must obey the rules that state the basic properties of probability:
  1. $0 \le P(A) \le 1$ for any event A.
  2. $P(S) = 1$.
  3. **Addition rule:** Events A and B are **disjoint** if they have no outcomes in common. If A and B are disjoint, then $P(A \text{ or } B) = P(A) + P(B)$.
  4. For any event A, $P(A \text{ does not occur}) = 1 - P(A)$.

- When a sample space S contains finitely many possible values, a **discrete probability model** assigns each of these values a probability between 0 and 1 such that the sum of all the probabilities is exactly 1. The probability of any event is the sum of the probabilities of all the values that make up the event.

- A sample space can contain all values in some interval of numbers. A **continuous probability model** assigns probabilities as areas under a **density curve.** The probability of any event is the area under the curve above the values that make up the event.

- A **random variable** is a variable taking numerical values determined by the outcome of a random phenomenon. The **probability distribution** of a random variable X tells us what the possible values of X are and how probabilities are assigned to those values.

- A random variable X and its distribution can be **discrete** or **continuous.** A **discrete random variable** has finitely many possible values. Its distribution gives the probability of each value. A **continuous random variable** takes all values in some interval of numbers. A density curve describes the probability distribution of a continuous random variable.

9.18 You read in a book on poker that the probability of being dealt three of a kind in a five-card poker hand is 1/50. This means that
(a) if you deal thousands of poker hands, the fraction of them that contain three of a kind will be very close to 1/50.
(b) if you deal 50 poker hands, exactly 1 of them will contain three of a kind.
(c) if you deal 10,000 poker hands, exactly 200 of them will contain three of a kind.

9.19 A basketball player shoots 8 free throws during a game. The sample space for counting the number she makes is
(a) S = any number between 0 and 1.
(b) S = whole numbers 0 to 8.
(c) S = all sequences of 8 hits or misses, like HMMHHHHMH.

9.20 Here is the probability model for the blood type of a randomly chosen person in the United States:

Blood type	O	A	B	AB
Probability	0.45	0.40	0.11	?

This probability model is
(a) continuous.　(b) discrete.　(c) equally likely.

9.21 The probability that a randomly chosen American has type AB blood must be
(a) any number between 0 and 1.　(b) 0.04.　(c) 0.4.

9.22 In a table of random digits such as Table B, each digit is equally likely to be any of 0, 1, 2, 3, 4, 5, 6, 7, 8, or 9. What is the probability that a digit in the table is 7 or greater?
(a) 7/10　(b) 4/10　(c) 3/10

9.23 Choose an American household at random and let the random variable X be the number of cars (including SUVs and light trucks) they own. Here is the probability model if we ignore the few households that own more than 5 cars:

Number of cars X	0	1	2	3	4	5
Probability	0.09	0.36	0.35	0.13	0.05	0.02

A housing company builds houses with two-car garages. What percent of households have more cars than the garage can hold?
(a) 20%　(b) 45%　(c) 55%

9.24 Choose a common fruit fly *Drosophila melanogaster* at random. Call the length of the thorax (where the wings and legs attach) Y. The random variable Y has the Normal distribution with mean $\mu = 0.800$ millimeter (mm) and standard deviation $\sigma = 0.078$ mm. The probability $P(Y > 1)$ that the fly you choose has a thorax more than 1 mm long is about
(a) 0.995.   (b) 0.5.   (c) 0.005.

CHAPTER 9 EXERCISES

9.25 Sample space. In each of the following situations, describe a sample space S for the random phenomenon.
(a) A basketball player shoots four free throws. You record the sequence of hits and misses.
(b) A basketball player shoots four free throws. You record the number of baskets she makes.

9.26 Probability models? In each of the following situations, state whether or not the given assignment of probabilities to individual outcomes is legitimate, that is, satisfies the rules of probability. If not, give specific reasons for your answer.
(a) Roll a die and record the count of spots on the up-face:
$P(1) = 0$ $P(2) = 1/6$ $P(3) = 1/3$
$P(4) = 1/3$ $P(5) = 1/6$ $P(6) = 0$
(b) Deal a card from a shuffled deck:
$P(\text{clubs}) = 12/52$ $P(\text{diamonds}) = 12/52$
$P(\text{hearts}) = 12/52$ $P(\text{spades}) = 16/52$
(c) Choose a college student at random and record sex and enrollment status:
$P(\text{female full-time}) = 0.56$ $P(\text{male full-time}) = 0.44$
$P(\text{female part-time}) = 0.24$ $P(\text{male part-time}) = 0.17$

9.27 Education among young adults. Choose a young adult (aged 25 to 29) at random. The probability is 0.13 that the person chosen did not complete high school, 0.29 that the person has a high school diploma but no further education, and 0.30 that the person has at least a bachelor's degree.
(a) What must be the probability that a randomly chosen young adult has some education beyond high school but does not have a bachelor's degree?
(b) What is the probability that a randomly chosen young adult has at least a high school education?

9.28 Land in Canada. Canada's national statistics agency, Statistics Canada, says that the land area of Canada is 9,094,000 square kilometers. Of this land, 4,176,000 square kilometers are forested. Choose a square kilometer of land in Canada at random.
(a) What is the probability that the area you choose is forested?
(b) What is the probability that it is not forested?

9.29 Foreign-language study. Choose a student in grades 9 to 12 at random and ask if he or she is studying a language other than English. Here is the distribution of results:

Language	Spanish	French	German	All others	None
Probability	0.26	0.09	0.03	0.03	0.59

(a) Explain why this is a legitimate probability model.
(b) What is the probability that a randomly chosen student is studying a language other than English?
(c) What is the probability that a randomly chosen student is studying French, German, or Spanish?

9.30 Car colors. Choose a new car or light truck at random and note its color. Here are the probabilities of the most popular colors for vehicles made in North America in 2007:[7]

Color	White	Silver	Black	Red	Gray	Blue
Probability	0.19	0.18	0.16	0.13	0.12	0.12

(a) What is the probability that the vehicle you choose has any color other than the six listed?
(b) What is the probability that a randomly chosen vehicle is neither silver nor white?

9.31 Drawing cards. You are about to draw a card at random (that is, all choices have the same probability) from a set of 7 cards. Although you can't see the cards, here they are:

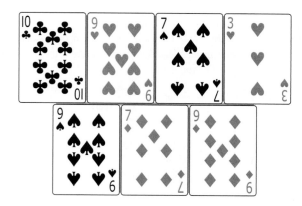

(a) What is the probability that you draw a 9?
(b) What is the probability that you draw a red 9?
(c) What is the probability that you do not draw a 7?

9.32 Loaded dice. There are many ways to produce crooked dice. To *load* a die so that 6 comes up too often and 1 (which is opposite 6) comes up too seldom, add a bit of lead to the filling of the spot on the 1 face. If a die is loaded so that 6 comes up with probability 0.2 and the probabilities of the 2, 3, 4, and 5 faces are not affected, what is the assignment of probabilities to the six faces?

9.33 A door prize. A party host gives a door prize to one guest chosen at random. There are 48 men and 42 women at the party. What is the probability that the prize goes to a woman? Explain how you arrived at your answer.

9.34 Race and ethnicity. The Census Bureau allows each person to choose from a long list of races. That is, in the eyes of the Census Bureau, you belong to whatever race you say you belong to. "Hispanic/Latino" is a separate category; Hispanics may be of any race. If we choose a resident of the United States at random, the Census Bureau gives these probabilities:[8]

	Hispanic	Not Hispanic
Asian	0.001	0.044
Black	0.006	0.124
White	0.139	0.674
Other	0.003	0.009

(a) Verify that this is a legitimate assignment of probabilities.
(b) What is the probability that a randomly chosen American is Hispanic?
(c) Non-Hispanic whites are the historical majority in the United States. What is the probability that a randomly chosen American is not a member of this group?

Choose at random a young adult aged 19 to 22 years. Ask their age and where they live (with their parents, in their own place, or in some other place such as a college dormitory). Here is the probability model for the 12 possible answers:[9]

	Age in Years			
	19	20	21	22
With parents	0.11	0.13	0.11	0.11
Own place	0.04	0.09	0.13	0.16
Other	0.03	0.04	0.03	0.02

Exercises 9.35 to 9.37 use this probability model.

9.35 Where do young people live?
(a) Why is this a legitimate discrete probability model?
(b) What is the probability that the person chosen is a 19-year-old who lives in his or her own place?
(c) What is the probability that the person is 19 years old?
(d) What is the probability that the person chosen lives in his or her own place?

9.36 Where do young people live, continued.
(a) List the outcomes that make up the event

$$A = \{\text{The person chosen is } either \text{ 19 years old } or \text{ lives in his or her own place, or both}\}$$

(b) What is $P(A)$? Explain carefully why $P(A)$ is not the sum of the probabilities you found in parts (b) and (c) of the previous exercise.

9.37 Where do young people live, continued.
(a) What is the probability that the person chosen is 21 years old or older?
(b) What is the probability that the person chosen does not live with his or her parents?

9.38 Spelling errors. Spell-checking software catches "nonword errors" that result in a string of letters that is not a word, as when "the" is typed as "teh." When undergraduates are asked to type a 250-word essay (without spell-checking), the number X of nonword errors has the following distribution:

Value of X	0	1	2	3	4
Probability	0.1	0.2	0.3	0.3	0.1

(a) Is the random variable X discrete or continuous? Why?
(b) Write the event "at least one nonword error" in terms of X. What is the probability of this event?
(c) Describe the event $X \leq 2$ in words. What is its probability? What is the probability that $X < 2$?

9.39 First digits again. A crook who never heard of Benford's law might fake invoices so that the first digits of the amounts are equally likely to be any of 1, 2, 3, 4, 5, 6, 7, 8, or 9. Call the first digit of a randomly chosen fake invoice W for short.
(a) Write the probability distribution for the random variable W.
(b) Find $P(W \geq 6)$ and compare your result with the Benford's law probability from Example 9.6.

9.40 Who goes to Paris? Abby, Deborah, Mei-Ling, Sam, and Roberto work in a firm's public relations office. Their employer must choose two of them to attend a conference in Paris. To avoid unfairness, the choice will be made by drawing two names from a hat. (This is an SRS of size 2.)
(a) Write down all possible choices of two of the five names. This is the sample space.
(b) The random drawing makes all choices equally likely. What is the probability of each choice?
(c) What is the probability that Mei-Ling is chosen?
(d) What is the probability that neither of the two men (Sam and Roberto) is chosen?

9.41 Birth order. A couple plans to have three children. There are 8 possible arrangements of girls and boys. For example, GGB means the first two children are girls and the third child is a boy. All 8 arrangements are (approximately) equally likely.

(a) Write down all 8 arrangements of the sexes of three children. What is the probability of any one of these arrangements?

(b) Let X be the number of girls the couple has. What is the probability that $X = 2$?

(c) Starting from your work in (a), find the distribution of X. That is, what values can X take, and what are the probabilities for each value?

9.42 Random numbers. Many random number generators allow users to specify the range of the random numbers to be produced. Suppose that you specify that the random number Y can take any value between 0 and 2. Then the density curve of the outcomes has constant height between 0 and 2, and height 0 elsewhere.

(a) Is the random variable Y discrete or continuous? Why?

(b) What is the height of the density curve between 0 and 2? Draw a graph of the density curve.

(c) Use your graph from (b) and the fact that probability is area under the curve to find $P(Y \leq 1)$.

9.43 More random numbers. Find these probabilities as areas under the density curve you sketched in Exercise 9.42.

(a) $P(0.5 < Y < 1.3)$

(b) $P(Y \geq 0.8)$

9.44 Did you vote? A sample survey contacted an SRS of 663 registered voters in Oregon shortly after an election and asked respondents whether they had voted. Voter records show that 56% of registered voters had actually voted. We will see later that in this situation the proportion of the sample who voted (call this proportion V) has approximately the Normal distribution with mean $\mu = 0.56$ and standard deviation $\sigma = 0.019$.

(a) If the respondents answer truthfully, what is $P(0.52 \leq V \leq 0.60)$? This is the probability that the sample proportion V estimates the population proportion 0.56 within plus or minus 0.04.

(b) In fact, 72% of the respondents said they had voted ($V = 0.72$). If respondents answer truthfully, what is $P(V \geq 0.72)$? This probability is so small that it is good evidence that some people who did not vote claimed that they did vote.

9.45 Friends. How many close friends do you have? Suppose that the number of close friends adults claim to have varies from person to person with mean $\mu = 9$ and standard deviation $\sigma = 2.5$. An opinion poll asks this question of an SRS of 1100 adults. We will see later that in this situation the sample mean response $\bar{x}$ has approximately the Normal distribution with mean 9 and standard deviation 0.075. What is $P(8.9 \leq \bar{x} \leq 9.1)$, the probability that the sample result $\bar{x}$ estimates the population truth $\mu = 9$ to within ± 0.1?

9.46 Unusual dice. Nonstandard dice can produce interesting distributions of outcomes. You have two balanced, six-sided dice. One is a standard die, with faces having 1, 2, 3, 4, 5, and 6 spots. The other die has three faces with 0 spots and three faces with 6 spots. Find the probability distribution for the total number of spots Y on the up-faces when you roll these two dice. (*Hint:* Start with a picture like Figure 9.2 for the possible up-faces. Label the three 0 faces on the second die 0a, 0b, 0c in your picture, and similarly distinguish the three 6 faces.)

9.47 Playing Pick 4. The Pick 4 games in many state lotteries announce a four-digit winning number each day. Each of the 10,000 possible numbers 0000 to 9999 has the same chance of winning. You win if your choice matches the winning digits. Suppose your chosen number is 5974.

(a) What is the probability that the winning number matches your number exactly?

(b) What is the probability that the winning number has the same digits as your number *in any order*?

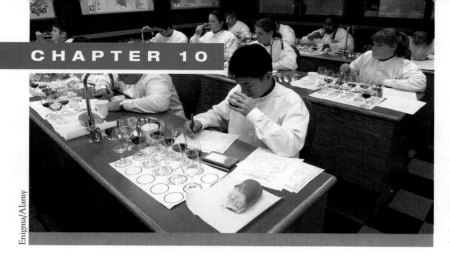
Enigma/Alamy

Evaluating wine is serious
business. Example 10.2 has data
on one source of "off-odors" in
wine.

Sampling Distributions

**IN THIS CHAPTER
WE COVER...**

▪ Parameters and statistics

▪ Statistical estimation and the law
  of large numbers

▪ Sampling distributions

▪ The mean and standard deviation
  of $\bar{x}$

▪ The central limit theorem

What is the average income of American households? Each March, the government's Current Population Survey asks detailed questions about income. The 53,800 households contacted in March 2008 had a mean "total money income" of $67,609 in 2007.[1] (The median income was of course lower, $50,233.) That $67,609 describes the sample, but we use it to estimate the mean income of all households. This is an example of statistical inference: we use information from a sample to infer something about a wider population.

Because the results of random samples and randomized comparative experiments include an element of chance, we can't guarantee that our inferences are correct. What we can guarantee is that our methods usually give correct answers. The reasoning of statistical inference rests on asking, "How often would this method give a correct answer if I used it very many times?" If our data come from random sampling or randomized comparative experiments, the laws of probability answer the question "What would happen if we did this many times?" This chapter presents some facts about probability that help answer this question.

Parameters and statistics

As we begin to use sample data to draw conclusions about a wider population, we must take care to keep straight whether a number describes a sample or a population. Here is the vocabulary we use.

> **PARAMETER, STATISTIC**
>
> A **parameter** is a number that describes the population. In statistical practice, the value of a parameter is not known because we cannot examine the entire population.
>
> A **statistic** is a number that can be computed from the sample data without making use of any unknown parameters. In practice, we often use a statistic to estimate an unknown parameter.

EXAMPLE 10.1 Household earnings

The mean income of the sample of 53,800 households contacted by the Current Population Survey was $\bar{x} = \$67,609$. The number $67,609 is a *statistic* because it describes this one Current Population Survey sample. The population that the poll wants to draw conclusions about is all 117 million U.S. households. The *parameter* of interest is the mean income of all of these households. We don't know the value of this parameter. ■

Remember **s** and **p**: **s**tatistics come from **s**amples, and **p**arameters come from **p**opulations. As long as we were just doing data analysis, the distinction between population and sample was not important. Now, however, it is essential. The notation we use

population mean μ reflects this distinction. We write μ (the Greek letter mu) for the **mean of a population.**
sample mean $\bar{x}$ This parameter has a fixed value, but we don't know what it is. The **mean of the sample** is the familiar $\bar{x}$, the average of the observations in the sample. This statistic would almost certainly take a different value if we chose another sample from the same population. The sample mean $\bar{x}$ from a sample or an experiment is an estimate of the mean μ of the underlying population.

APPLY YOUR KNOWLEDGE

10.1 Effects of caffeine. How does caffeine affect our bodies? In a matched pairs experiment, subjects pushed a button as quickly as they could after taking a caffeine pill and also after taking a placebo pill. The mean pushes per minute were **283** for the placebo and **311** for caffeine. Is each of the boldface numbers a parameter or a statistic?

10.2 Florida voters. Florida has played a key role in recent presidential elections. Voter registration records show that **41%** of Florida voters are registered as Democrats and **37%** as Republicans. (Most of the others did not choose a party.) To test a random digit dialing device, you use it to call 250 randomly chosen residential telephones in Florida. Of the registered voters contacted, **33%** are registered Democrats. Is each of the boldface numbers a parameter or a statistic?

Statistical estimation and the law of large numbers

Statistical inference uses sample data to draw conclusions about the entire population. Because good samples are chosen randomly, statistics such as $\bar{x}$ are random variables. We can describe the behavior of a sample statistic by a probability model that answers the question "What would happen if we did this many times?" Here is an example that will lead us toward the probability ideas most important for statistical inference.

Enigma/Alamy

EXAMPLE 10.2 Does this wine smell bad?

Sulfur compounds such as dimethyl sulfide (DMS) cause "off-odors" in wine, so winemakers want to know the odor threshold, the lowest concentration of DMS that the human nose can detect. Different people have different thresholds, so we start by asking about the mean threshold μ in the population of all adults. The number μ is a parameter that describes this population.

To estimate μ, we present tasters with both natural wine and the same wine spiked with DMS at different concentrations to find the lowest concentration at which they identify the spiked wine. Here are the odor thresholds (measured in micrograms of DMS per liter of wine) for 10 randomly chosen subjects:

$$28 \quad 40 \quad 28 \quad 33 \quad 20 \quad 31 \quad 29 \quad 27 \quad 17 \quad 21$$

The mean threshold for these subjects is $\overline{x} = 27.4$. It seems reasonable to use the sample result $\overline{x} = 27.4$ to estimate the unknown μ. An SRS should fairly represent the population, so the mean $\overline{x}$ of the sample should be somewhere near the mean μ of the population. Of course, we don't expect $\overline{x}$ to be exactly equal to μ. We realize that if we choose another SRS, the luck of the draw will probably produce a different $\overline{x}$. ■

If $\overline{x}$ is rarely exactly right and varies from sample to sample, why is it nonetheless a reasonable estimate of the population mean μ? Here is one answer: *if we keep on taking larger and larger samples, the statistic $\overline{x}$ is guaranteed to get closer and closer to the parameter μ*. If we can afford to keep on measuring more subjects, eventually we will estimate the mean odor threshold of all adults very accurately. This remarkable fact is called the *law of large numbers*. It is remarkable because it holds for *any* population, not just for some special class such as Normal distributions.

LAW OF LARGE NUMBERS

Draw observations at random from any population with finite mean μ. As the number of observations drawn increases, the mean $\overline{x}$ of the observed values gets closer and closer to the mean μ of the population.

The behavior of $\overline{x}$ is similar to the idea of probability. In the long run, the *proportion* of outcomes taking any value gets close to the probability of that value, and the *average* outcome gets close to the population mean. Figure 9.1 (page 164) shows how proportions approach probability in one example. Here is an example of how sample means approach the population mean.

EXAMPLE 10.3 The law of large numbers in action

In fact, the distribution of odor thresholds among all adults has mean 25. The mean $\mu = 25$ is the true value of the parameter we seek to estimate. Figure 10.1 shows how the sample mean $\overline{x}$ of an SRS drawn from this population changes as we add more subjects to our sample.

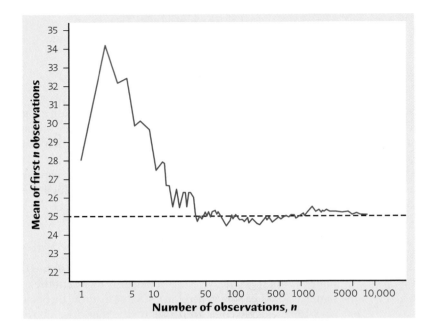

The first subject in Example 10.2 had threshold 28, so the line in Figure 10.1 starts there. The mean for the first two subjects is

$$\overline{x} = \frac{28 + 40}{2} = 34$$

This is the second point on the graph. At first, the graph shows that the mean of the sample changes as we take more observations. Eventually, however, the mean of the observations gets close to the population mean $\mu = 25$ and settles down at that value.

If we started over, again choosing people at random from the population, we would get a different path from left to right in Figure 10.1. The law of large numbers says that whatever path we get will always settle down at 25 as we draw more and more people. ■

The law of large numbers is the foundation of such business enterprises as gambling casinos and insurance companies. The winnings (or losses) of a gambler on a few plays are uncertain—that's why some people find gambling exciting. In Figure 10.1, the mean has not settled down close to μ even after 100 observations. It is only *in the long run* that the mean outcome is predictable. The house plays tens of thousands of times. So the house, unlike individual gamblers, can count on the long-run regularity described by the law of large numbers. The average winnings of the house on tens of thousands of plays will be very close to the mean of the distribution of winnings. Needless to say, this mean guarantees the house a profit. That's why gambling can be a business.

APPLY YOUR KNOWLEDGE

10.3 Insurance. The idea of insurance is that we all face risks that are unlikely but carry high cost. Think of a fire destroying your home. Insurance spreads the risk: we all pay a small amount, and the insurance policy pays a large amount to those few of us whose homes burn down. An insurance company looks at the records for millions of homeowners and sees that the mean loss from fire in a year is $\mu = \$250$ per person. (Most of us have no loss, but a few lose their homes. The $250 is the average loss.) The company plans to sell fire insurance for $250 plus enough to cover its costs and profit. Explain clearly why it would be unwise to sell only 12 policies. Then explain why selling thousands of such policies is a safe business.

Sampling distributions

The law of large numbers assures us that if we measure enough subjects, the statistic $\bar{x}$ will eventually get very close to the unknown parameter μ. But the odor threshold study in Example 10.2 had just 10 subjects. What can we say about estimating μ by $\bar{x}$ from a sample of 10 subjects? Put this one sample in the context of all such samples by asking, "What would happen if we took many samples of 10 subjects from this population?" Here's how to answer this question:

- Take a large number of samples of size 10 from the population.
- Calculate the sample mean $\bar{x}$ for each sample.
- Make a histogram of the values of $\bar{x}$.
- Examine the shape, center, and spread of the distribution displayed in the histogram.

It is too expensive to take many samples from a large population such as all adult U.S. residents. But we can imitate many samples by using software. Using software to imitate chance behavior is called **simulation.**

simulation

EXAMPLE 10.4 What would happen in many samples?

Extensive studies have found that the DMS odor threshold of adults follows roughly a Normal distribution with mean $\mu = 25$ micrograms per liter and standard deviation $\sigma = 7$ micrograms per liter. We call this the *population distribution* of odor threshold.

Figure 10.2 illustrates the process of choosing many samples and finding the sample mean threshold $\bar{x}$ for each one. Follow the flow of the figure from the population at the left, to choosing an SRS and finding the $\bar{x}$ for this sample, to collecting together the $\bar{x}$'s from many samples. The first sample has $\bar{x} = 26.42$. The second sample contains a different 10 people, with $\bar{x} = 24.28$, and so on. The histogram at the right of the figure shows the distribution of the values of $\bar{x}$ from 1000 separate SRSs of size 10. This histogram displays the *sampling distribution* of the statistic $\bar{x}$. ■

POPULATION DISTRIBUTION, SAMPLING DISTRIBUTION

The **population distribution** of a variable is the distribution of values of the variable among all the individuals in the population.

The **sampling distribution** of a statistic is the distribution of values taken by the statistic in all possible samples of the same size from the same population.

Be careful: The population distribution describes the *individuals* that make up the population. A sampling distribution describes how a *statistic* varies in many samples from the population. Strictly speaking, the sampling distribution is the ideal pattern that would

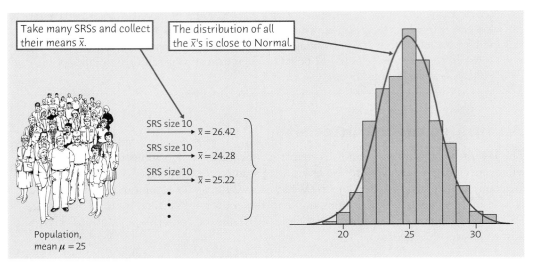

FIGURE 10.2

The idea of a sampling distribution: take many samples from the same population, collect the $\bar{x}$'s from all the samples, and display the distribution of the $\bar{x}$'s. The histogram shows the results of 1000 samples.

emerge if we looked at all possible samples of size 10 from our population. A distribution obtained from a fixed number of trials, like the 1000 trials in Figure 10.2, is only an approximation to the sampling distribution.

We can use the tools of data analysis to describe any distribution. Let's apply those tools to Figure 10.2. What can we say about the shape, center, and spread of this distribution?

- **Shape:** It looks Normal! Detailed examination confirms that the distribution of $\bar{x}$ from many samples is very close to Normal.
- **Center:** The mean of the 1000 $\bar{x}$'s is 24.95. That is, the distribution is centered very close to the population mean $\mu = 25$.
- **Spread:** The standard deviation of the 1000 $\bar{x}$'s is 2.217, notably smaller than the standard deviation $\sigma = 7$ of the population of individual subjects.

Although these results describe just one simulation of a sampling distribution, they reflect facts that are true whenever we use random sampling.

APPLY YOUR KNOWLEDGE

10.4 Sampling distribution versus population distribution. During World War II, 12,000 able-bodied male undergraduates at the University of Illinois participated in required physical training. Each student ran a timed mile. Their times followed the Normal distribution with mean 7.11 minutes and standard deviation 0.74 minute. An SRS of 100 of these students has mean time $\bar{x} = 7.15$ minutes. A second SRS of size 100 has mean $\bar{x} = 6.97$ minutes. After many SRSs, the many values of the sample mean $\bar{x}$ follow the Normal distribution with mean 7.11 minutes and standard deviation 0.074 minute.

(a) What is the population? What values does the population distribution describe? What is this distribution?

(b) What values does the sampling distribution of $\bar{x}$ describe? What is the sampling distribution?

10.5 Generating a sampling distribution. Let's illustrate the idea of a sampling distribution in the case of a very small sample from a very small population. The population is the scores of 10 students on an exam:

Student	0	1	2	3	4	5	6	7	8	9
Score	82	62	80	58	72	73	65	66	74	62

The parameter of interest is the mean score μ in this population. The sample is an SRS of size $n = 4$ drawn from the population. Because the students are labeled 0 to 9, a single random digit from Table B chooses one student for the sample.

(a) Find the mean of the 10 scores in the population. This is the population mean μ.

(b) Use the first digits in row 116 of Table B to draw an SRS of size 4 from this population. What are the four scores in your sample? What is their mean $\bar{x}$? This statistic is an estimate of μ.

(c) Repeat this process 9 more times, using the first digits in rows 117 to 125 of Table B. Make a histogram of the 10 values of $\bar{x}$. You are constructing the sampling distribution of $\bar{x}$. Is the center of your histogram close to μ?

The mean and standard deviation of $\bar{x}$

Figure 10.2 suggests that when we choose many SRSs from a population, the sampling distribution of the sample means is centered at the mean of the original population and is less spread out than the distribution of individual observations. Here are the facts.

MEAN AND STANDARD DEVIATION OF A SAMPLE MEAN[2]

Suppose that $\bar{x}$ is the mean of an SRS of size n drawn from a large population with mean μ and standard deviation σ. Then the sampling distribution of $\bar{x}$ has **mean** μ and **standard deviation $\sigma/\sqrt{n}$.**

These facts about the mean and the standard deviation of the sampling distribution of $\bar{x}$ are true for *any* population, not just for some special class such as Normal distributions. They have important implications for statistical inference:

- The mean of the statistic $\bar{x}$ is always equal to the mean μ of the population. That is, the sampling distribution of $\bar{x}$ is centered at μ. In repeated sampling, $\bar{x}$ will sometimes fall above the true value of the parameter μ and sometimes below, but there is no systematic tendency to overestimate or underestimate the parameter. This makes the idea of lack of bias in the sense of "no favoritism" more precise. Because the mean of $\bar{x}$ is equal to μ, we say that the statistic $\bar{x}$ is an **unbiased estimator** of the parameter μ.   *unbiased estimator*
- An unbiased estimator is "correct on the average" in many samples. How close the estimator falls to the parameter in most samples is determined by the spread of the sampling distribution. If individual observations have standard deviation σ, then sample means $\bar{x}$ from samples of size n have standard deviation $\sigma/\sqrt{n}$. That is, **averages are less variable than individual observations.**

- Not only is the standard deviation of the distribution of $\bar{x}$ smaller than the standard deviation of individual observations, but it gets smaller as we take larger samples. **The results of large samples are less variable than the results of small samples.**

The upshot of all this is that we can trust the sample mean from a large random sample to estimate the population mean accurately. If the sample size n is large, the standard deviation of $\bar{x}$ is small, and almost all samples will give values of $\bar{x}$ that lie very close to the true parameter μ. *However, the standard deviation of the sampling distribution gets smaller only at the rate $\sqrt{n}$. To cut the standard deviation of $\bar{x}$ in half, we must take four times as many observations, not just twice as many.* So very accurate estimates may be expensive.

APPLY YOUR KNOWLEDGE

10.6 Measurements in the lab. Juan makes a measurement in a chemistry laboratory and records the result in his lab report. The standard deviation of students' lab measurements is $\sigma = 10$ milligrams. Juan repeats the measurement 3 times and records the mean $\bar{x}$ of his 3 measurements.

   (a) What is the standard deviation of Juan's mean result? (That is, if Juan kept on making 3 measurements and averaging them, what would be the standard deviation of all his $\bar{x}$'s?)

   (b) How many times must Juan repeat the measurement to reduce the standard deviation of $\bar{x}$ to 5? Explain to someone who knows no statistics the advantage of reporting the average of several measurements rather than the result of a single measurement.

The central limit theorem

The facts about the mean and standard deviation of $\bar{x}$ are true no matter what the shape of the population distribution may be. But what is the shape of the sampling distribution? *It is a remarkable fact that as the sample size increases, the distribution of $\bar{x}$ changes shape: it looks less like that of the population and more like a Normal distribution.* When the sample is large enough, the distribution of $\bar{x}$ is very close to Normal. This is true no matter what shape the population distribution has, as long as the population has a finite standard deviation σ. This famous fact of probability theory is called the *central limit theorem.*

CENTRAL LIMIT THEOREM

Draw an SRS of size n from any population with mean μ and finite standard deviation σ. The **central limit theorem** says that when n is large the sampling distribution of the sample mean $\bar{x}$ is approximately Normal:

$$\bar{x} \text{ is approximately } N\left(\mu, \frac{\sigma}{\sqrt{n}}\right)$$

The central limit theorem allows us to use Normal probability calculations to answer questions about sample means from many observations.

How large a sample size n is needed for $\bar{x}$ to be close to normal depends on the population distribution. In fact, *if the population distribution itself is exactly Normal, then the sampling distribution of $\bar{x}$ is exactly Normal*. No real population has an exactly Normal distribution, so this fact is much less important than the central limit theorem. If the shape of the population distribution is far from Normal, more observations are required in order for $\bar{x}$ to be close to Normal. Here is an example in which the population is very far from Normal.

EXAMPLE 10.5 **The central limit theorem in action**

Figure 10.3(a) shows a strongly right-skewed population distribution that has its most probable outcomes near 0. The mean μ of this distribution is 1, and its standard deviation σ is also 1. This particular distribution is called an *exponential distribution*. Exponential distributions are used as models for the lifetime in service of electronic components and for the time required to serve a customer or repair a machine.

Figures 10.3(b), (c), and (d) are the density curves of the sample means of 2, 10, and 25 observations from this population. As n increases, the shape becomes more Normal. The mean remains at $\mu = 1$, and the standard deviation decreases, taking the value $1/\sqrt{n}$. The density curve for 10 observations is still somewhat skewed to the right but already resembles a Normal curve having $\mu = 1$ and $\sigma = 1/\sqrt{10} = 0.32$. The density curve for $n = 25$ is yet more Normal. The contrast between the shapes of the population distribution and of the distribution of the means of 10 or 25 observations is striking. ■

Comparing Figure 10.3(a) with Figures 10.3(b), (c), and (d) illustrates the two most important ideas of this chapter.

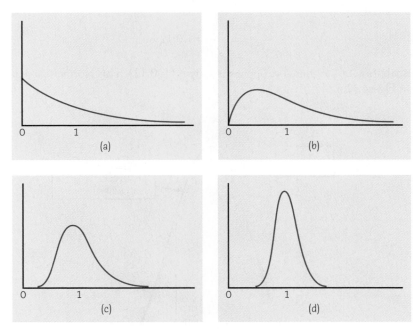

FIGURE 10.3

The central limit theorem in action, for Example 10.5. The distribution of sample means $\bar{x}$ from a strongly non-Normal population becomes more Normal as the sample size increases. **(a)** The distribution of 1 observation. **(b)** The distribution of $\bar{x}$ for 2 observations. **(c)** The distribution of $\bar{x}$ for 10 observations. **(d)** The distribution of $\bar{x}$ for 25 observations.

THINKING ABOUT SAMPLE MEANS

Means of random samples are **less variable** than individual observations.

Means of random samples are **more Normal** than individual observations.

Let's use Normal calculations based on the central limit theorem to answer a question about the very non-Normal distribution in Figure 10.3(a).

EXAMPLE 10.6 **Maintaining air conditioners**

STATE: The time (in hours) that a technician requires to perform preventive maintenance on an air-conditioning unit is governed by the exponential distribution whose density curve appears in Figure 10.3(a). The mean time is $\mu = 1$ hour and the standard deviation is $\sigma = 1$ hour. Your company has a contract to maintain 70 of these units in an apartment building. You must schedule technicians' time for a visit to this building. Is it safe to budget an average of 1.1 hours for each unit? Or should you budget an average of 1.25 hours?

PLAN: We can treat these 70 air conditioners as an SRS from all units of this type. What is the probability that the average maintenance time for 70 units exceeds 1.1 hours? That the average time exceeds 1.25 hours?

SOLVE: The central limit theorem says that the sample mean time $\bar{x}$ spent working on 70 units has approximately the Normal distribution with mean equal to the population mean $\mu = 1$ hour and standard deviation

$$\frac{\sigma}{\sqrt{70}} = \frac{1}{\sqrt{70}} = 0.12 \text{ hour}$$

The distribution of $\bar{x}$ is therefore approximately $N(1, 0.12)$. This Normal curve is the solid curve in Figure 10.4.

FIGURE 10.4

The exact distribution (dotted) and the Normal approximation from the central limit theorem (solid) for the average time needed to maintain an air conditioner, for Example 10.6. The probability we want is the area to the right of 1.1.

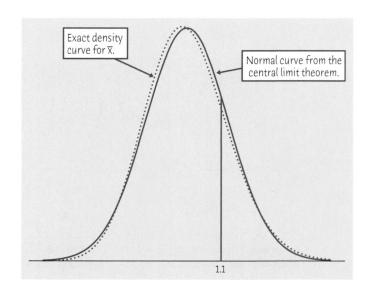

Using this Normal distribution, the probabilities we want are

$$P(\bar{x} > 1.10 \text{ hours}) = 0.2014$$

$$P(\bar{x} > 1.25 \text{ hours}) = 0.0182$$

Software gives these probabilities immediately, or you can standardize and use Table A. For example,

$$P(\bar{x} > 1.10) = P\left(\frac{\bar{x} - 1}{0.12}\right) > P\left(\frac{1.10 - 1}{0.12}\right)$$

$$= P(Z > 0.83) = 1 - 0.7967 = 0.2033$$

with the usual roundoff error. Don't forget to use standard deviation 0.12 in your software or when you standardize $\bar{x}$.

CONCLUDE: If you budget 1.1 hours per unit, there is a 20% chance that the technicians will not complete the work in the building within the budgeted time. This chance drops to 2% if you budget 1.25 hours. You therefore budget 1.25 hours per unit. ■

Using more mathematics, we can start with the exponential distribution and find the actual density curve of $\bar{x}$ for 70 observations. This is the dotted curve in Figure 10.4. You can see that the solid Normal curve is a good approximation. The exactly correct probability for 1.1 hours is the area to the right of 1.1 under the dotted density curve. It is 0.1977. The central limit theorem Normal approximation 0.2014 is off by only about 0.004.

APPLY YOUR KNOWLEDGE

10.7 Population versus sample. The blood cholesterol level of all men aged 20 to 34 follows the Normal distribution with mean $\mu = 188$ milligrams per deciliter (mg/dl) and standard deviation $\sigma = 41$ mg/dl. A sample survey measures the blood cholesterol level of an SRS of 10 such men.

(a) What are the mean and standard deviation of the sampling distribution of the sample mean $\bar{x}$?

(b) Draw two Normal curves on the same graph, one for the population distribution of individual measurements and another for the sampling distribution of the mean of 10 measurements. Comparing the two curves illustrates the fact that averages are less variable than individuals.

10.8 Larger sample, more accurate estimate. The blood cholesterol level of all men aged 20 to 34 follows a population distribution with mean $\mu = 188$ milligrams per deciliter (mg/dl) and standard deviation $\sigma = 41$ mg/dl.

(a) Choose an SRS of 100 men from this population. According to the central limit theorem, what is the approximate sampling distribution of $\bar{x}$? What is the probability that $\bar{x}$ takes a value between 185 and 191 mg/dl? This is the probability that $\bar{x}$ estimates μ within ±3 mg/dl.

(b) Choose an SRS of 1000 men from this population. Now what is the probability that $\bar{x}$ falls within ±3 mg/dl of μ? The larger sample is much more likely to give an accurate estimate of μ.

10.9 More on insurance. An insurance company knows that in the entire population of millions of homeowners, the mean annual loss from fire is $\mu = \$250$ and the standard deviation of the loss is $\sigma = \$1000$. The distribution of losses is strongly right-skewed: most policies have $0 loss, but a few have large losses. If the company sells 10,000 policies, can it safely base its rates on the assumption that its average loss will be no greater than $275? Follow the four-step process as illustrated in Example 10.6.

CHAPTER 10 SUMMARY

■ A **parameter** in a statistical problem is a number that describes a population, such as the **population mean** μ. To estimate an unknown parameter, use a **statistic** calculated from a sample, such as the **sample mean** $\overline{x}$.

■ The **law of large numbers** states that the actually observed mean outcome $\overline{x}$ must approach the mean μ of the population as the number of observations increases.

■ The **population distribution** of a variable describes the values of the variable for all individuals in a population.

■ The **sampling distribution** of a statistic describes the values of the statistic in all possible samples of the same size from the same population.

■ When the sample is an SRS from the population, the **mean** of the sampling distribution of the sample mean $\overline{x}$ is the same as the population mean μ. That is, $\overline{x}$ is an **unbiased estimator** of μ.

■ The **standard deviation** of the sampling distribution of $\overline{x}$ is $\sigma/\sqrt{n}$ for an SRS of size n if the population has standard deviation σ. That is, averages are less variable than individual observations.

■ Choose an SRS of size n from any population with mean μ and finite standard deviation σ. The **central limit theorem** states that when n is large the sampling distribution of $\overline{x}$ is approximately Normal. That is, averages are more Normal than individual observations. We can use the $N(\mu, \sigma/\sqrt{n})$ distribution to calculate approximate probabilities for events involving $\overline{x}$.

CHECK YOUR SKILLS

10.10 The Bureau of Labor Statistics announces that last month it interviewed all members of the labor force in a sample of 60,000 households; **4.9%** of the people interviewed were unemployed. The boldface number is a
(a) sampling distribution.   (b) parameter.   (c) statistic.

10.11 A study of voting chose 663 registered voters at random shortly after an election. Of these, 72% said they had voted in the election. Election records show that only **56%** of registered voters voted in the election. The boldface number is a
(a) sampling distribution.   (b) parameter.   (c) statistic.

10.12 Annual returns on the more than 5000 common stocks available to investors vary a lot. In a recent year, the mean return was 8.3% and the standard deviation of returns was 28.5%. The law of large numbers says that

(a) you can get an average return higher than the mean 8.3% by investing in a large number of stocks.
(b) as you invest in more and more stocks chosen at random, your average return on these stocks gets ever closer to 8.3%.
(c) if you invest in a large number of stocks chosen at random, your average return will have approximately a Normal distribution.

10.13 Scores on the mathematics part of the SAT exam in a recent year were roughly Normal with mean 515 and standard deviation 114. You choose an SRS of 100 students and average their SAT math scores. If you do this many times, the mean of the average scores you get will be close to
(a) 515.   (b) $515/100 = 5.15$.   (c) $515/\sqrt{100} = 51.5$.

10.14 Scores on the mathematics part of the SAT exam in a recent year were roughly Normal with mean 515 and

standard deviation 114. You choose an SRS of 100 students and average their SAT math scores. If you do this many times, the standard deviation of the average scores you get will be close to
(a) 114.   (b) $114/100 = 1.14$.   (c) $114/\sqrt{100} = 11.4$.

10.15 The number of hours a light bulb burns before failing varies from bulb to bulb. The distribution of burnout times is strongly skewed to the right. The central limit theorem says that
(a) as we look at more and more bulbs, their average burnout time gets ever closer to the mean μ for all bulbs of this type.
(b) the average burnout time of a large number of bulbs has a distribution of the same shape (strongly skewed) as the distribution for individual bulbs.
(c) the average burnout time of a large number of bulbs has a distribution that is close to Normal.

10.16 The length of human pregnancies from conception to birth varies according to a distribution that is approximately Normal with mean 266 days and standard deviation 16 days. The probability that the average pregnancy length for 6 randomly chosen women exceeds 270 days is about
(a) 0.40.   (b) 0.27.   (c) 0.07.

CHAPTER 10 EXERCISES

10.17 Testing glass. How well materials conduct heat matters when designing houses. As a test of a new measurement process, 10 measurements are made on pieces of glass known to have conductivity **1**. The average of the 10 measurements is **1.09**. Is each of the boldface numbers a parameter or a statistic? Explain your answer.

10.18 Small classes in school. The Tennessee STAR experiment randomly assigned children to regular or small classes during their first four years of school. When these children reached high school, **40.2%** of blacks from small classes took the ACT or SAT college entrance exams. Only **31.7%** of blacks from regular classes took one of these exams. Is each of the boldface numbers a parameter or a statistic? Explain your answer.

10.19 Roulette. A roulette wheel has 38 slots, of which 18 are black, 18 are red, and 2 are green. When the wheel is spun, the ball is equally likely to come to rest in any of the slots. One of the simplest wagers chooses red or black. A bet of $1 on red returns $2 if the ball lands in a red slot. Otherwise, the player loses his dollar. When gamblers bet on red or black, the two green slots belong to the house. Because the probability of winning $2 is 18/38, the mean payoff from a $1 bet is twice 18/38, or 94.7 cents. Explain what the law of large numbers tells

us about what will happen if a gambler makes very many bets on red.

10.20 Lightning strikes. The number of lightning strikes on a square kilometer of open ground in a year has mean 6 and standard deviation 2.4. (These values are typical of much of the United States.) The National Lightning Detection Network uses automatic sensors to watch for lightning in a sample of 10 square kilometers. What are the mean and standard deviation of $\bar{x}$, the mean number of strikes per square kilometer?

10.21 Heights of male students. To estimate the mean height μ of male students on your campus, you will measure an SRS of students. Heights of people of the same sex and similar ages are close to Normal. You know from government data that the standard deviation of the heights of young men is about 2.8 inches. Suppose that (unknown to you) the mean height of all male students is 70 inches.
(a) If you choose one student at random, what is the probability that he is between 69 and 71 inches tall?
(b) You measure 25 students. What is the sampling distribution of their average height $\bar{x}$?
(c) What is the probability that the mean height of your sample is between 69 and 71 inches?

10.22 Glucose testing. A pregnant women is classified as having gestational diabetes if her blood glucose level is above 140 milligrams per deciliter (mg/dl) one hour after having a sugary drink. The glucose level isn't fixed, but varies from day to day. Shelia's glucose level one hour after the sugary drink varies according to the Normal distribution with $\mu = 125$ mg/dl and $\sigma = 10$ mg/dl.
(a) If a single glucose measurement is made, what is the probability that Shelia is diagnosed as having gestational diabetes?
(b) If measurements are made on 4 separate days and the mean result is compared with the criterion 140 mg/dl, what is the probability that Shelia is diagnosed as having gestational diabetes?

10.23 Durable press fabrics. "Durable press" cotton fabrics are treated to improve their recovery from wrinkles after washing. Unfortunately, the treatment also reduces the strength of the fabric. The breaking strength of untreated fabric is Normally distributed with mean 58 pounds and standard deviation 2.3 pounds. The same type of fabric after treatment has Normally distributed breaking strength with mean 30 pounds and standard deviation 1.6 pounds.[3] A clothing manufacturer tests an SRS of 5 specimens of each fabric.
(a) What is the probability that the mean breaking strength of the 5 untreated specimens exceeds 50 pounds?
(b) What is the probability that the mean breaking strength of the 5 treated specimens exceeds 50 pounds?

10.24 Pollutants in auto exhausts. The entire fleet of light vehicles sold in the United States by any manufacturer must emit an average of no more than 0.07 grams per mile (g/mi) of nitrogen oxides (NOX). NOX emissions for one car model vary Normally with mean 0.05 g/mi and standard deviation 0.01 g/mi.
(a) What is the probability that a single car of this model emits more than 0.07 g/mi of NOX?
(b) A company has 25 cars of this model in its fleet. What is the probability that the average NOX level $\overline{x}$ of these cars is above 0.07 g/mi?

10.25 Auto accidents. The number of accidents per week at a hazardous intersection varies with mean 2.2 and standard deviation 1.4. This distribution takes only whole-number values, so it is certainly not Normal.
(a) Let $\overline{x}$ be the mean number of accidents per week at the intersection during a year (52 weeks). What is the approximate distribution of $\overline{x}$ according to the central limit theorem?
(b) What is the approximate probability that $\overline{x}$ is less than 2?
(c) What is the approximate probability that there are fewer than 100 accidents at the intersection in a year? (*Hint:* Restate this event in terms of $\overline{x}$.)

10.26 Returns on stocks. Andrew plans to retire in 40 years. He plans to invest part of his retirement funds in stocks, so he seeks out information on past returns. He learns that over the entire 20th century the real (that is, adjusted for inflation) annual returns on U.S. common stocks had mean 8.7% and standard deviation 20.2%.[4] The distribution of annual returns on common stocks is roughly symmetric, so the mean return over even a moderate number of years is close to Normal. What is the probability (assuming that the past pattern of variation continues) that the mean annual return on common stocks over the next 40 years will exceed 10%? What is the probability that the mean return will be less than 5%? Follow the four-step process as illustrated in Example 10.6.

10.27 Airline passenger weights. The Federal Aviation Administration tells airlines to assume that passengers average 190 pounds in the summer, including clothing and carry-on baggage. But passengers vary, and the FAA does not specify a standard deviation. A reasonable standard deviation is 35 pounds. Weights are not Normally distributed, but they are not very non-Normal. A commuter plane carries 19 passengers. What is the approximate probability that the total weight of the passengers exceeds 4000 pounds? Use the four-step process to guide your work. (*Hint:* To apply the central limit theorem, restate the problem in terms of the mean weight.)

10.28 Sampling male students. To estimate the mean height μ of male students on your campus, you will measure an SRS of students. You know from government data that heights of young men are approximately Normal with standard deviation about 2.8 inches. How large an SRS must you take to reduce the standard deviation of the sample mean to one-half inch?

10.29 Sampling male students, continued. To estimate the mean height μ of male students on your campus, you will measure an SRS of students. You know from government data that heights of young men are approximately Normal with standard deviation about 2.8 inches. You want your sample mean $\overline{x}$ to estimate μ with an error of no more than one-half inch in either direction.
(a) What standard deviation must $\overline{x}$ have so that 99.7% of all samples give an $\overline{x}$ within one-half inch of μ? (Use the 68–95–99.7 rule.)
(b) How large an SRS do you need to reduce the standard deviation of $\overline{x}$ to the value you found in part (a)?

10.30 Playing the numbers. The numbers racket is a well-entrenched illegal gambling operation in most large cities. One version works as follows: you choose one of the 1000 three-digit numbers 000 to 999 and pay your local numbers runner a dollar to enter your bet. Each day, one three-digit number is chosen at random and pays off $600. The mean payoff for the population of thousands of bets is $\mu = 60$ cents. Joe makes one bet every day for many years. Explain what the law of large numbers says about Joe's results as he keeps on betting.

10.31 Playing the numbers: a gambler gets chance outcomes. The law of large numbers tells us what happens in the long run. Like many games of chance, the numbers racket has outcomes so variable—one three-digit number wins $600 and all others win nothing—that gamblers never reach "the long run." Even after many bets, their average winnings may not be close to the mean. For the numbers racket, the mean payout for single bets is $0.60 (60 cents) and the standard deviation of payouts is about $18.96. If Joe plays 350 days a year for 40 years, he makes 14,000 bets.
(a) What are the mean and standard deviation of the average payout $\overline{x}$ that Joe receives from his 14,000 bets?
(b) The central limit theorem says that his average payout is approximately Normal with the mean and standard deviation you found in part (a). What is the approximate probability that Joe's average payout per bet is between $0.50 and $0.70? You see that Joe's average may not be very close to the mean $0.60 even after 14,000 bets.

10.32 Playing the numbers: the house has a business. Unlike Joe (see the previous exercise) the operators of the numbers racket can rely on the law of large numbers. It is said that the New York City mobster Casper Holstein took as many as 25,000 bets per day in the Prohibition era. That's 150,000 bets in a week if he takes Sunday off. Casper's mean winnings per bet are $0.40 (he pays out 60 cents of each dollar bet to people like Joe and keeps the other 40 cents.) His standard deviation for single bets is about $18.96, the same as Joe's.

(a) What are the mean and standard deviation of Casper's average winnings $\bar{x}$ on his 150,000 bets?

(b) According to the central limit theorem, what is the approximate probability that Casper's average winnings per bet are between $0.30 and $0.50? After only a week, Casper can be pretty confident that his winnings will be quite close to $0.40 per bet.

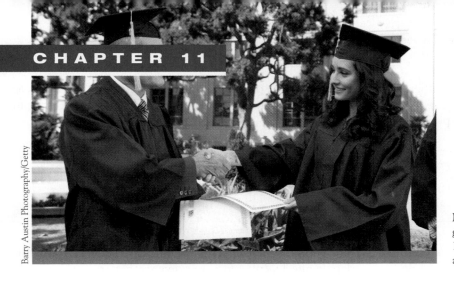
Barry Austin Photography/Getty

More women than men now graduate from college. Exercises 11.34 and 11.35 give data and ask for probabilities.

General Rules of Probability*

IN THIS CHAPTER WE COVER...

- Independence and the multiplication rule
- The general addition rule
- Conditional probability
- The general multiplication rule
- Tree diagrams

Although we are interested in probability mainly because it is the foundation for statistical inference, the mathematics of chance is important in many fields of study. Our introduction to probability in Chapter 9 concentrated on basic ideas and facts. Now we look at some further details. To start, recall the four rules of probability that we met in Chapter 9.

PROBABILITY RULES

Rule 1. For any event A, $0 \leq P(A) \leq 1$.

Rule 2. If S is the sample space, $P(S) = 1$.

Rule 3. **Addition rule:** If A and B are **disjoint** events,

$$P(A \text{ or } B) = P(A) + P(B)$$

Rule 4. For any event A,

$$P(A \text{ does not occur}) = 1 - P(A)$$

Independence and the multiplication rule

Rule 3, the addition rule for disjoint events, describes the probability that *one or the other* of two events A and B occurs in the special situation when A and B cannot

---

*This more advanced chapter introduces some of the mathematics of probability. The material is not needed to read the rest of the book.

occur together. Now we will describe the probability that *both* events A and B occur, again only in a special situation. To display relations among several events, it is often helpful to draw a picture.

VENN DIAGRAM

A picture that shows the sample space S as a rectangular area and events as areas within S is called a **Venn diagram.**

Figures 11.1 and 11.2 are Venn diagrams. Events A and B in Figure 11.1 are disjoint because they do not overlap. Figure 11.2 illustrates two events that are not disjoint. The event {A and B} appears as the overlapping area that is common to both A and B. Can we find the probability $P(A \text{ and } B)$ that both events occur if we know the individual probabilities $P(A)$ and $P(B)$?

FIGURE 11.1

Venn diagram showing disjoint events A and B.

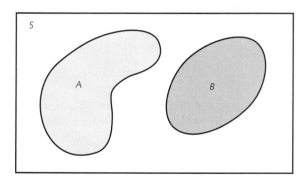

FIGURE 11.2

Venn diagram showing events A and B that are not disjoint. The event {A and B} consists of outcomes common to A and B.

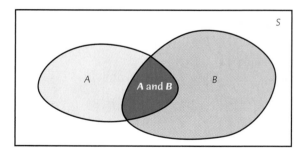

EXAMPLE 11.1 **Can you taste PTC?**

That molecule in the diagram is PTC, a substance with an unusual property: 70% of people find that it has a bitter taste and the other 30% can't taste it at all. The difference is genetic, depending on a single gene. Ask two people chosen at random to taste PTC. We are interested in the events

$$A = \{\text{first person can taste PTC}\}$$
$$B = \{\text{second person can taste PTC}\}$$

We know that $P(A) = 0.7$ and $P(B) = 0.7$. What is the probability $P(A \text{ and } B)$ that both can taste PTC?

We can think our way to the answer. The first person chosen can taste PTC in 70% of all samples and then the second person can taste it in 70% of those samples. We will get two tasters in 70% of 70% of all samples. That's $P(A \text{ and } B) = 0.7 \times 0.7 = 0.49$. ▪

The argument in Example 11.1 works because knowing that the first person can taste PTC tells us nothing about the second person. The probability is still 0.7 that the second person can taste PTC whether or not the first person can. We say that the events "first person can taste PTC" and "second person can taste PTC" are **independent.** Now we have another rule of probability.

independent events

MULTIPLICATION RULE FOR INDEPENDENT EVENTS

Two events A and B are **independent** if knowing that one occurs does not change the probability that the other occurs. If A and B are independent,

$$P(A \text{ and } B) = P(A)P(B)$$

EXAMPLE 11.2 Independent or not?

To use this multiplication rule, we must decide whether events are independent. In Example 11.1, we think that the ability of one randomly chosen person to taste PTC tells us nothing about whether or not a second person, also randomly chosen, can taste PTC. That's independence. But if the two people are members of the same family, the fact that ability to taste PTC is inherited warns us that they are not independent.

Independence is clearest in artificial settings such as games of chance. Because a coin has no memory, it is safe to assume that successive coin tosses are independent. On the other hand, the colors of successive cards dealt from the same deck are not independent. A standard 52-card deck contains 26 red and 26 black cards. For the first card dealt from a shuffled deck, the probability of a red card is $26/52 = 0.50$. Once we see that the first card is red, we know that there are only 25 reds among the remaining 51 cards. The probability that the second card is red is therefore only $25/51 = 0.49$. Knowing the outcome of the first deal changes the probabilities for the second. ▪

If two events A and B are independent, the event that A does not occur is also independent of B, and so on. Moreover, the multiplication rule extends to collections of more than two events, provided that all are independent. Independence of several events means that no information about any collection of the events can change the probabilities of the remaining events.

EXAMPLE 11.3 Can you taste PTC?

Carmen buys a package of PTC taste strips online and offers them to friends at a party to see who can taste PTC. Take A_i to be the event that the ith person Carmen meets can taste PTC. The probability that the first 3 people can all taste PTC is

$$P(A_1 \text{ and } A_2 \text{ and } A_3) = P(A_1)P(A_2)P(A_3)$$
$$= (0.7)(0.7)(0.7) = 0.343$$

The probability that the 5th person is the first who can't taste PTC is

$$P(A_1)P(A_2)P(A_3)P(A_4)(1 - P(A_5)) = (0.7)(0.7)(0.7)(0.7)(0.3)$$
$$= (0.7)^4(0.3) = 0.072$$

You see how independence allows you to find the probability of any string of outcomes. ■

EXAMPLE 11.4 Rapid HIV testing

STATE: Many people who come to clinics to be tested for HIV, the virus that causes AIDS, don't come back to learn the test results. Clinics now use "rapid HIV tests" that give a result while the client waits. The trade-off for fast results is that rapid tests are less accurate than slower laboratory tests. Applied to people who have no HIV antibodies, one rapid test has probability about 0.004 of producing a false positive (that is, of falsely indicating that antibodies are present).[1] If a clinic tests 200 people who are free of HIV antibodies, what is the chance that at least one false positive will occur?

PLAN: It is reasonable to assume that the test results for different individuals are independent. We have 200 independent events, each with probability 0.004. What is the probability that at least one of these events occurs?

SOLVE: "At least one positive" combines many outcomes. It is easier to find the probability of "no positives" and use the fact that

$$P(\text{at least one positive}) = 1 - P(\text{no positives})$$

The probability of a negative result for any one person is $1 - 0.004 = 0.996$. To find the probability that all 200 people tested have negative results, use the multiplication rule:

$$P(\text{no positives}) = P(\text{all 200 negative})$$
$$= (0.996)(0.996) \cdots (0.996)$$
$$= 0.996^{200} = 0.4486$$

The probability we want is therefore

$$P(\text{at least one positive}) = 1 - 0.4486 = 0.5514$$

CONCLUDE: The probability is greater than 1/2 that at least one of the 200 people will test positive for HIV, even though no one has the virus. ■

The multiplication rule $P(A \text{ and } B) = P(A)P(B)$ holds if A and B are independent but not otherwise. The addition rule $P(A \text{ or } B) = P(A) + P(B)$ holds if A and B are disjoint but not otherwise. Resist the temptation to use these simple rules when the circumstances that justify them are not present. Be careful not to confuse disjointness and independence. If A and B are disjoint, then the fact that A occurs tells us that B cannot occur—look again at Figure 11.1. So disjoint events are not independent. Unlike disjointness, we cannot picture independence in a Venn diagram, because it involves the probabilities of the events rather than just the outcomes that make up the events.

APPLY YOUR KNOWLEDGE

11.1 Older college students. Government data show that 8% of adults are full-time college students and that 30% of adults are age 55 or older. Nonetheless, we can't conclude that, because $(0.08)(0.30) = 0.024$, about 2.4% of adults are college students 55 or older. Why not?

11.2 Common names. The Census Bureau says that the 10 most common names in the United States are (in order) Smith, Johnson, Williams, Brown, Jones, Miller, Davis, Garcia, Rodriguez, and Wilson. These names account for 9.6% of all U.S. residents. Out of curiosity, you look at the authors of the textbooks for your current courses. There are 9 authors in all. Would you be surprised if none of the names of these authors were among the 10 most common? (Assume that authors' names are independent and follow the same probability distribution as the names of all residents.)

11.3 Lost Internet sites. Internet sites often vanish or move, so that references to them can't be followed. In fact, 13% of Internet sites referenced in major scientific journals are lost within two years after publication.[2] If a paper contains seven Internet references, what is the probability that all seven are still good two years later? What specific assumptions did you make in order to calculate this probability?

The general addition rule

We know that if A and B are disjoint events, then $P(A \text{ or } B) = P(A) + P(B)$. If events A and B are *not* disjoint, they can occur together. The probability that one or the other occurs is then *less* than the sum of their probabilities. As Figure 11.3 illustrates, outcomes common to both are counted twice when we add probabilities, so we must subtract this probability once. Here is the addition rule for any two events, disjoint or not.

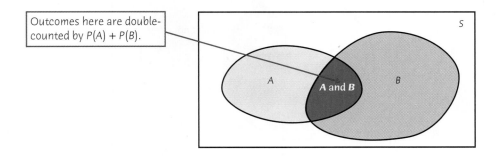

Outcomes here are double-counted by $P(A) + P(B)$.

FIGURE 11.3

The general addition rule: for any events A and B,
$P(A \text{ or } B) =$
$P(A) + P(B) - P(A \text{ and } B)$.

ADDITION RULE FOR ANY TWO EVENTS

For any two events A and B,

$$P(A \text{ or } B) = P(A) + P(B) - P(A \text{ and } B)$$

If A and B are disjoint, the event $\{A \text{ and } B\}$ that both occur contains no outcomes and therefore has probability 0. So the general addition rule includes Rule 3, the addition rule for disjoint events.

EXAMPLE 11.5 Motor vehicle sales

Motor vehicles sold in the United States (ignoring heavy trucks) are classified as either cars or light trucks and as either domestic or imported. "Light trucks" include SUVs and minivans. "Domestic" means made in Canada, Mexico, or the United States, so that a Toyota made in Canada counts as domestic.

In a recent year, 77% of the new vehicles sold to individuals were domestic, 52% were light trucks, and 44% were domestic light trucks.[3] Choose a vehicle sale at random. Then

$$P(\text{domestic or light truck}) = P(\text{domestic}) + P(\text{light truck}) - P(\text{domestic light truck})$$
$$= 0.77 + 0.52 - 0.44 = 0.85$$

That is, 85% of vehicles sold were either domestic or light trucks. ■

Venn diagrams clarify events and their probabilities because you can just think of adding and subtracting areas. Figure 11.4 shows all the events formed from "domestic" and "truck" in Example 11.5. The four probabilities that appear in the figure add to 1 because they refer to four disjoint events that make up the entire sample space. All of these probabilities come from the information in Example 11.5. For example, the probability that a randomly chosen vehicle sale is a domestic car ("D and not T" in the figure) is

$$P(\text{domestic car}) = P(\text{domestic}) - P(\text{domestic light truck})$$
$$= 0.77 - 0.44 = 0.33$$

FIGURE 11.4
Venn diagram and probabilities for motor vehicle sales, for Example 11.5.

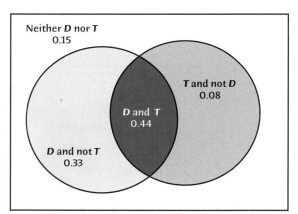

D = vehicle is domestic   T = vehicle is a light truck

Barry Austin Photography/Getty

APPLY YOUR KNOWLEDGE

11.4 College degrees. Of all college degrees awarded in the United States, 50% are bachelor's degrees, 59% are earned by women, and 29% are bachelor's degrees earned by women. Make a Venn diagram and use it to answer these questions.

(a) What percent of all degrees are earned by men?

(b) What percent of all degrees are bachelor's degrees earned by men?

11.5 Distance learning. A study of the students taking distance learning courses at a university finds that they are mostly older students not living in the university town. Choose a distance learning student at random. Let A be the event that the student is 25 years old or older and B the event that the student is local. The study finds that $P(A) = 0.7$, $P(B) = 0.25$, and $P(A \text{ and } B) = 0.05$.

(a) Make a Venn diagram similar to Figure 11.4 showing the events {A and B}, {A and not B}, {B and not A}, and {neither A nor B}.

(b) Describe each of these events in words.

(c) Find the probabilities of all four events and add the probabilities to your Venn diagram.

Conditional probability

The probability we assign to an event can change if we know that some other event has occurred. This idea is the key to many applications of probability.

EXAMPLE 11.6 **Trucks among imported motor vehicles**

Figure 11.4, based on the information in Example 11.5, gives the following probabilities for a randomly chosen light motor vehicle sold at retail in the United States:

	Domestic	Imported	Total
Light truck	0.44	0.08	0.52
Car	0.33	0.15	0.48
Total	0.77	0.23	1

The four probabilities in the body of the table add to 1 because they describe all vehicles sold. We obtain the "Total" row and column from these probabilities by the addition rule.

Now we are told that the vehicle chosen is imported. That is, it is one of the 23% in the "Imported" column of the table. The probability that a vehicle is a light truck, *given the information that it is imported,* is the proportion of trucks in the "Imported" column,

$$P(\text{truck} \mid \text{imported}) = \frac{0.08}{0.23} = 0.35$$

This is a **conditional probability.** You can read the bar | as "given the information that." ∎

conditional probability

Although 52% of all vehicles sold are trucks, only 35% of imported vehicles are trucks. It's common sense that knowing that one event (the vehicle is imported) occurs often changes the probability of another event (the vehicle is a truck). The example also shows how we should define conditional probability. The conditional probability $P(B \mid A)$ of one event B given that another event A occurs is the proportion *of all occurrences of* A for which B also occurs.

CONDITIONAL PROBABILITY

When $P(A) > 0$, the **conditional probability** of B given A is

$$P(B \mid A) = \frac{P(A \text{ and } B)}{P(A)}$$

Be sure to keep in mind the distinct roles of the events A and B in $P(B \mid A)$*. Event A represents the information we are given, and B is the event whose probability we are calculating. Here is an example that emphasizes this distinction.*

EXAMPLE 11.7 **Imports among trucks, trucks among imports**

What is the conditional probability that a randomly chosen vehicle is imported, *given the information that it is a truck?* Using the definition of conditional probability,

$$P(\text{imported} \mid \text{truck}) = \frac{P(\text{imported and truck})}{P(\text{truck})}$$

$$= \frac{0.08}{0.52} = 0.15$$

Only 15% of trucks sold are imports. We have now found two conditional probabilities:

$$P(\text{truck} \mid \text{imported}) = 0.35$$
$$P(\text{imported} \mid \text{truck}) = 0.15$$

The first answers the question "What proportion of imports are trucks?" The second answers "What proportion of trucks are imports?" ■

The conditional probability $P(B \mid A)$ is generally not the same as the unconditional probability $P(B)$. If these two probabilities *are* the same, knowing that A occurs gives no additional information about B. That's what we mean when we say that A and B are independent. So the precise definition of independence is expressed in terms of conditional probability.

INDEPENDENT EVENTS

Two events A and B that both have positive probability are **independent** if

$$P(B \mid A) = P(B)$$

APPLY YOUR KNOWLEDGE

11.6 College degrees. In the setting of Exercise 11.4, what is the conditional probability that a degree is earned by a woman, given that it is a bachelor's degree?

11.7 Distance learning. In the setting of Exercise 11.5, what is the conditional probability that a student is local, given that he or she is less than 25 years old?

11.8 Independent? The Clemson University Fact Book for 2007 shows that 123 of the university's 338 assistant professors were women, along with 76 of the 263 associate professors and 73 of the 375 full professors.

(a) What is the probability that a randomly chosen Clemson professor is a woman?

(b) What is the conditional probability that a randomly chosen professor is a woman, given that the person chosen is a full professor?

(c) Are the rank and gender of Clemson professors independent? How do you know?

The general multiplication rule

The definition of conditional probability reminds us that in principle all probabilities, including conditional probabilities, can be found from the assignment of probabilities to events that describes a random phenomenon. More often, however, conditional probabilities are part of the information given to us in a probability model. The definition of conditional probability then turns into a rule for finding the probability that both of two events occur.

MULTIPLICATION RULE FOR ANY TWO EVENTS

The probability that both of two events A and B happen together can be found by

$$P(A \text{ and } B) = P(A)P(B \mid A)$$

In words, this rule says that for both of two events to occur, first one must occur and then, given that the first event has occurred, the second must occur. If the A and B are independent, then the conditional probability $P(B \mid A)$ is the same as the unconditional probability $P(B)$. So the general multiplication rule includes the multiplication rule for independent events.

EXAMPLE 11.8   Teens with online profiles

The Pew Internet and American Life Project finds that 93% of teenagers (ages 12 to 17) use the Internet, and that 55% of online teens have posted a profile on a social networking site.[4] What percent of teens are online *and* have posted a profile?

Use the multiplication rule:

$$P(\text{online}) = 0.93$$
$$P(\text{profile} \mid \text{online}) = 0.55$$
$$P(\text{online and have profile}) = P(\text{online}) \times P(\text{profile} \mid \text{online})$$
$$= (0.93)(0.55) = 0.5115$$

That is, about 51% of all teens use the Internet and have a profile on a social networking site.

You can think your way through this: if 93% of teens are online and 55% *of these* have posted a profile, then 55% of 93% are both online and have a profile. ■

The multiplication rule extends to find the probability that all of several events occur. Just condition each event on the occurrence of *all* of the preceding events. For any three events A, B, and C,

$$P(A \text{ and } B \text{ and } C) = P(A)P(B \mid A)P(C \mid \text{both } A \text{ and } B)$$

Here is an example of the extended multiplication rule.

EXAMPLE 11.9   Fundraising by telephone

STATE: A charity raises funds by calling a list of prospective donors to ask for pledges. It is able to talk with 40% of the names on its list. Of those the charity reaches, 30% make a pledge. But only half of those who pledge actually make a contribution. What percent of the donor list contributes?

PLAN: Express the information we are given in terms of events and their probabilities:

If A = {the charity reaches a prospect}   then $P(A) = 0.4$
If B = {the prospect makes a pledge}   then $P(B \mid A) = 0.3$
If C = {the prospect makes a contribution}   then $P(C \mid \text{both } A \text{ and } B) = 0.5$

We want to find $P(A \text{ and } B \text{ and } C)$.

SOLVE: Use the multiplication rule:

$$P(A \text{ and } B \text{ and } C) = P(A)P(B \mid A)P(C \mid \text{both } A \text{ and } B)$$
$$= 0.4 \times 0.3 \times 0.5 = 0.06$$

CONCLUDE: Only 6% of the prospective donors make a contribution. ■

APPLY YOUR KNOWLEDGE

11.9 At the gym. Suppose that 10% of adults belong to health clubs, and 40% of these health club members go to the club at least twice a week. What percent of all adults go to a health club at least twice a week? Write the information given in terms of probabilities and use the general multiplication rule.

11.10 Teens online. We saw in Example 11.8 that 93% of teenagers are online and that 55% of online teens have posted a profile on a social networking site. Of online teens with a profile, 76% have placed comments on a friend's blog. What percent of all teens are online, have a profile, and comment on a friend's blog? Define events and probabilities and follow the pattern of Example 11.9.

11.11 The probability of a flush. A poker player holds a flush when all 5 cards in the hand belong to the same suit (clubs, diamonds, hearts, or spades). We will find the probability of a flush when 5 cards are dealt. Remember that a deck contains 52 cards, 13 of each suit, and that when the deck is well shuffled, each card dealt is equally likely to be any of those that remain in the deck.

(a) Concentrate on spades. What is the probability that the first card dealt is a spade? What is the conditional probability that the second card is a spade, given that the first is a spade? (*Hint:* How many cards remain? How many of these are spades?)

(b) Continue to count the remaining cards to find the conditional probabilities of a spade on the third, the fourth, and the fifth card, given in each case that all previous cards are spades.

(c) The probability of being dealt 5 spades is the product of the 5 probabilities you have found. What is this probability?

(d) The probability of being dealt 5 hearts or 5 diamonds or 5 clubs is the same as the probability of being dealt 5 spades. What is the probability of being dealt a flush?

Tree diagrams

Probability models often have several stages, with probabilities at each stage conditional on the outcomes of earlier states. These models require us to combine several of the basic rules into a more elaborate calculation. Here is an example.

EXAMPLE 11.10   Who visits YouTube?

STATE: Video sharing sites, led by YouTube, are popular destinations on the Internet. Let's look only at adult Internet users, age 18 and over. About 27% of adult Internet users are 18 to 29 years old, another 45% are 30 to 49 years old, and the remaining 28% are 50 and over. The Pew Internet and American Life Project finds that 70% of Internet users aged 18 to 29 have visited a video sharing site, along with 51% of those aged 30 to 49 and 26% of those 50 or older. What percent of all adult Internet users visit video sharing sites?

Jim Craigmyle/CORBIS

PLAN: To use the tools of probability, restate all of these percents as probabilities. If we choose an online adult at random,

$$P(\text{age 18 to 29}) = 0.27$$
$$P(\text{age 30 to 49}) = 0.45$$
$$P(\text{age 50 and older}) = 0.28$$

These three probabilities add to 1 because all adult Internet users are in one of the three age groups. The percents of each group who visit video sharing sites are *conditional* probabilities:

$$P(\text{video yes} \mid \text{age 18 to 29}) = 0.70$$
$$P(\text{video yes} \mid \text{age 30 to 49}) = 0.51$$
$$P(\text{video yes} \mid \text{age 50 and older}) = 0.26$$

We want to find the unconditional probability $P(\text{video yes})$.

SOLVE: The **tree diagram** in Figure 11.5 organizes this information. Each segment in the tree is one stage of the problem. Each complete branch shows a path through the two stages. The probability written on each segment is the conditional probability of an Internet user following that segment, given that he or she has reached the node from which it branches.

tree diagram

Starting at the left, an Internet user falls into one of the three age groups. The probabilities of these groups mark the leftmost segments in the tree. Look at age 18 to 29, the top

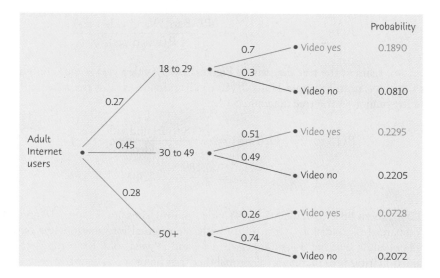

FIGURE 11.5
Tree diagram for use of the Internet and video sharing sites such as YouTube, for Example 11.10. The three disjoint paths to the outcome that an adult Internet user visits video sharing sites are colored red.

branch. The two segments going out from the "18 to 29" branch point carry the conditional probabilities

$$P(\text{video yes} \mid \text{age 18 to 29}) = 0.70$$
$$P(\text{video no} \mid \text{age 18 to 29}) = 0.30$$

The full tree shows the probabilities for all three age groups.

Now use the multiplication rule. The probability that a randomly chosen Internet user is an 18- to 29-year-old who visits video sharing sites is

$$P(\text{18 to 29 and video yes}) = P(\text{18 to 29})P(\text{video yes} \mid \text{18 to 29})$$
$$= (0.27)(0.70) = 0.1890$$

This probability appears at the end of the topmost branch. The multiplication rule says that the probability of any complete branch in the tree is the product of the probabilities of the segments in that branch.

There are three disjoint paths to "video yes," one for each of the three age groups. These paths are colored red in Figure 11.5. Because the three paths are disjoint, the probability that an adult Internet user visits video sharing sites is the sum of their probabilities:

$$P(\text{video yes}) = (0.27)(0.70) + (0.45)(0.51) + (0.28)(0.26)$$
$$= 0.1890 + 0.2295 + 0.0728 = 0.4913$$

CONCLUDE: About 49% of all adult Internet users have visited a video sharing site. ■

It takes longer to explain a tree diagram than it does to use it. Once you have understood a problem well enough to draw the tree, the rest is easy. Here is another question about video sharing sites that the tree diagram helps us answer.

EXAMPLE 11.11 **Young adults at video sharing sites**

STATE: What percent of adult Internet users who visit video sharing sites are age 18 to 29?

PLAN: In probability language, we want the conditional probability $P(\text{18 to 29} \mid \text{video yes})$. Use the tree diagram and the definition of conditional probability:

$$P(\text{18 to 29} \mid \text{video yes}) = \frac{P(\text{18 to 29 and video yes})}{P(\text{video yes})}$$

SOLVE: Look again at the tree diagram in Figure 11.5. $P(\text{video yes})$ is the sum of the three red probabilities, as in Example 11.10. $P(\text{18 to 29 and video yes})$ is the result of following just the top branch in the tree diagram. So

$$P(\text{18 to 29} \mid \text{video yes}) = \frac{P(\text{18 to 29 and video yes})}{P(\text{video yes})}$$
$$= \frac{0.1890}{0.4913} = 0.3847$$

CONCLUDE: About 38% of adults who visit video sharing sites are between 18 and 29 years old. Compare this conditional probability with the original information (unconditional) that 27% of adult Internet users are between 18 and 29 years old. Knowing that a person visits video sharing sites increases the probability that he or she is young. ■

Examples 11.10 and 11.11 illustrate a common setting for tree diagrams. Some outcome (such as visiting video sharing sites) has several sources (such as the three age groups). Starting from

- the probability of each source, and
- the conditional probability of the outcome given each source

the tree diagram leads to the overall probability of the outcome. Example 11.10 does this. You can then use the probability of the outcome and the definition of conditional probability to find the conditional probability of one of the sources, given that the outcome occurred. Example 11.11 shows how.

APPLY YOUR KNOWLEDGE

11.12 Peanut and tree nut allergies. About 1% of the American population is allergic to peanuts or tree nuts.[5] Choose 5 individuals at random and let the random variable X be the number in this sample who are allergic to peanuts or tree nuts. The possible values X can take are 0, 1, 2, 3, 4, and 5. Make a five-stage tree diagram of the outcomes (allergic or not allergic) for the 5 individuals and use it to find the probability distribution of X.

11.13 Testing for HIV. Enzyme immunoassay tests are used to screen blood specimens for the presence of antibodies to HIV, the virus that causes AIDS. Antibodies indicate the presence of the virus. The test is quite accurate but is not always correct. Here are approximate probabilities of positive and negative test results when the blood tested does and does not actually contain antibodies to HIV:[6]

	Test Result	
	Positive	Negative
Antibodies present	0.9985	0.0015
Antibodies absent	0.0060	0.9940

Suppose that 1% of a large population carry antibodies to HIV in their blood.

(a) Draw a tree diagram for selecting a person from this population (outcomes: antibodies present or absent) and testing his or her blood (outcomes: test positive or negative).

(b) What is the probability that the test is positive for a randomly chosen person from this population?

11.14 Peanut and tree nut allergies. Continue your work from Exercise 11.12. What is the conditional probability that exactly 1 of the people will be allergic to peanuts or tree nuts, given that at least 1 of the 5 people suffers from one of these allergies?

11.15 False HIV positives. Continue your work from Exercise 11.13. What is the probability that a person has the antibody, given that the test is positive? (Your result illustrates a fact that is important when considering proposals for widespread testing for HIV, illegal drugs, or agents of biological warfare: if the condition being tested is uncommon in the population, most positives will be false positives.)

CHAPTER 11 SUMMARY

■ Events A and B are **disjoint** if they have no outcomes in common. In that case, $P(A \text{ or } B) = P(A) + P(B)$.

■ The **conditional probability** $P(B \mid A)$ of an event B given an event A is defined by

$$P(B \mid A) = \frac{P(A \text{ and } B)}{P(A)}$$

when $P(A) > 0$. In practice, we most often find conditional probabilities from directly available information rather than from the definition.

■ Events A and B are **independent** if knowing that one event occurs does not change the probability we would assign to the other event; that is, $P(B \mid A) = P(B)$. In that case, $P(A \text{ and } B) = P(A)P(B)$.

■ Any assignment of probability obeys these rules:

Addition rule for disjoint events: If events $A, B, C, \ldots$ are all disjoint in pairs, then

$$P(\text{at least one of these events occurs}) = P(A) + P(B) + P(C) + \cdots$$

Multiplication rule for independent events: If events $A, B, C, \ldots$ are independent, then

$$P(\text{all of these events occur}) = P(A)P(B)P(C)\cdots$$

General addition rule: For any two events A and B,

$$P(A \text{ or } B) = P(A) + P(B) - P(A \text{ and } B)$$

General multiplication rule: For any two events A and B,

$$P(A \text{ and } B) = P(A)P(B \mid A)$$

■ **Tree diagrams** organize probability models that have several stages.

CHECK YOUR SKILLS

11.16 An instant lottery game gives you probability 0.02 of winning on any one play. Plays are independent of each other. If you play 3 times, the probability that you win on none of your plays is about
(a) 0.98.   (b) 0.94.   (c) 0.000008.

11.17 Choose an American adult at random. The probability that you choose a woman is 0.52. The probability that the person you choose has never married is 0.25. The probability that you choose a woman who has never married is 0.11. The probability that the person you choose is either a woman or never married (or both) is therefore about
(a) 0.77.   (b) 0.66.   (c) 0.13.

Accidents, suicide, and murder are the leading causes of death for young adults. Following are the counts of violent deaths in a recent year among people 20 to 24 years of age.

	Female	Male
Accidents	1818	6457
Homicide	457	2870
Suicide	345	2152

Exercises 11.18 to 11.21 are based on this table.

11.18 Choose a violent death in this age group at random. The probability that the victim was male is about
(a) 0.81.   (b) 0.78.   (c) 0.19.

11.19 The conditional probability that the victim was male, given that the death was accidental, is about
(a) 0.81.   (b) 0.78.   (c) 0.56.

11.20 The conditional probability that the death was accidental, given that the victim was male, is about
(a) 0.81.   (b) 0.78.   (c) 0.56.

11.21 Let A be the event that a victim of violent death was a woman and B the event that the death was a suicide. The proportion of suicides among violent deaths of women is expressed in probability notation as
(a) $P(A \text{ and } B)$.   (b) $P(A \mid B)$.   (c) $P(B \mid A)$.

11.22 Of people who died in the United States in recent years, 86% were white, 12% were black, and 2% were Asian. (This ignores a small number of deaths among other races.) Diabetes caused 2.8% of deaths among whites, 4.4% among blacks, and 3.5% among Asians. The probability that a randomly chosen death is a white who died of diabetes is about
(a) 0.107.   (b) 0.030.   (c) 0.024.

CHAPTER 11 EXERCISES

11.23 Playing the lottery. New York State's "Quick Draw" lottery moves right along. Players choose between one and ten numbers from the range 1 to 80; 20 winning numbers are displayed on a screen every four minutes. If you choose just one number, your probability of winning is 20/80, or 0.25. Lester plays one number 8 times as he sits in a bar. What is the probability that all 8 bets lose?

11.24 Universal blood donors. People with type O-negative blood are universal donors. That is, any patient can receive a transfusion of O-negative blood. Only 7.2% of the American population have O-negative blood. If 10 people appear at random to give blood, what is the probability that at least 1 of them is a universal donor?

11.25 Playing the slots. Before electronics took over, slot machines were like this: you pull the lever to spin three wheels; each wheel has 20 symbols, all equally likely to show when the wheel stops spinning; the three wheels are independent of each other. Suppose that the middle wheel has 9 cherries among its 20 symbols, and the left and right wheels have 1 cherry each.
(a) You win the jackpot if all three wheels show cherries. What is the probability of winning the jackpot?
(b) There are three ways that the three wheels can show two cherries and one symbol other than a cherry. Find the probability of each of these ways.
(c) What is the probability that the wheels stop with exactly two cherries showing among them?

11.26 A random walk on Wall Street? The "random walk" theory of stock prices says that price movements in disjoint time periods are independent of each other. Suppose that we record only whether the price is up or down each year, and that the probability that our portfolio rises in price in any one year is 0.65.

(a) What is the probability that our portfolio goes up for three consecutive years?
(b) What is the probability that the portfolio's value moves in the same direction (either up or down) for three consecutive years?

11.27 Getting into college. Ramon has applied to both Princeton and Stanford. He thinks the probability that Princeton will admit him is 0.4, the probability that Stanford will admit him is 0.5, and the probability that both will admit him is 0.2. Make a Venn diagram. Then answer these questions.
(a) What is the probability that neither university admits Ramon?
(b) What is the probability that he gets into Stanford but not Princeton?
(c) Are admission to Princeton and admission to Stanford independent events?

11.28 Tendon surgery. You have torn a tendon and are facing surgery to repair it. The surgeon explains the risks to you: infection occurs in 3% of such operations, the repair fails in 14%, and both infection and failure occur together in 1%. What percent of these operations succeed and are free from infection? Follow the four-step process in your answer.

11.29 Screening job applicants. A company retains a psychologist to assess whether job applicants are suited for assembly-line work. The psychologist classifies applicants as one of A (well suited), B (marginal), or C (not suited). The company is concerned about the event D that an employee leaves the company within a year of being hired. Data on all people hired in the past five years give these probabilities:

$P(A) = 0.4$ $P(B) = 0.3$ $P(C) = 0.3$
$P(A \text{ and } D) = 0.1$ $P(B \text{ and } D) = 0.1$ $P(C \text{ and } D) = 0.2$

Sketch a Venn diagram of the events A, B, C, and D and mark on your diagram the probabilities of all combinations of psychological assessment and leaving (or not) within a year. What is $P(D)$, the probability that an employee leaves within a year?

11.30 Foreign-language study. Choose a student in grades 9 to 12 at random and ask if he or she is studying a language other than English. Here is the distribution of results:

Language	Spanish	French	German	All others	None
Probability	0.26	0.09	0.03	0.03	0.59

What is the conditional probability that a student is studying Spanish, given that he or she is studying some language other than English?

11.31 Income tax returns. Here is the distribution of the adjusted gross income (in thousands of dollars) reported on individual federal income tax returns in 2006:

Income	< 15	15–49	50–99	100–199	≥ 200
Probability	0.272	0.394	0.217	0.087	0.030

(a) What is the probability that a randomly chosen return shows an adjusted gross income of $50,000 or more?
(b) Given that a return shows an income of at least $50,000, what is the conditional probability that the income is at least $100,000?

11.32 Computer games. Here is the distribution of computer games sold by type of game:[7]

Game type	Probability
Strategy	0.354
Role playing	0.139
Family entertainment	0.127
Shooters	0.109
Children's	0.057
Other	0.214

What is the conditional probability that a computer game is a role-playing game, given that it is not a strategy game?

11.33 A probability teaser. Suppose (as is roughly correct) that each child born is equally likely to be a boy or a girl and that the sexes of successive children are independent. If we let BG mean that the older child is a boy and the younger child is a girl, then each of the combinations BB, BG, GB, GG has probability 0.25. Ashley and Brianna each have two children.
(a) You know that at least one of Ashley's children is a boy. What is the conditional probability that she has two boys?
(b) You know that Brianna's older child is a boy. What is the conditional probability that she has two boys?

11.34 College degrees. A striking trend in higher education is that more women than men reach each level of attainment. Here are the counts (in thousands) of earned degrees in the United States in the 2010–2011 academic year, classified by level and by the sex of the degree recipient:[8]

	Bachelor's	Master's	Professional	Doctorate	Total
Female	986	411	52	32	1481
Male	693	260	45	27	1025
Total	1679	671	97	59	2506

(a) If you choose a degree recipient at random, what is the probability that the person you choose is a woman?
(b) What is the conditional probability that you choose a woman, given that the person chosen received a doctorate?
(c) Are the events "choose a woman" and "choose a doctoral degree recipient" independent? How do you know?

11.35 College degrees. Exercise 11.34 gives the counts (in thousands) of earned degrees in the United States in the 2010–2011 academic year. Use these data to answer the following questions.
(a) What is the probability that a randomly chosen degree recipient is a man?
(b) What is the conditional probability that the person chosen received a bachelor's degree, given that he is a man?
(c) Use the multiplication rule to find the probability of choosing a male bachelor's degree recipient. Check your result by finding this probability directly from the table of counts.

11.36 Deer and pine seedlings. As suburban gardeners know, deer will eat almost anything green. In a study of pine seedlings at an environmental center in Ohio, researchers noted how deer damage varied with how much of the seedling was covered by thorny undergrowth:[9]

	Deer Damage	
Thorny cover	Yes	No
None	60	151
< 1/3	76	158
1/3 to 2/3	44	177
> 2/3	29	176

(a) What is the probability that a randomly selected seedling was damaged by deer?
(b) What are the conditional probabilities that a randomly selected seedling was damaged, given each level of cover?
(c) Does knowing about the amount of thorny cover on a seedling change the probability of deer damage? If so, cover and damage are not independent.

11.37 Deer and pine seedlings. In the setting of Exercise 11.36, what percent of the trees that were damaged by deer were less than 1/3 covered by thorny plants?

11.38 Deer and pine seedlings. In the setting of Exercise 11.36, what percent of the trees that were not damaged by deer were more than 2/3 covered by thorny plants?

Julie is graduating from college. She has studied biology, chemistry, and computing and hopes to use her science background in crime investigation. Late one night she thinks about some jobs for which she has applied. Let A, B, and C be the events that Julie is offered a job by

A = the Connecticut Office of the Chief Medical Examiner

B = the New Jersey Division of Criminal Justice

C = the federal Disaster Mortuary Operations Response Team

Julie writes down her personal probabilities for being offered these jobs:

$P(A) = 0.6$	$P(B) = 0.4$	$P(C) = 0.2$
$P(A \text{ and } B) = 0.1$	$P(A \text{ and } C) = 0.05$	$P(B \text{ and } C) = 0.05$
$P(A \text{ and } B \text{ and } C) = 0$		

Make a Venn diagram of the events A, B, and C. As in Figure 11.4, mark the probabilities of every intersection involving these events. Use this diagram for Exercises 11.39 to 11.41.

11.39 Will Julie get a job offer? What is the probability that Julie is offered at least one of the three jobs?

11.40 Will Julie get just these offers? What is the probability that Julie is offered both the Connecticut and New Jersey jobs, but not the federal job?

11.41 Julie's conditional probabilities. If Julie is offered the federal job, what is the conditional probability that she is also offered the New Jersey job? If Julie is offered the New Jersey job, what is the conditional probability that she is also offered the federal job?

11.42 The geometric distributions. You are tossing a pair of balanced dice in a board game. Tosses are independent. You land in a danger zone that requires you to roll doubles (both faces show the same number of spots) before you are allowed to play again. How long will you wait to play again?

(a) What is the probability of rolling doubles on a single toss of the dice? (If you need review, the possible outcomes appear in Figure 9.2 (page 167). All 36 outcomes are equally likely.)

(b) What is the probability that you do not roll doubles on the first toss, but you do on the second toss?

(c) What is the probability that the first two tosses are not doubles and the third toss is doubles? This is the probability that the first doubles occurs on the third toss.

(d) Now you see the pattern. What is the probability that the first doubles occurs on the fourth toss? On the fifth toss? Give the general result: what is the probability that the first doubles occurs on the kth toss?

(*Comment:* The distribution of the number of trials to the first success is called a *geometric distribution*. In this problem you have found geometric distribution probabilities when the probability of a success on each trial is 1/6. The same idea works for any probability of success.)

11.43 Winning at tennis. A player serving in tennis has two chances to get a serve into play. If the first serve is out, the player serves again. If the second serve is also out, the player loses the point. Here are probabilities based on four years of the Wimbledon Championship:[10]

$$P(\text{1st serve in}) = 0.59$$
$$P(\text{win point} \mid \text{1st serve in}) = 0.73$$
$$P(\text{2nd serve in} \mid \text{1st serve out}) = 0.86$$
$$P(\text{win point} \mid \text{1st serve out and 2nd serve in}) = 0.59$$

Make a tree diagram for the results of the two serves and the outcome (win or lose) of the point. (The branches in your tree have different numbers of stages depending on the outcome of the first serve.) What is the probability that the serving player wins the point?

11.44 Urban voters. The voters in a large city are 40% white, 40% black, and 20% Hispanic. (Hispanics may be of any race in official statistics, but here we are speaking of political blocks.) A black mayoral candidate anticipates attracting 30% of the white vote, 90% of the black vote, and 50% of the Hispanic vote. Draw a tree diagram with probabilities for the race (white, black, or Hispanic) and vote (for or against the candidate) of a randomly chosen voter. What percent of the overall vote does the candidate expect to get? Use the four-step process to guide your work.

11.45 Winning at tennis, continued. Based on your work in Exercise 11.43, in what percent of points won by the server was the first serve in? (Write this as a conditional probability and use the definition of conditional probability.)

11.46 Where do the votes come from? In the election described in Exercise 11.44, what percent of the candidate's votes come from black voters? (Write this as a conditional probability and use the definition of conditional probability.)

11.47 Lactose intolerance. Lactose intolerance causes difficulty digesting dairy products that contain lactose (milk sugar). It is particularly common among people of African and Asian ancestry. In the United States (ignoring other groups and people who consider themselves to belong to more than one race), 82% of the population is white, 14% is black, and 4% is Asian. Moreover, 15% of whites, 70% of blacks, and 90% of Asians are lactose intolerant.[11]

(a) What percent of the entire population is lactose intolerant?

(b) What percent of people who are lactose intolerant are Asian?

FIGURE 11.6

Tree diagram for fundraising by telephone, for Exercise 11.48. The three stages are the type of prospect called, whether or not the person makes a pledge, and whether or not a person who pledges actually makes a contribution.

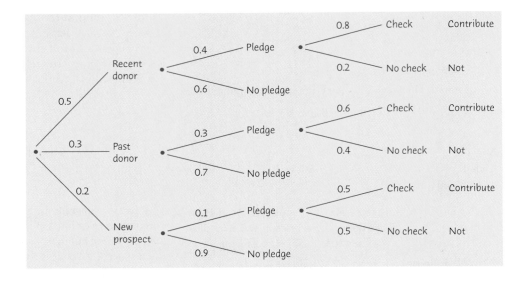

11.48 Fundraising by telephone. Tree diagrams can organize problems having more than two stages. Figure 11.6 shows probabilities for a charity calling potential donors by telephone.[12] Each person called is either a recent donor, a past donor, or a new prospect. At the next stage, the person called either does or does not pledge to contribute, with conditional probabilities that depend on the donor class the person belongs to. Finally, those who make a pledge either do or don't actually make a contribution.
(a) What percent of calls result in a contribution?
(b) What percent of those who contribute are recent donors?

Mendelian inheritance. *Some traits of plants and animals depend on inheritance of a single gene. This is called Mendelian inheritance, after Gregor Mendel (1822–1884). Exercises 11.49 to 11.52 are based on the following information about Mendelian inheritance of blood type.*

Each of us has an ABO blood type, which describes whether two characteristics called A and B are present. Every human being has two blood type alleles (gene forms), one inherited from our mother and one from our father. Each of these alleles can be A, B, or O. Which two we inherit determines our blood type. The table shows what our blood type is for each combination of two alleles.

Alleles inherited	Blood type
A and A	A
A and B	AB
A and O	A
B and B	B
B and O	B
O and O	O

We inherit each of a parent's two alleles with probability 0.5. We inherit independently from our mother and father.

11.49 Rachel and Jonathan both have alleles A and B.
(a) What blood types can their children have?
(b) What is the probability that their next child has each of these blood types?

11.50 Sarah and David both have alleles B and O.
(a) What blood types can their children have?
(b) What is the probability that their next child has each of these blood types?

11.51 Isabel has alleles A and O. Carlos has alleles A and B. They have two children.
(a) What is the probability that both children have blood type A?
(b) What is the probability that both children have the same blood type?

11.52 Jasmine has alleles A and O. Tyrone has alleles B and O.
(a) What is the probability that a child of these parents has blood type O?
(b) If Jasmine and Tyrone have three children, what is the probability that all three have blood type O?
(c) What is the probability that the first child has blood type O and the next two do not?

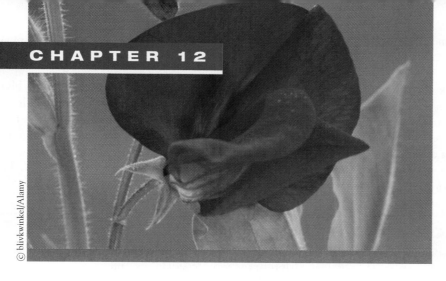

The color of sweet pea blossoms follows laws of inheritance expressed in probabilities (Exercise 12.28).

CHAPTER 12

Binomial Distributions*

**IN THIS CHAPTER
WE COVER...**

- The binomial setting and binomial distributions
- Binomial distributions in statistical sampling
- Binomial probabilities
- Binomial mean and standard deviation
- The Normal approximation to binomial distributions

A basketball player shoots 5 free throws. How many does she make? A sample survey dials 1200 residential phone numbers at random. How many live people answer the phone? You plant 10 dogwood trees. How many live through the winter? In all these situations, we want a probability model for a *count* of successful outcomes.

The binomial setting and binomial distributions

The distribution of a count depends on how the data are produced. Here is a common situation.

THE BINOMIAL SETTING

1. There are a fixed number n of observations.
2. The n observations are all **independent.** That is, knowing the result of one observation does not change the probabilities we assign to other observations.
3. Each observation falls into one of just two categories, which for convenience we call "success" and "failure."
4. The probability of a success, call it p, is the same for each observation.

---

*This more advanced chapter concerns a special topic in probability. The material is not needed to read the rest of the book.

Think of tossing a coin n times as an example of the binomial setting. Each toss gives either heads or tails. Knowing the outcome of one toss doesn't change the probability of a head on any other toss, so the tosses are independent. If we call heads a success, then p is the probability of a head and remains the same as long as we toss the same coin. For tossing a coin, p is close to 0.5. If we spin the coin on a flat surface rather than toss it, p is not equal to 0.5. The number of heads we count is a discrete random variable X. The distribution of X is called a *binomial distribution*.

BINOMIAL DISTRIBUTION

The count X of successes in the binomial setting has the **binomial distribution** with parameters n and p. The parameter n is the number of observations, and p is the probability of a success on any one observation. The possible values of X are the whole numbers from 0 to n.

The binomial distributions are an important class of discrete probability models. *Pay attention to the binomial setting, because not all counts have binomial distributions.*

EXAMPLE 12.1 **Counting boys**

Choose two births at random from the last year's births at a large hospital and count the number of boys (0, 1, or 2). The genders of children born to different mothers are surely independent. The probability that a randomly chosen birth in Canada and the United States is a boy is about 0.52. So the count of boys has a binomial distribution with $n = 2$ and $p = 0.52$.

Next, observe successive births at a large hospital and let X be the number of births until the first boy is born. Births are independent and each has probability 0.52 of being a boy. Yet X is *not* binomial, because there is no fixed number of observations. "Count observations until the first success" is a different setting than "count the number of successes in a fixed number of observations." ∎

Binomial distributions in statistical sampling

The binomial distributions are important in statistics when we wish to make inferences about the proportion p of "successes" in a population. Here is a typical example.

EXAMPLE 12.2 **Choosing an SRS of DVDs**

A distributor inspects an SRS of 10 DVDs from a shipment of 10,000 DVDs of a popular film. Suppose that (unknown to the distributor) 10% of the DVDs in the shipment have defective copy-protection schemes that will harm personal computers. Count the number X of bad DVDs in the sample.

This is not quite a binomial setting. Removing one DVD changes the proportion of bad DVDs remaining in the shipment. So the probability that the second DVD chosen is bad changes when we know whether the first is good or bad. But removing one DVD from a shipment of 10,000 changes the makeup of the remaining 9999 DVDs very little. In practice, the distribution of X is very close to the binomial distribution with $n = 10$ and $p = 0.1$. ▪

Example 12.2 shows how we can use the binomial distributions in the statistical setting of selecting an SRS. When the population is much larger than the sample, a count of successes in an SRS of size n has approximately the binomial distribution with n equal to the sample size and p equal to the proportion of successes in the population.

> **SAMPLING DISTRIBUTION OF A COUNT**
>
> Choose an SRS of size n from a population with proportion p of successes. When the population is much larger than the sample, the count X of successes in the sample has approximately the binomial distribution with parameters n and p.

APPLY YOUR KNOWLEDGE

In each of Exercises 12.1 to 12.3, X is a count. Does X have a binomial distribution? Give your reasons in each case.

12.1 Random digit dialing. When an opinion poll calls residential telephone numbers at random, only 20% of the calls reach a live person. You watch the random dialing machine make 15 calls. X is the number that reach a live person.

12.2 Random digit dialing. When an opinion poll calls residential telephone numbers at random, only 20% of the calls reach a live person. You watch the random dialing machine make calls. X is the number of calls until the first live person answers.

12.3 Computer instruction. A student studies binomial distributions using computer-assisted instruction. After the lesson, the computer presents 10 problems. The student solves each problem and enters her answer. The computer gives additional instruction between problems if the answer is wrong. The count X is the number of problems that the student gets right.

12.4 Teens feel the heat. Opinion polls find that 63% of American teens say that their parents put at least some pressure on them to get into a good college.[1] If you take an SRS of 1000 teens, what is the approximate distribution of the number in your sample who say they feel at least some pressure from their parents to get into a good college?

Binomial probabilities

We can find a formula for the probability that a binomial random variable takes any value by starting from the multiplication rule for independent events (page 201).

BINOMIAL PROBABILITY

If X has the binomial distribution with n observations and probability p of success on each observation, the possible values of X are 0, 1, 2, ..., n. If k is any one of these values, the **binomial probability** of k successes is

$$P(X = k) = \frac{n!}{k!\,(n-k)!}\,p^k(1-p)^{n-k}$$

This expression uses the **factorial** notation:

$$n! = n \times (n-1) \times (n-2) \times \cdots \times 3 \times 2 \times 1$$

In addition, we define $0! = 1$.

EXAMPLE 12.3 **Inheriting blood type**

The blood types of successive children born to the same parents are independent and have fixed probabilities that depend on the genetic makeup of the parents. Each child born to a particular set of parents has probability 0.25 of having blood type O. If these parents have 5 children, what is the probability that exactly 2 of them have type O blood?

The number X of children with type O blood has the binomial distribution with $n = 5$ and $p = 0.25$. The probability we want is

$$P(X = 2) = \frac{5!}{2!\,3!}\,(0.25)^2(0.75)^3$$

Calculating a binomial probability is made easier by the fact that the larger of the two factorials in the denominator will cancel much of the $n!$ in the numerator:

$$P(X = 2) = \frac{(5)(4)(3)(2)(1)}{(2)(1) \times (3)(2)(1)}\,(0.25)^2(0.75)^3$$

$$= \frac{(5)(4)}{(2)(1)}\,(0.25)^2(0.75)^3$$

$$= 10(0.25)^2(0.75)^3 = 0.2637 \;\blacksquare$$

The binomial probability formula is awkward to use unless the number of observations n is quite small. Graphing calculators and software will give you binomial probabilities $P(X = k)$ and cumulative probabilities $P(X \leq k)$. Here, for example, is Minitab's output for the binomial probability in Example 12.3:

```
Binomial with n = 5 and p = 0.25

x   P(X=x)
2    0.263672
```

Optional: Where does the formula come from? We can arrive at the binomial probability formula used in Example 12.3 as follows. The multiplication rule says that the probability that (say) the first and third children have type O blood is

$$(0.25)(0.75)(0.25)(0.75)(0.75) = (0.25)^2(0.75)^3$$

You see that *any* arrangement of 2 successes and 3 failures among the 5 children has this same probability. So the overall probability of exactly 2 successes is $(0.25)^2(0.75)^3$ times the number of ways of arranging 2 successes and 3 failures. You can write these out as SSFFF, SFSFF, and so on to see that there are 10 such arrangements. In general, the number of ways of arranging k successes and $n - k$ failures among n trials is the $n!/k!(n - k)!$ in the binomial probability formula. This expression is called a **binomial coefficient.**

binomial coefficient

APPLY YOUR KNOWLEDGE

12.5 Proofreading. Typing errors in a text are either nonword errors (as when "the" is typed as "teh") or word errors that result in a real but incorrect word. Spell-checking software will catch nonword errors but not word errors. Human proofreaders catch 70% of word errors. You ask a fellow student to proofread an essay in which you have deliberately made 10 word errors.

(a) If the student matches the usual 70% rate, what is the distribution of the number of errors caught? What is the distribution of the number of errors missed?

(b) Missing 3 or more out of 10 errors seems a poor performance. What is the probability that a proofreader who catches 70% of word errors misses exactly 3 out of 10? If you use software, also find the probability of missing 3 or more out of 10.

12.6 Random digit dialing. When an opinion poll calls residential telephone numbers at random, only 20% of the calls reach a live person. You watch the random digit dialing machine make 15 calls.

(a) What is the probability that exactly 3 calls reach a person?

(b) What is the probability that at most 3 calls reach a person?

(c) What is the probability that at least 3 calls reach a person?

(d) What is the probability that fewer than 3 calls reach a person?

(e) What is the probability that more than 3 calls reach a person?

Binomial mean and standard deviation

If a count X has the binomial distribution based on n observations with probability p of success, what is its mean μ? That is, in very many repetitions of the binomial setting, what will be the average count of successes? We can guess the answer. If a basketball player makes 80% of her free throws, the mean number made in 10 tries should be 80% of 10, or 8. In general, the mean of a binomial distribution should be $\mu = np$. Here are the facts.

BINOMIAL MEAN AND STANDARD DEVIATION

If a count X has the binomial distribution with number of observations n and probability of success p, the **mean** and **standard deviation** of X are

$$\mu = np$$
$$\sigma = \sqrt{np(1 - p)}$$

EXAMPLE 12.4 **Inheriting blood type**

Continuing Example 12.3, the count X of children with type O blood is binomial with $n = 5$ and $p = 0.25$. The histogram in Figure 12.1 displays this probability distribution. (Because probabilities are long-run proportions, using probabilities as the heights of the bars shows what the distribution of X would be in very many repetitions.) The distribution is skewed to the right.

The mean and standard deviation of the binomial distribution in Figure 12.1 are

$$\mu = np$$
$$= (5)(0.25) = 1.25$$
$$\sigma = \sqrt{np(1-p)}$$
$$= \sqrt{(5)(0.25)(0.75)} = \sqrt{0.9375} = 0.9682$$

The mean is marked on the probability histogram in Figure 12.1. Notice that the mean need not be a whole number even though all of the possible outcomes are whole numbers. If we look at very many couples with these genetic makeups who have 5 children, the average number of their children who have type O blood is 1.25. ■

FIGURE 12.1

Probability histogram for the binomial distribution with $n = 5$ and $p = 0.25$, for Example 12.4.

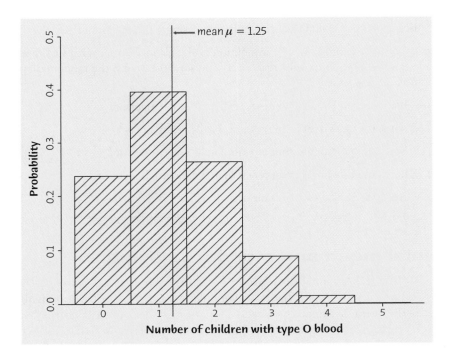

APPLY YOUR KNOWLEDGE

12.7 Proofreading. Return to the proofreading setting of Exercise 12.5.

(a) If X is the number of word errors missed, what is the distribution of X? If Y is the number of word errors caught, what is the distribution of Y?

(b) What is the mean number of errors caught? What is the mean number of errors missed? The mean counts of successes and of failures always add to n, the number of observations.

(c) What is the standard deviation of the number of errors caught? What is the standard deviation of the number of errors missed? The standard deviations of the count of successes and the count of failures are always the same.

12.8 Random digit dialing. When an opinion poll calls residential telephone numbers at random, only 20% of the calls reach a live person. You watch the random digit dialing machine make 15 calls.

(a) What is the mean number of calls that reach a person?

(b) What is the standard deviation σ of the count of calls that reach a person?

(c) If calls are made to New York City rather than nationally, the probability that a call reaches a person is only $p = 0.08$. How does this new p affect the standard deviation? What would be the standard deviation if $p = 0.01$? What does your work show about the behavior of the standard deviation of a binomial distribution as the probability of a success gets closer to 0?

The Normal approximation to binomial distributions

It isn't practical to use the formula for binomial probabilities when the number of observations n is large. Software or a graphing calculator will handle many problems that are beyond the reach of hand calculation. If technology does not rescue you, there is another alternative: *as the number of observations n gets larger, the binomial distribution gets close to a Normal distribution.* When n is large, we can use Normal probability calculations to approximate binomial probabilities. Here are the facts.

> **NORMAL APPROXIMATION FOR BINOMIAL DISTRIBUTIONS**
>
> Suppose that a count X has the binomial distribution with n observations and success probability p. When n is large, the distribution of X is approximately Normal, $N(np, \sqrt{np(1-p)}\,)$.
>
> As a rule of thumb, we will use the Normal approximation when n is so large that $np \geq 10$ and $n(1-p) \geq 10$.

The Normal approximation is easy to remember because it says to act as if X is Normal with exactly the same mean and standard deviation as the binomial. The accuracy of the Normal approximation improves as the sample size n increases. It is most accurate for any fixed n when p is close to 1/2 and least accurate when p is near 0 or 1. This is why the rule of thumb in the box depends on p as well as n.

EXAMPLE 12.5 Attitudes toward shopping

Sample surveys show that fewer people enjoy shopping than in the past. A survey asked a nationwide random sample of 2500 adults if they agreed or disagreed that "I like buying new clothes, but shopping is often frustrating and time-consuming."[2] The population that the poll wants to draw conclusions about is all U.S. residents aged 18 and over. Suppose that in fact 60% of all adult U.S. residents would say "Agree" if asked the same question. What is the probability that 1520 or more of the sample agree? ■

Erica Shires/zefa/CORBIS

FIGURE 12.2
Probability histogram for the binomial distribution with $n = 2500$, $p = 0.6$. The bars at and above 1520 are shaded to highlight the probability of getting at least 1520 successes. The shape of this binomial probability distribution closely resembles a Normal curve.

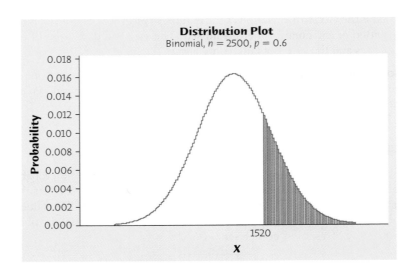

Because there are about 235 million adults in the United States, the responses of 2500 randomly chosen adults are very close to independent. So the number in our sample who agree that shopping is frustrating is a random variable X having the binomial distribution with $n = 2500$ and $p = 0.6$. Figure 12.2 is a probability histogram of this distribution, from Minitab. As the Normal approximation suggests, the shape of the distribution looks Normal.

To find the probability $P(X \geq 1520)$ that at least 1520 of the people in the sample find shopping frustrating, we must add the binomial probabilities of all outcomes from $X = 1520$ to $X = 2500$. This is is the sum of the heights of the shaded bars in Figure 12.2. Statistical software can find the exact probability. In most cases, software finds cumulative probabilities $P(X \leq x)$. So start by writing

$$P(X \geq 1520) = 1 - P(X \leq 1519)$$

Here is Minitab's answer for $P(X \leq 1519)$:

```
Binomial with n = 2500 and p = 0.6

    x      P(X<=x)
 1519     0.786861
```

The probability we want is $1 - 0.786861 = 0.213139$, correct to 6 decimal places. We can avoid the need for software by using the Normal approximation.

EXAMPLE 12.6 **Normal calculation of a binomial probability**

Act as though the count X has the Normal distribution with the same mean and standard deviation as the binomial distribution:

$$\mu = np = (2500)(0.6) = 1500$$

$$\sigma = \sqrt{np(1 - p)} = \sqrt{(2500)(0.6)(0.4)} = 24.49$$

Standardizing X gives a standard Normal variable Z. The probability we want is

$$P(X \geq 1520) = P\left(\frac{X - 1500}{24.49} \geq \frac{1520 - 1500}{24.49}\right)$$

$$= P(Z \geq 0.82)$$

$$= 1 - 0.7939 = 0.2061$$

The Normal approximation 0.2061 misses the true probability by about 0.007. ■

Whether or not the Normal approximation is satisfactory depends on how accurate your calculations need to be. For most statistical purposes, great accuracy is not required. Our rule of thumb for use of the Normal approximation reflects this judgment.

APPLY YOUR KNOWLEDGE

12.9 Using Benford's law. According to Benford's law (Example 9.6, page 171) the probability that the first digit of the amount of a randomly chosen invoice is a 1 or a 2 is 0.477. You examine 90 invoices from a vendor and find that 29 have first digits 1 or 2. If Benford's law holds, the count of 1s and 2s will have the binomial distribution with $n = 90$ and $p = 0.477$. Too few 1s and 2s suggests fraud. What is the approximate probability of 29 or fewer if the invoices follow Benford's law? Do you suspect that the invoice amounts are not genuine?

12.10 College admissions. A small liberal arts college would like to have an entering class of 415 students next year. Past experience shows that about 27% of the students admitted will decide to attend. The college therefore plans to admit 1535 students. Suppose that students make their decisions independently and that the probability is 0.27 that a randomly chosen student will accept the offer of admission.

(a) What are the mean and standard deviation of the number of students who accept the admissions offer from this college?

(b) Use the Normal approximation: what is the approximate probability that the college gets more students than it wants?

(c) Use software to compute the exact probability that the college gets more students than it wants. How good is the approximation in part (b)?

12.11 Checking for survey errors. One way of checking the effect of undercoverage, nonresponse, and other sources of error in a sample survey is to compare the sample with known facts about the population. About 12% of American adults are black. The number X of blacks in random samples of 1500 adults should therefore vary with the binomial ($n = 1500$, $p = 0.12$) distribution.

(a) What are the mean and standard deviation of X?

(b) Use the Normal approximation to find the probability that the sample will contain between 165 and 195 blacks. Be sure to check that you can safely use the approximation.

CHAPTER 12 SUMMARY

■ A count X of successes has a **binomial distribution** in the **binomial setting:** there are n observations; the observations are independent of each other; each observation results in a success or a failure; each observation has the same probability p of a success.

■ The binomial distribution with n observations and probability p of success gives a good approximation to the sampling distribution of the count of successes in an SRS of size n from a large population containing proportion p of successes.

■ If X has the binomial distribution with parameters n and p, the possible values of X are the whole numbers $0, 1, 2, \ldots, n$. The **binomial probability** that X takes any of these values is

$$P(X = k) = \frac{n!}{k!\,(n-k)!}\, p^k (1-p)^{n-k}$$

Binomial probabilities in practice are best found using software. Here the **factorial $n!$** is

$$n! = n \times (n-1) \times (n-2) \times \cdots \times 3 \times 2 \times 1$$

for positive whole numbers n, and $0! = 1$.

■ The **mean** and **standard deviation** of a binomial count X are

$$\mu = np$$

$$\sigma = \sqrt{np(1-p)}$$

■ The **Normal approximation** to the binomial distribution says that if X is a count having the binomial distribution with parameters n and p, then when n is large, X is approximately $N(np, \sqrt{np(1-p)}\,)$. Use this approximation only when $np \geq 10$ and $n(1-p) \geq 10$.

CHECK YOUR SKILLS

12.12 Joe reads that 1 out of 4 eggs contains salmonella bacteria. So he never uses more than 3 eggs in cooking. If eggs do or don't contain salmonella independently of each other, the number of contaminated eggs when Joe uses 3 chosen at random has the distribution

(a) binomial with $n = 4$ and $p = 1/4$.
(b) binomial with $n = 3$ and $p = 1/4$.
(c) binomial with $n = 3$ and $p = 1/3$.

12.13 In a group of 10 college students, 4 are business majors. You choose 3 of the 10 students at random and ask their major. The distribution of the number of business majors you choose is

(a) binomial with $n = 10$ and $p = 0.4$.
(b) binomial with $n = 3$ and $p = 0.4$.
(c) not binomial.

12.14 A basketball player makes 70% of her free throws. She takes 7 free throws in a game. If the shots are independent of each other, the probability that she makes the first 5 and misses

the last 2 is about
(a) 0.635.   (b) 0.318.   (c) 0.015.

12.15 A basketball player makes 70% of her free throws. She takes 7 free throws in a game. If the shots are independent of each other, the probability that she makes 5 out of the 7 shots is about
(a) 0.635.   (b) 0.318.   (c) 0.015.

Each entry in a table of random digits like Table B has probability 0.1 of being a 0, and digits are independent of each other. Exercises 12.16 to 12.18 use this setting.

12.16 The probability of finding exactly 4 0s in a line 40 digits long is about
(a) 0.0000225.   (b) 0.0225.   (c) 0.2059.

12.17 The mean number of 0s in a line 40 digits long is
(a) 4.   (b) 3.098.   (c) 0.4.

12.18 Ten lines in the table contain 400 digits. The count of 0s in these lines is approximately Normal with
(a) mean 40 and standard deviation 36.
(b) mean 40 and standard deviation 6.
(c) mean 36 and standard deviation 6.

12.19 Binomial setting? In each situation below, is it reasonable to use a binomial distribution for the random variable X? Give reasons for your answer in each case.

(a) An auto manufacturer chooses one car from each hour's production for a detailed quality inspection. One variable recorded is the count X of finish defects (dimples, ripples, etc.) in the car's paint.

(b) The pool of potential jurors for a murder case contains 100 persons chosen at random from the adult residents of a large city. Each person in the pool is asked whether he or she opposes the death penalty; X is the number who say "Yes."

(c) Joe buys a ticket in his state's Pick 3 lottery game every week; X is the number of times in a year that he wins a prize.

12.20 Binomial setting? A binomial distribution will be approximately correct as a model for one of these two sports settings and not for the other. Explain why by briefly discussing both settings.

(a) A National Football League kicker has made 80% of his field goal attempts in the past. This season he attempts 20 field goals. The attempts differ widely in distance, angle, wind, and so on.

(b) A National Basketball Association player has made 80% of his free-throw attempts in the past. This season he takes 150 free throws. Basketball free throws are always attempted from 15 feet away with no interference from other players.

12.21 Testing ESP. In a test for ESP (extrasensory perception), a subject is told that cards the experimenter but not the subject can see contain either a star, a circle, a wave, or a square. As the experimenter looks at each of 20 cards in turn, the subject names the shape on the card. A subject who is just guessing has probability 0.25 of guessing correctly on each card.

(a) The count of correct guesses in 20 cards has a binomial distribution. What are n and p?

(b) What is the mean number of correct guesses in many repetitions of the experiment?

(c) What is the probability of exactly 5 correct guesses?

12.22 Random stock prices. A believer in the random walk theory of stock markets thinks that an index of stock prices has probability 0.65 of increasing in any year. Moreover, the change in the index in any given year is not influenced by whether it rose or fell in earlier years. Let X be the number of years among the next 5 years in which the index rises.

(a) X has a binomial distribution. What are n and p?

(b) What are the possible values that X can take?

(c) Find the probability of each value of X. Draw a probability histogram for the distribution of X. (See Figure 12.1 for an example of a probability histogram.)

(d) What are the mean and standard deviation of this distribution? Mark the location of the mean on your histogram.

12.23 On the Web. What kinds of Web sites do males aged 18 to 34 visit? About 50% of male Internet users in this age group visit an auction site such as eBay at least once a month.[3] Interview a random sample of 12 male Internet users aged 18 to 34.

(a) What is the distribution of the number who have visited an online auction site in the past month?

(b) What is the probability that exactly 8 of the 12 have visited an auction site in the past month? If you have software, also find the probability that at least 8 of the 12 have visited an auction site in the past month.

12.24 The pill. Many women take oral contraceptives to prevent pregnancy. Under ideal conditions, 1% of women taking the pill become pregnant within one year. In typical use, however, 5% become pregnant.[4] Choose at random 20 women taking the pill. How many become pregnant in the next year?

(a) Explain why this is a binomial setting.

(b) What is the probability that at least one of the women becomes pregnant under ideal conditions? What is the probability in typical use?

12.25 On the Web, continued. A study of Internet usage interviews a random sample of 500 men aged 18 to 34. Based on the information in Exercise 12.23, what is the probability that at least 235 of the men in the sample visit an online auction site at least once a month? (Check that the Normal approximation is permissible and use it to find this probability. If your software allows, find the exact binomial probability and compare the two results.)

12.26 The pill, continued. A study of the effectiveness of oral contraceptives interviews a random sample of 500 women who are taking the pill.

(a) Based on the information about typical use in Exercise 12.24, what is the probability that at least 25 of these women become pregnant in the next year? (Check that the Normal approximation is permissible and use it to find this probability. If your software allows, find the exact binomial probability and compare the two results.)

(b) We can't use the Normal approximation to the binomial distributions to find this probability under ideal conditions as described in Exercise 12.24. Why not?

12.27 Hitting the fairway. One statistic used to assess professional golfers is driving accuracy, the percent of drives that land in the fairway. Driving accuracy for PGA Tour professionals ranges from about 40% to about 75%. Tiger Woods hits the fairway about 60% of the time.[5]

(a) Tiger hits 14 drives in a round. What assumptions must you make in order to use a binomial distribution for the count X of fairways he hits? Which of these assumptions is least realistic?
(b) Assuming that a binomial distribution can be used, what is the most likely number of fairways that Tiger hits in a round in which he hits 14 drives?

12.28 Genetics. According to genetic theory, the blossom color in the second generation of a certain cross of sweet peas should be red or white in a 3:1 ratio. That is, each plant has probability 3/4 of having red blossoms, and the blossom colors of separate plants are independent.
(a) What is the probability that exactly 6 out of 8 of these plants have red blossoms?
(b) What is the mean number of red-blossomed plants when 80 plants of this type are grown from seeds?
(c) What is the probability of obtaining at least 60 red-blossomed plants when 80 plants are grown from seeds? Use the Normal approximation. If your software allows, find the exact binomial probability and compare the two results.

12.29 False positives in testing for HIV. A rapid test for the presence in the blood of antibodies to HIV, the virus that causes AIDS, gives a positive result with probability about 0.004 when a person who is free of HIV antibodies is tested. A clinic tests 1000 people who are all free of HIV antibodies.
(a) What is the distribution of the number of positive tests?
(b) What is the mean number of positive tests?
(c) You cannot safely use the Normal approximation for this distribution. Explain why.

12.30 High school dropouts in Canada. The high school dropout rate is lower in Canada than in the United States: among Canadians aged 20 to 24, 14% of men and 9% of women lack a high school diploma and are not attending school.[6] A provincial "second chance system" mails a flyer to 25,000 young men aged 20 to 24 inviting dropouts to return to school.
(a) If the mailing list can be considered a random sample of the population, what is the mean number of high school dropouts who will receive the flyer?
(b) What is the approximate probability that at least 3600 dropouts will receive the flyer?

12.31 Survey demographics. According to the Census Bureau, 13% of American adults (age 18 and over) are Hispanic. An opinion poll plans to contact an SRS of 1200 adults.
(a) What is the mean number of Hispanics in such samples? What is the standard deviation?
(b) According to the 68–95–99.7 rule, what range will include the counts of Hispanics in 95% of all such samples?

(c) How large a sample is required to make the mean number of Hispanics at least 200?

12.32 Multiple-choice tests. Here is a simple probability model for multiple-choice tests. Suppose that each student has probability p of correctly answering a question chosen at random from a universe of possible questions. (A strong student has a higher p than a weak student.) Answers to different questions are independent.
(a) Jodi is a good student for whom $p = 0.75$. Use the Normal approximation to find the probability that Jodi scores between 70% and 80% on a 100-question test.
(b) If the test contains 250 questions, what is the probability that Jodi will score between 70% and 80%? You see that Jodi's score on the longer test is more likely to be close to her "true score."

12.33 Is this coin balanced? While he was a prisoner of war during World War II, John Kerrich tossed a coin 10,000 times. He got 5067 heads. If the coin is perfectly balanced, the probability of a head is 0.5. Is there reason to think that Kerrich's coin was not balanced? To answer this question, find the probability that tossing a balanced coin 10,000 times would give a count of heads at least this far from 5000 (that is, at least 5067 heads or no more than 4933 heads).

Whooping cough. *Whooping cough (pertussis) is a highly contagious bacterial infection that was a major cause of childhood deaths before the development of vaccines. About 80% of unvaccinated children who are exposed to whooping cough will develop the infection, as opposed to only about 5% of vaccinated children. Exercises 12.34 to 12.37 are based on this information.*

12.34 Vaccination at work. A group of 20 children at a nursery school are exposed to whooping cough by playing with an infected child.
(a) If all 20 have been vaccinated, what is the mean number of new infections? What is the probability that no more than 2 of the 20 children develop infections?
(b) If none of the 20 have been vaccinated, what is the mean number of new infections? What is the probability that 18 or more of the 20 children develop infections?

12.35 A whooping cough outbreak. In 2007, Bob Jones University ended its fall semester a week early because of a whooping cough outbreak; 158 students were isolated and another 1200 given antibiotics as a precaution.[7] Because the effect of childhood vaccination often wears off by late adolescence, treat the Bob Jones students as if they were unvaccinated. It appears that about 1400 students were exposed. What is the probability that at least 75% of these students develop infections if not treated? (Fortunately, whooping cough is much less serious after infancy.)

12.36 A mixed group: means. A group of 20 children at a nursery school are exposed to whooping cough by playing with an infected child. Of these children 17 have been vaccinated and 3 have not.
(a) What is the distribution of the number of new infections among the 17 vaccinated children? What is the mean number of new infections?
(b) What is the distribution of the number of new infections among the 3 unvaccinated children? What is the mean number of new infections?
(c) Add your means from parts (a) and (b). This is the mean number of new infections among all 20 exposed children.

12.37 A mixed group: probabilities. We would like to find the probability that exactly 2 of the 20 exposed children in the previous exercise develop whooping cough.
(a) One way to get 2 infections is to get 1 among the 17 vaccinated children and 1 among the 3 unvaccinated children. Find the probability of exactly 1 infection among the 17 vaccinated children. Find the probability of exactly 1 infection among the 3 unvaccinated children. These events are independent: what is the probability of exactly 1 infection in each group?
(b) Write down all the ways in which 2 infections can be divided between the two groups of children. Follow the pattern of part (a) to find the probability of each of these possibilities. Add all of your results (including the result of part (a)) to obtain the probability of exactly 2 infections among the 20 children.

12.38 The continuity correction. One reason why the Normal approximation may fail to give accurate estimates of binomial probabilities is that the binomial distributions are discrete and the Normal distributions are continuous. That is, counts take only whole number values but Normal variables can take any value. We can improve the Normal approximation by treating each whole number count as if it occupied the interval from 0.5 below the number to 0.5 above the number. For example, approximate a binomial probability $P(X \geq 10)$ by finding the Normal probability $P(X \geq 9.5)$. Be careful: binomial $P(X > 10)$ is approximated by Normal $P(X \geq 10.5)$.

We saw in Exercise 12.27 that Tiger Woods hits the fairway in 60% of his drives. We will assume that his drives are independent and that each has probability 0.6 of hitting the fairway. Tiger drives 25 times. The exact binomial probability that he hits 15 or more fairways is 0.5858.
(a) Show that this setting satisfies the rule of thumb for use of the Normal approximation (just barely).
(b) What is the Normal approximation to $P(X \geq 15)$?
(c) What is the Normal approximation using the continuity correction? That's a lot closer to the true binomial probability.

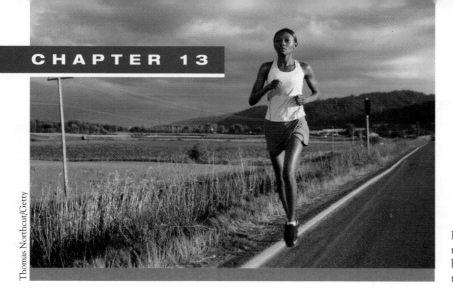

Thomas Northcut/Getty

Body mass index (BMI) measures weight relative to height (Example 13.1). Distance runners usually have low BMI.

Introduction to Inference

IN THIS CHAPTER WE COVER...

- The reasoning of statistical estimation

- Confidence intervals for a population mean

- The reasoning of statistical tests

- Stating hypotheses

- *P*-values

- Tests for a population mean

- Statistical significance

After we have selected a sample, we know the responses of the individuals in the sample. The usual reason for taking a sample is not to learn about the individuals in the sample but to *infer* from the sample data some conclusion about the wider population that the sample represents.

STATISTICAL INFERENCE

Statistical inference provides methods for drawing conclusions about a population from sample data.

Because a different sample might lead to different conclusions, we can't be certain that our conclusions are correct. Statistical inference uses the language of probability to say how trustworthy our conclusions are. This chapter introduces the two most common types of inference, *confidence intervals* for estimating the value of a population parameter and *tests of significance* for assessing the evidence for a claim about a population. Both types of inference are based on the sampling distributions of statistics. That is, both use probability to say what would happen if we applied the inference method many times.

This chapter presents the basic reasoning of statistical inference. To make the reasoning as clear as possible, we start with a setting that is too simple to be realistic. Here is the setting for our work in this chapter.

SIMPLE CONDITIONS FOR INFERENCE ABOUT A MEAN

1. We have an SRS from the population of interest. There is no nonresponse or other practical difficulty.
2. The variable we measure has an exactly Normal distribution $N(\mu, \sigma)$ in the population.
3. We don't know the population mean μ. But we do know the population standard deviation σ.

The conditions that we have a perfect SRS, that the population is exactly Normal, and that we know the population σ are all unrealistic. Later chapters will deal with inference in realistic settings.

The reasoning of statistical estimation

Body mass index (BMI) is used to screen for possible weight problems. It is calculated as weight divided by the square of height, measuring weight in kilograms and height in meters. Many online BMI calculators allow you to enter weight in pounds and height in inches. Adults with BMI less than 18.5 are considered underweight and those with BMI greater than 25 may be overweight. For data about BMI, we turn to the National Health and Nutrition Examination Survey (NHANES), a government sample survey that monitors the health of the American population.

Thomas Northcut/Getty

EXAMPLE 13.1 **Body mass index of young women**

The most recent NHANES report gives data for 654 women aged 20 to 29 years.[1] The mean BMI of these 654 women was $\bar{x} = 26.8$. On the basis of this sample, we want to estimate the mean BMI μ in the population of all 18 million women in this age group.

To match the "simple conditions," we will treat the NHANES sample as an SRS from a Normal population with standard deviation $\sigma = 7.5$. ▪

Here is the reasoning of statistical estimation in a nutshell:

1. To estimate the unknown population mean BMI μ, use the mean $\bar{x} = 26.8$ of the random sample. We don't expect $\bar{x}$ to be exactly equal to μ, so we want to say how accurate this estimate is.
2. We know the sampling distribution of $\bar{x}$. In repeated samples, $\bar{x}$ has the Normal distribution with mean μ and standard deviation $\sigma/\sqrt{n}$. So the average BMI $\bar{x}$ of an SRS of 654 young women has standard deviation

$$\frac{\sigma}{\sqrt{n}} = \frac{7.5}{\sqrt{654}} = 0.3 \ \text{(rounded off)}$$

3. The 95 part of the 68–95–99.7 rule for Normal distributions says that $\bar{x}$ is within 0.6 (that's two standard deviations) of the mean μ in 95% of all samples. That is, for 95% of all samples of size 654, the distance between the sample mean $\bar{x}$ and the population mean μ is less than 0.6. So if we estimate that μ lies somewhere in the

interval from $\overline{x} - 0.6$ to $\overline{x} + 0.6$, *we'll be right for 95% of all possible samples*. For this particular sample, this interval is

$$\overline{x} - 0.6 = 26.8 - 0.6 = 26.2$$

to

$$\overline{x} + 0.6 = 26.8 + 0.6 = 27.4$$

4. Because we got the interval 26.2 to 27.4 from a method that captures the population mean for 95% of all possible samples, we say that we are 95% *confident* that the mean BMI μ of all young women is some value in that interval, no lower than 26.2 and no higher than 27.4.

The sampling distribution of $\overline{x}$ tells us how close to μ the sample mean $\overline{x}$ is likely to be. Statistical estimation just turns that information around to say how close to $\overline{x}$ the unknown population mean μ is likely to be. The interval of numbers between the values $\overline{x} \pm 0.6$ is a 95% *confidence interval* for μ. For this particular sample $\overline{x} = 26.8$, so our confidence interval is 26.8 ± 0.6. Most confidence intervals have a form similar to this,

$$\text{estimate} \pm \text{margin of error}$$

The estimate ($\overline{x} = 26.8$ in our example) is our guess for the value of the unknown parameter. The **margin of error** ± 0.6 shows how accurate we believe our guess is. The **confidence level** for this interval is 95% because the interval $\overline{x} \pm 0.6$ catches the unknown parameter in 95% of all possible samples.

margin of error
confidence level

CONFIDENCE INTERVAL

A **level C confidence interval** for a parameter has two parts:

- An interval calculated from the data, usually of the form

$$\text{estimate} \pm \text{margin of error}$$

- A **confidence level** C, which gives the probability that the interval will capture the true parameter value in repeated samples. That is, the confidence level is the success rate for the method.

We can choose the confidence level we want, usually 90% or higher because we usually want to be quite sure of our conclusions. The most common confidence level is 95%.

EXAMPLE 13.2 Statistical estimation in pictures

Figure 13.1 shows how 95% confidence intervals behave. Draw many SRSs from the same population and calculate a 95% confidence interval from each sample. The center of each interval is at $\overline{x}$ and therefore varies from sample to sample. The sampling distribution of $\overline{x}$ appears at the top of the figure to show the long-term pattern of this variation. The population mean μ is at the center of the sampling distribution. The 95% confidence intervals from 25 SRSs appear underneath. The center $\overline{x}$ of each interval is marked by a dot. The

Twenty-five samples from the same population gave these 95% confidence intervals. In the long run, 95% of all samples give an interval that contains the population mean μ.

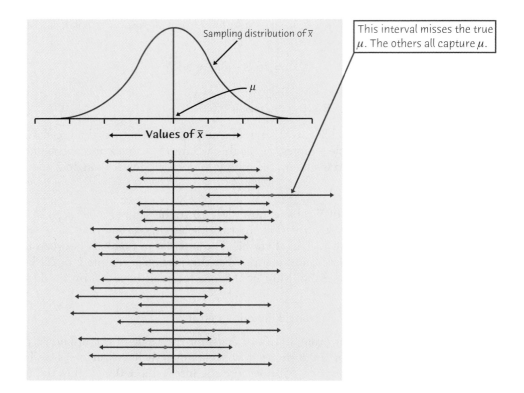

arrows on either side of the dot span the confidence interval. All except one of these 25 intervals capture the true value of μ. If we take a very large number of samples, 95% of the confidence intervals will contain μ. ■

INTERPRETING A CONFIDENCE INTERVAL

The confidence level is the success rate of the method that produces the interval. We don't know whether the 95% confidence interval from a particular sample is one of the 95% that capture μ or one of the unlucky 5% that miss.

To say that we are **95% confident** that the unknown μ lies between 26.2 and 27.4 is shorthand for **"We got these numbers using a method that gives correct results 95% of the time."**

APPLY YOUR KNOWLEDGE

13.1 Number skills of young men. The National Assessment of Educational Progress (NAEP) gave a test of basic arithmetic and the ability to apply it in everyday life to a sample of 840 men 21 to 25 years of age.[2] Scores range from 0 to 500. The mean score for these 840 young men was $\bar{x} = 272$. We want to estimate the mean score μ in the population of all young men. Consider the NAEP sample as an SRS from a Normal population with standard deviation $\sigma = 60$.

(a) If we take many samples, the sample mean $\bar{x}$ varies from sample to sample according to a Normal distribution with mean equal to the unknown mean score μ in the population. What is the standard deviation of this sampling distribution?

(b) According to the 95 part of the 68–95–99.7 rule, 95% of all values of $\bar{x}$ fall within _____ on either side of the unknown mean μ. What is the missing number?

(c) What is the 95% confidence interval for the population mean score μ based on this one sample?

13.2 Explaining confidence. A student reads that a 95% confidence interval for the mean body mass index (BMI) of young American women is 26.8 ± 0.6. Asked to explain the meaning of this interval, the student says, "95% of all young women have BMI between 26.2 and 27.4." Explain in simple language what a 95% confidence interval is and why the student's explanation is incorrect.

Confidence intervals for a population mean

To find a 95% confidence interval for the mean BMI of young women, we first caught the central 95% of the Normal sampling distribution by going out two standard deviations in both directions from the mean. To find a level C confidence interval, we first catch the central area C under the Normal sampling distribution. Because all Normal distributions are the same in the standard scale, we can obtain everything we need from the standard Normal curve.

Figure 13.2 shows how the central area C under a standard Normal curve is marked off by two points z^* and $-z^*$. Numbers like z^* that mark off specified areas are called **critical values** of the standard Normal distribution. Values of z^* for many choices of C appear at the bottom of Table C in the back of the book, in the row labeled z^*. Here are the entries for the most common confidence levels:

critical value

Confidence level C	90%	95%	99%
Critical value z^*	1.645	1.960	2.576

You see that for C = 95% the critical value is $z^* = 1.960$. This is a bit more precise than the approximate value $z^* = 2$ based on the 68–95–99.7 rule. Software will give you critical values z^* for any confidence level, as well as the entire confidence interval.

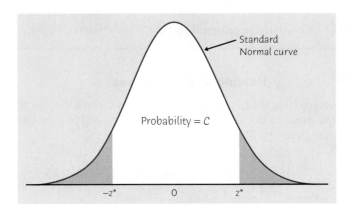

FIGURE 13.2
The critical value z^* is the number that catches central probability C under a standard Normal curve between $-z^*$ and z^*.

Because there is area C under the standard Normal curve between $-z^*$ and z^*, *any* Normal curve has area C within z^* standard deviations on either side of its mean. In particular, the Normal sampling distribution of $\overline{x}$ has area C within $z^*\sigma/\sqrt{n}$ on either side of the population mean μ because is has mean μ and standard deviation $\sigma/\sqrt{n}$. If we start at $\overline{x}$ and go out $z^*\sigma/\sqrt{n}$ in both directions, we get an interval that contains the population mean μ in a porportion C of all samples. This interval is

$$\text{from}\quad \overline{x} - z^*\frac{\sigma}{\sqrt{n}} \quad\text{to}\quad \overline{x} + z^*\frac{\sigma}{\sqrt{n}}$$

or

$$\overline{x} \pm z^*\frac{\sigma}{\sqrt{n}}$$

It is a level C confidence interval for μ.

CONFIDENCE INTERVAL FOR THE MEAN OF A NORMAL POPULATION

Draw an SRS of size n from a Normal population having unknown mean μ and known standard deviation σ. A level C **confidence interval for μ** is

$$\overline{x} \pm z^*\frac{\sigma}{\sqrt{n}}$$

The critical value z^* is illustrated in Figure 13.2 and found in the z^* row of Table C.

The steps in finding a confidence interval mirror the overall four-step process for organizing statistical problems.

CONFIDENCE INTERVALS: THE FOUR-STEP PROCESS

STATE: What is the practical question that requires estimating a parameter?

PLAN: Identify the parameter, choose a level of confidence, and select the type of confidence interval that fits your situation.

SOLVE: Carry out the work in two phases:

1.   **Check the conditions** for the interval you plan to use.
2.   Calculate the **confidence interval.**

CONCLUDE: Return to the practical question to describe your results in this setting.

EXAMPLE 13.3   Healing of skin wounds

STATE: Biologists studying the healing of skin wounds measured the rate at which new cells closed a razor cut made in the skin of an anesthetized newt. Here are data from 18 newts, measured in micrometers (millionths of a meter) per hour:[3]

29	27	34	40	22	28	14	35	26
35	12	30	23	18	11	22	23	33

We want to estimate the mean healing rate.

PLAN: We will estimate the mean rate μ for all newts of this species by giving a 95% confidence interval. The confidence interval $\bar{x} \pm z^*\sigma/\sqrt{n}$ fits this situation.

SOLVE: We should start by checking the conditions for inference. For this example, we will first find the interval and then discuss how statistical practice deals with conditions that are never perfectly satisfied.

The mean of the sample is $\bar{x} = 25.67$. As part of the "simple conditions," suppose that from past experience with this species of newts we know that the standard deviation of healing rates is $\sigma = 8$ micrometers per hour. For 95% confidence, the critical value is $z^* = 1.960$. A 95% confidence interval for μ is therefore

$$\bar{x} \pm z^* \frac{\sigma}{\sqrt{n}} = 25.67 \pm 1.960 \frac{8}{\sqrt{18}}$$

$$= 25.67 \pm 3.70$$

$$= 21.97 \text{ to } 29.37$$

CONCLUDE: We are 95% confident that the mean healing rate for all newts of this species is between 21.97 and 29.37 micrometers per hour. ▪

In practice, the first part of the *Solve* step is to check the conditions for inference. The "simple conditions" are as follows:

1. **SRS:** We don't have an actual SRS from the population of all newts of this species. Scientists usually act as if animal subjects are an SRS from their species or genetic type if there is nothing special about how the subjects were obtained.
2. **Normal distribution:** The biologists expect from past experience that measurements like this on several animals of the same species under the same conditions will follow approximately a Normal distribution. We can't look at the population, but we can examine the sample. Figure 13.3 is a stemplot, with split stems. The shape is irregular, but there are no outliers or strong skewness. Shapes like this often occur in small samples from Normal populations, so we have no reason to doubt that the population distribution is Normal.
3. **Known σ:** It really is unrealistic to suppose that we know that $\sigma = 8$. We will see in Chapter 16 that it is easy to do away with the need to know σ.

```
1 | 1 2 4
1 | 8
2 | 2 2 3 3
2 | 6 7 8 9
3 | 0 3 4
3 | 5 5
4 | 0
```

FIGURE 13.3

Stemplot of the healing rates in Example 13.3.

As this discussion suggests, inference methods are often used when conditions like SRS and Normal population are not exactly satisfied. In this introductory chapter, we act as though the "simple conditions" are satisfied. In reality, wise use of inference requires judgment. Chapter 14 and the later chapters on each inference method will give you a better basis for judgment.

APPLY YOUR KNOWLEDGE

13.3 Find a critical value. The critical value z^* for confidence level 97.5% is not in Table C. Use software or Table A of standard Normal probabilities to find z^*. Include in your answer a sketch like Figure 13.2 with C = 0.975 and your critical value z^* marked on the axis.

13.4 Measuring conductivity. The National Institute of Standards and Technology (NIST) supplies "standard materials" that have known properties. Here are 6 measurements of the electrical conductivity of the same standard liquid, which is supposed to have conductivity 5:

5.32   4.88   5.10   4.73   5.15   4.75

NIST knows the variability of its measurements very well, so it is quite realistic to assume that the population of all measurements of the same liquid has the Normal distribution with mean μ equal to the true conductivity and standard deviation $\sigma = 0.2$. NIST wants to give the buyer of this liquid a 90% confidence interval for its true conductivity. What is this interval? Follow the four-step process as illustrated in Example 13.3.

13.5 IQ test scores. Here are the IQ test scores of 31 seventh-grade girls in a Midwest school district:[4]

114	100	104	89	102	91	114	114	103	105
108	130	120	132	111	128	118	119	86	72
111	103	74	112	107	103	98	96	112	112	93

(a) These 31 girls are an SRS of all seventh-grade girls in the school district. Suppose that the standard deviation of IQ scores in this population is known to be $\sigma = 15$. We expect the distribution of IQ scores to be close to Normal. Make a stemplot of the distribution of these 31 scores (split the stems) to verify that there are no major departures from Normality. You have now checked the "simple conditions" to the extent possible.

(b) Estimate the mean IQ score for all seventh-grade girls in the school district, using a 99% confidence interval. Follow the four-step process as illustrated in Example 13.3.

The reasoning of statistical tests

Confidence intervals are one of the two most common types of statistical inference. Use a confidence interval when your goal is to estimate a population parameter. The second common type of inference, called *tests of significance,* has a different goal: to assess the evidence provided by data about some claim concerning a population. Here is the reasoning of statistical tests in a nutshell.

> **EXAMPLE 13.4** **I'm a great free-throw shooter**
>
> I claim that I make 80% of my basketball free throws. To test my claim, you ask me to shoot 20 free throws. I make only 8 of the 20. "Aha!" you say, "Someone who makes 80% of his free throws would almost never make only 8 out of 20. So I don't believe your claim."
>
> Your reasoning is based on asking what would happen if my claim were true and we repeated the sample of 20 free throws many times—I would almost never make as few as 8. This outcome is so unlikely that it gives strong evidence that my claim is not true.
>
> You can say how strong the evidence against my claim is by giving the probability that I would make as few as 8 out of 20 free throws if I really make 80% in the long run. This probability is 0.0001. I would make as few as 8 of 20 only once in 10,000 tries in the long run if my claim to make 80% were true. The small probability convinces you that my claim is false. ■

Statistical tests use an elaborate vocabulary, but the basic idea is simple: *an outcome that would rarely happen if a claim were true is good evidence that the claim is not true*. That is, tests as well as confidence intervals are based on what would happen if we repeated the sample or experiment many times. We will act as if the "simple conditions" listed on page xxx are true: we have a perfect SRS from an exactly Normal population with standard deviation σ known to us. Here is an example we will explore.

EXAMPLE 13.5   Sweetness loss in colas

Diet colas gradually lose their sweetness over time. Manufacturers therefore test new colas for loss of sweetness before marketing them. Trained tasters score the cola on a "sweetness score" of 1 to 10 before and after storage. Our data are the sweetness losses (score before storage minus score after storage) as judged by a panel of 10 tasters.

Ramin/Talaie/CORBIS

To match the "simple conditions," we will treat the 10 tasters as an SRS from the population of all trained tasters and assume that in this population sweetness losses for any cola are Normal with unknown mean μ and standard deviation $\sigma = 1$. The population mean μ measures true loss of sweetness and is different for different colas.

For a cola already on the market, 10 tasters had mean loss $\overline{x} = 0.3$. The taste test for a new cola gives $\overline{x} = 1.02$. Is there good evidence that either of these colas loses sweetness in storage? ■

The reasoning is the same as in Example 13.4. We make a claim and ask if the data give evidence *against* it. Let's spell out the steps.

1. We seek evidence that there *is* a sweetness loss, so the claim we test is that there *is not* a loss. This claim says that the mean loss for the population of all trained testers is $\mu = 0$.
2. If the claim that $\mu = 0$ is true, the sampling distribution of $\overline{x}$ from 10 tasters is Normal with mean $\mu = 0$ and standard deviation

$$\frac{\sigma}{\sqrt{n}} = \frac{1}{\sqrt{10}} = 0.316$$

Figure 13.4 shows this sampling distribution.

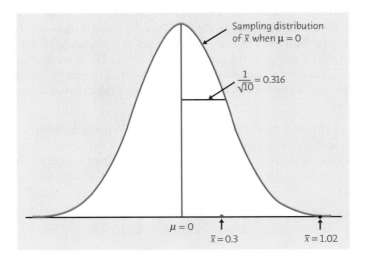

FIGURE 13.4

If a cola does not lose sweetness in storage, the mean score $\overline{x}$ for 10 tasters will have this sampling distribution. The actual result for one cola was $\overline{x} = 0.3$. That could easily happen just by chance. Another cola had $\overline{x} = 1.02$. That's so far out on the Normal curve that it is good evidence that this cola did lose sweetness.

3. An outcome $\bar{x}$ that would rarely happen if $\mu = 0$ were true is evidence that μ is not 0. To see if an observed value of $\bar{x}$ would rarely happen, locate it on the distribution in Figure 13.4.

EXAMPLE 13.6 Sweetness loss in colas

For a cola already on the market, 10 tasters had mean loss $\bar{x} = 0.3$. Look at Figure 13.4. It is clear that $\bar{x} = 0.3$ could easily occur just by chance when the population mean is $\mu = 0$. This outcome is not good evidence against the claim that $\mu = 0$.

The taste test for a new cola produced $\bar{x} = 1.02$. That's way out on the Normal curve in Figure 13.4—so far out that *an observed value this large would rarely occur just by chance if the true μ were 0*. This observed value is good evidence that the true μ is in fact greater than 0, that is, that the cola lost sweetness. The manufacturer must reformulate the cola and try again. ■

APPLY YOUR KNOWLEDGE

13.6 Student attitudes. The Survey of Study Habits and Attitudes (SSHA) is a psychological test that measures students' study habits and attitude toward school. Scores range from 0 to 200. The mean score for college students is about 115, and the standard deviation is about 30. A teacher suspects that the mean μ for older students is higher than 115. She gives the SSHA to an SRS of 25 students who are at least 30 years old. Suppose we know that scores in the population of older students are Normally distributed with standard deviation $\sigma = 30$.

  (a) We seek evidence *against* the claim that $\mu = 115$. What is the sampling distribution of the mean score $\bar{x}$ of a sample of 25 students if the claim is true? Draw the density curve of this distribution. (Sketch a Normal curve, then mark on the axis the values of the mean and 1, 2, and 3 standard deviations on either side of the mean.)

  (b) Suppose that the sample data give $\bar{x} = 118.6$. Mark this point on the axis of your sketch. In fact, the result was $\bar{x} = 125.8$. Mark this point on your sketch. Using your sketch, explain in simple language why one result is good evidence that the mean score of all older students is greater than 115 and why the other outcome is not.

13.7 Measuring conductivity. The National Institute of Standards and Technology (NIST) supplies a "standard liquid" whose electrical conductivity is supposed to be exactly 5. Is there reason to think that the true conductivity of a shipment of this liquid is not 5? To find out, NIST measures the conductivity 6 times. These measurements are an SRS from the population of all possible measurements of this shipment. This population has a Normal distribution with mean μ equal to the true conductivity and standard deviation $\sigma = 0.2$.

  (a) We seek evidence *against* the claim that $\mu = 5$. What is the sampling distribution of the mean $\bar{x}$ in many samples of 6 measurements if the claim is true? Make a sketch of the Normal curve for this distribution. (Draw a Normal curve, then mark on the axis the values of the mean and 1, 2, and 3 standard deviations on either side of the mean.)

  (b) Suppose that the sample mean is $\bar{x} = 4.98$. Mark this value on the axis of your sketch. Another shipment of liquid has $\bar{x} = 4.7$ for 6 measurements. Mark this value on the axis as well. Explain in simple language why one result is good evidence that the true conductivity differs from 5 and why the other result gives no reason to doubt that 5 is correct.

Stating hypotheses

A statistical test starts with a careful statement of the claims we want to compare. In Example 13.6, we saw that the taste test data are not plausible if the new cola loses no sweetness. Because the reasoning of tests looks for evidence *against* a claim, we start with the claim we seek evidence against, such as "no loss of sweetness."

NULL AND ALTERNATIVE HYPOTHESES

The claim tested by a statistical test is called the **null hypothesis.** The test is designed to assess the strength of the evidence against the null hypothesis. Usually the null hypothesis is a statement of "no effect" or "no difference."

The claim about the population that we are trying to find evidence *for* is the **alternative hypothesis.** The alternative hypothesis is **one-sided** if it states that a parameter is *larger than* the null hypothesis value or if it states that a parameter is *smaller than* the null hypothesis value. It is **two-sided** if it states that the parameter is *different from* the null value (it could be either smaller or larger).

We abbreviate the null hypothesis as H_0 and the alternative hypothesis as H_a. *Hypotheses always refer to a population, not to a particular outcome. Be sure to state H_0 and H_a in terms of population parameters.*

In Example 13.6, we are seeking evidence *for* loss in sweetness. The null hypothesis says "no loss" on the average in a large population of tasters. The alternative hypothesis says "there is a loss." So the hypotheses are

$$H_0: \mu = 0$$
$$H_a: \mu > 0$$

The alternative hypothesis is *one-sided* because we are interested only in whether the cola *lost* sweetness.

EXAMPLE 13.7   **Studying job satisfaction**

Does the job satisfaction of assembly workers differ when their work is machine-paced rather than self-paced? Assign workers either to an assembly line moving at a fixed pace or to a self-paced setting. All subjects work in both settings, in random order. This is a matched pairs design. After two weeks in each work setting, the workers take a test of job satisfaction. The response variable is the difference in satisfaction scores, self-paced minus machine-paced.

The parameter of interest is the mean μ of the differences in scores in the population of all assembly workers. The null hypothesis says that there is no difference between self-paced and machine-paced work, that is,

$$H_0: \mu = 0$$

The authors of the study wanted to know if the two work conditions have different levels of job satisfaction. They did not specify the direction of the difference. The alternative hypothesis is therefore *two-sided:*

$$H_a: \mu \neq 0 \;\blacksquare$$

The hypotheses should express the hopes or suspicions you have *before* you see the data. If you do not have a specific direction firmly in mind in advance, use a two-sided alternative.

APPLY YOUR KNOWLEDGE

13.8 Student attitudes. State the null and alternative hypotheses for the study of older students' attitudes described in Exercise 13.6. (Is the alternative hypothesis one-sided or two-sided?)

13.9 Measuring conductivity. State the null and alternative hypotheses for the study of electrical conductivity described in Exercise 13.7. (Is the alternative hypothesis one-sided or two-sided?)

13.10 Grading a teaching assistant. The examinations in a large accounting class are scaled after grading so that the mean score is 50. The professor thinks that one teaching assistant is a poor teacher and suspects that his students have a lower mean score than the class as a whole. The TA's students this semester can be considered a sample from the population of all students in the course, so the professor compares their mean score with 50. State the hypotheses H_0 and H_a.

P-values

The reasoning of a statistical test is that *an outcome that would rarely happen if a claim were true is good evidence that the claim is not true.* The claim we seek evidence against is the null hypothesis H_0. We assess the strength of the evidence by giving a probability that says how rarely an outcome like this would happen if H_0 were true. This probability is called a *P-value.* Statistical tests generally work like this:

TEST STATISTIC AND P-VALUE

A **test statistic** calculated from the sample data measures how far the data diverge from what we would expect if the null hypothesis H_0 were true. Large values of the statistic show that the data are not consistent with H_0.

The probability, computed assuming that H_0 is true, that the test statistic would take a value as extreme or more extreme than that actually observed is called the **P-value** of the test. The smaller the P-value, the stronger the evidence against H_0 provided by the data.

Small *P*-values are evidence against H_0 because they say that the observed result would be unlikely to occur if H_0 were true. Large *P*-values fail to give evidence against H_0. Statistical software will give you the *P*-value of a test when you enter your null and alternative hypotheses and your data. So your most important task is to understand what a *P*-value says.

EXAMPLE 13.8 **Sweetness loss in colas: one-sided *P*-value**

The study of sweetness loss in Examples 13.5 and 13.6 tests the hypotheses

$$H_0: \mu = 0$$
$$H_a: \mu > 0$$

Because the alternative hypothesis says that $\mu > 0$, values of $\bar{x}$ greater than 0 favor H_a over H_0. The test statistic compares the observed $\bar{x}$ with the hypothesized value $\mu = 0$. For now, let's concentrate on the *P*-value.

For a cola already on the market, 10 tasters found mean sweetness loss $\bar{x} = 0.3$. For a new cola, the tasters reported $\bar{x} = 1.02$. *The P-value for each test is the probability of getting an $\bar{x}$ this large when the mean sweetness loss is really $\mu = 0$.*

The shaded area in Figure 13.5 shows the *P*-value when $\bar{x} = 0.3$. The Normal curve is the sampling distribution of $\bar{x}$ when the null hypothesis $H_0: \mu = 0$ is true. A Normal probability calculation (Exercise 13.11) shows that the *P*-value is $P(\bar{x} \geq 0.3) = 0.1714$. A value as large as $\bar{x} = 0.3$ would appear just by chance in 17% of all samples when $H_0: \mu = 0$ is true. So observing $\bar{x} = 0.3$ is not strong evidence against H_0.

On the other hand, you can calculate that the probability that $\bar{x}$ is 1.02 or larger when in fact $\mu = 0$ is only 0.0006. We would very rarely observe a mean sweetness loss of 1.02 or larger if H_0 were true. This small *P*-value provides strong evidence against H_0 and in favor of the alternative $H_a: \mu > 0$. ∎

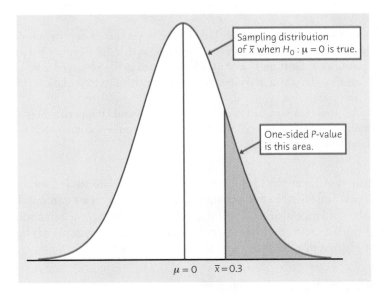

FIGURE 13.5

The one-sided *P*-value for the cola with mean sweetness loss $\bar{x} = 0.3$ in Example 13.8.

Sampling distribution of $\bar{x}$ when $H_0 : \mu = 0$ is true.

One-sided *P*-value is this area.

$\mu = 0$ $\bar{x} = 0.3$

The alternative hypothesis sets the direction that counts as evidence against H_0. In Example 13.8, only large positive values count because the alternative is one-sided on the high side. If the alternative is two-sided, both directions count.

FIGURE 13.6

The two-sided P-value for sample mean $\bar{x} = 17$ in Example 13.9.

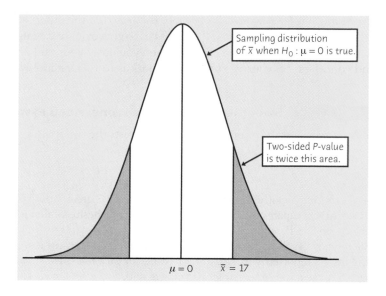

EXAMPLE 13.9 Job satisfaction: two-sided P-value

The study of job satisfaction in Example 13.7 requires that we test

$$H_0: \mu = 0$$
$$H_a: \mu \neq 0$$

Suppose we know that differences in job satisfaction scores (self-paced minus machine-paced) in the population of all workers follow a Normal distribution with standard deviation $\sigma = 60$.

Data from 18 workers give $\bar{x} = 17$. That is, these workers prefer the self-paced environment on the average. Because the alternative is two-sided, the P-value is the probability of getting an $\bar{x}$ at least as far from $\mu = 0$ *in either direction* as the observed $\bar{x} = 17$. The shaded areas in Figure 13.6 show this P-value. A Normal probability calculation (Exercise 13.12) finds that $P = 0.2293$.

Values as far from 0 as $\bar{x} = 17$ (in either direction) would happen 23% of the time when the true population mean is $\mu = 0$. An outcome that would occur so often when H_0 is true is not good evidence against H_0. ■

The conclusion of Example 13.9 is *not* that H_0 is true. The study looked for evidence against $H_0: \mu = 0$ and failed to find strong evidence. That is all we can say. Tests of significance assess the evidence against H_0. If the evidence is strong, we can confidently reject H_0 in favor of the alternative. *Failing to find evidence against H_0 means only that the data are consistent with H_0, not that we have clear evidence that H_0 is true.*

APPLY YOUR KNOWLEDGE

13.11 Sweetness loss in colas: find the P-value. The P-value for the first cola in Example 13.8 is the probability (taking the null hypothesis $\mu = 0$ to be true) that $\bar{x}$ takes a value at least as large as 0.3.

(a) What is the sampling distribution of $\overline{x}$ when $\mu = 0$? (Remember that the population standard deviation is $\sigma = 1$.) This distribution appears in Figure 13.5.

(b) Do a Normal probability calculation to find the P-value. Your result should agree with Example 13.8 up to roundoff error.

13.12 Job satisfaction: find the *P*-value. The P-value in Example 13.9 is the probability (taking the null hypothesis $\mu = 0$ to be true) that $\overline{x}$ takes a value at least as far from 0 as 17.

(a) What is the sampling distribution of $\overline{x}$ when $\mu = 0$? (Remember that the population standard deviation is $\sigma = 60$.) This distribution appears in Figure 13.6.

(b) Do a Normal probability calculation to find the P-value. Your result should agree with Example 13.9 up to roundoff error.

Tests for a population mean

We have used tests for hypotheses about the mean μ of a population, under the "simple conditions," to introduce statistical tests. The test compares the sample mean $\overline{x}$ with the claimed population mean stated by the null hypothesis H_0. The P-value says how unlikely an $\overline{x}$ this extreme is if H_0 is true. Now we can reduce this test to a rule.

z TEST FOR A POPULATION MEAN

Draw an SRS of size n from a Normal population that has unknown mean μ and known standard deviation σ. To **test the null hypothesis that μ has a specified value,**

$$H_0: \mu = \mu_0$$

calculate the **one-sample z test statistic**

$$z = \frac{\overline{x} - \mu_0}{\sigma/\sqrt{n}}$$

In terms of a variable Z having the standard Normal distribution, the P-value for a test of H_0 against

$H_a: \mu > \mu_0$ is $P(Z \geq z)$

$H_a: \mu < \mu_0$ is $P(Z \leq z)$

$H_a: \mu \neq \mu_0$ is $2P(Z \geq |z|)$

The test statistic z measures how far the observed sample mean $\bar{x}$ deviates from the hypothesized population value μ_0. The measurement is in the standard scale obtained by dividing by the standard deviation of $\bar{x}$. When H_0 is true, z has the standard Normal distribution. The pictures that illustrate the P-value look just like Figures 13.5 and 13.6 except that they are in the standard scale.

In practice, the steps in carrying out a test of significance mirror the overall four-step process for organizing realistic statistical problems.

TESTS OF SIGNIFICANCE: THE FOUR-STEP PROCESS

STATE: What is the practical question that requires a statistical test?

PLAN: Identify the parameter, state null and alternative hypotheses, and choose the type of test that fits your situation.

SOLVE: Carry out the test in three phases:

1. **Check the conditions** for the test you plan to use.
2. Calculate the **test statistic.**
3. Find the **P-value.**

CONCLUDE: Return to the practical question to describe your results in this setting.

EXAMPLE 13.10 **Executives' blood pressures**

STATE: The National Center for Health Statistics reports that the systolic blood pressure for males 35 to 44 years of age has mean 128 and standard deviation 15. The medical director of a large company looks at the medical records of 72 executives in this age group and finds that the mean systolic blood pressure in this sample is $\bar{x} = 126.07$. Is this evidence that the company's executives have a different mean blood pressure from the general population?

ImageState/Alamy

PLAN: The null hypothesis is "no difference" from the national mean $\mu_0 = 128$. The alternative is two-sided, because the medical director did not have a particular direction in mind before examining the data. So the hypotheses about the unknown mean μ of the executive population are

$$H_0: \mu = 128$$
$$H_a: \mu \neq 128$$

The one-sample z test is appropriate for these hypotheses under the "simple conditions."

SOLVE: As part of the "simple conditions," suppose we know that executives' blood pressures follow a Normal distribution with standard deviation $\sigma = 15$. Software can now calculate z and P for you. Going ahead by hand, the **test statistic** is

$$z = \frac{\bar{x} - \mu_0}{\sigma/\sqrt{n}} = \frac{126.07 - 128}{15/\sqrt{72}}$$
$$= -1.09$$

To help find the **P-value,** sketch the standard Normal curve and mark on it the observed value of z. Figure 13.7 shows that the P-value is the probability that a standard

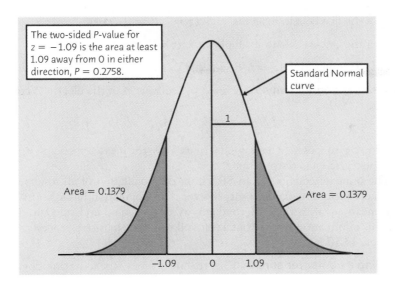

FIGURE 13.7
The *P*-value for the two-sided
test in Example 13.10. The
observed value of the test
statistic is $z = -1.09$.

Normal variable *Z* takes a value at least 1.09 away from zero. From Table A or software, this probability is

$$P = 2P(Z < -1.09) = (2)(0.1379) = 0.2758$$

CONCLUDE: More than 27% of the time, an SRS of size 72 from the general male population would have a mean blood pressure at least as far from 128 as that of the executive sample. The observed $\bar{x} = 126.07$ is therefore not good evidence that executives differ from other men. ▪

In this chapter we are acting as if the "simple conditions" stated on page 232 are true. In practice, you must verify these conditions.

1. **SRS:** The most important condition is that the 72 executives in the sample are an SRS from the population of all middle-aged male executives in the company. We should check this requirement by asking where the data came from. If medical records are available only for executives with recent medical problems, for example, the data are of little value for our purpose because of the obvious health bias. It turns out that all executives are given a free annual medical exam, and that the medical director selected 72 exam results at random.

2. **Normal distribution:** We should also examine the distribution of the 72 observations to look for signs that the population distribution is not Normal.

3. **Known σ:** It really is unrealistic to suppose that we know that $\sigma = 15$. We will see in Chapter 16 that it is easy to do away with the need to know σ.

APPLY YOUR KNOWLEDGE

13.13 The z statistic. Published reports of research work are terse. They often report just a test statistic and *P*-value. For example, the conclusion of Example 13.10 might be stated as "($z = -1.09$, $P = 0.2758$)." Find the values of the one-sample z statistic needed to complete these conclusions:

(a) For the first cola in Example 13.8, ($z = ?$, $P = 0.1714$).

(b) For the second cola in Example 13.8, ($z = ?$, $P = 0.0006$).

(c) For Example 13.9, ($z = ?$, $P = 0.2293$).

13.14 Measuring conductivity. Here are 6 measurements of the electrical conductivity of a liquid:

5.32   4.88   5.10   4.73   5.15   4.75

The liquid is supposed to have conductivity 5. Do the measurements give good evidence that the true conductivity is not 5?

The 6 measurements are an SRS from the population of all results we would get if we kept measuring conductivity forever. This population has a Normal distribution with mean equal to the true conductivity of the liquid and standard deviation 0.2. Use this information to carry out a test, following the four-step process as illustrated in Example 13.10.

13.15 Reading a computer screen. Does the use of fancy type fonts slow down the reading of text on a computer screen? Adults can read four paragraphs of text in an average time of 22 seconds in the common Times New Roman font. Ask 25 adults to read this text in the ornate font named Gigi. Here are their times:[5]

23.2 21.2 28.9 27.7 29.1 27.3 16.1 22.6 25.6
34.2 23.9 26.8 20.5 34.3 21.4 32.6 26.2 34.1
31.5 24.6 23.0 28.6 24.4 28.1 41.3

Suppose that reading times are Normal with $\sigma = 6$ seconds. Is there good evidence that the mean reading time for Gigi is greater than 22 seconds? Follow the four-step process as illustrated in Example 13.10.

Statistical significance

In Examples 13.8 and 13.9, we decided that P-value $P = 0.0006$ was strong evidence against the null hypothesis and that P-values $P = 0.1714$ and $P = 0.2293$ did not give convincing evidence. There is no rule for how small a P-value we should require to reject H_0—it's a matter of judgment and depends on the specific circumstances.

Nonetheless, we can compare a P-value with some fixed values that are in common use as standards for evidence against H_0. The most common fixed values are 0.05 and 0.01. If $P \leq 0.05$, there is no more than 1 chance in 20 that a sample would give evidence this strong just by chance when H_0 is actually true. If $P \leq 0.01$, we have a result that in the long run would happen no more than once per 100 samples if H_0 were true. These fixed standards for P-values are called **significance levels.** We use α, the Greek letter alpha, to stand for a significance level.

significance level

> **STATISTICAL SIGNIFICANCE**
>
> If the P-value is as small or smaller than α, we say that the data are **statistically significant at level α.**

"Significant" in the statistical sense does not mean "important." It means simply "not likely to happen just by chance." The significance level α makes "not likely" more exact. Significance at level 0.01 is often expressed by writing "The results were significant ($P < 0.01$)." Here P stands for the P-value. The actual P-value is more informative than a statement of significance because it allows us to assess significance at any level we choose. For example, a result with $P = 0.03$ is significant at the $\alpha = 0.05$ level but is not significant at the $\alpha = 0.01$ level.

Before technology that gives P-values quickly and accurately became common, *tables of critical values* were used to assess significance. Critical values for the z statistic appear in the z^* row at the bottom of Table C, the same table we used for confidence intervals. At the top of the table, you see the confidence level C for each z^*. At the bottom of the table, you see both the one-sided and two-sided P-values for each z^*. Values of a test statistic z that are farther out than a z^* (in the direction given by the alternative hypothesis) are significant at the level that matches z^*. To assess significance at the $\alpha = 0.05$ level, for example, just compare your z with the z^* for $P = 0.05$. Because P-values are more informative than just "significant or not," it is better to use the table to get an approximate P-value.

SIGNIFICANCE FROM A TABLE OF CRITICAL VALUES

To find the approximate P-value for any z statistic, compare z (ignoring its sign) with the critical values in the z^* row of Table C. If z falls between two values of z^*, the P-value falls between the two corresponding values of P in the "One-sided P" or the "Two-sided P" row of Table C.

EXAMPLE 13.11   **Is it significant?**

The z statistic for a one-sided test is $z = 2.13$. How significant is this result? Compare $z = 2.13$ with the z^* row in Table C. It lies between $z^* = 2.054$ and $z^* = 2.326$. So the P-value lies between the corresponding entries in the "One-sided P" row, which are $P = 0.02$ and $P = 0.01$. This z is significant at the $\alpha = 0.02$ level and *is not* significant at the $\alpha = 0.01$ level.

z^*	2.054	2.326
One-sided P	.02	.01

Figure 13.8 illustrates the situation. The shaded area under the Normal curve is the P-value for $z = 2.13$. You can see that P falls between the areas to the right of the two critical values, for $P = 0.02$ and $P = 0.01$.

The z statistic in Example 13.10 is $z = -1.09$. The alternative hypothesis is two-sided. Compare $z = -1.09$ (ignoring the minus sign) with the z^* row in Table C. It lies between $z^* = 1.036$ and $z^* = 1.282$. So the P-value lies between the matching entries in the "Two-sided P" row, $P = 0.30$ and $P = 0.20$. This is enough to conclude that the data do not provide good evidence against the null hypothesis. ■

z^*	1.036	1.282
Two-sided P	.30	.20

APPLY YOUR KNOWLEDGE

13.16 Protecting long-distance runners. A randomized comparative experiment compared vitamin C with a placebo as protection against respiratory infections after running a very long distance. The report of the study said:[6]

FIGURE 13.8

Is it significant? The test statistic value $z = 2.13$ falls between the critical values required for significance at the $\alpha = 0.02$ and $\alpha = 0.01$ levels. So the test *is* significant at $\alpha = 0.02$ and *is not* significant at $\alpha = 0.01$.

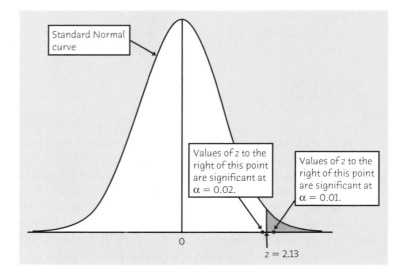

Sixty-eight percent of the runners in the placebo group reported the development of symptoms of upper respiratory tract infection after the race; this was significantly more (P < 0.01) than that reported by the vitamin C-supplemented group (33%).

(a) Explain to someone who knows no statistics why "significantly more" means there is good reason to think that vitamin C works.

(b) Now explain more exactly: what does $P < 0.01$ mean?

13.17 Significance from a table. A test of $H_0: \mu = 1$ against $H_a: \mu > 1$ has test statistic $z = 1.776$. Is this test significant at the 5% level ($\alpha = 0.05$)? Is it significant at the 1% level ($\alpha = 0.01$)?

13.18 Significance from a table. A test of $H_0: \mu = 1$ against $H_a: \mu \neq 1$ has test statistic $z = 1.776$. Is this test significant at the 5% level ($\alpha = 0.05$)? Is it significant at the 1% level?

13.19 Testing software. You have computer software that is supposed to generate observations from a standard Normal distribution. If this is true, the numbers generated come from a population with $\mu = 0$ and $\sigma = 1$. A command to generate 100 observations gives outcomes with mean $\bar{x} = -0.2213$. Assume that the population σ remains fixed. We want to test

$$H_0: \mu = 0$$
$$H_a: \mu \neq 0$$

(a) Calculate the value of the z test statistic.

(b) Use Table C: is z significant at the 5% level ($\alpha = 0.05$)?

(c) Use Table C: is z significant at the 1% level ($\alpha = 0.01$)?

(d) Between which two Normal critical values z^* in the bottom row of Table C does z lie? Between what two numbers does the P-value lie? Does the test give good evidence against the null hypothesis?

CHAPTER 13 SUMMARY

■ A **confidence interval** uses sample data to estimate an unknown population parameter with an indication of how accurate the estimate is and of how confident we are that the result is correct.

■ Any confidence interval has two parts: an interval calculated from the data and a confidence level C. The **interval** often has the form

$$\text{estimate} \pm \text{margin of error}$$

■ The **confidence level** is the success rate of the method that produces the interval. That is, C is the probability that the method will give a correct answer. If you use 95% confidence intervals often, in the long run 95% of your intervals will contain the true parameter value. You do not know whether or not a 95% confidence interval calculated from a particular set of data contains the true parameter value.

■ A level C **confidence interval for the mean** μ of a Normal population with known standard deviation σ, based on an SRS of size n, is given by

$$\overline{x} \pm z^* \frac{\sigma}{\sqrt{n}}$$

The **critical value** z^* is chosen so that the standard Normal curve has area C between $-z^*$ and z^*.

■ A **test of significance** assesses the evidence provided by data against a **null hypothesis** H_0 in favor of an **alternative hypothesis** H_a.

■ Hypotheses are always stated in terms of population parameters. Usually H_0 is a statement that no effect is present, and H_a says that a parameter differs from its null value in a specific direction (**one-sided alternative**) or in either direction (**two-sided alternative**).

■ The essential reasoning of a significance test is as follows. Suppose for the sake of argument that the null hypothesis is true. If we repeated our data production many times, would we often get data as inconsistent with H_0 as the data we actually have? Data that would rarely occur if H_0 were true provide evidence against H_0.

■ A test is based on a **test statistic** that measures how far the sample outcome is from the value stated by H_0.

■ The **P-value** of a test is the probability, computed supposing H_0 to be true, that the test statistic will take a value at least as extreme as that actually observed. Small P-values indicate strong evidence against H_0. To calculate a P-value we must know the sampling distribution of the test statistic when H_0 is true.

■ If the P-value is as small or smaller than a specified value α, the data are **statistically significant** at significance level α.

■ **Significance tests for the null hypothesis H_0: $\mu = \mu_0$** concerning the unknown mean μ of a population are based on the **one-sample z test statistic**

$$z = \frac{\overline{x} - \mu_0}{\sigma/\sqrt{n}}$$

The z test assumes an SRS of size n from a Normal population with known population standard deviation σ. P-values can be obtained either with computations from the standard Normal distribution or by using software.

A laboratory scale is known to have a standard deviation of $\sigma = 0.001$ gram in repeated weighings. Scale readings in repeated weighings are Normally distributed, with mean equal to the true weight of the specimen. Three weighings of a specimen on this scale give 3.412, 3.416, and 3.414 grams. Exercises 13.20 through 13.22 use this information.

13.20 A 95% confidence interval for the true weight of this specimen is
(a) 3.414 ± 0.00113.   (b) 3.414 ± 0.00065.
(c) 3.414 ± 0.00196.

13.21 The z statistic for testing $H_0: \mu = 3.41$ based on these 3 measurements is
(a) $z = 0.004$.   (b) $z = 4$.   (c) $z = 6.928$.

13.22 Another specimen is weighed 8 times on this scale. The average weight is 4.1602 grams. A 99% confidence interval for the true weight of this specimen is
(a) 4.1602 ± 0.00032.   (b) 4.1602 ± 0.00069.
(c) 4.1602 ± 0.00091.

13.23 Psychologists often measure how long it takes mice to find their way through a maze. The mean time is 18 seconds for one particular maze. A researcher thinks that a loud noise will cause the mice to complete the maze faster. She measures how long each of 10 mice takes with a noise as stimulus. The sample mean is $\bar{x} = 16.5$ seconds. The null hypothesis for the significance test is
(a) $H_0: \mu = 18$.   (b) $H_0: \mu = 16.5$.   (c) $H_0: \mu < 18$.

13.24 The alternative hypothesis for the test in Exercise 13.23 is
(a) $H_a: \mu \neq 18$.   (b) $H_a: \mu < 18$.   (c) $H_a: \mu = 16.5$.

13.25 You use software to carry out a test of significance. The program tells you that the P-value is $P = 0.027$. This result is
(a) not significant at either $\alpha = 0.05$ or $\alpha = 0.01$.
(b) significant at $\alpha = 0.05$ but not at $\alpha = 0.01$.
(c) significant at both $\alpha = 0.05$ and $\alpha = 0.01$.

13.26 You use software to carry out a test of significance. The program tells you that the P-value is $P = 0.027$. This means that
(a) the probability that the null hypothesis is true is 0.027.
(b) the value of the test statistic is 0.027.
(c) a test statistic as extreme as these data give would happen with probability 0.027 if the null hypothesis were true.

13.27 Women's heights. The average height of 18-year-old American women is 64.2 inches. You wonder whether the mean height of this year's female graduates from your local high school is different from the national average. You measure an SRS of 78 female graduates and find that $\bar{x} = 63.1$ inches. What are your null and alternative hypotheses?

13.28 Stating hypotheses. In planning a study of the birth weights of babies whose mothers did not see a doctor before delivery, a researcher states the hypotheses as

$$H_0: \bar{x} = 1000 \text{ grams}$$
$$H_a: \bar{x} < 1000 \text{ grams}$$

What's wrong with this?

In all exercises that call for P-values, give the actual value if you use software; otherwise, use Table C to give values between which P must fall.

13.29 Student study times. A class survey in a large first-year college class asked, "About how many minutes do you study on a typical weeknight?" The mean response of the 269 students was $\bar{x} = 137$ minutes. Suppose that we know that study time follows a Normal distribution with standard deviation $\sigma = 65$ minutes in the population of all first-year students at this university.
(a) Use the survey result to give a 99% confidence interval for the mean study time of all first-year students.
(b) What condition not yet mentioned must be met for your confidence interval to be valid?

13.30 I want more muscle. Young men in North America and Europe tend to think they need more muscle to be attractive. One study presented 200 young American men with 100 images of men with various levels of muscle.[7] Researchers measure level of muscle in kilograms per square meter (kg/m^2) of fat-free body mass. Typical young men have about 20 kg/m^2. Each subject chose two images, one that represented his own level of body muscle and one that he thought represented "what women prefer." The mean gap between self-image and "what women prefer" was 2.35 kg/m^2.
    Suppose that the "muscle gap" in the population of all young men has a Normal distribution with standard deviation 2.5 kg/m^2. Give a 90% confidence interval for the mean amount of muscle young men think they should add to be attractive to women. (In fact, women prefer a level close to that of typical men.)

13.31 An outlier strikes. There were actually 270 responses to the class survey in Exercise 13.29. One student claimed to study 30,000 minutes per night. We know he's joking, so we left out this value. If we did a calculation without looking at the data, we would get $\bar{x} = 248$ minutes for all 270 students. Now what is the 99% confidence interval for the population mean? (Continue to use $\sigma = 65$.) Compare the new interval with that in Exercise 13.29. The message is clear: always look at your data, because outliers can greatly change your result.

13.32 Explaining confidence. Here is an explanation from the Associated Press concerning one of its opinion polls. Explain briefly but clearly in what way this explanation is incorrect.

> For a poll of 1,600 adults, the variation due to sampling error is no more than three percentage points either way. The error margin is said to be valid at the 95 percent confidence level. This means that, if the same questions were repeated in 20 polls, the results of at least 19 surveys would be within three percentage points of the results of this survey.

13.33 Student study times. Exercise 13.29 describes a class survey in which students claimed to study an average of $\overline{x} = 137$ minutes on a typical weeknight. Regard these students as an SRS from the population of all first-year students at this university. Does the study give good evidence that students claim to study more than 2 hours per night on the average?
(a) State null and alternative hypotheses in terms of the mean study time in minutes for the population.
(b) What is the value of the test statistic z?
(c) What is the P-value of the test? Can you conclude that students do claim to study more than two hours per weeknight on the average?

13.34 I want more muscle. If young men thought that their own level of muscle was about what women prefer, the mean "muscle gap" in the study described in Exercise 13.30 would be 0. We suspect (before seeing the data) that young men think women prefer more muscle.
(a) State null and alternative hypotheses for testing this suspicion.
(b) What is the value of the test statistic z?
(c) You can tell just from the value of z that the evidence in favor of the alternative is very strong (that is, the P-value is very small). Explain why this is true.

13.35 Hotel managers' personalities. Successful hotel managers must have personality characteristics often thought of as feminine (such as "compassionate") as well as those often thought of as masculine (such as "forceful"). A personality test measures "femininity" on a scale of 1 to 7. A sample of 148 male general managers of three-star and four-star hotels had mean femininity score $\overline{y} = 5.29$.[8] The mean score for the general male population is $\mu = 5.19$. Do hotel managers on the average differ significantly in femininity score from men in general? Assume that the standard deviation of scores in the

population of all male hotel managers is the same as the $\sigma = 0.78$ for the adult male population.
(a) State null and alternative hypotheses in terms of the mean femininity score μ for male hotel managers.
(b) Find the z test statistic.
(c) What is the P-value for your z? What do you conclude about male hotel managers?

13.36 Is this what P means? When asked to explain the meaning of "the P-value was $P = 0.03$," a student says, "This means there is only probability 0.03 that the null hypothesis is true." Explain what $P = 0.03$ really means in a way that makes it clear that the student's explanation is wrong.

13.37 Pig skulls show that you were rich. In grave sites from ancient China, skulls of sacrificed pigs tend to appear along with expensive ornaments. This suggests that the pigs, like the ornaments, signal the wealth and prestige of the person buried. A study of burials from around 3500 B.C. concluded that "there are striking differences in grave goods between burials with pig skulls and burials without them. . . . A test indicates that the two samples of total artifacts are significantly different at the 0.01 level."[9] Explain clearly why "significantly different at the 0.01 level" gives good reason to think that there really is a systematic difference between burials that contain pig skulls and those that lack them.

13.38 Cicadas as fertilizer? Every 17 years, swarms of cicadas emerge from the ground in eastern North America, live for about six weeks, then die. There are so many cicadas that their dead bodies can serve as fertilizer. In an experiment, a researcher added cicadas under some plants in a natural plot of bellflowers on the forest floor, leaving other plants undisturbed. "In this experiment, cicada-supplemented bellflowers from a natural field population produced foliage with 12% greater nitrogen content relative to controls ($P = 0.031$)."[10] A friend who knows no statistics says that an increase of 12% isn't a lot—maybe it's just an accident due to natural variation among the plants. Explain in simple language how "$P = 0.031$" answers this objection.

13.39 Forests and windstorms. Does the destruction of large trees in a windstorm change forests in any important way? Here is the conclusion of a study that found that the answer is "No":

> We found surprisingly little divergence between treefall areas and adjacent control areas in the richness of woody plants ($P = 0.62$), in total stem densities ($P = 0.98$), or in population size or structure for any individual shrub or tree species.[11]

The two P-values refer to null hypotheses that say "no change" in measurements between treefall and control areas. Explain clearly why these values provide no evidence of change.

13.40 5% versus 1%. Sketch the standard Normal curve for the z test statistic and mark off areas under the curve to show why a value of z that is significant at the 1% level in a one-sided test is always significant at the 5% level. If z is significant at the 5% level, what can you say about its significance at the 1% level?

13.41 The wrong alternative. One of your friends is comparing movie ratings by female and male students for a class project. She starts with no expectations as to which sex will rate a movie more highly. After seeing that women rate a particular movie more highly than men, she tests a one-sided alternative about the mean ratings,

$$H_0: \mu_F = \mu_M$$
$$H_a: \mu_F > \mu_M$$

She finds $z = 2.1$ with one-sided P-value $P = 0.0179$.
(a) Explain why your friend should have used the two-sided alternative hypothesis.
(b) What is the correct P-value for $z = 2.1$?

13.42 The wrong P. The report of a study of seat belt use by drivers says, "Hispanic drivers were not significantly more likely than White/non-Hispanic drivers to overreport safety belt use (27.4 vs. 21.1%, respectively; $z = 1.33$, $P > 1.0$)."[12] How do you know that the P-value given is incorrect? What is the correct one-sided P-value for test statistic $z = 1.33$?

*Exercises 13.43 to 13.49 ask you to answer questions from data. Assume that the "simple conditions" hold in each case. The exercise statements give you the **State** step of the four-step process. In your work, follow the **Plan, Solve,** and **Conclude** steps, illustrated in Example 13.3 for a confidence interval and in Example 13.10 for a test of significance.*

13.43 Pulling wood apart. How heavy a load (pounds) is needed to pull apart pieces of Douglas fir 4 inches long and 1.5 inches square? Here are data from students doing a laboratory exercise:

33,190	31,860	32,590	26,520	33,280
32,320	33,020	32,030	30,460	32,700
23,040	30,930	32,720	33,650	32,340
24,050	30,170	31,300	28,730	31,920

(a) We are willing to regard the wood pieces prepared for the lab session as an SRS of all similar pieces of Douglas fir. Engineers commonly assume that characteristics of materials vary Normally. Make a graph to show the shape of the distribution for these data. Does the Normality condition appear safe?
(b) Suppose that the strength of pieces of wood like these follows a Normal distribution with standard deviation 3000 pounds. Give a 90% confidence interval for the mean load required to pull the wood apart.

13.44 Bone loss by nursing mothers. Breast-feeding mothers secrete calcium into their milk. Some of the calcium may come from their bones, so mothers may lose bone mineral. Researchers measured the percent change in mineral content of the spines of 47 mothers during three months of breast-feeding.[13] Here are the data:

−4.9	−2.7	−0.8	−5.3	−8.3	−2.1	−6.8	−4.3
−3.1	−1.0	−6.5	−1.8	−5.2	−5.7	−7.0	−2.2
−3.0	−3.6	−5.2	−2.0	−2.1	−5.6	−4.4	−3.3
−4.7	−3.8	−5.9	−2.5	−0.3	−6.2	−6.8	1.7
0.4	−5.3	0.2	−2.2	−5.1	−4.7	−2.5	2.2
−6.5	−1.0	−4.0	−4.9	0.3	−2.3	−7.8	

(a) The researchers are willing to consider these 47 women as an SRS from the population of all nursing mothers. Suppose that the percent change in this population has standard deviation $\sigma = 2.5\%$. Make a stemplot of the data to see that they appear to follow a Normal distribution quite closely. (Don't forget that you need both a 0 and a −0 stem because there are both positive and negative values.)
(b) Use a 99% confidence interval to estimate the mean percent change in the population.

13.45 Pulling wood apart. Exercise 13.43 gives data on the pounds of load needed to pull apart pieces of Douglas fir. The data are a random sample from a Normal distribution with standard deviation 3000 pounds.
(a) Is there significant evidence at the $\alpha = 0.10$ level against the hypothesis that the mean is 32,000 pounds for the two-sided alternative?
(b) Is there significant evidence at the $\alpha = 0.10$ level against the hypothesis that the mean is 31,500 pounds for the two-sided alternative?

13.46 Bone loss by nursing mothers. Exercise 13.44 gives the percent change in the mineral content of the spine for 47 mothers during three months of nursing a baby. As in that exercise, suppose that the percent change in the population of all nursing mothers has a Normal distribution with standard deviation $\sigma = 2.5\%$. Do these data give good evidence that on the average nursing mothers lose bone mineral?

13.47 This wine stinks. Sulfur compounds cause "off-odors" in wine, so winemakers want to know the odor threshold, the lowest concentration of a compound that the human nose can detect. The odor threshold for dimethyl sulfide (DMS) in trained wine tasters is about 25 micrograms per liter of wine (μg/l). The untrained noses of consumers may be less sensitive, however. Here are the DMS odor thresholds for 10 untrained students:

31 31 43 36 23 34 32 30 20 24

(a) Assume that the standard deviation of the odor threshold for untrained noses is known to be $\sigma = 7$ μg/l. Briefly discuss the other two "simple conditions," using a stemplot to verify that the distribution is roughly symmetric with no outliers.
(b) Give a 95% confidence interval for the mean DMS odor threshold among all students.

13.48 Eye grease. Athletes performing in bright sunlight often smear black eye grease under their eyes to reduce glare. Does eye grease work? In one study, 16 student subjects took a test of sensitivity to contrast after 3 hours facing into bright sun, both with and without eye grease. This is a matched pairs design. Here are the differences in sensitivity, with eye grease minus without eye grease:[14]

0.07 0.64 −0.12 −0.05 −0.18 0.14 −0.16 0.03
0.05 0.02 0.43 0.24 −0.11 0.28 0.05 0.29

We want to know whether eye grease increases sensitivity on the average.
(a) What are the null and alternative hypotheses? Say in words what mean μ your hypotheses concern.
(b) Suppose that the subjects are an SRS of all young people with normal vision, that contrast differences follow a Normal distribution in this population, and that the standard deviation of differences is $\sigma = 0.22$. Carry out a test of significance.

13.49 This wine stinks. Are untrained students less sensitive on the average than trained tasters in detecting "off-odors" in wine? Exercise 13.47 gives the lowest levels of dimethyl sulfide (DMS) that 10 students could detect. The units are micrograms of DMS per liter of wine (μg/l). Assume that the odor threshold for untrained noses is Normally distributed with $\sigma = 7$ μg/l. Is there evidence that the mean threshold for untrained tasters is greater than 25 μg/l?

13.50 Tests from confidence intervals. A confidence interval for the population mean μ tells us which values of μ are plausible (those inside the interval) and which values are not plausible (those outside the interval) at the chosen level of confidence. You can use this idea to carry out a test of any null hypothesis H_0: $\mu = \mu_0$ starting with a confidence interval: *reject H_0 if μ_0 is outside the interval and fail to reject if μ_0 is inside the interval.*
The alternative hypothesis is always two-sided, H_a: $\mu \neq \mu_0$, because the confidence interval extends in both directions from $\bar{x}$. A 95% confidence interval leads to a test at the 5% significance level because the interval is wrong 5% of the time. In general, confidence level C leads to a test at significance level $\alpha = 1 - C$.
(a) In Example 13.10, a medical director found mean blood pressure $\bar{x} = 126.07$ for an SRS of 72 executives. The standard deviation of the blood pressures of all executives is $\sigma = 15$. Give a 90% confidence interval for the mean blood pressure μ of all executives.
(b) The hypothesized value $\mu_0 = 128$ falls *inside* this confidence interval. Carry out the z test for H_0: $\mu = 128$ against the two-sided alternative. Show that the test is *not significant* at the 10% level.
(c) The hypothesized value $\mu_0 = 129$ falls *outside* this confidence interval. Carry out the z test for H_0: $\mu = 129$ against the two-sided alternative. Show that the test *is significant* at the 10% level.

13.51 Tests from confidence intervals. A 95% confidence interval for a population mean is 31.5 ± 3.4. Use the method described in the previous exercise to answer these questions.
(a) With a two-sided alternative, can you reject the null hypothesis that $\mu = 34$ at the 5% ($\alpha = 0.05$) significance level? Why or why not?
(b) With a two-sided alternative, can you reject the null hypothesis that $\mu = 35$ at the 5% significance level? Why or why not?

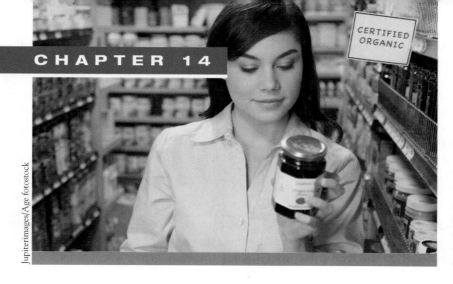

"Do you feel confident or not confident that the food available at most grocery stores is safe to eat?" Exercise 14.6 describes an opinion poll that asked this question.

Thinking about Inference

IN THIS CHAPTER WE COVER...

- Conditions for inference in practice
- How confidence intervals behave
- Sample size for confidence intervals
- How significance tests behave

To this point, we have met just two procedures for statistical inference. Both concern inference about the mean μ of a population when the "simple conditions" (page 232) are true: the data are an SRS, the population has a Normal distribution, and we know the standard deviation σ of the population. Under these conditions, a confidence interval for the mean μ is

$$\bar{x} \pm z^* \frac{\sigma}{\sqrt{n}}$$

To test a hypothesis H_0: $\mu = \mu_0$ we use the one-sample z statistic:

$$z = \frac{\bar{x} - \mu_0}{\sigma/\sqrt{n}}$$

We call these **z procedures** because they both start with the one-sample z statistic and use the standard Normal distribution.

z procedures

This chapter expands our discussion of confidence intervals and tests, still using the z procedures as examples. In later chapters we will modify these procedures for inference about a population mean to make them useful in practice. We will also introduce procedures for confidence intervals and tests in most of the settings we met in learning to explore data. The understanding needed to use statistical inference effectively is the same, no matter how elaborate the details of the procedure are.

Conditions for inference in practice

Any confidence interval or significance test can be trusted only under specific conditions. It's up to you to understand these conditions and judge whether they fit your problem. With that in mind, let's look back at the "simple conditions" for the z procedures.

The final "simple condition," that we know the standard deviation σ of the population, is rarely satisfied in practice. The z procedures are therefore of little practical use. Chapter 16 shows that it is easy to remove this condition. The first two "simple conditions" (SRS, Normal population) are harder to escape. In fact, they represent the kinds of conditions needed if we are to trust almost any statistical inference. As you plan inference, you should always ask, "Where did the data come from?" and you must often also ask, "What is the shape of the population distribution?"

Where did the data come from? *The most important requirement for any inference procedure is that the data come from a process to which the laws of probability apply.* Inference is most reliable when the data come from a random sample or a randomized comparative experiment. Random samples use chance to choose respondents. Randomized comparative experiments use chance to assign subjects to treatments. The deliberate use of chance ensures that the laws of probability apply to the outcomes, and this in turn ensures that statistical inference makes sense.

WHERE THE DATA COME FROM MATTERS

When you use statistical inference, you are acting as if your data are a random sample or come from a randomized comparative experiment.

If a study's data don't come from a random sample or a randomized comparative experiment, the conclusions may be suspect. It is common to apply statistical inference to data that are not produced by random selection. When you see such a study, ask whether the data can be trusted as a basis for the stated conclusions.

EXAMPLE 14.1 **The psychologist and the sociologist**

A psychologist is interested in how our visual perception can be fooled by optical illusions. Her subjects are students in Psychology 101 at her university. Most psychologists would agree that it's safe to treat the students as an SRS of all people with normal vision. There is nothing special about being a student that changes visual perception.

A sociologist at the same university uses students in Sociology 101 to examine attitudes toward poor people. Students as a group are younger than the adult population as a whole. Even among young people, students as a group come from more prosperous and better-educated homes. Even among students, this university isn't typical of all campuses. Even on this campus, students in a sociology course may have opinions that are quite different from those of engineering students. The sociologist can't reasonably act as if these students are a random sample from any interesting population. ■

Our first examples of inference, using the z procedures, act as if the data are an SRS from the population of interest. Let's look back at the examples in Chapter 13.

EXAMPLE 14.2 **Is it really an SRS?**

The NHANES survey that produced the body mass data for Example 13.1 used a complex multistage sample design, so it's a bit oversimplified to treat the data as coming from an SRS from the population of young women.[1] The overall effect of the NHANES sample is close to an SRS, however.

The 18 newts for the skin-healing study in Example 13.3 were chosen at random from a laboratory population of newts to receive one of several treatments being compared in a randomized comparative experiment. Scientists usually act as if the available animal subjects are an SRS from their species or genetic type if there is nothing special about where the subjects came from. We can treat these newts as an SRS from this species.

The cola taste test in Example 13.5 uses scores from 10 tasters. All were examined to be sure that they have no medical condition that interferes with normal taste and then carefully trained to score sweetness using a set of standard drinks. We are willing to take their scores as an SRS from the population of trained tasters.

The medical director who examined executives' blood pressures in Example 13.10 actually chose an SRS from the medical records of all executives in this company. ■

These examples are typical. One is an actual SRS, two are situations in which common practice is to act as if the sample were an SRS, and in the remaining example procedures that assume an SRS can be used for a quick analysis of data from a more complex random sample. *There is no simple rule for deciding when you can act as if a sample is an SRS. Pay attention to these cautions:*

- *Practical problems such as nonresponse in samples or dropouts from an experiment can hinder inference even from a well-designed study.* The NHANES survey has about an 80% response rate. This is much higher than opinion polls and most other national surveys, so by realistic standards NHANES data are quite trustworthy. (NHANES uses advanced methods to try to correct for nonresponse, but these methods work best when response is high to start with.)

- *Different methods are needed for different designs.* The z procedures aren't correct for random sampling designs more complex than an SRS. We won't discuss inference for really complex designs like that used by NHANES.

- *There is no cure for fundamental flaws like voluntary response surveys or uncontrolled experiments.* Look back at the bad examples in Chapters 7 and 8 and steel yourself to just ignore data from such studies.

What is the shape of the population distribution? Most statistical inference procedures require some conditions on the shape of the population distribution. Many basic methods of inference are designed for Normal populations. That's the case for the z procedures and also for the more practical procedures for inference about means that we will meet in Chapters 16 and 17. Fortunately, this condition is less essential than where the data come from.

This is true because the z procedures and many other procedures designed for Normal distributions are based on Normality of the sample mean $\bar{x}$, not Normality of individual observations. The central limit theorem tells us that $\bar{x}$ is more Normal than the individual observations and that $\bar{x}$ becomes more Normal as the size of the sample increases. In practice, the z procedures are reasonably accurate for any roughly symmetric distribution for samples of even moderate size. If the sample is large, $\bar{x}$ will be close to Normal even if individual measurements are strongly skewed, as Figure 10.3 (page 191) illustrates. Later chapters give practical guidelines for specific inference procedures.

There is one important exception to the principle that the shape of the population is less critical than how the data were produced. Outliers can distort the results of inference. *Any inference procedure based on sample statistics like the sample mean $\bar{x}$ that are not resistant to outliers can be strongly influenced by a few extreme observations.*

How can we decide if the population distribution is roughly Normal? Sometimes *experience with similar data* suggests that our data are likely to come from a roughly Normal distribution, or not. For example, heights of people of the same sex and similar ages are close to Normal, but weights are not. Sometimes we rely on *data analysis*. Always explore your data before doing inference. When the data are chosen at random from a population, the shape of the data distribution mirrors the shape of the population distribution. Make a stemplot or histogram of your data and look to see whether the shape is roughly Normal. Remember that small samples have a lot of chance variation, so that Normality is hard to judge from just a few observations. Always look for outliers and try to correct them or justify their removal before performing the z procedures or other inference based on statistics like $\bar{x}$ that are not resistant.

When outliers are present or the data suggest that the population is strongly non-Normal, a statistician can suggest alternative methods that don't require Normality and are not sensitive to outliers.

APPLY YOUR KNOWLEDGE

14.1 Rate that movie. A professor interested in the opinions of college-age adults about a new hit movie asks the 25 students in her course on documentary filmmaking to rate the entertainment value of the movie on a scale of 0 to 5. Which of the following is the most important reason why a confidence interval for the mean rating by all college-age adults based on these data is of little use? Comment briefly on each reason to explain your answer.

(a) The sample is small, so the margin of error will be large.

(b) Many of the students in the course will probably refuse to respond.

(c) Students in a course on filmmaking can't be considered a random sample from the population of all college-age adults.

Ilene MacDonald/Alamy

14.2 Running red lights. A survey asked a sample of licensed drivers, "Of every ten motorists who run a red light, about how many do you think will be caught?" The mean result for 880 respondents was $\bar{x} = 1.92$ and the standard deviation was $s = 1.83$.[2] For this large sample, s will be close to the population standard deviation σ, so suppose we know that $\sigma = 1.83$.

(a) Give a 95% confidence interval for the mean opinion in the population of all licensed drivers.

(b) The distribution of responses is skewed to the right rather than Normal. This will not strongly affect the z confidence interval for this sample. Why not?

(c) The 880 respondents are an SRS from completed calls among 45,956 calls to randomly chosen residential telephone numbers listed in telephone directories. Only 5029 of the calls were completed. This information gives two reasons to suspect that the sample may not represent all licensed drivers. What are these reasons?

14.3 Sampling shoppers. A marketing consultant observes 50 consecutive shoppers at a supermarket on a Sunday morning, recording how much each shopper spends in the store. Suggest some reasons why it may be risky to act as if these shoppers are an SRS of all shoppers at this store.

How confidence intervals behave

The z confidence interval $\bar{x} \pm z^*\sigma/\sqrt{n}$ for the mean of a Normal population illustrates several important properties that are shared by all confidence intervals in common use. The user chooses the confidence level, and the margin of error follows from this choice. We would like high confidence and also a small margin of error. High confidence says that our method almost always gives correct answers. A small margin of error says that we have pinned down the parameter quite precisely. The factors that influence the margin of error of the z confidence interval are typical of most confidence intervals.

How do we get a small margin of error? The margin of error for the z confidence interval is

$$\text{margin of error} = z^* \frac{\sigma}{\sqrt{n}}$$

The numerator contains z^* and σ, and the denominator is $\sqrt{n}$. This margin of error gets smaller when

- z^* gets smaller. Smaller z^* is the same as lower confidence level C.
- σ is smaller. The standard deviation σ measures the variation in the population. You can think of the variation among individuals in the population as noise that obscures the average value μ. It is easier to pin down μ when σ is small.
- n gets larger. Increasing the sample size n reduces the margin of error for any confidence level. That is, larger samples allow more precise estimates.

You can't change the population standard deviation σ. But you can decide what confidence level you want and how many observations you will take. These decisions change the margin of error.

EXAMPLE 14.3 **Changing the margin of error**

In Example 13.3 (page 236), biologists measured the rate of healing of the skin of 18 newts. The data gave $\bar{x} = 25.67$ micrometers per hour and we know that $\sigma = 8$ micrometers per hour. The z confidence interval for the mean healing rate for all newts is $\bar{x} \pm z^*\sigma/\sqrt{n}$. Here are the intervals for several levels of confidence:

99% confidence	$25.67 \pm 2.576\dfrac{8}{\sqrt{18}}$	$= 25.67 \pm 4.86$
95% confidence	$25.67 \pm 1.960\dfrac{8}{\sqrt{18}}$	$= 25.67 \pm 3.70$
90% confidence	$25.67 \pm 1.645\dfrac{8}{\sqrt{18}}$	$= 25.67 \pm 3.10$

There is a trade-off between the confidence level and the margin of error. To obtain a smaller margin of error from the same data, you must be willing to accept lower confidence.

Here are the 95% confidence intervals for 9, 18, and 36 newts (the actual sample size 18, plus samples half as large and twice as large):

sample size 9 $25.67 \pm 1.960\dfrac{8}{\sqrt{9}} = 25.67 \pm 5.23$

sample size 18 $25.67 \pm 1.960\dfrac{8}{\sqrt{18}} = 25.67 \pm 3.70$

sample size 36 $25.67 \pm 1.960\dfrac{8}{\sqrt{36}} = 25.67 \pm 2.61$

As the sample size increases, the margin of error gets smaller. *Because the sample size n appears under a square root sign, you need four times as many observations to cut the margin of error in half.* ▨

What does the margin of error include? The most important caution about confidence intervals in general is a consequence of the use of a sampling distribution. A sampling distribution shows how a statistic such as $\overline{x}$ varies in repeated random sampling. This variation causes *random sampling error* because the statistic misses the true parameter by a random amount. No other source of variation or bias in the sample data influences the sampling distribution. So *the margin of error in a confidence interval ignores everything except the sample-to-sample variation due to choosing the sample randomly.*

> **THE MARGIN OF ERROR DOESN'T COVER ALL ERRORS**
>
> The margin of error in a confidence interval covers only random sampling errors.
>
> Practical difficulties such as undercoverage and nonresponse are often more serious than random sampling error. The margin of error does not take such difficulties into account.

Recall from Chapter 7 that national opinion polls often have response rates less than 50%. The announced margin of error for these polls is unrealistically small.

APPLY YOUR KNOWLEDGE

14.4 Confidence level and margin of error. Example 13.1 (page 232) described NHANES survey data on the body mass index (BMI) of 654 young women. The mean BMI in the sample was $\overline{x} = 26.8$. We treated these data as an SRS from a Normally distributed population with standard deviation $\sigma = 7.5$.

(a) Give three confidence intervals for the mean BMI μ in this population, using 90%, 95%, and 99% confidence.

(b) What are the margins of error for 90%, 95%, and 99% confidence? How does increasing the confidence level change the margin of error of a confidence interval when the sample size and population standard deviation remain the same?

14.5 Sample size and margin of error. Example 13.1 (page 232) described NHANES survey data on the body mass index (BMI) of 654 young women. The mean BMI in the sample was $\bar{x} = 26.8$. We treated these data as an SRS from a Normally distributed population with standard deviation $\sigma = 7.5$.

(a) Suppose that we had an SRS of just 100 young women. What would be the margin of error for 95% confidence?

(b) Find the margins of error for 95% confidence based on SRSs of 400 young women and 1600 young women.

(c) Compare the three margins of error. How does increasing the sample size change the margin of error of a confidence interval when the confidence level and population standard deviation remain the same?

14.6 Is your food safe? "Do you feel confident or not confident that the food available at most grocery stores is safe to eat?" When a Gallup Poll asked this question, 87% of the sample said they were confident.[3] Gallup announced the poll's margin of error for 95% confidence as ±3 percentage points. Which of the following sources of error are included in this margin of error?

Jupiterimages/Age fotostock

(a) Gallup dialed landline telephone numbers at random and so missed all people without landline phones, including people whose only phone is a cell phone.

(b) Some people whose numbers were chosen never answered the phone in several calls or answered but refused to participate in the poll.

(c) There is chance variation in the random selection of telephone numbers.

Sample size for confidence intervals

A wise user of statistics never plans a sample or an experiment without at the same time planning the inference. The number of observations is a critical part of planning a study. You can obtain a confidence interval that has both high confidence and a small margin of error by taking enough observations.

The margin of error of the z confidence interval for the mean of a Normally distributed population is $m = z^*\sigma/\sqrt{n}$. To obtain a desired margin of error m, put in the value of z^* for your desired confidence level, and solve for the sample size n. Here is the result.

> **SAMPLE SIZE FOR DESIRED MARGIN OF ERROR**
>
> The z confidence interval for the mean of a Normal population will have a specified margin of error m when the sample size is
>
> $$n = \left(\frac{z^*\sigma}{m}\right)^2$$

EXAMPLE 14.4 How many observations?

Example 13.3 (page 236) reports a study of the healing rate of cuts in the skin of newts. We know that the population standard deviation is $\sigma = 8$ micrometers per hour. We want to estimate the mean healing rate μ for this species of newts within ±3 micrometers per hour with 90% confidence. How many newts must we measure?

The desired margin of error is $m = 3$. For 90% confidence, Table C gives $z^* = 1.645$. Therefore,

$$n = \left(\frac{z^*\sigma}{m}\right)^2 = \left(\frac{1.645 \times 8}{3}\right)^2 = 19.2$$

Because 19 newts will give a slightly larger margin of error than desired, and 20 newts a slightly smaller margin of error, we must measure 20 newts. *Always round up to the next higher whole number when finding n.* ■

APPLY YOUR KNOWLEDGE

14.7 Body mass index of young women. Example 13.1 (page 232) assumed that the body mass index (BMI) of all American young women follows a Normal distribution with standard deviation $\sigma = 7.5$. How large a sample would be needed to estimate the mean BMI μ in this population to within ± 1 with 95% confidence?

14.8 Number skills of young men. Suppose that scores of men aged 21 to 25 years on the quantitative part of the National Assessment of Educational Progress (NAEP) test follow a Normal distribution with standard deviation $\sigma = 60$. You want to estimate the mean score within ± 10 with 90% confidence. How large an SRS of scores must you choose?

How significance tests behave

Significance tests are widely used in most areas of statistical work. New pharmaceutical products require significant evidence of effectiveness and safety. Courts inquire about statistical significance in hearing class action discrimination cases. Marketers want to know whether a new package design will significantly increase sales. Medical researchers want to know whether a new therapy performs significantly better. In all these uses, statistical significance is valued because it points to an effect that is unlikely to occur simply by chance. Here are some points to keep in mind when you use or interpret significance tests.

How small a *P* is convincing? The purpose of a test of significance is to describe the degree of evidence provided by the sample against the null hypothesis. The P-value does this. But how small a P-value is convincing evidence against the null hypothesis? This depends mainly on two circumstances:

■ *How plausible is H_0?* If H_0 represents an assumption that the people you must convince have believed for years, strong evidence (small P) will be needed to persuade them.
■ *What are the consequences of rejecting H_0?* If rejecting H_0 in favor of H_a means making an expensive changeover from one type of product packaging to another, you need strong evidence that the new packaging will boost sales.

These criteria are a bit subjective. Different people will often insist on different levels of significance. Giving the P-value allows each of us to decide individually if the evidence is sufficiently strong.

Users of statistics have often emphasized standard levels of significance such as 10%, 5%, and 1%. For example, courts have tended to accept 5% as a standard in discrimination cases.[4] This emphasis reflects the time when tables of critical values rather than software dominated statistical practice. The 5% level ($\alpha = 0.05$) is particularly common. *There is no sharp border between "significant" and "not significant," only increasingly strong evidence as the P-value decreases. There is no practical distinction between the P-values 0.049 and 0.051. It makes no sense to treat $P \leq 0.05$ as a universal rule for what is significant.*

Significance depends on the alternative hypothesis You may have noticed that the P-value for a one-sided test is one-half the P-value for the two-sided test of the same null hypothesis based on the same data. The two-sided P-value combines two equal areas, one in each tail of a Normal curve. The one-sided P-value is just one of these areas, in the direction specified by the alternative hypothesis. It makes sense that the evidence against H_0 is stronger when the alternative is one-sided, because it is based on the data *plus* information about the direction of possible deviations from H_0. If you lack this added information, always use a two-sided alternative hypothesis.

Significance depends on sample size Significance depends both on the size of the effect you observe *and* on the size of the sample. Understanding this fact is essential to understanding significance tests.

EXAMPLE 14.5 Coaching and SAT scores

On the average, high school juniors who retake the SAT exam as seniors improve their mathematics score by 13 points. Professor Gamma has designed a rigorous coaching program that she thinks will produce a larger increase. A group of juniors goes through this program and retakes the SAT as seniors. Their scores improve by an average of $\overline{x} = 15$ points. Is this significant evidence that the coaching program raises scores by more than 13 points on the average?

We'll assume the simple conditions: the students in the program are an SRS of the population of all juniors who take the SAT, and the distribution of math score gains in the entire population is Normal with unknown mean μ and known standard deviation $\sigma = 30$. For testing

$$H_0: \mu = 13$$

$$H_a: \mu > 13$$

the z test statistic is

$$z = \frac{\overline{x} - \mu_0}{\sigma/\sqrt{n}} = \frac{15 - 13}{30/\sqrt{n}}$$

The gain of 2 points is not very impressive. But how significant it is depends on the sample size n:

Sample size	z statistic	P-value
50	0.4714	0.3187
100	0.6667	0.2525
500	1.4907	0.0680
1000	2.1082	0.0175
5000	4.7140	0.000001

There you have it: a very small effect can be highly significant if the sample size is very large. To see why, think of the z test statistic as follows:

$$z = \frac{\overline{x} - \mu_0}{\sigma/\sqrt{n}} = \frac{\text{size of the observed effect}}{\text{size of chance variation}}$$

The numerator $\overline{x} - \mu_0$ shows how far the data diverge from the null hypothesis. How significant this effect is depends on the size of the chance variation from sample to sample, measured by the standard deviation of $\overline{x}$ that is the denominator of z.

SAMPLE SIZE AFFECTS STATISTICAL SIGNIFICANCE

Because large random samples have small chance variation, very small population effects can be highly significant if the sample is large.

Because small random samples have a lot of chance variation, even large population effects can fail to be significant if the sample is small.

Statistical significance does not tell us whether an effect is large enough to be important. That is, **statistical significance is not the same thing as practical importance.**

Keep in mind that statistical significance means "the sample showed an effect larger than would often occur just by chance." Significance says nothing about how large the effect actually is. *Always look at the actual size of an effect as well as at its statistical significance*. A confidence interval is often helpful. For example, the 95% confidence interval for the mean score gain in Example 14.5 with a sample of size 1000 is

$$\overline{x} \pm z^* \frac{\sigma}{\sqrt{n}} = 2 \pm 1.960 \frac{30}{\sqrt{1000}}$$

$$= 2 \pm 1.86$$

$$= 0.14 \text{ to } 3.86 \text{ points}$$

An improvement this small, even if it is statistically significant, doesn't justify an intensive coaching program.

Beware of multiple analyses Statistical significance ought to mean that you have found an effect that you were looking for. The reasoning behind statistical significance works well if you decide what effect you are seeking, design a study to search for it, and use a test of significance to weigh the evidence you get. In other settings, significance may have little meaning.

EXAMPLE 14.6 **Cell phones and brain cancer**

Might the radiation from cell phones be harmful to users? Many studies have found little or no connection between using cell phones and various illnesses. Here is part of a news account of one study:

A hospital study that compared brain cancer patients and a similar group without brain cancer found no statistically significant association between cell phone use and a group of brain cancers known as gliomas. But when 20 types of glioma were considered separately an association was found between phone use and one rare form. Puzzlingly, however, this risk appeared to decrease rather than increase with greater mobile phone use.[5]

Think for a moment. Suppose that the 20 null hypotheses (no association) for these 20 significance tests are all true. Then each test has a 5% chance of being significant at the 5% level. That's what $\alpha = 0.05$ means: results this extreme occur 5% of the time just by chance when the null hypothesis is true. Because 5% is 1/20, we expect about 1 of 20 tests to give a significant result just by chance. That's what the study observed. ■

Running one test and reaching the 5% level of significance is reasonably good evidence that you have found something. Running 20 tests and reaching that level only once is not. The caution about multiple analyses applies to confidence intervals as well. A single 95% confidence interval has probability 0.95 of capturing the true parameter each time you use it. The probability that all of 20 confidence intervals will capture their parameters is much less than 95%. If you think that multiple tests or intervals may have discovered an important effect, you need to gather new data to do inference about that specific effect.

APPLY YOUR KNOWLEDGE

14.9 Is it significant? In the absence of special preparation SAT mathematics scores in recent years have varied Normally with mean $\mu = 518$ and $\sigma = 114$. Fifty students go through a rigorous training program designed to raise their scores. Either by hand or by using software, carry out a test of

$$H_0: \mu = 518$$
$$H_a: \mu > 518$$

(with $\sigma = 114$) in each of the following situations:

(a) The students' average score is $\bar{x} = 544$. Is this result significant at the 5% level?

(b) The average score is $\bar{x} = 545$. Is this result significant at the 5% level?
The difference between the two outcomes in (a) and (b) is of no importance. Beware attempts to treat $\alpha = 0.05$ as sacred.

14.10 Detecting acid rain. Emissions of sulfur dioxide by industry result in "acid rain." The acidity of liquids is measured by pH on a scale of 0 to 14. Distilled water has pH 7.0, and lower pH values indicate acidity. Normal rain is somewhat acidic, so acid rain is sometimes defined as rainfall with a pH below 5.0. Suppose that pH measurements of rainfall on different days in a Canadian forest follow a Normal distribution with standard deviation $\sigma = 0.5$. A sample of n days finds that the mean pH is $\bar{x} = 4.8$. Is this good evidence that the mean pH μ for all rainy days is less than 5.0? The answer depends on the size of the sample.

Either by hand or using software, carry out three tests of

$$H_0: \mu = 5.0$$
$$H_a: \mu < 5.0$$

Use $\sigma = 0.5$ and $\bar{x} = 4.8$ in all three tests. But use three different sample sizes, $n = 5$, $n = 15$, and $n = 40$.

(a) What are the P-values for the three tests? *The P-value of the same result $\bar{x} = 4.8$ gets smaller (more significant) as the sample size increases.*

(b) For each test, sketch the Normal curve for the sampling distribution of $\bar{x}$ when H_0 is true. This curve has mean 5.0 and standard deviation $0.5/\sqrt{n}$. Mark the observed $\bar{x} = 4.8$ on each curve. *The same result $\bar{x} = 4.8$ gets more extreme on the sampling distribution as the sample size increases.*

14.11 Confidence intervals help. Give a 95% confidence interval for the mean pH μ for each sample size in the previous exercise. The intervals, unlike the P-values, give a clear picture of what mean pH values are plausible for each sample.

14.12 Searching for ESP. A researcher looking for evidence of extrasensory perception (ESP) tests 500 subjects. Four of these subjects do significantly better ($P < 0.01$) than random guessing.

(a) You can't conclude that these four people have ESP. Why not?

(b) What should the researcher now do to test whether any of these four subjects have ESP?

CHAPTER 14 SUMMARY

- A specific confidence interval or test is correct only under specific conditions. The most important conditions concern the method used to produce the data. Other factors such as the shape of the population distribution may also be important.

- Whenever you use statistical inference, you are acting as if your data are a random sample or come from a randomized comparative experiment.

- Always do data analysis before inference to detect outliers or other problems that would make inference untrustworthy.

- Other things being equal, the margin of error of a confidence interval gets smaller as
  - the confidence level C decreases,
  - the population standard deviation σ decreases,
  - the sample size n increases.

- The margin of error in a confidence interval accounts for only the chance variation due to random sampling. In practice, errors due to nonresponse or undercoverage are often more serious.

- The z confidence interval for a Normal mean has specified margin of error m when the sample size is

$$n = \left(\frac{z^*\sigma}{m} \right)^2$$

  Here z^* is the critical value for the desired level of confidence. Always round n up when you use this formula.

- There is no universal rule for how small a P-value in a test of significance is convincing evidence against the null hypothesis. Beware of placing too much weight on traditional significance levels such as $\alpha = 0.05$.

- Very small effects can be highly significant (small P) when a test is based on a large sample. A statistically significant effect need not be practically important. Plot the data to display the effect you are seeking, and use confidence intervals to estimate the actual values of parameters.

- On the other hand, lack of significance does not imply that H_0 is true. Even a large effect can fail to be significant when a test is based on a small sample.

- Many tests run at once will probably produce some significant results by chance alone, even if all the null hypotheses are true.

CHECK YOUR SKILLS

14.13 The most important condition for sound conclusions from statistical inference is usually
(a) that the data can be thought of as a random sample from the population of interest.
(b) that the population distribution is exactly Normal.
(c) that the data contain no outliers.

14.14 The coach of a college men's basketball team records the resting heart rates of the 15 team members. You should not trust a confidence interval for the mean resting heart rate of all male students at this college based on these data because
(a) with only 15 observations, the margin of error will be large.
(b) heart rates may not have a Normal distribution.
(c) the members of the basketball team can't be considered a random sample of all students.

14.15 You turn your Web browser to the online Harris Interactive poll. Based on 6748 responses from people who chose to click on this site, the poll reports that 16% of U.S. adults sometimes use the Internet to make telephone calls.[6] You should refuse to calculate a 95% confidence interval based on this sample because
(a) the poll was taken a week ago.
(b) inference from a voluntary response sample can't be trusted.
(c) the sample is too large.

14.16 Many sample surveys use well-designed random samples but half or more of the original sample can't be contacted or refuse to take part. Any errors due to this nonresponse
(a) have no effect on the accuracy of confidence intervals.
(b) are included in the announced margin of error.
(c) are in addition to the random variation accounted for by the announced margin of error.

14.17 A writer in a medical journal says: "An uncontrolled experiment in 17 women found a significantly improved mean clinical symptom score after treatment. Methodologic flaws make it difficult to interpret the results of this study." The writer is skeptical about the significant improvement because
(a) there is no control group, so the improvement might be due to the placebo effect or to the fact that many medical conditions improve over time.

(b) the P-value given was $P = 0.03$, which is too large to be convincing.
(c) the response variable might not have an exactly Normal distribution in the population.

14.18 Vigorous exercise helps people live several years longer (on the average). Whether mild activities like slow walking extend life is not clear. Suppose that the added life expectancy from regular slow walking is just 2 months. A statistical test is more likely to find a significant increase in mean life if
(a) it is based on a very large random sample.
(b) it is based on a very small random sample.
(c) The size of the sample doesn't have any effect on the significance of the test.

14.19 A laboratory scale is known to have a standard deviation of $\sigma = 0.001$ gram in repeated weighings. Scale readings in repeated weighings are Normally distributed, with mean equal to the true weight of the specimen. How many times must you weigh a specimen on this scale in order to get a margin of error no larger than ± 0.0005 with 95% confidence?
(a) 4 times   (b) 15 times   (c) 16 times

CHAPTER 14 EXERCISES

14.20 Color blindness in Africa. An anthropologist claims that color blindness is less common in societies that live by hunting and gathering than in agricultural societies. He tests a number of adults in two populations in Africa, one of each type. The proportion of color-blind people is significantly lower ($P < 0.05$) in the hunter-gatherer population. What additional information would you want to help you decide whether you believe the anthropologist's claim?

14.21 Hotel managers. In Exercise 13.35 (page 253) you carried out a test of significance based on data from 148 general managers of three-star and four-star hotels. Before you trust your results, you would like more information about the data. What facts would you most like to know?

14.22 Sampling at the mall. A market researcher chooses at random from women entering a large suburban shopping mall. One outcome of the study is a 95% confidence interval for the mean of "the highest price you would pay for a pair of casual shoes."

(a) Explain why this confidence interval does not give useful information about the population of all women.

(b) Explain why it may give useful information about the population of women who shop at large suburban malls.

14.23 Hotel managers. In Exercise 13.35 (page 253) you carried out a test of significance based on the femininity scores of 148 male general managers of three-star and four-star hotels. You now realize that a confidence interval for the mean score of male hotel managers would be more informative than a test. You would be satisfied to estimate the mean to within ±0.2 with 99% confidence. The standard deviation of the scores is probably close to the value $\sigma = 0.78$ for the adult male population. How large an SRS of hotel managers do you need?

14.24 Sensitive questions. The National AIDS Behavioral Surveys found that 170 individuals in its random sample of 2673 adult heterosexuals said they had multiple sexual partners in the past year. That's 6.36% of the sample. Why is this estimate likely to be biased? Does the margin of error of a 95% confidence interval for the proportion of all adults with multiple partners allow for this bias?

14.25 Pulling wood apart. You want to estimate the mean load needed to pull apart the pieces of wood in Exercise 13.43 (page 254) to within ±1000 pounds with 95% confidence. How large a sample is needed?

14.26 College degrees. At the Census Bureau Web site www.census.gov you can find the percent of adults in each state who have at least a bachelor's degree. It makes no sense to find $\bar{x}$ for these data and use it to get a confidence interval for the mean percent μ in all 50 states. Why not?

14.27 An outlier strikes. You have data on an SRS of recent graduates from your college that shows how long each student took to complete a bachelor's degree. The data contain one high outlier. Will this outlier have a greater effect on a confidence interval for mean completion time if your sample is small or large? Why?

14.28 Can we trust this interval? Here are data on the percent change in the total mass (in tons) of wildlife in several West African game preserves in the years 1971 to 1999:[7]

1971	1972	1973	1974	1975	1976	1977	1978
2.9	3.1	−1.2	−1.1	−3.3	3.7	1.9	−0.3

1979	1980	1981	1982	1983	1984	1985	1986
−5.9	−7.9	−5.5	−7.2	−4.1	−8.6	−5.5	−0.7

1987	1988	1989	1990	1991	1992	1993	1994
−5.1	−7.1	−4.2	0.9	−6.1	−4.1	−4.8	−11.3

1995	1996	1997	1998	1999			
−9.3	−10.7	−1.8	−7.4	−22.9			

Software gives the 95% confidence interval for the mean annual percent change as −6.66% to −2.55%. There are several reasons why we might not trust this interval.

(a) Examine the distribution of the data. What feature of the distribution throws doubt on the validity of statistical inference?

(b) Plot the percents against year. What trend do you see in this time series? Explain why a trend over time casts doubt on the condition that years 1971 to 1999 can be treated as an SRS from a larger population of years.

14.29 When to use pacemakers. A medical panel prepared guidelines for when cardiac pacemakers should be implanted in patients with heart problems. The panel reviewed a large number of medical studies to judge the strength of the evidence supporting each recommendation. For each recommendation, they ranked the evidence as level A (strongest), B, or C (weakest). Here, in scrambled order, are the panel's descriptions of the three levels of evidence.[8] Which is A, which B, and which C? Explain your ranking.

Evidence was ranked as level _____ when data were derived from a limited number of trials involving comparatively small numbers of patients or from well-designed data analysis of nonrandomized studies or observational data registries.

Evidence was ranked as level _____ if the data were derived from multiple randomized clinical trials involving a large number of individuals.

Evidence was ranked as level _____ when consensus of expert opinion was the primary source of recommendation.

14.30 What is significance good for? Which of the following questions does a test of significance answer? Briefly explain your replies.

(a) Is the sample or experiment properly designed?

(b) Is the observed effect due to chance?

(c) Is the observed effect important?

14.31 Why are larger samples better? Statisticians prefer large samples. Describe briefly the effect of increasing the size of a sample (or the number of subjects in an experiment) on each of the following:

(a) The margin of error of a 95% confidence interval.

(b) The P-value of a test, when H_0 is false and all facts about the population remain unchanged as n increases.

14.32 Predicting success of trainees. What distinguishes managerial trainees who eventually become executives from those who don't succeed and leave the company? We have lots of data on past trainees—data on their personalities and goals, their college preparation and performance, even their family backgrounds and their hobbies. Statistical software makes it easy to perform dozens of significance tests on these dozens of variables to see which ones best predict later success. We find that future executives are significantly more likely than washouts to have an urban or suburban upbringing and an undergraduate degree in a technical field. Explain clearly why using these "significant" variables to select future trainees is not wise.

14.33 A test goes wrong. Software can generate samples from (almost) exactly Normal distributions. Here is a random sample of size 5 from the Normal distribution with mean 10 and standard deviation 2:

$$6.47 \quad 7.51 \quad 10.10 \quad 13.63 \quad 9.91$$

These data match the conditions for a z test better than real data will: the population is very close to Normal and has known standard deviation $\sigma = 2$, and the population mean is $\mu = 10$. Test the hypotheses

$$H_0: \mu = 8$$
$$H_a: \mu \neq 8$$

(a) What are the z statistic and its P-value? Is the test significant at the 5% level?

(b) We know that the null hypothesis does not hold, but the test failed to give strong evidence against H_0. Explain why this is not surprising.

14.34 Helping welfare mothers. A study compares two groups of mothers who were on welfare two years ago. One group attended a voluntary training program offered free of charge at a local vocational school. The other group did not choose to attend the training program. The study finds a significant difference ($P < 0.01$) between the proportions of the mothers in the two groups who are still on welfare. The difference is not only significant but quite large. The report says that with 95% confidence the percent of the nonattending group still on welfare is 21% ± 4% higher than that of the group who attended the program. You are on the staff of a member of Congress who is interested in the plight of welfare mothers and who asks you about the report.

(a) Explain in simple language what "a significant difference ($P < 0.01$)" means.

(b) Explain clearly and briefly what "95% confidence" means.

(c) Explain why this study does not provide good evidence that requiring job training of all welfare mothers would greatly reduce the percent who remain on welfare for several years.

14.35 How far do rich parents take us? How much education children get is strongly associated with the wealth and social status of their parents. In social science jargon, this is "socioeconomic status," or SES. But the SES of parents has little influence on whether children who have graduated from college go on to yet more education. One study looked at whether or not college graduates took the LSAT admissions test for law school. The effects of the parents' SES on taking the LSAT were "both statistically insignificant and small."

(a) What does "statistically insignificant" mean?

(b) Why is it important that the effects were small in size as well as insignificant?

Elephants sometimes damage crops in Africa. Can beehives keep elephants away from trees? See Exercise 15.5.

From Exploration to Inference: Part II Review

IN THIS CHAPTER WE COVER...

- Part II Summary
- Review Exercises
- Supplementary Exercises
- Optional Exercises

Part II Summary

In Part I of this book, you mastered **data analysis,** the use of graphs and numerical summaries to organize and explore any set of data. Part II has introduced designs for data production, probability, and the reasoning of statistical inference. Parts III and IV will deal with inference in practice.

Designs for producing data are essential if the data are intended to represent some wider population or process. Figures 15.1 and 15.2 display the big ideas visually. You should now understand good designs for producing data and also why bad designs often produce data that are worthless for inference. The deliberate use of chance in producing data is a central idea in statistics. It not only reduces bias but allows us to use **probability,** the mathematics of chance, as the basis for inference. Fortunately, we need only some basic facts about probability in order to understand statistical inference.

Figure 15.1 STATISTICS IN SUMMARY

Simple Random Sample

Population → All samples of size n are equally likely → Sample data $x_1, x_2, \dots, x_n$

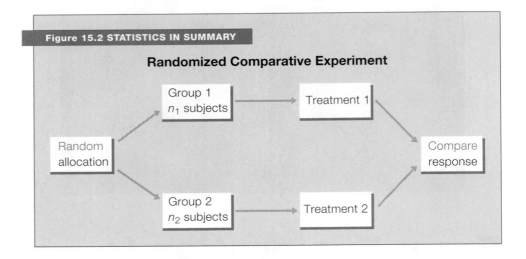

Figure 15.2 STATISTICS IN SUMMARY

Randomized Comparative Experiment

Statistical inference draws conclusions about a population on the basis of sample data and uses probability to indicate how reliable the conclusions are. A confidence interval estimates an unknown parameter. A significance test shows how strong the evidence is for some claim about a parameter.

The probabilities in both confidence intervals and tests tell us what would happen if we used the method for the interval or test very many times.

■ A confidence level is the success rate of the method for a confidence interval. This is the probability that the method actually produces an interval that captures the unknown parameter. A 95% confidence interval gives a correct result 95% of the time when we use it repeatedly.

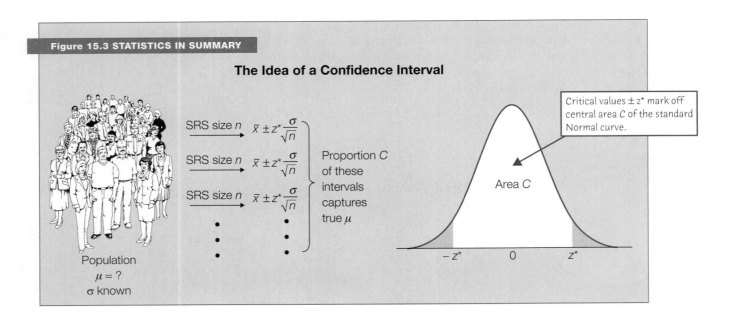

Figure 15.3 STATISTICS IN SUMMARY

The Idea of a Confidence Interval

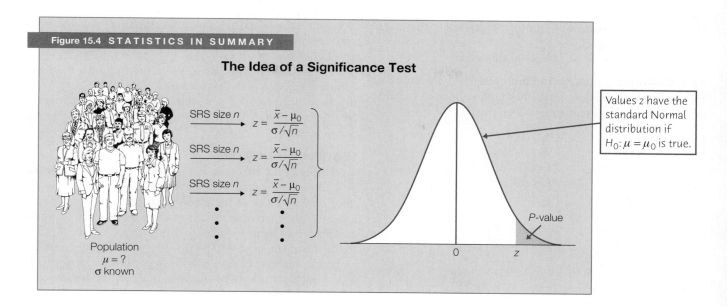

Figure 15.4 STATISTICS IN SUMMARY

The Idea of a Significance Test

Values z have the standard Normal distribution if $H_0: \mu = \mu_0$ is true.

- A P-value tells us how surprising the observed outcome would be if the null hypothesis were true. That is, P is the probability that the test would produce a result at least as extreme as the observed result if the null hypothesis really were true. Very surprising outcomes (small P-values) are good evidence that the null hypothesis is not true.

Figures 15.3 and 15.4 use the z procedures introduced in Chapter 13 to present in picture form the big ideas of confidence intervals and significance tests. These ideas are the foundation for the rest of this book. We will have much to say about many statistical methods and their use in practice. In every case, the basic reasoning of confidence intervals and significance tests remains the same.

REVIEW EXERCISES

Review exercises help you solidify the basic ideas and skills in Chapters 7 to 14. In exercises that ask for a P-value, you may use either Table A or software.

15.1 Spoofing. Online criminals use "spoofing" to direct Internet users to fraudulent Web sites in order to collect information such as passwords. In one study of Internet fraud, students were warned about spoofing and then asked to log in to their university account starting from the university's home page. In some cases, the log-in link led to the genuine dialog box. In others, the box looked genuine but in fact was linked to a different site that recorded the ID and password the student entered. An alert student could detect the fraud by looking at the true Internet address displayed in the browser status bar below the window, but most just entered their ID and password. Is this study an experiment? Why? What are the explanatory and response variables?

15.2 Student counseling. A university offers its students up to 8 sessions per semester of free psychological counseling. To evaluate satisfaction with this service, the counseling office mails questionnaires to 200 of the 1400 students who participated in counseling last semester. Only 93 students return the questionnaire. What is the population in this study? What is the sample?

15.3 How much do students earn? A university's financial aid office wants to know how much it can expect students to earn from summer employment. This information will be used to set the level of financial aid. The population contains 3478 students who have completed at least one year of study but have not yet graduated. The university will send a questionnaire to an SRS of 100 of these students, drawn from an alphabetized list.

(a) Describe how you will label the students in order to select the sample.

(b) Use Table B, beginning at line 105, to select the first 5 students in the sample.

(c) What is the response variable in this study?

15.4 California's endangered animals. The California Department of Fish and Game publishes a list of the state's endangered animals. Here are the reptiles on the list:

Desert tortoise	Green sea turtle
Loggerhead sea turtle	Olive Ridley sea turtle
Leatherback sea turtle	Barefoot banded gecko
Island night lizard	Alameda whipsnake
Coachella Valley fringe-toed lizard	Flat-tailed horned lizard
Southern rubber boa	Blunt-nosed leopard lizard
Giant garter snake	San Francisco garter snake

Your class can't decide which 3 endangered reptiles to choose for special study, so you agree to choose an SRS from the list. Use software or Table B at line 111 to choose an SRS of 3 of these species.

15.5 Elephants and bees. Elephants sometimes damage crops in Africa. It turns out that elephants dislike bees. They recognize beehives in areas where they are common and avoid them. Can this be used to keep elephants away from trees? A group in Kenya placed active beehives in some trees and empty beehives in others. Will elephant damage be less in trees with hives? Will even empty hives keep elephants away?[1]

(a) Outline the design of an experiment to answer these questions using 72 acacia trees (be sure to include a control group).

(b) Use software to choose the trees for the active-hive group, or Table B at line 137 to choose the first 4 trees in that group.

(c) What is the response variable in this experiment?

15.6 Does chocolate cause headaches? The evidence linking chocolates to chronic headaches is inconsistent. In one study, 64 women with chronic headaches ate a restricted diet for two weeks. They then ate candy bars containing either chocolate or carob, prepared to taste the same, and reported whether they had a headache in the next 12 hours.[2]

(a) Outline the design of this experiment.

(b) Use software to choose the 32 members of the chocolate group (list only the first 10), or use Table B at line 110 to choose the first 5 members of the chocolate group.

15.7 Cash to find work? Will cash bonuses speed the return to work of unemployed people? The Illinois Department of Employment Security designed an experiment to find out. The subjects were 10,065 people aged 20 to 54 who were filing claims for unemployment insurance. Some were offered $500 if they found a job within 11 weeks and held it for at least 4 months. Others could tell potential employers that the state would pay the employer $500 for hiring them. A control group got neither kind of bonus.[3]

(a) Suggest two response variables of interest to the state and outline the design of the experiment.

(b) How will you label the subjects for random assignment? Use Table B at line 127 to choose the first 3 subjects for the first treatment.

15.8 Effects of day care. The Carolina Abecedarian Project investigated the effect of high-quality preschool programs on children from poor families. Children were randomly assigned to two groups. One group participated in a year-round preschool program from the age of three months. The control group received social services but no preschool. At age 21, **35%** of the treatment group and **14%** of the control group were attending a four-year college or had already graduated from college. Is each of the boldface numbers a parameter or a statistic? Why?

15.9 *NOVA* takes a sample. The Web site of the PBS television program *NOVA Science Now* invites viewers to vote on issues such as re-creating the virus responsible for the deadly flu epidemic of 1918. This online poll is unusual in offering detailed arguments for both sides. Of the 790 viewers who read the arguments and voted, 64% said that re-creating the virus was justified.[4] Explain to someone who knows no statistics why these 790 responses probably don't represent the opinions of all American adults.

15.10 Marijuana and driving. Questioning a sample of young people in New Zealand revealed a positive association between use of marijuana (cannabis) and traffic accidents caused by the members of the sample. Both cannabis use and accidents were measured by interviewing the young people themselves. The study report says, "It is unlikely that self reports of cannabis use and accident rates will be perfectly accurate."[5] Is the response bias likely to make the reported association stronger or weaker than the true association? Why?

15.11 Fuel economy. The Environmental Protection Agency (EPA) fuel economy ratings say that the Toyota Prius hybrid car gets 48 miles per gallon (mpg) on the highway. Deborah wonders whether the actual long-term average highway mileage of her new Prius is less than 48 mpg. She keeps careful records of gas mileage for 3000 miles of highway driving. Her result is $\bar{x} = 47.2$ mpg. What are her null and alternative hypotheses?

15.12 Did you work hard in high school? The average amount of time that high school students spend on homework is about 5 hours per week. Only 25% of college freshmen say they spent at least 6 hours per week on homework in high school. Your college wonders if the average for its freshmen differs from the national average. A random sample of 200 freshmen claims to have spent an average of $\bar{x} = 6.2$ hours per week on homework in high school. State the null and alternative hypotheses for a comparison of freshmen at your college with national freshmen.

15.13 Blood cholesterol in Canadian men. The distribution of blood cholesterol level in the population of Canadian men aged 18 to 34 years is close to Normal with standard deviation $\sigma = 0.9$ millimoles per liter (mmol/l).[6] You measure the blood cholesterol of 14 cross-country runners. The mean level is $\bar{x} = 4.4$ mmol/l. Assuming that σ is the same as in the general population, give a 90% confidence interval for the mean level μ among cross-country runners.

15.14 Testing blood cholesterol. The mean blood cholesterol level for all Canadian men aged 18 to 34 years is $\mu = 4.6$ mmol/l. Does the sample in the previous exercise give good evidence that the mean for cross-country runners is lower? State hypotheses, find the z test statistic, and give the P-value. Is the result significant at the $\alpha = 0.10$ level? At $\alpha = 0.05$? At $\alpha = 0.01$?

15.15 Smaller margin of error. How large a sample is needed to cut the margin of error in Exercise 15.13 in half? How large a sample is needed to cut the margin of error to ± 0.1 mmol/l?

15.16 More significant results. You increase the sample of cross-country runners in Exercise 15.13 from 14 to 56. Suppose that this larger sample gives the same mean level, $\bar{x} = 4.4$ mmol/l. Redo the test in Exercise 15.14. What is the P-value now? At which of the levels $\alpha = 0.10$, $\alpha = 0.05$, $\alpha = 0.01$ is the result significant? What general fact about significance tests does comparing your results here and in Exercise 15.14 illustrate?

15.17 Pesticides in whale blubber: estimation. The level of pesticides found in the blubber of whales is a measure of pollution of the oceans by runoff from land and can also be used to identify different populations of whales. A sample of 8 male minke whales in the West Greenland area of the North Atlantic found the mean concentration of the insecticide dieldrin to be $\bar{x} = 357$ nanograms per gram of blubber (ng/g).[7] Suppose that the concentration in all such whales varies Normally with standard deviation $\sigma = 50$ ng/g. Use a 95% confidence interval to estimate the mean level. Be sure to state your conclusion in plain language.

15.18 Pesticides in whale blubber: testing. The Food and Drug Administration regulates the amount of dieldrin in raw food. For some foods, no more than 100 ng/g is allowed. Using the information in Exercise 15.17, is there good evidence that the mean concentration in whale blubber is above 100 ng/g? State hypotheses, carry out a test assuming that the "simple conditions" (page 232) hold, and give your conclusion in plain language.

15.19 Other confidence levels. Use the information in Exercise 15.17 to give an 80% confidence interval and a 90% confidence interval for the mean concentration of dieldrin in the whale population. What general fact about confidence intervals do the margins of error of your three intervals illustrate?

15.20 Birth weight and IQ: estimation. Infants weighing less than 1500 grams at birth are classed as "very low birth weight." Low birth weight carries many risks. One study followed 113 male infants with very low birth weight to adulthood. At age 20, the mean IQ score for these men was $\bar{x} = 87.6$.[8] IQ scores vary Normally with standard deviation $\sigma = 15$. Give a 95% confidence interval for the mean IQ score at age 20 for all very-low-birth-weight males.

15.21 Birth weight and IQ: testing. IQ tests are scaled so that the mean score in a large population should be $\mu = 100$. We suspect that the very-low-birth-weight population has mean score less than 100. Does the study described in the previous exercise give good evidence that this is true? State hypotheses, carry out a test assuming that the "simple conditions" (page 232) hold, and give your conclusion in plain language.

15.22 Birth weight and IQ: causation? Very-low-birth-weight babies are more likely to be born to unmarried mothers and to mothers who did not complete high school.
(a) Explain why the study of Exercise 15.20 was not an experiment.
(b) Explain clearly why confounding prevents us from concluding that very low birth weight in itself reduces adult IQ.

15.23 Sample space. A randomly chosen subject arrives for a study of exercise and fitness. Describe a sample space for each of the following. (In some cases, you may have some freedom in your choice of S.)
(a) The subject is either female or male.
(b) After 10 minutes on an exercise bicycle, you ask the subject to rate his or her effort on the Rate of Perceived Exertion (RPE) scale. RPE ranges in whole-number steps from 6 (no exertion at all) to 20 (maximal exertion).
(c) You measure VO2, the maximum volume of oxygen consumed per minute during exercise. VO2 is generally between 2.5 and 6.1 liters per minute.
(d) You measure the maximum heart rate (beats per minute).

15.24 Internet search engines. Internet search sites compete for users because they sell advertising space on their sites and can charge more if they are heavily used. Choose an

Internet search attempt at random. Here is the probability distribution for the site the search uses:[9]

Site	Google	Yahoo	MSN	Ask.com	Others
Probability	0.66	0.21	0.07	0.04	?

(a) What is the probability that a search attempt is made at a site other than the leading four?
(b) What is the probability that a search attempt is directed to a site other than Google?

15.25 How many in the house? In government data, a household consists of all occupants of a dwelling unit. Here is the distribution of household size in the United States:

Number of persons	1	2	3	4	5	6	7
Probability	0.26	0.33	0.16	0.15	0.07	0.02	0.01

Choose an American household at random and let the random variable Y be the number of persons living in the household.
(a) Express "more than one person lives in this household" in terms of Y. What is the probability of this event?
(b) What is $P(2 < Y \le 4)$?
(c) What is $P(Y \ne 2)$?

15.26 How many children? How many children do women give birth to during their childbearing years? Choose at random an American woman who is past childbearing:[10]

Number of children	0	1	2	3	4	5
Probability	0.193	0.174	0.344	0.181	0.074	0.034

(The few women with 6 or more children are included in the "5 children" group.)
(a) Check that this distribution satisfies the two requirements for a legitimate discrete probability model.
(b) Describe in words the event $P(X \le 2)$. What is the probability of this event?
(c) What is $P(X < 2)$?
(d) Write the event "a woman gives birth to three or more children" in terms of values of X. What is the probability of this event?

15.27 Reaction times. The time that people require to react to a stimulus usually has a right-skewed distribution, because lack of attention causes a few lengthy reaction times. Reaction times for children with attention deficit hyperactivity disorder (ADHD) are more skewed, because their condition causes more frequent lack of attention. In one study, children with ADHD were asked to press the spacebar on a computer keyboard when any letter other than X appeared on the screen.

With 2 seconds between letters, the mean reaction time was 445 milliseconds (ms) and the standard deviation was 82 ms.[11] Take these values to be the population μ and σ for ADHD children.
(a) What are the mean and standard deviation of the mean reaction time $\bar{x}$ for a randomly chosen group of 15 ADHD children? For a group of 150 such children?
(b) The distribution of reaction time is strongly skewed. Explain briefly why we hesitate to regard $\bar{x}$ as Normally distributed for 15 children but are willing to use a Normal distribution for the mean reaction time of 150 children.
(c) What is the approximate probability that the mean reaction time in a group of 150 ADHD children is greater than 450 ms?

15.28 An IQ test. The Wechsler Adult Intelligence Scale (WAIS) is a common "IQ test" for adults. The distribution of WAIS scores for persons over 16 years of age is approximately Normal with mean 100 and standard deviation 15.
(a) What is the probability that a randomly chosen individual has a WAIS score of 105 or higher?
(b) What are the mean and standard deviation of the average WAIS score $\bar{x}$ for an SRS of 60 people?
(c) What is the probability that the average WAIS score of an SRS of 60 people is 105 or higher?
(d) Would your answers to any of (a), (b), or (c) be affected if the distribution of WAIS scores in the adult population were distinctly non-Normal?

15.29 Does chocolate cause headaches, continued. Here are some of the results of the experiment described in Exercise 15.6. There was no significant difference in headaches between the chocolate and carob groups ($P = 0.68$). But subjects who said they had a mild headache before eating the candy bar were more likely to report a headache afterward ($P < 0.001$). Explain carefully why $P = 0.68$ means there is no evidence that chocolate and carob differ in their effects and why $P < 0.001$ is evidence that having a headache before eating the candy bar does increase reports of a headache after eating.

15.30 Brains at work. When our brains store information, complicated chemical changes take place. In trying to understand these changes, researchers blocked some processes in brain cells taken from rats and compared these cells with a control group of normal cells. They say that "no differences were seen" between the two groups in four response variables. They give P-values 0.45, 0.83, 0.26, and 0.84 for these four comparisons.[12]
(a) Say clearly what P-value $P = 0.45$ says about the response that was observed.

(b) It isn't literally true that "no differences were seen." That is, the mean responses were not exactly alike in the two groups. Explain what the researchers mean when they give $P = 0.45$ and say "no differences were seen."

SUPPLEMENTARY EXERCISES

Supplementary exercises apply the skills you have learned in ways that require more thought or more elaborate use of technology.

15.31 Sampling students. You want to investigate the attitudes of students at your school toward the school's policy on sexual harassment. You have a grant that will pay the costs of contacting about 500 students.
(a) Specify the exact population for your study. For example, will you include part-time students?
(b) Describe your sample design. Will you use a stratified sample?
(c) Briefly discuss the practical difficulties that you anticipate. For example, how will you contact the students in your sample?

15.32 The placebo effect. A survey of physicians found that some doctors give a placebo to a patient who complains of pain for which the physician can find no cause. If the patient's pain improves, these doctors conclude that it had no physical basis. The medical school researchers who conducted the survey claimed that these doctors do not understand the placebo effect. Why?

15.33 Informed consent. The requirement that human subjects give their informed consent to participate in an experiment can greatly reduce the number of available subjects. For example, a study of new teaching methods asks the consent of parents for their children to be taught by either a new method or the standard method. Many parents do not return the forms, so their children must continue to follow the standard curriculum. Why is it not correct to consider these children as part of the control group along with children who are randomly assigned to the standard method?

15.34 Fixing health care. The cost of health care and health insurance is the biggest health concern among Americans, even ahead of cancer and other diseases. Changing to a national government health insurance system is controversial. An opinion poll will give different results depending on the wording of the question asked. For each of the following claims, say whether including it in the question would *increase* or *decrease* the percent of a poll sample who support a government health insurance system.
(a) A national system would mean that everybody has health insurance.

(b) A national system would probably require an increase in taxes.
(c) Eliminating private insurance companies and their profits would reduce insurance costs.
(d) A national system would limit the medical treatments available in order to contain costs.

15.35 Market research. Stores advertise price reductions to attract customers. What type of price cut is most attractive? Market researchers prepared ads for athletic shoes announcing different levels of discounts (20%, 40%, or 60%). The student subjects who read the ads were also given "inside information" about the fraction of shoes on sale (50% or 100%). Each subject then rated the attractiveness of the sale on a scale of 1 to 7.[13]
(a) There are two factors. Make a sketch like Figure 8.2 (page 148) that displays the treatments formed by all combinations of levels of the factors.
(b) Outline a completely randomized design using 60 student subjects. Use software or Table B at line 111 to choose the subjects for the first treatment.

15.36 Making french fries. Few people want to eat discolored french fries. Potatoes are kept refrigerated before being cut for french fries to prevent spoiling and preserve flavor. But immediate processing of cold potatoes causes discoloring due to complex chemical reactions. The potatoes must therefore be brought to room temperature before processing. Design an experiment in which tasters will rate the color and flavor of french fries prepared from several groups of potatoes. The potatoes will be freshly picked or stored for a month at room temperature or stored for a month refrigerated. They will then be sliced and cooked either immediately or after an hour at room temperature.
(a) What are the factors and their levels, the treatments, and the response variables?
(b) Describe and outline the design of this experiment.
(c) It is efficient to have each taster rate fries from all treatments. How will you use randomization in presenting fries to the tasters?

15.37 The addition rule. The addition rule for probabilities, $P(A \text{ or } B) = P(A) + P(B)$, is not always true. Give (in words) an example of real-world events A and B for which this rule is not true.

15.38 Comparing wine tasters. Two wine tasters rate each wine they taste on a scale of 1 to 5. From data on their ratings of a large number of wines, we obtain the following probabilities for both tasters' ratings of a randomly chosen wine (see the chart).

	Taster 2				
Taster 1	1	2	3	4	5
1	0.03	0.02	0.01	0.00	0.00
2	0.02	0.08	0.05	0.02	0.01
3	0.01	0.05	0.25	0.05	0.01
4	0.00	0.02	0.05	0.20	0.02
5	0.00	0.01	0.01	0.02	0.06

(a) Why is this a legitimate discrete probability model?
(b) What is the probability that the tasters agree when rating a wine?
(c) What is the probability that Taster 1 rates a wine higher than Taster 2? What is the probability that Taster 2 rates a wine higher than Taster 1?

15.39 Distributions: means versus individuals. The z confidence interval and test are based on the sampling distribution of the sample mean $\bar{x}$. Suppose that the distribution of body mass index (BMI) among young women is Normal with mean $\mu = 27$ and standard deviation $\sigma = 7.5$.
(a) You take an SRS of 100 young women. According to the 99.7 part of the 68–95–99.7 rule, about what range of BMI values do you expect to see in your sample?
(b) You look at many SRSs of size 100. About what range of sample mean BMIs $\bar{x}$ do you expect to see?

15.40 Distributions: larger samples. In the setting of the previous exercise, how many women must you sample to cut the range of values of $\bar{x}$ in half? This will also cut the margin of error of a confidence interval for μ in half. Do you expect the range of individual BMI values in the new sample to also be much less than in a sample of size 100? Why?

15.41 Alcohol and mortality. It appears that people who drink alcohol in moderation have lower death rates than either people who drink heavily or people who do not drink at all. The protection offered by moderate drinking is concentrated among people over 50 and on deaths from heart disease. The Nurses' Health Study played an essential role in establishing these facts for women. This part of the study followed 85,709 female nurses for 12 years, during which time 2658 of the subjects died. The nurses completed a questionnaire that described their diet, including their use of alcohol. They were reexamined every two years. Conclusion: "As compared with nondrinkers and heavy drinkers, light-to-moderate drinkers had a significantly lower risk of death."[14]
(a) Was this study an experiment? Explain your answer.
(b) What does "significantly lower risk of death" mean in simple language?
(c) Suggest some lurking variables that might be confounded

with how much a person drinks. The investigators used advanced statistical methods to adjust for many such variables before concluding that the moderate drinkers really have a lower risk of death.

15.42 Time in a restaurant. The owner of a pizza restaurant in France knows that the time customers spend in the restaurant on Saturday evening has mean 90 minutes and standard deviation 15 minutes. He has read that pleasant odors can influence customers, so he spreads a lavender odor throughout the restaurant. Here are the times (minutes) for customers on the next Saturday evening:[15]

92	126	114	106	89	137	93	76	98	108
124	105	129	103	107	109	94	105	102	108
95	121	109	104	116	88	109	97	101	106

(a) Make a stemplot of the times. The distribution is roughly symmetric and single-peaked, so the distribution of $\bar{x}$ should be close to Normal.
(b) Suppose that the standard deviation $\sigma = 15$ minutes is not changed by the odor. Is there reason to think that the lavender odor has changed the mean time customers spend in the restaurant? Follow the four-step process for significance tests (page 246).

15.43 Normal body temperature? Here are the daily average body temperatures (degrees Fahrenheit) for 20 healthy adults:[16]

98.74	98.83	96.80	98.12	97.89	98.09	97.87
97.42	97.30	97.84	100.27	97.90	99.64	97.88
98.54	98.33	97.87	97.48	98.92	98.33	

(a) Make a stemplot of the data. The distribution is roughly symmetric and single-peaked. There is one mild outlier. We expect the distribution of the sample mean $\bar{x}$ to be close to Normal.
(b) Do these data give evidence that the mean body temperature for all healthy adults is not equal to the traditional 98.6 degrees? Follow the four-step process for significance tests (page 246). (Suppose that body temperature varies Normally with standard deviation 0.7 degree.)

15.44 Time in a restaurant. Use the data in Exercise 15.42 to estimate the mean time customers spend in this restaurant on Saturday evenings with 95% confidence. Follow the four-step process for confidence intervals (page 236).

15.45 Normal body temperature. Use the data in Exercise 15.43 to estimate mean body temperature with 90% confidence. Follow the four-step process for confidence intervals (page 236).

These exercises concern the material in Chapters 11 and 12.

15.46 Is business success just chance? Investors like to think that some companies are consistently successful. Academic researchers looked at data for many companies to determine whether each firm's sales growth was above the median for all firms in each year. They found that a simple "just chance" model fit well: years are independent, and the probability of being above the median in any one year is 1/2.[17] If this model holds, what is the probability that a particular firm is above average for two consecutive years? For all of four years?

15.47 Sharing music online. A sample survey reports that 29% of Internet users download music files online, 21% share music files from their computers, and 12% both download and share music.[18] Make a Venn diagram that displays this information. What percent of Internet users neither download nor share music files?

15.48 Really high incomes. The Internal Revenue Service received 138,394,754 individual income tax returns for 2006. Of these, 354,093 reported an adjusted gross income of $1 million or more and 40,931 reported at least $5 million.[19]
(a) What is the probability that a randomly chosen return shows an income of at least $5 million?
(b) If you know that a randomly chosen return shows an income of $1 million or more, what is the conditional probability that the income is at least $5 million?

15.49 Comparing wine tasters. In the setting of Exercise 15.38, Taster 1's rating for a wine is 3. What is the conditional probability that Taster 2's rating is higher than 3?

15.50 Latinos online. "Latinos comprise 14% of the U.S. adult population and about half of this growing group (56%) goes online."[20] Take A to be the event that a randomly chosen adult is a Latino and B the event that a randomly chosen adult goes online. Express the two percents given as probabilities. Find the percent of U.S. adults who are Latino and go online.

15.51 A baseball cliché. How often have you heard a baseball radio or TV announcer say something like "Scott has hit safely in 9 of the last 12 games," as if this were an impressive performance? Let's find out how impressive. Major league starting players (leaving out pitchers) hit safely in about 67% of their games.[21]
(a) It's reasonable to take games as independent. What is the distribution of the number of games out of 12 in which a typical player hits safely?

(b) What is the probability that a player hits safely in 9 or more out of 12 games? In 8 or more out of 12?

15.52 Text messaging. Suppose (as is roughly true) that 40% of all cell phone owners have sent or received text messages. A sample survey interviews an SRS of 2000 cell phone owners.
(a) What is the actual distribution of the number X in the sample who have sent or received text messages?
(b) What is the probability that 750 or fewer of the people in the sample have sent or received text messages? (Use software or a suitable approximation.)

15.53 Athletes breaking bones. The intense training needed to reach the Olympics carries risks. About 70% of the members of U.S. Winter Olympics teams have suffered one or more broken bones in the past.
(a) The 2006 team had 211 members. What distribution describes the number of team members who had broken bones in the past?
(b) What is the probability that 150 or more of the 211 team members had broken bones in the past? (Use software or an approximation.)

15.54 Airline overbooking. Airlines sell more tickets than a plane has seats because some passengers don't show up and an empty seat is worth nothing once the plane takes off. You are planning ticket sales for a Boeing 737 with 132 seats. You know that about 12% of people who book the flight won't show up. Use binomial distributions (software or the Normal approximation) to answer these questions.
(a) If you sell 145 seats, what is the probability that no more than 132 passengers will show up?
(b) On the average, each passenger without a seat costs the airline $250, either as a reward for voluntarily giving up a seat or as a penalty if a passenger is bumped. If you sell 145 seats, what is the probability that this extra cost is no more than $1000?

15.55 Cystic fibrosis. Cystic fibrosis is a lung disorder that often results in death. It is inherited but can be inherited only if both parents are carriers of an abnormal gene. In 1989, the CF gene that is abnormal in carriers of cystic fibrosis was identified. The probability that a randomly chosen person of European ancestry carries an abnormal CF gene is 1/25. (The probability is less in other ethnic groups.) The CF20m test detects most but not all harmful mutations of the CF gene. The test is positive for 90% of people who are carriers. It is (ignoring human error) never positive for people who are not carriers. What is the probability that a randomly chosen person of European ancestry tests positive?

15.56 Cystic fibrosis, continued. Jason tests positive on the CF20m test. What is the probability that he is a carrier of the abnormal CF gene?

15.57 Smoking and social class. As the dangers of smoking have become more widely known, clear class differences in smoking have emerged. British government statistics classify adult men by occupation as "managerial and professional" (43% of the population), "intermediate" (34%), or "routine and manual" (23%). A survey finds that 20% of men in managerial and professional occupations smoke, 29% of the intermediate group smoke, and 38% in routine and manual occupations smoke.[22] Use a tree diagram to find the percent of all adult British men who smoke.

15.58 Smoking and social class, continued. Use your work from the previous exercise to find the percent of male smokers who have routine and manual occupations. (Start by expressing this as a conditional probability.) This information is used in planning antismoking campaigns.

15.59 Do the rich stay that way? We like to think that anyone can rise to the top. That's possible, but it's easier if you start near the top. Divide families by the income of the parents into the top 20%, the bottom 20%, and the middle 60%. Here are the conditional probabilities that a child of each class of parents ends up in each income class as an adult.[23] For example, a child of parents in the top 20% has probability 0.42 of also being in the top 20%.

	Child's Class		
Parents' class	Top 20%	Middle 60%	Bottom 20%
Top 20%	0.42	0.52	0.06
Middle 60%	0.15	0.68	0.17
Bottom 20%	0.07	0.56	0.37

Suppose that these probabilities stay the same for three generations. Draw a tree diagram to show the path of a child and grandchild of parents in the top 20% of incomes. For example, the child might drop to the middle and the grandchild might then rise back to the top. What is the probability that the grandchild of people in the top 20% is also in the top 20%?

Inference about Variables

PART III

QUANTITATIVE RESPONSE VARIABLE

CHAPTER 16 Inference about a Population Mean

CHAPTER 17 Two-Sample Problems

CATEGORICAL RESPONSE VARIABLE

CHAPTER 18 Inference about a Population Proportion

CHAPTER 19 Comparing Two Proportions

CHAPTER 20 Part III Review

With the principles in hand, we proceed to practice, that is, to inference in realistic settings. In the remaining chapters of this book, you will meet some of the most commonly used statistical procedures. We have grouped these procedures into two classes, corresponding to our division of data analysis into exploring variables and distributions and exploring relationships. The five chapters of Part III concern inference about the distribution of a single variable and inference for comparing the distributions of two variables. Part IV deals with inference for relationships among variables. In Chapters 16 and 17, we analyze data on quantitative variables. We begin with the familiar Normal distribution for a quantitative variable. Chapters 18 and 19 concern categorical variables, so that inference begins with counts and proportions of outcomes. Chapter 20 reviews this part of the text.

The four-step process for approaching a statistical problem can guide much of your work in these chapters. You should review the outlines of the four-step process for a confidence interval (page 236) and for a test of significance (page 246). The statement of an exercise usually does the *State* step for you, leaving the *Plan, Solve,* and *Conclude* steps for you to complete. It is helpful to first summarize the *State* step in your own words to organize your thinking. Many examples and exercises in these chapters involve both carrying out inference and thinking about inference in practice. Remember that any inference method is useful only under certain conditions, and that you must judge these conditions before rushing to inference.

Eric Nathan/Alamy

Geologists want to estimate the chemical composition of small diamonds deep in the earth (Exercises 16.13 and 16.14).

Inference about a Population Mean

This chapter describes confidence intervals and significance tests for the mean μ of a population. We used the z procedures in this same setting to introduce the ideas of confidence intervals and tests. Now we discard the unrealistic condition that we know the population standard deviation σ and present procedures for practical use. We also pay more attention to the real-data setting of our work. The details of confidence intervals and tests change only slightly when you don't know σ. More important, you can interpret your results exactly as before. To emphasize this, Examples 16.2 and 16.3 repeat the most important examples from Chapter 13.

IN THIS CHAPTER WE COVER...

- Conditions for inference about a mean
- The t distributions
- The one-sample t confidence interval
- The one-sample t test
- Using technology
- Matched pairs t procedures
- Robustness of t procedures

Conditions for inference about a mean

Confidence intervals and tests of significance for the mean μ of a Normal population are based on the sample mean $\overline{x}$. Here are the conditions needed for realistic inference about a population mean.

CONDITIONS FOR INFERENCE ABOUT A MEAN

- We can regard our data as a **simple random sample** (SRS) from the population. This condition is very important.
- Observations from the population have a **Normal distribution** with mean μ and standard deviation σ. In practice, it is enough that the distribution be symmetric and single-peaked unless the sample is very small. Both μ and σ are unknown parameters.

There is another condition that applies to all of the inference methods in this book: *the population must be much larger than the sample, say at least 20 times as large.*[1] All of our examples and exercises satisfy this condition. Practical settings in which the sample is a large part of the population are rather special, and we will not discuss them.

When the conditions for inference are satisfied, the sample mean $\overline{x}$ has the Normal distribution with mean μ and standard deviation $\sigma/\sqrt{n}$. Because we don't know σ, we estimate it by the sample standard deviation s. We then estimate the standard deviation of $\overline{x}$ by $s/\sqrt{n}$. This quantity is called the *standard error* of the sample mean $\overline{x}$.

STANDARD ERROR

When the standard deviation of a statistic is estimated from data, the result is called the **standard error** of the statistic. The standard error of the sample mean $\overline{x}$ is $s/\sqrt{n}$.

APPLY YOUR KNOWLEDGE

16.1 Travel time to work. A study of commuting times reports the travel times to work of a random sample of 20 employed adults in New York State. The mean is $\overline{x} = 31.25$ minutes and the standard deviation is $s = 21.88$ minutes. What is the standard error of the mean?

16.2 Is that light moving? When two lights close together blink alternately, we "see" one light moving back and forth if the time between blinks is short. What is the longest interval of time between blinks that preserves the illusion of motion? Ask subjects to turn a knob that slows the blinking until they "see" two lights rather than one light moving. A report gives the results in the form "mean plus or minus the standard error of the mean."[2] Data for 12 subjects are summarized as 251 ± 45 (in milliseconds). What are $\overline{x}$ and s for these subjects? (This exercise is also a warning to read carefully: that 251 ± 45 is *not* a confidence interval, yet summaries in this form are common in scientific reports.)

The *t* distributions

If we knew the value of σ, we would base confidence intervals and tests for μ on the one-sample z statistic

$$z = \frac{\overline{x} - \mu}{\sigma/\sqrt{n}}$$

This z statistic has the standard Normal distribution $N(0, 1)$. In practice, we don't know σ, so we substitute the standard error $s/\sqrt{n}$ of $\overline{x}$ for its standard deviation $\sigma/\sqrt{n}$. The statistic that results does not have a Normal distribution. It has a distribution that is new to us, called a *t distribution*.

> ### THE ONE-SAMPLE *t* STATISTIC AND THE *t* DISTRIBUTIONS
>
> Draw an SRS of size *n* from a large population that has the Normal distribution with mean μ and standard deviation σ. The **one-sample *t* statistic**
>
> $$t = \frac{\overline{x} - \mu}{s/\sqrt{n}}$$
>
> has the ***t* distribution** with $n - 1$ degrees of freedom.

The *t* statistic has the same interpretation as any standardized statistic: it says how far $\overline{x}$ is from its mean μ in standard deviation units. There is a different *t* distribution for each sample size. We specify a particular *t* distribution by giving its **degrees of freedom.** The degrees of freedom for the one-sample *t* statistic come from the sample standard deviation *s* in the denominator of *t*. We saw in Chapter 2 (page 38) that *s* has $n - 1$ degrees of freedom. There are other *t* statistics with different degrees of freedom, some of which we will meet later. We will write the *t* distribution with $n - 1$ degrees of freedom as $t(n - 1)$ for short.

degrees of freedom

Figure 16.1 compares the density curves of the standard Normal distribution and the *t* distributions with 2 and 9 degrees of freedom. The figure illustrates these facts about the *t* distributions:

- The density curves of the *t* distributions are similar in shape to the standard Normal curve. They are symmetric about 0, single-peaked, and bell-shaped.
- The spread of the *t* distributions is a bit greater than that of the standard Normal distribution. The *t* distributions in Figure 16.1 have more probability in the tails and less in the center than does the standard Normal. This is true because substituting the estimate *s* for the fixed parameter σ introduces more variation into the statistic.

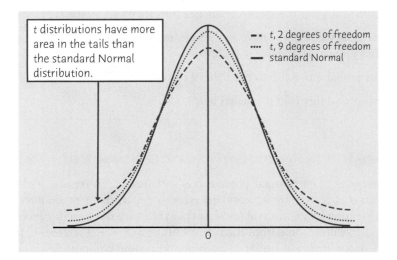

FIGURE 16.1

Density curves for the *t* distributions with 2 and 9 degrees of freedom and the standard Normal distribution. All are symmetric with center 0. The *t* distributions are somewhat more spread out.

■ As the degrees of freedom increase, the t density curve approaches the $N(0, 1)$ curve ever more closely. This happens because s estimates σ more accurately as the sample size increases. So using s in place of σ causes little extra variation when the sample is large.

Table C in the back of the book gives critical values for the t distributions. Each row in the table contains critical values for the t distribution whose degrees of freedom appear at the left of the row. For convenience, we label the table entries both by the confidence level C (in percent) required for confidence intervals and by the one-sided and two-sided P-values for each critical value. You have already used the standard Normal critical values in the z^* row at the bottom of Table C. By looking down any column, you can check that the t critical values approach the Normal values as the degrees of freedom increase. If you use statistical software, you don't need Table C.

EXAMPLE 16.1 *t* **critical values**

Figure 16.1 shows the density curve for the t distribution with 9 degrees of freedom. What point on this distribution has probability 0.05 to its right? In Table C, look in the df = 9 row above one-sided P-value .05 and you will find that this critical value is $t^* = 1.833$. To use software, enter the degrees of freedom and the probability you want to the *left*, 0.95 in this case. Here is Minitab's output:

```
Student's t distribution with 9 DF
P(X<=x)          x
   0.95   1.83311  ■
```

APPLY YOUR KNOWLEDGE

16.3 Critical values. Use Table C or software to find

(a) the critical value for a one-sided test with level $\alpha = 0.05$ based on the $t(5)$ distribution.

(b) the critical value for a 98% confidence interval based on the $t(21)$ distribution.

16.4 More critical values. You have an SRS of size 25 and calculate the one-sample t statistic. What is the critical value t^* such that

(a) t has probability 0.025 to the right of t^*?

(b) t has probability 0.75 to the left of t^*?

The one-sample *t* confidence interval

To analyze samples from Normal populations with unknown σ, just replace the standard deviation $\sigma/\sqrt{n}$ of $\overline{x}$ by its standard error $s/\sqrt{n}$ in the z procedures of Chapters 13 and 14. The confidence interval and test that result are *one-sample t procedures*. Critical values and P-values come from the t distribution with $n - 1$ degrees of freedom. The one-sample t procedures are similar in both reasoning and computational detail to the z procedures.

THE ONE-SAMPLE *t* CONFIDENCE INTERVAL

Draw an SRS of size *n* from a large population having unknown mean μ. A level C **confidence interval for μ** is

$$\bar{x} \pm t^* \frac{s}{\sqrt{n}}$$

where t^* is the critical value for the $t(n-1)$ density curve with area C between $-t^*$ and t^*. This interval is exact when the population distribution is Normal and is approximately correct for large *n* in other cases.

EXAMPLE 16.2   **Healing of skin wounds**

Let's look again at the biological study we met in Example 13.3. We follow the four-step process for a confidence interval, outlined on page 236.

STATE: Biologists studying the healing of skin wounds measured the rate at which new cells closed a razor cut made in the skin of an anesthetized newt. Here are data from 18 newts, measured in micrometers (millionths of a meter) per hour:[3]

29	27	34	40	22	28	14	35	26
35	12	30	23	18	11	22	23	33

This is one of several sets of measurements made under different conditions. We want to estimate the mean rate for comparison with rates under other conditions.

PLAN: We will estimate the mean rate μ for all newts of this species by giving a 95% confidence interval.

SOLVE: We must first check the conditions for inference.

- As in Chapter 13 (page 237), we are willing to regard these newts as an SRS from their species.
- The stemplot in Figure 16.2 does not suggest any strong departures from Normality.

We can proceed to calculation. For these data,

$$\bar{x} = 25.67 \quad \text{and} \quad s = 8.324$$

The degrees of freedom are $n - 1 = 17$. From Table C we find that for 95% confidence $t^* = 2.110$. The confidence interval is

$$\bar{x} \pm t^* \frac{s}{\sqrt{n}} = 25.67 \pm 2.110 \frac{8.324}{\sqrt{18}}$$

$$= 25.67 \pm 4.14$$

$$= 21.53 \text{ to } 29.81 \text{ micrometers per hour}$$

CONCLUDE: We are 95% confident that the mean healing rate for all newts of this species is between 21.53 and 29.81 micrometers per hour. ∎

The one-sample *t* confidence interval has the form

$$\text{estimate} \pm t^* \text{SE}_{\text{estimate}}$$

1	1 2 4
1	8
2	2 2 3 3
2	6 7 8 9
3	0 3 4
3	5 5
4	0

FIGURE 16.2

Stemplot of the healing rates in Example 16.2.

where "SE" stands for "standard error." We will meet a number of confidence intervals that have this common form. In Example 16.2, the estimate is the sample mean $\overline{x}$, and its standard error is

$$SE_{\overline{x}} = \frac{s}{\sqrt{n}}$$

$$= \frac{8.324}{\sqrt{18}} = 1.962$$

Software will find $\overline{x}$, s, $SE_{\overline{x}}$, and the confidence interval from the data. Figure 16.5 (page 293) displays typical software output for Example 16.2.

APPLY YOUR KNOWLEDGE

16.5 Critical values. What critical value t^* from Table C would you use for a confidence interval for the mean of the population in each of the following situations?

(a) A 95% confidence interval based on $n = 10$ observations.

(b) A 99% confidence interval from an SRS of 20 observations.

(c) A 90% confidence interval from a sample of size 7.

16.6 To gamble or not to gamble. Our decisions depend on how the options are presented to us. Here's an experiment that illustrates this phenomenon. Tell 20 subjects that they have been given $50 but can't keep it all. Then present them with a long series of choices between bets they can make with the $50. Scattered among these choices in random order are 64 choices between a fixed amount and an all-or-nothing gamble. The odds for the gamble are always the same, but 32 of the fixed options read "Keep $20" and the other 32 read "Lose $30." These two options are exactly the same except for their wording, but people are more likely to gamble if the fixed option says they lose money. Here are the percent differences ("Lose $30" minus "Keep $20") in the numbers of trials on which the 20 subjects chose to gamble:[4]

37.5	30.8	6.2	17.6	14.3	8.3	16.7	20.0	10.5	21.7
30.8	27.3	22.7	38.5	8.3	10.5	8.3	10.5	25.0	7.7

(a) Make a stemplot. Is there any sign of a major deviation from Normality?

(b) All 20 subjects gambled more often when faced with a sure loss than when faced with a sure win. Give a 95% confidence interval for the mean percent increase in gambling when faced with a sure loss.

16.7 Ancient air. To discover the nature of the earth's atmosphere long ago, we can examine the gas in bubbles inside ancient amber. Amber is tree resin that has hardened and been trapped in rocks. The gas in bubbles within amber should be a sample of the atmosphere at the time the amber was formed. Measurements on specimens of amber from the late Cretaceous era (75 to 95 million years ago) give these percents of nitrogen:[5]

63.4	65.0	64.4	63.3	54.8	64.5	60.8	49.1	51.0

Assume that these observations are an SRS from the late Cretaceous atmosphere. Use a 90% confidence interval to estimate the mean percent of nitrogen in ancient air. Follow the four-step process as illustrated in Example 16.2.

The one-sample *t* test

The *t* test for a population mean is very similar to the *z* test we met on page 245. The only difference is that *P*-values come from a *t* distribution rather than the standard Normal distribution.

THE ONE-SAMPLE *t* TEST

Draw an SRS of size *n* from a large population having unknown mean μ. To **test the hypothesis** H_0: $\mu = \mu_0$, compute the **one-sample *t* statistic**

$$t = \frac{\bar{x} - \mu_0}{s/\sqrt{n}}$$

Find *P*-values from the *t* distribution with $n - 1$ degrees of freedom.

These *P*-values are exact if the population distribution is Normal and are approximately correct for large *n* in other cases.

EXAMPLE 16.3   **Sweetness loss in colas**

Here is a more realistic analysis of the cola sweetness example from Chapter 13. We follow the four-step process for a significance test, outlined on page 246.

STATE: Cola makers test new recipes for loss of sweetness during storage. Trained tasters rate the sweetness before and after storage. Here are the sweetness losses (sweetness before storage minus sweetness after storage) found by 10 tasters for one new cola recipe:

$$2.0 \quad 0.4 \quad 0.7 \quad 2.0 \quad -0.4 \quad 2.2 \quad -1.3 \quad 1.2 \quad 1.1 \quad 2.3$$

Are these data good evidence that the cola lost sweetness?

PLAN: Tasters vary in their perception of sweetness loss. So we ask the question in terms of the mean loss μ for a large population of tasters. The null hypothesis is "no loss," and the alternative hypothesis says "there is a loss."

$$H_0: \mu = 0$$
$$H_a: \mu > 0$$

SOLVE: First check the conditions for inference. As before, we are willing to regard these 10 carefully trained tasters as an SRS from a large population of all trained tasters. Figure 16.3 is a stemplot of the data. We can't judge Normality from just 10 observations; there are no outliers but the data are somewhat skewed. *P*-values for the *t* test may be only approximately accurate.

The basic statistics are

$$\bar{x} = 1.02 \quad \text{and} \quad s = 1.196$$

The one-sample *t* statistic is

$$t = \frac{\bar{x} - \mu_0}{s/\sqrt{n}} = \frac{1.02 - 0}{1.196/\sqrt{10}}$$
$$= 2.697$$

−1	3
−0	4
0	4 7
1	1 2
2	0 0 2 3

FIGURE 16.3

Stemplot of the sweetness losses in Example 16.3.

FIGURE 16.4
The P-value for the one-sided t test in Example 16.3.

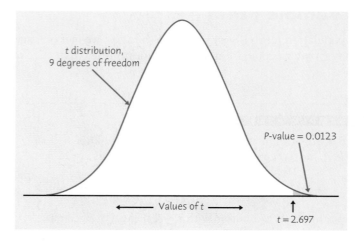

t distribution,
9 degrees of freedom

P-value = 0.0123

← Values of t →

↑
t = 2.697

df = 9

t^*	2.398	2.821
One-sided P	.02	.01

The P-value for $t = 2.697$ is the area to the right of 2.697 under the t distribution curve with degrees of freedom $n - 1 = 9$. Figure 16.4 shows this area. Software (see Figure 16.6) tells us that $P = 0.0123$.

Without software, we can pin P between two values by using Table C. Search the df $= 9$ row of Table C for entries that bracket $t = 2.697$. The observed t lies between the critical values for one-sided P-values 0.02 and 0.01.

CONCLUDE: There is quite strong evidence ($P < 0.02$) for a loss of sweetness. ∎

APPLY YOUR KNOWLEDGE

16.8 Is it significant? The one-sample t statistic for testing

$$H_0: \mu = 0$$
$$H_a: \mu > 0$$

from a sample of $n = 15$ observations has the value $t = 1.82$.

(a) What are the degrees of freedom for this statistic?

(b) Give the two critical values t^* from Table C that bracket t. What are the one-sided P-values for these two entries?

(c) Is the value $t = 1.82$ significant at the 5% level? Is it significant at the 1% level?

16.9 Is it significant? The one-sample t statistic from a sample of $n = 25$ observations for the two-sided test of

$$H_0: \mu = 64$$
$$H_a: \mu \neq 64$$

has the value $t = 1.12$.

(a) What are the degrees of freedom for t?

(b) Locate the two critical values t^* from Table C that bracket t. What are the two-sided P-values for these two entries?

(c) Is the value $t = 1.12$ statistically significant at the 10% level? At the 5% level?

16.10 Ancient air, continued. Do the data of Exercise 16.7 give good reason to think that the percent of nitrogen in the air during the Cretaceous era was different from the present 78.1%? Carry out a test of significance, following the four-step process as illustrated in Example 16.3.

Using technology

Any technology suitable for statistics will implement the one-sample t procedures. As usual, you can read and use almost any output now that you know what to look for. Figure 16.5 displays output for the 95% confidence interval of Example 16.2 from a graphing calculator, a statistical program, and a spreadsheet program. The calculator and Minitab outputs are straightforward. All three give the estimate $\overline{x}$ and the confidence

FIGURE 16.5
The t confidence interval of Example 16.2: output from a graphing calculator, a statistical program, and a spreadsheet program.

Texas Instruments Graphing Calculator

Minitab

Excel

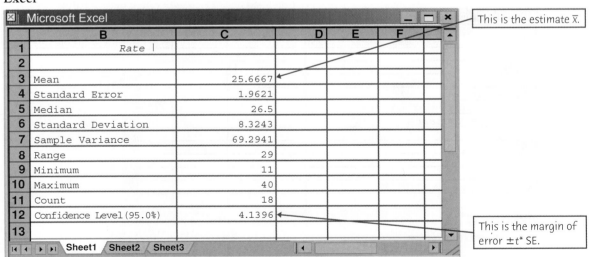

interval plus a clearly labeled selection of other information. The confidence interval agrees with our hand calculation in Example 16.2. In general, software results are more accurate because of the rounding in hand calculations. Excel gives several descriptive measures but does not give the confidence interval. The entry labeled "Confidence Level (95.0%)" is the margin of error. You can use this together with $\bar{x}$ to get the interval using either a calculator or the spreadsheet's formula capability.

Figure 16.6 displays output for the t test in Example 16.3. The graphing calculator and Minitab give the sample mean $\bar{x}$, the t statistic, and its P-value. Accurate P-values are the biggest advantage of software for the t procedures. Excel is as usual more awkward than

Texas Instruments Graphing Calculator

Minitab

Excel

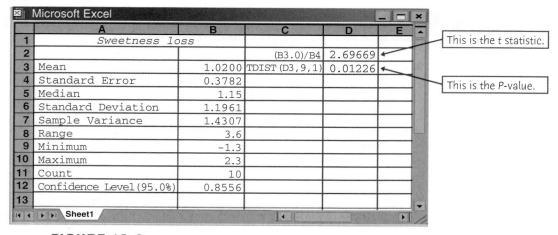

FIGURE 16.6

The t test of Example 16.3: output from a graphing calculator, a statistical program, and a spreadsheet program.

software designed for statistics. It lacks a one-sample *t* test menu selection but does have a function named TDIST for tail areas under *t* density curves. The Excel output shows functions for the *t* statistic and its *P*-value to the right of the main display, along with their values $t = 2.69669$ and $P = 0.01226$.

Matched pairs *t* procedures

Comparative studies are more convincing than single-sample investigations. For that reason, one-sample inference is less common than comparative inference. One common design to compare two treatments makes use of one-sample procedures. In a **matched pairs design,** subjects are matched in pairs and each treatment is given to one subject in each pair. Another situation calling for matched pairs is before-and-after observations on the same subjects. The taste test of Example 16.3 is a matched pairs study because the same 10 tasters rate before-and-after sweetness.

matched pairs design

MATCHED PAIRS *t* PROCEDURES

To compare the responses to the two treatments in a matched pairs design, find the difference between the responses within each pair. Then apply the one-sample *t* procedures to these differences.

The parameter μ in a matched pairs *t* procedure is the mean difference in the responses to the two treatments within matched pairs of subjects in the entire population.

EXAMPLE 16.4 Do chimpanzees collaborate?

STATE: Will chimpanzees recruit another chimp when solving a problem requires collaboration? Present chimpanzee subjects with food outside their cage that they can bring within reach by pulling two ropes, one attached to each end of the food tray. If a chimp pulls only one rope, the rope comes loose and the food is lost. Another chimp is available as a partner, but only if the subject opens a door joining two cages. The same 8 chimpanzees faced this problem in two versions: the two ropes were close enough together that one chimp could pull both (no collaboration needed) or the two ropes were too far apart for one chimp to pull both (collaboration needed). Table 16.1 shows how often in 24 trials each subject opened

Manoj Shah/Getty

TABLE 16.1 Trials (out of 24) on which chimpanzees recruited a partner

| | COLLABORATION NEEDED | | |
CHIMPANZEE	YES	NO	DIFFERENCE
Namuiska	16	0	16
Kalema	16	1	15
Okech	23	5	18
Baluku	19	3	16
Umugenzi	15	4	11
Indi	20	9	11
Bili	24	16	8
Asega	24	20	4

the door to recruit another chimp as partner.[6] Is there evidence that chimpanzees recruit partners more often when a problem requires collaboration?

PLAN: Take μ to be the mean difference (collaboration required minus not) in the number of times a subject recruited a partner. The null hypothesis says that the need for collaboration has no effect, and H_a says that partners are recruited more often when the problem requires collaboration. So we test the hypotheses

$$H_0: \mu = 0$$
$$H_a: \mu > 0$$

SOLVE: The subjects are "semi-free-ranging chimpanzees at Ngamba Island Chimpanzee Sanctuary in Uganda." We are willing to regard them as an SRS from their species. To analyze the data, subtract the "no collaboration needed" count from the "collaboration needed" count for each subject. The 8 differences form a single sample from a population with unknown mean μ. They appear in the "Difference" column in Table 16.1. All of the chimpanzees recruited a partner more often when the ropes were too far apart to be pulled by one chimp.

The stemplot in Figure 16.7 creates the impression of a left skew. This is a bit misleading, as the *dotplot* in the bottom part of Figure 16.7 shows. A dotplot simply places the observations on an axis, stacking observations that have the same value. It gives a good picture of distributions with only whole-number values. We can't assess Normality from just 8 observations, but there are no signs of major departures from Normality. The researchers used the matched pairs t test.

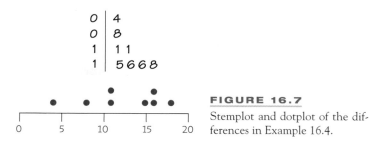

FIGURE 16.7
Stemplot and dotplot of the differences in Example 16.4.

The 8 differences have

$$\bar{x} = 12.375 \quad \text{and} \quad s = 4.749$$

The one-sample t statistic is therefore

$$t = \frac{\bar{x} - 0}{s/\sqrt{n}} = \frac{12.375 - 0}{4.749/\sqrt{8}}$$
$$= 7.37$$

df = 7		
t^*	4.785	5.408
One-sided P	.001	.0005

Find the P-value from the $t(7)$ distribution. (Remember that the degrees of freedom are 1 less than the sample size.) Table C shows that 7.37 is greater than the critical value for one-sided $P = 0.0005$. The P-value is therefore less than 0.0005. Software says that $P = 0.000077$.

CONCLUDE: The data give very strong evidence ($P < 0.0005$) that chimpanzees recruit a collaborator more often when faced with a problem that requires a collaborator to solve. That is, chimpanzees recognize when collaboration is necessary, a skill that they share with humans. ■

Example 16.4 illustrates how to turn matched pairs data into single-sample data by taking differences within each pair. We are making inferences about a single population, the population of all differences within matched pairs. *It is incorrect to ignore the matching and analyze the data as if we had two samples of chimpanzees, one facing ropes close together and the other facing ropes far apart.* Inference procedures for comparing two samples assume that the samples are selected independently of each other. This condition does not hold when the same subjects are measured twice.

APPLY YOUR KNOWLEDGE

Many exercises from this point on ask you to give the P-value of a t test. If you have suitable technology, give the exact P-value. Otherwise, use Table C to give two values between which P lies.

16.11 The brain responds to sound. The usual way to study the brain's response to sounds is to have subjects listen to "pure tones." The response to recognizable sounds may differ. To compare responses, researchers anesthetized macaque monkeys. They fed pure tones and also monkey calls directly to their brains by inserting electrodes. Response to the stimulus was measured by the firing rate (electrical spikes per second) of neurons in various areas of the brain. Table 16.2 contains the responses for 37 neurons.[7] Researchers suspected that the response to monkey calls would be stronger than the response to a pure tone. Do the data support this idea? Complete the *Plan, Solve,* and *Conclude* steps of the four-step process, following the model of Example 16.4.

TABLE 16.2 Neuron response to tones and monkey calls

TONE	CALL	TONE	CALL	TONE	CALL	TONE	CALL
474	500	145	42	71	134	35	103
256	138	141	241	68	65	31	70
241	485	129	194	59	182	28	192
226	338	113	123	59	97	26	203
185	194	112	182	57	318	26	135
174	159	102	141	56	201	21	129
176	341	100	118	47	279	20	193
168	85	74	62	46	62	20	54
161	303	72	112	41	84	19	66
150	208						

16.12 The brain responds, continued. How much more strongly do monkey brains respond to monkey calls than to pure tones? Give a 90% confidence interval to answer this question.

Robustness of *t* procedures

The *t* confidence interval and test are exactly correct when the distribution of the population is exactly Normal. No real data are exactly Normal. The usefulness of the *t* procedures in practice therefore depends on how strongly they are affected by lack of Normality.

> ### ROBUST PROCEDURES
>
> A confidence interval or significance test is called **robust** if the confidence level or P-value does not change very much when the conditions for use of the procedure are violated.

The condition that the population is Normal rules out outliers, so the presence of outliers shows that this condition is not fulfilled. The t procedures are not robust against outliers unless the sample is large, because $\overline{x}$ and s are not resistant to outliers.

Fortunately, the t procedures are quite robust against non-Normality of the population except when outliers or strong skewness are present. (Skewness is more serious than other kinds of non-Normality.) As the size of the sample increases, the central limit theorem ensures that the distribution of the sample mean $\overline{x}$ becomes more nearly Normal and that the t distribution becomes more accurate for critical values and P-values of the t procedures.

Always make a plot to check for skewness and outliers before you use the t procedures for small samples. For most purposes, you can safely use the one-sample t procedures when $n \geq 15$ unless an outlier or quite strong skewness is present. Here are practical guidelines for inference on a single mean.[8]

> ### USING THE t PROCEDURES
>
> - Except in the case of small samples, the condition that the data are an SRS from the population of interest is more important than the condition that the population distribution is Normal.
> - *Sample size less than 15:* Use t procedures if the data appear close to Normal (roughly symmetric, single peak, no outliers). If the data are clearly skewed or if outliers are present, do not use t.
> - *Sample size at least 15:* The t procedures can be used except in the presence of outliers or strong skewness.
> - *Large samples:* The t procedures can be used even for clearly skewed distributions when the sample is large, roughly $n \geq 40$.

EXAMPLE 16.5 Can we use *t*?

Figure 16.8 shows plots of several data sets. For which of these can we safely use the t procedures?[9]

- Figure 16.8(a) is a histogram of the percent of each state's adult residents who are college graduates. *We have data on the entire population of 50 states, so inference is not needed.* We can calculate the exact mean for the population. There is no uncertainty due to having only a sample from the population, and no need for a confidence interval or test. *If these data were an SRS from a larger population, t inference would be safe despite the mild skewness because n = 50.*

(a)

```
23 | 0
24 | 0
25 |
26 | 5
27 |
28 | 7
29 |
30 | 2 5 9
31 | 3 9 9
32 | 0 3 3 6 7 7
33 | 0 2 3 6
```

(b)

```
37 | 4 8 9
38 | 0 0 1 1 2 2 8 9
39 | 2 6 8
40 | 6 7
41 | 5 7 9 9
42 | 0 2
43 | 1
```

(c)

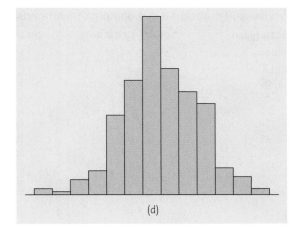

(d)

FIGURE 16.8

Can we use *t* procedures for these data? **(a)** Percent of adult college graduates in the 50 states. *No, this is an entire population, not a sample.* **(b)** Force required to pull apart 20 pieces of Douglas fir. *No, there are just 20 observations and strong skewness.* **(c)** Lengths of 23 tropical flowers of the same variety. *Yes, the sample is large enough to overcome the mild skewness.* **(d)** Heights of college students. *Yes, for any size sample,* because the distribution is close to Normal.

- Figure 16.8(b) is a stemplot of the force required to pull apart 20 pieces of Douglas fir. *The data are strongly skewed to the left with possible low outliers, so we cannot trust the t procedures for n = 20.*
- Figure 16.8(c) is a stemplot of the lengths of 23 specimens of the red variety of the tropical flower *Heliconia*. *The data are mildly skewed to the right and there are no outliers. We can use the t distributions for such data.*
- Figure 16.8(d) is a histogram of the heights of the students in a college class. *This distribution is quite symmetric and appears close to Normal. We can use the t procedures for any sample size.* ▪

Eric Nathan/Alamy

16.13 Diamonds. Earth scientists studied the small diamonds found in a nodule of rock carried up to the earth's surface in surrounding rock. This is a sample from a single population of diamonds formed in a single event deep in the earth.[10] Table 16.3 presents data on the nitrogen content (parts per million) and the abundance of carbon-13 in these diamonds. (Carbon has several isotopes, forms with different numbers of neutrons in the nuclei of their atoms. Carbon-12 makes up almost 99% of natural carbon. The abundance of carbon-13 is measured by the ratio of carbon-13 to carbon-12, in parts per thousand more or less than a standard. The minus signs in the data mean that the ratio is smaller in these diamonds than in standard carbon.)

We would like to estimate the mean abundance of both nitrogen and carbon-13 in the population of diamonds represented by this sample. Examine the data for nitrogen. Can we use a t confidence interval for mean nitrogen? Explain your answer. Give a 95% confidence interval if you think the result can be trusted.

TABLE 16.3 Nitrogen and carbon-13 in a sample of diamonds

DIAMOND	NITROGEN (ppm)	CARBON-13 RATIO	DIAMOND	NITROGEN (ppm)	CARBON-13 RATIO
1	487	−2.78	13	273	−2.73
2	1430	−1.39	14	94	−2.33
3	60	−4.26	15	69	−3.83
4	244	−1.19	16	262	−2.04
5	196	−2.12	17	120	−2.82
6	274	−2.87	18	302	−0.84
7	41	−3.68	19	75	−3.57
8	54	−3.29	20	242	−2.42
9	473	−3.79	21	115	−3.89
10	30	−4.06	22	65	−3.87
11	98	−1.83	23	311	−1.58
12	41	−4.03	24	61	−3.97

16.14 Diamonds, continued. Examine the data in Table 16.3 on abundance of carbon-13. Can we use a t confidence interval for mean carbon-13? Explain your answer. Give a 95% confidence interval if you think the result can be trusted.

CHAPTER 16 SUMMARY

■ Tests and confidence intervals for the mean μ of a Normal population are based on the sample mean $\overline{x}$ of an SRS. Because of the central limit theorem, the resulting procedures are approximately correct for other population distributions when the sample is large.

■ In practice, we do not know the population standard deviation σ. Estimate the standard deviation $\sigma/\sqrt{n}$ of $\overline{x}$ by the **standard error** $s/\sqrt{n}$ to get the **one-sample t statistic**

$$t = \frac{\overline{x} - \mu}{s/\sqrt{n}}$$

The t statistic has the **t distribution** with $n - 1$ degrees of freedom.

- There is a t distribution for every positive **degrees of freedom.** All are symmetric distributions similar in shape to the standard Normal distribution. The t distribution approaches the $N(0, 1)$ distribution as the degrees of freedom increase.

- A level C **confidence interval for the mean** μ of a Normal population is

$$\bar{x} \pm t^* \frac{s}{\sqrt{n}}$$

The **critical value** t^* is chosen so that the t curve with $n - 1$ degrees of freedom has area C between $-t^*$ and t^*.

- **Significance tests** for H_0: $\mu = \mu_0$ are based on the t statistic. Use P-values or fixed significance levels from the $t(n - 1)$ distribution.

- Use these one-sample procedures to analyze **matched pairs** data by first taking the difference within each matched pair to produce a single sample.

- The t procedures are quite **robust** when the population is non-Normal, especially for larger sample sizes. The t procedures are useful for non-Normal data when $n \geq 15$ unless the data show outliers or strong skewness.

CHECK YOUR SKILLS

16.15 We prefer the t procedures to the z procedures for inference about a population mean because
(a) z can be used only for large samples.
(b) z requires that you know the population standard deviation σ.
(c) z requires that you can regard your data as an SRS from the population.

16.16 You are testing H_0: $\mu = 10$ against H_a: $\mu < 10$ based on an SRS of 20 observations from a Normal population. The data give $\bar{x} = 8$ and $s = 4$. The value of the t statistic is
(a) -0.5.   (b) -10.   (c) -2.24.

16.17 You are testing H_0: $\mu = 10$ against H_a: $\mu < 10$ based on an SRS of 20 observations from a Normal population. The t statistic is $t = -2.25$. The degrees of freedom for this statistic are
(a) 19.   (b) 20.   (c) 21.

16.18 You have an SRS of 15 observations from a Normally distributed population. What critical value would you use to obtain a 98% confidence interval for the mean μ of the population?
(a) 2.326   (b) 2.602   (c) 2.624

16.19 Data on the blood cholesterol levels of 24 rats (milligrams per deciliter of blood) give $\bar{x} = 85$ and $s = 12$. A 95% confidence interval for the mean blood cholesterol of rats under this condition is
(a) 79.9 to 90.1.   (b) 80.2 to 89.8.   (c) 84.0 to 86.0.

16.20 Which of the following would cause the most worry about the validity of the confidence interval you calculated in the previous exercise?
(a) There is a clear outlier in the data.
(b) A stemplot of the data shows a mild right skew.
(c) You do not know the population standard deviation σ.

16.21 Which of these settings does *not* allow use of a matched pairs t procedure?
(a) You interview both the husband and the wife in 64 married couples and ask each about their ideal number of children.
(b) You interview a sample of 64 unmarried male students and another sample of 64 unmarried female students and ask each about their ideal number of children.
(c) You interview 64 female students in their freshman year and again in their senior year and ask each about their ideal number of children.

CHAPTER 16 EXERCISES

16.22 Read carefully. You read in the report of a psychology experiment: "Separate analyses for our two groups of 12 participants revealed no overall placebo effect for our student group (mean $= 0.08$, SD $= 0.37$, $t(11) = 0.49$) and a significant effect for our non-student group (mean $= 0.35$, SD $= 0.37$, $t(11) = 3.25$, $p < 0.01$)."[11] The null hypothesis is that the mean effect is zero. What are the correct values of the two t statistics based on the means and standard deviations? Compare each correct t-value with the critical values in Table C. What can you say about the two-sided P-value in each case?

16.23 Body mass index of young women. In Example 13.1 (page 232) we developed a 95% z confidence interval for the mean body mass index (BMI) of women aged 20 to 29 years, based on a national random sample of 654 such women. We assumed there that the population standard deviation was known to be $\sigma = 7.5$. In fact, the sample data had mean BMI $\bar{x} = 26.8$ and standard deviation $s = 7.42$. What is the 95% t confidence interval for the mean BMI of all young women?

16.24 Reading scores in Atlanta. The Trial Urban District Assessment (TUDA) is a government-sponsored study of student achievement in large urban school districts. TUDA gives a reading test scored from 0 to 500. A score of 243 is a "basic" reading level and a score of 281 is "proficient." Scores for a random sample of 1470 eighth-graders in Atlanta had $\bar{x} = 240$ with standard error 1.1.[12]
(a) We don't have the 1470 individual scores, but use of the t procedures is surely safe. Why?
(b) Give a 99% confidence interval for the mean score of all Atlanta eighth-graders. (Be careful: the report gives the standard error of $\bar{x}$, not the standard deviation s.)
(c) Urban children often perform below the basic level. Is there good evidence that the mean for all Atlanta eighth-graders is less than the basic level?

16.25 Calcium and blood pressure. In a randomized comparative experiment on the effect of calcium in the diet on blood pressure, researchers divided 54 healthy white males at random into two groups. One group received calcium; the other, a placebo. At the beginning of the study, the researchers measured many variables on the subjects. The paper reporting the study gives $\bar{x} = 114.9$ and $s = 9.3$ for the seated systolic blood pressure of the 27 members of the placebo group.
(a) Give a 95% confidence interval for the mean blood pressure in the population from which the subjects were recruited.
(b) What conditions for the population and the study design are required by the procedure you used in (a)? Which of these conditions are important for the validity of the procedure in this case?

16.26 The placebo effect. The placebo effect is particularly strong in patients with Parkinson's disease. To understand the workings of the placebo effect, measure activity at a key point in the brain when patients receive a placebo that they think is an active drug and also when no treatment is given.[13] The same six patients were measured both with and without the placebo, at different times.
(a) Explain why the proper procedure to compare the mean response to placebo with control (no treatment) is a matched pairs t test.

(b) The six differences (treatment minus control) had $\bar{x} = -0.326$ and $s = 0.181$. Is there significant evidence of a difference between treatment and control?

16.27 The conductivity of glass. How well materials conduct heat matters when designing houses, for example. Conductivity is measured in terms of watts of heat power transmitted per square meter of surface per degree Celsius of temperature difference on the two sides of the material. In these units, glass has conductivity about 1. The National Institute of Standards and Technology (NIST) provides data on properties of materials. Here are 11 NIST measurements of the heat conductivity of a particular type of glass:[14]

1.11 1.07 1.11 1.07 1.12 1.08 1.08 1.18 1.18 1.18 1.12

(a) We can consider this an SRS of all specimens of glass of this type. Make a stemplot. Is there any sign of major deviation from Normality?
(b) Give a 95% confidence interval for the mean conductivity.
(c) Is there significant evidence at the 5% level that the mean conductivity of this type of glass is not 1?

16.28 Learning Blissymbols. Blissymbols are pictographs (think of Egyptian hieroglyphs) sometimes used to help learning-disabled children. In a study of computer-assisted learning, 12 normal-ability schoolchildren were assigned at random to each of four computer learning programs. After they used the program, they attempted to recognize 24 Blissymbols. Here are the counts correct for one of the programs:[15]

12 22 9 14 20 15 9 10 11 11 15 6

(a) Make a stemplot (split the stems). Are there outliers or strong skewness that would forbid use of the t procedures?
(b) Give a 90% confidence interval for the mean count correct among all children of this age who use the program.

16.29 A big toe problem. Hallux abducto valgus (call it HAV) is a deformation of the big toe that often requires surgery. Doctors used X-rays to measure the angle (in degrees) of deformity in 38 consecutive patients under the age of 21 who came to a medical center for surgery to correct HAV. The angle is a measure of the seriousness of the deformity. Here are the data:[16]

28 32 25 34 38 26 25 18 30 26 28 13 20
21 17 16 21 23 14 32 25 21 22 20 18 26
16 30 30 20 50 25 26 28 31 38 32 21

It is reasonable to regard these patients as a random sample of young patients who require HAV surgery. Carry out the *Solve* and *Conclude* steps for a 95% confidence interval for the mean HAV angle in the population of all such patients.

Wellcome Trust Medical Library/Custom Medical Stock Photo

16.30 An outlier's effect. Our bodies have a natural electrical field that helps wounds heal. Does changing the field strength slow healing? A series of experiments with newts investigated this question. In one experiment, the two hind limbs of 12 newts were assigned at random to either experimental or control groups. This is a matched pairs design. The electrical field in the experimental limbs was reduced to zero by applying a voltage. The control limbs were left alone. Here are the rates at which new cells closed a razor cut in each limb, in micrometers per hour:[17]

Newt	1	2	3	4	5	6	7	8	9	10	11	12
Control limb	36	41	39	42	44	39	39	56	33	20	49	30
Experimental limb	28	31	27	33	33	38	45	25	28	33	47	23

(a) Make a stemplot of the differences between limbs of the same newt (control limb minus experimental limb). There is a high outlier.
(b) A good way to judge the effect of an outlier is to do your analysis twice, once with the outlier and a second time without it. Carry out two t tests to see if the mean healing rate is significantly lower in the experimental limbs, one including all 12 newts and another that omits the outlier. What are the test statistics and their P-values? Does the outlier have a strong influence on your conclusion?

16.31 An outlier's effect. A good way to judge the effect of an outlier is to do your analysis twice, once with the outlier and a second time without it. The data in Exercise 16.29 follow a Normal distribution quite closely except for one patient with HAV angle 50 degrees, a high outlier.
(a) Find the 95% confidence interval for the population mean based on the 37 patients who remain after you drop the outlier.

(b) Compare your interval in (a) with your interval from Exercise 16.29. What is the most important effect of removing the outlier?

16.32 Genetic engineering for cancer treatment. Here's a new idea for treating advanced melanoma, the most serious kind of skin cancer. Genetically engineer white blood cells to better recognize and destroy cancer cells, then infuse these cells into patients. The subjects in a small initial study were 11 patients whose melanoma had not responded to existing treatments. One question was how rapidly the new cells would multiply after infusion, as measured by the doubling time in days. Here are the doubling times:[18]

1.4   1.0   1.3   1.0   1.3   2.0   0.6   0.8   0.7   0.9   1.9

(a) Examine the data. Is it reasonable to use the t procedures?
(b) Give a 90% confidence interval for the mean doubling time. Are you willing to use this interval to make an inference about the mean doubling time in a population of similar patients?

16.33 Genetic engineering for cancer treatment, continued. Another outcome in the cancer experiment described in Exercise 16.32 is measured by a test for the presence of cells that trigger an immune response in the body and so may help fight cancer. Here are data for the 11 subjects: counts of active cells per 100,000 cells before and after infusion of the modified cells. The difference (after minus before) is the response variable.

Before	14	0	1	0	0	0	0	20	1	6	0
After	41	7	1	215	20	700	13	530	35	92	108
Difference	27	7	0	215	20	700	13	510	34	86	108

(a) Examine the data. Is it reasonable to use the t procedures?
(b) If your conclusion in part (a) is Yes, do the data give convincing evidence that the count of active cells is higher after treatment?

16.34 Growing trees faster. The concentration of carbon dioxide (CO_2) in the atmosphere is increasing due to our use of fossil fuels. Because plants use CO_2 to fuel photosynthesis, more CO_2 may cause trees and other plants to grow faster. An elaborate apparatus allows researchers to pipe extra CO_2 to a 30-meter circle of forest. They selected two nearby circles in each of three parts of a pine forest and randomly chose one of each pair to receive extra CO_2. The response variable is the mean increase in base area for 30 to 40 trees in a circle during a growing season. We measure this in percent increase per year. The table presents one year's data.[19]

Pair	Control plot	Treated plot
1	9.752	10.587
2	7.263	9.244
3	5.742	8.675

(a) State the null and alternative hypotheses. Explain clearly why the investigators used a one-sided alternative.
(b) Carry out a test and report your conclusion in simple language.
(c) The investigators used the test you just carried out. Any use of the t procedures with samples this size is risky. Why?

16.35 Fungus in the air. Fungus in the air in poultry-processing plants can affect the health of the workers. The problem is most serious during the summer. To measure the presence of spores, air samples are pumped to an agar plate and "colony-forming units (CFUs)" are counted after an incubation period. Here are data from two locations in a plant that processes 37,000 turkeys per day, taken on four days in the summer. The units are CFUs per cubic meter of air.[20]

	Day 1	Day 2	Day 3	Day 4
Kill room	3175	2526	1763	1090
Processing	529	141	362	224

(a) Explain carefully why these are matched pairs data.
(b) The spore count is clearly higher in the kill room. Give sample means and a 90% confidence interval to estimate how much higher. Be sure to state your conclusion in plain English.
(c) You will often see the t procedures used for data like these. You should regard the results as only rough approximations. Why?

16.36 Weeds among the corn. Velvetleaf is a particularly annoying weed in corn fields. It produces lots of seeds, and the seeds wait in the soil for years until conditions are right. How many seeds do velvetleaf plants produce? Here are counts from 28 plants that came up in a corn field when no herbicide was used:[21]

2450	2504	2114	1110	2137	8015	1623
1531	2008	1716	721	863	1136	2819
1911	2101	1051	218	1711	164	2228
363	5973	1050	1961	1809	130	880

We would like to give a confidence interval for the mean number of seeds produced by velvetleaf plants. Alas, the t interval can't be safely used for these data. Why not?

16.37 How much oil? How much oil wells in a given field will ultimately produce is key information in deciding whether to drill more wells. Here are the estimated total amounts of oil recovered from 64 wells in the Devonian Richmond Dolomite area of the Michigan basin, in thousands of barrels:[22]

21.71	53.2	46.4	42.7	50.4	97.7	103.1	51.9
43.4	69.5	156.5	34.6	37.9	12.9	2.5	31.4
79.5	26.9	18.5	14.7	32.9	196	24.9	118.2
82.2	35.1	47.6	54.2	63.1	69.8	57.4	65.6
56.4	49.4	44.9	34.6	92.2	37.0	58.8	21.3
36.6	64.9	14.8	17.6	29.1	61.4	38.6	32.5
12.0	28.3	204.9	44.5	10.3	37.7	33.7	81.1
12.1	20.1	30.5	7.1	10.1	18.0	3.0	2.0

Take these wells to be an SRS of wells in this area.
(a) Give a 95% t confidence interval for the mean amount of oil recovered from all wells in this area.
(b) Make a graph of the data. The distribution is very skewed, with several high outliers. A computer-intensive method that gives accurate confidence intervals without assuming any specific shape for the distribution gives a 95% confidence interval of 40.28 to 60.32. How does the t interval compare with this? Should the t procedures be used with these data?

The following exercises ask you to answer questions from data without having the details outlined for you. The four-step process is illustrated in Examples 16.2, 16.3, and 16.4. The exercise statements give you the **State** *step. Follow the* **Plan, Solve,** *and* **Conclude** *steps in your work.*

16.38 Gold in the Yukon. Mining of gold, silver, and copper continues to be big business in Canada's Yukon Territory. Mining companies release assay results to attract investors. Here are the results of gold assays (grams of gold per ton of ore) from 30 test holes at the Sherwood Copper Corporation's Minto mine in the Yukon:[23]

2.48	0.50	0.64	0.80	1.37	0.40	1.19	0.82	0.44	0.51
0.50	0.63	0.36	0.20	0.92	3.43	0.02	0.51	0.17	0.09
0.04	0.13	0.09	0.05	0.22	1.07	0.30	0.25	0.09	0.10

Assuming (this is risky) that these holes are randomly located in a new area of the mine, what can you say about the gold content in this area?

16.39 Does nature heal better? Our bodies have a natural electrical field that helps wounds heal. Does changing the field strength slow healing? A series of experiments with newts investigated this question. The data below are the healing rates of cuts (micrometers per hour) in a matched pairs experiment. The pairs are the two hind limbs of the same newt, with the body's natural field in one limb (control) and half the natural value in the other limb (experimental).[24] Is there good evidence that changing the electrical field from its natural level slows healing?

TABLE 16.4 A mutual fund versus its benchmark index

YEAR	FUND RETURN	INDEX RETURN	YEAR	FUND RETURN	INDEX RETURN
1984	−1.02	7.38	1996	14.65	6.05
1985	56.94	56.16	1997	4.12	1.78
1986	56.71	69.44	1998	16.93	20.00
1987	12.48	24.63	1999	26.34	26.96
1988	11.61	28.27	2000	−8.60	−14.17
1989	24.76	10.54	2001	−18.92	−21.44
1990	−12.05	−23.45	2002	−17.79	−15.94
1991	4.74	12.13	2003	34.45	38.59
1992	−5.79	−12.17	2004	18.95	20.25
1993	44.74	32.56	2005	15.00	13.54
1994	0.76	7.78	2006	25.92	26.34
1995	14.89	11.21	2007	15.98	11.17

Newt	1	2	3	4	5	6	7	8	9	10	11	12	13	14
Control	25	13	44	45	57	42	50	36	35	38	43	31	26	48
Experimental	24	23	47	42	26	46	38	33	28	28	21	27	25	45

16.40 How much better does nature heal? Give a 90% confidence interval for the difference in healing rates (control minus experimental) in the previous exercise.

16.41 Mutual fund performance. Mutual funds often compare their performance with a benchmark provided by an "index" that describes the performance of the class of assets in which the fund invests. For example, the Vanguard International Growth Fund benchmarks its performance against the EAFE (Europe, Australasia, Far East) index. Table 16.4 gives annual returns (percent) for the fund and the index.

Does the fund's performance differ significantly from that of its benchmark?
(a) Explain clearly why the matched pairs t test is the proper choice to answer this question.
(b) Do a complete analysis that answers the question posed.

16.42 Right versus left. The design of controls and instruments affects how easily people can use them. Timothy Sturm investigated this effect in a course project, asking 25 right-handed students to turn a knob (with their right hands) that moved an indicator by screw action. There were two identical instruments, one with a right-hand thread (the knob turns clockwise) and the other with a left-hand thread (the knob turns counterclockwise). Table 16.5 gives the times

TABLE 16.5 Performance times (seconds) using right-hand and left-hand threads

SUBJECT	RIGHT THREAD	LEFT THREAD	SUBJECT	RIGHT THREAD	LEFT THREAD
1	113	137	14	107	87
2	105	105	15	118	166
3	130	133	16	103	146
4	101	108	17	111	123
5	138	115	18	104	135
6	118	170	19	111	112
7	87	103	20	89	93
8	116	145	21	78	76
9	75	78	22	100	116
10	96	107	23	89	78
11	122	84	24	85	101
12	103	148	25	88	123
13	116	147			

in seconds each subject took to move the indicator a fixed distance.[25]

(a) Each of the 25 students used both instruments. Explain briefly how you would use randomization in arranging the experiment.

(b) The project hoped to show that right-handed people find right-hand threads easier to use. Do an analysis that leads to a conclusion about this issue.

16.43 Comparing two drugs. Makers of generic drugs must show that they do not differ significantly from the "reference" drugs that they imitate. One aspect in which drugs might differ is their extent of absorption in the blood. Table 16.6 gives data taken from 20 healthy nonsmoking male subjects for one pair of drugs.[26] This is a matched pairs design. Numbers 1 to 20 were assigned at random to the subjects. Subjects 1 to 10 received the generic drug first, and Subjects 11 to 20 received the reference drug first. In all cases, a washout period separated the two drugs so that the first had disappeared from the blood before the subject took the second. Do the drugs differ significantly in absorption?

16.44 Practical significance? Give a 90% confidence interval for the mean time advantage of right-hand over left-hand threads in the setting of Exercise 16.42. Do you think that the time saved would be of practical importance if the task were performed many times—for example, by an assembly-line worker? To help answer this question, find the mean time for right-hand threads as a percent of the mean time for left-hand threads.

TABLE 16.6 Absorption extent for two versions of a drug

SUBJECT	REFERENCE DRUG	GENERIC DRUG
15	4108	1755
3	2526	1138
9	2779	1613
13	3852	2254
12	1833	1310
8	2463	2120
18	2059	1851
20	1709	1878
17	1829	1682
2	2594	2613
4	2344	2738
16	1864	2302
6	1022	1284
10	2256	3052
5	938	1287
7	1339	1930
14	1262	1964
11	1438	2549
1	1735	3340
19	1020	3050

Hugh Clark/Frank Lane Picture Agency/CORBIS

A blue titmouse. Exercises 17.35 to 17.37 show how these small birds time their breeding based on the previous year's experience.

CHAPTER 17

Two-Sample Problems

**IN THIS CHAPTER
WE COVER...**

- Comparing two population means
- Two-sample *t* procedures
- Using technology
- Robustness again

Comparing two populations or two treatments is one of the most common situations encountered in statistical practice. We call such situations *two-sample problems*.

TWO-SAMPLE PROBLEMS

- The goal of inference is to compare the responses to two treatments or to compare the characteristics of two populations.
- We have a separate sample from each treatment or each population.

Unlike the matched pairs designs studied earlier, there is no matching of the individuals in the two samples, and the two samples can be of different sizes. Inference procedures for two-sample data differ from those for matched pairs. Here are some typical two-sample problems.

EXAMPLE 17.1 Physical therapy

Does regular physical therapy help lower back pain? A randomized experiment assigned patients with lower back pain to two groups: 142 received an examination and advice from a physical therapist; another 144 received regular physical therapy for up to five weeks. After a year, the change in their level of disability (0% to 100%) was assessed by a doctor who did not know which treatment the patients had received. ■

EXAMPLE 17.2 Social insight

A psychologist develops a test that measures social insight. He compares the social insight of female college students with that of male college students by giving the test to a sample of female students and a separate sample of male students. ■

Which data design? *Each situation described in Exercises 17.1 to 17.4 requires inference about a mean or means. Identify each as involving (1) a single sample, (2) matched pairs, or (3) two independent samples. The procedures of Chapter 16 apply to designs (1) and (2). We are about to learn procedures for (3).*

17.1 Looking back on love. Choose 40 romantically attached couples in their midtwenties. Interview the man and woman separately about a romantic attachment they had at age 15 or 16. Compare the attitudes of men and women.

17.2 Whom do you trust? Companies often place advertisements to improve the image of their brand rather than to promote specific products. In a randomized comparative experiment, business students read ads that cited either the *Wall Street Journal* or the *National Enquirer* for important facts about a fictitious company. The students rated the trustworthiness of the advertisement on a 7-point scale. Compare the mean score for the two types of advertisement.

17.3 Chemical analysis. To check a new analytical method, a chemist obtains a reference specimen of known concentration from the National Institute of Standards and Technology. She makes 20 measurements of the concentration of this specimen with the new method and checks for bias by comparing the mean result with the known concentration.

17.4 Chemical analysis, continued. Another chemist is checking the same new method. He has no reference specimen, but a familiar analytic method is available. He wants to know if the new and old methods agree. He takes a specimen of unknown concentration and measures the concentration 10 times with the new method and 10 times with the old method.

Comparing two population means

Comparing two populations or the responses to two treatments starts with data analysis: make stemplots (for small samples) or histograms (for larger samples) and compare the shapes, centers, and spreads of the two samples. The most common goal of inference is to compare the average or typical responses in the two populations. When data analysis suggests that both population distributions are symmetric, and especially when they are at least approximately Normal, we want to compare the population means. Here are the conditions for inference about means.

CONDITIONS FOR INFERENCE COMPARING TWO MEANS

■ We have **two SRSs,** from two distinct populations. The samples are **independent.** That is, one sample has no influence on the other. Matching violates independence, for example. We measure the same response variable for both samples.

■ Both populations are **Normally distributed.** The means and standard deviations of the populations are unknown. In practice, it is enough that the distributions have similar shapes and that the data have no strong outliers.

Call the variable we measure x_1 in the first population and x_2 in the second because the variable may have different distributions in the two populations. Here is how we describe the two populations:

Population	Variable	Mean	Standard deviation
1	x_1	μ_1	σ_1
2	x_2	μ_2	σ_2

There are four unknown parameters, the two means and the two standard deviations. The subscripts remind us which population a parameter describes. We want to compare the two population means, either by giving a confidence interval for their difference $\mu_1 - \mu_2$ or by testing the hypothesis of no difference, $H_0: \mu_1 = \mu_2$.

We use the sample means and standard deviations to estimate the unknown parameters. Again, subscripts remind us which sample a statistic comes from. Here is how we describe the samples:

Population	Sample size	Sample mean	Sample standard deviation
1	n_1	$\overline{x}_1$	s_1
2	n_2	$\overline{x}_2$	s_2

To do inference about the difference $\mu_1 - \mu_2$ between the means of the two populations, we start from the difference $\overline{x}_1 - \overline{x}_2$ between the means of the two samples.

EXAMPLE 17.3 Daily activity and obesity

STATE: People gain weight when they take in more energy from food than they expend. James Levine and his collaborators at the Mayo Clinic investigated the link between obesity and energy spent on daily activity.[1]

Choose 20 healthy volunteers who don't exercise. Deliberately choose 10 who are lean and 10 who are mildly obese. Attach sensors that monitor the subjects' every move for 10 days. Table 17.1 presents data on the time (in minutes per day) that the subjects spent standing or walking, sitting, and lying down. Do lean and obese people differ in the average time they spend standing and walking?

PLAN: Examine the data and carry out a test of hypotheses. We suspect in advance that lean subjects (Group 1) are more active than obese subjects (Group 2), so we test the hypotheses

$$H_0: \mu_1 = \mu_2$$
$$H_a: \mu_1 > \mu_2$$

SOLVE (first steps): Are the conditions for inference met? The subjects are volunteers, so they are not SRSs from all lean and mildly obese adults. The study tried to recruit comparable groups: all worked in sedentary jobs, none smoked or were taking medication, and so on. The subjects were not told that they were chosen from a larger group of volunteers because they did not exercise and were either lean or mildly obese. Because their willingness to volunteer isn't related to the purpose of the experiment, we will treat them as two independent SRSs.

A back-to-back stemplot (Figure 17.1) displays the data in detail. (We rounded the data to the nearest 10 minutes and used 100s as stems and 10s as leaves.) The distributions are a bit irregular, as we expect with just 10 observations. There are no clear departures from Normality such as extreme outliers or skewness. The lean subjects as a group spend much

Lean		Obese
	2	6 7
7 2	3	5 6 7
	4	1 1 2 3 6
8 8 6 4 1 0	5	
8 1	6	

FIGURE 17.1

Back-to-back stemplot of the times spent walking or standing from Example 17.3.

TABLE 17.1 Time (minutes per day) spent in three different postures by lean and obese subjects

GROUP	SUBJECT	STAND/WALK	SIT	LIE
Lean	1	511.100	370.300	555.500
Lean	2	607.925	374.512	450.650
Lean	3	319.212	582.138	537.362
Lean	4	584.644	357.144	489.269
Lean	5	578.869	348.994	514.081
Lean	6	543.388	385.312	506.500
Lean	7	677.188	268.188	467.700
Lean	8	555.656	322.219	567.006
Lean	9	374.831	537.031	531.431
Lean	10	504.700	528.838	396.962
Obese	11	260.244	646.281	521.044
Obese	12	464.756	456.644	514.931
Obese	13	367.138	578.662	563.300
Obese	14	413.667	463.333	532.208
Obese	15	347.375	567.556	504.931
Obese	16	416.531	567.556	448.856
Obese	17	358.650	621.262	460.550
Obese	18	267.344	646.181	509.981
Obese	19	410.631	572.769	448.706
Obese	20	426.356	591.369	412.919

more time standing and walking than do the obese subjects. Calculating the group means confirms this:

Group	n	Mean $\bar{x}$	Std. dev. s
Group 1 (lean)	10	525.751	107.121
Group 2 (obese)	10	373.269	67.498

The observed difference in mean time per day spent standing or walking is

$$\bar{x}_1 - \bar{x}_2 = 525.751 - 373.269 = 152.482 \text{ minutes}$$

To complete the *Solve* step, we must learn the details of inference comparing two means. ■

Two-sample *t* procedures

Whether an observed difference is surprising depends on the spread of the observations as well as on the two means. Widely different means can arise just by chance if the individual observations vary a great deal. To take variation into account, we standardize the observed difference $\bar{x}_1 - \bar{x}_2$ by dividing by its standard deviation. This standard deviation is

$$\sqrt{\frac{\sigma_1^2}{n_1} + \frac{\sigma_2^2}{n_2}}$$

standard error Because we don't know the population standard deviations, we estimate them by the sample standard deviations from our two samples. The result is the **standard error,** or estimated standard deviation, of the difference in sample means:

$$\sqrt{\frac{s_1^2}{n_1} + \frac{s_2^2}{n_2}}$$

When we standardize the estimate by dividing it by its standard error, the result is the **two-sample *t* statistic:**

$$t = \frac{\overline{x}_1 - \overline{x}_2}{\sqrt{\dfrac{s_1^2}{n_1} + \dfrac{s_2^2}{n_2}}}$$

two-sample t statistic

The statistic *t* has the same interpretation as any *z* or *t* statistic: it says how far $\overline{x}_1 - \overline{x}_2$ is from 0 in standard deviation units.

The two-sample *t* statistic does not have exactly a *t* distribution even if the populations are both exactly Normal. In practice, however, a *t* approximation is very accurate. There are two practical options for using the two-sample *t* procedures:

Option 1. With software, use the *t* statistic with accurate critical values from the approximating *t* distribution. The degrees of freedom are calculated from the data by a somewhat messy formula that we won't give. Moreover, the degrees of freedom may not be a whole number.

Option 2. Without software, use the *t* statistic with critical values from the *t* distribution with *degrees of freedom equal to the smaller of* $n_1 - 1$ *and* $n_2 - 1$. These procedures are always conservative for any two Normal populations. The confidence interval has a margin of error *as large as or larger than* is needed for the desired confidence level. The significance test gives a *P*-value *equal to or greater than* the true *P*-value.

The two options are exactly the same except for the degrees of freedom used for *t* critical values and *P*-values. As the sample sizes increase, confidence levels and *P*-values from Option 2 become more accurate. The gap between what Option 2 reports and the truth is quite small unless the sample sizes are both small and unequal.[2]

THE TWO-SAMPLE *t* PROCEDURES

Draw an SRS of size n_1 from a large Normal population with unknown mean μ_1, and draw an independent SRS of size n_2 from another large Normal population with unknown mean μ_2. A level C **confidence interval for** $\mu_1 - \mu_2$ is given by

$$(\overline{x}_1 - \overline{x}_2) \pm t^* \sqrt{\frac{s_1^2}{n_1} + \frac{s_2^2}{n_2}}$$

Here t^* is the critical value for confidence level C for the *t* distribution with degrees of freedom from either Option 1 (software) or Option 2 (the smaller of $n_1 - 1$ and $n_2 - 1$).

To **test the hypothesis** $H_0: \mu_1 = \mu_2$, calculate the **two-sample *t* statistic**

$$t = \frac{\overline{x}_1 - \overline{x}_2}{\sqrt{\dfrac{s_1^2}{n_1} + \dfrac{s_2^2}{n_2}}}$$

Find *P*-values from the *t* distribution with degrees of freedom from either Option 1 (software) or Option 2 (the smaller of $n_1 - 1$ and $n_2 - 1$).

EXAMPLE 17.4 Daily activity and obesity

We can now complete Example 17.3.

SOLVE (inference): The two-sample t statistic comparing the average minutes spent standing and walking in Group 1 (lean) and Group 2 (obese) is

$$t = \frac{\overline{x}_1 - \overline{x}_2}{\sqrt{\dfrac{s_1^2}{n_1} + \dfrac{s_2^2}{n_2}}}$$

$$= \frac{525.751 - 373.269}{\sqrt{\dfrac{107.121^2}{10} + \dfrac{67.498^2}{10}}}$$

$$= \frac{152.482}{40.039} = 3.808$$

Software (Option 1) gives one-sided P-value $P = 0.0008$ based on df = 15.174.

Without software, use the conservative Option 2. Because $n_1 - 1 = 9$ and $n_2 - 1 = 9$, there are 9 degrees of freedom. Because H_a is one-sided, the P-value is the area to the right of $t = 3.808$ under the $t(9)$ curve. Figure 17.2 illustrates this P-value. Table C shows that $t = 3.808$ lies between the critical values t^* for 0.0025 and 0.001. So $0.001 < P < 0.0025$. Option 2 gives a larger (more conservative) P-value than Option 1. As usual, the practical conclusion is the same for both versions of the test.

CONCLUDE: There is very strong evidence ($P = 0.0008$) that lean people spend more time walking and standing than do moderately obese people. ■

df = 9

t^*	3.690	4.297
One-sided P	.0025	.001

FIGURE 17.2

Using the conservative Option 2, the P-value in Example 17.4 comes from the t distribution with 9 degrees of freedom.

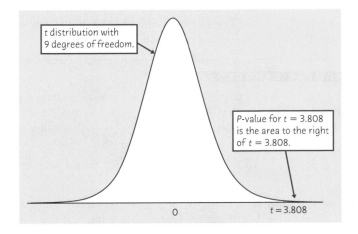

The analysis in Example 17.4 doesn't tell us whether lack of every-day activity *causes* obesity. It may be that some people are naturally more active and are therefore less likely to gain weight. Or it may be that people who gain weight reduce their activity level.

EXAMPLE 17.5 How much more active are lean people?

PLAN: Give a 90% confidence interval for $\mu_1 - \mu_2$, the difference in average daily minutes spent standing and walking between lean and mildly obese adults.

SOLVE and CONCLUDE: As in Example 17.4, the conservative Option 2 uses 9 degrees of freedom. Table C shows that the $t(9)$ critical value is $t^* = 1.833$. We are 90% confident that $\mu_1 - \mu_2$ lies in the interval

$$(\overline{x}_1 - \overline{x}_2) \pm t^* \sqrt{\frac{s_1^2}{n_1} + \frac{s_2^2}{n_2}}$$

$$= (525.751 - 373.269) \pm 1.833 \sqrt{\frac{107.121^2}{10} + \frac{67.498^2}{10}}$$

$$= 152.482 \pm 73.390$$

$$= 79.09 \text{ to } 225.87 \text{ minutes}$$

Software using Option 1 gives the 90% interval as 82.35 to 222.62 minutes, based on t with 15.174 degrees of freedom. The Option 2 interval is wider because this method is conservative. ∎

EXAMPLE 17.6 **Community service and attachment to friends**

STATE: Do college students who have volunteered for community service work differ from those who have not? A study obtained data from 57 students who had done service work and 17 who had not. One of the response variables was a measure of "attachment to friends." Here are the results:[3]

Group	Condition	*n*	$\overline{x}$	*s*
1	Service	57	105.32	14.68
2	No service	17	96.82	14.26

PLAN: The investigator had no specific direction for the difference in mind before looking at the data, so the alternative is two-sided. We will test the hypotheses

$$H_0: \mu_1 = \mu_2$$
$$H_a: \mu_1 \neq \mu_2$$

SOLVE: The investigator says that the individual scores, examined separately in the two samples, appear roughly Normal. There is a serious problem with the more important condition that the two samples can be regarded as SRSs from two student populations. We will discuss that after we illustrate the calculations.

The two-sample *t* statistic is

$$t = \frac{\overline{x}_1 - \overline{x}_2}{\sqrt{\dfrac{s_1^2}{n_1} + \dfrac{s_2^2}{n_2}}}$$

$$= \frac{105.32 - 96.82}{\sqrt{\dfrac{14.68^2}{57} + \dfrac{14.26^2}{17}}}$$

$$= \frac{8.5}{3.9677} = 2.142$$

Software (Option 1) says that the two-sided P-value is $P = 0.0414$.

Without software, use Option 2 to find a conservative P-value. There are 16 degrees of freedom, the smaller of

$$n_1 - 1 = 57 - 1 = 56 \quad \text{and} \quad n_2 - 1 = 17 - 1 = 16$$

Figure 17.3 illustrates the P-value. Find it by comparing $t = 2.142$ with the two-sided critical values for the $t(16)$ distribution. Table C shows that the P-value is between 0.05 and 0.04.

CONCLUDE: The data give moderately strong evidence ($P < 0.05$) that students who have engaged in community service are on the average more attached to their friends. ■

df = 16

t^*	2.120	2.235
Two-sided P	.05	.04

FIGURE 17.3
The P-value in Example 17.6. Because the alternative is two-sided, the P-value is double the area to the left of $t = -2.142$.

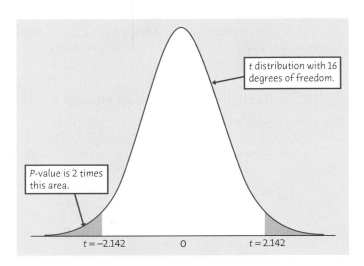

Is the t test in Example 17.6 justified? The student subjects were "enrolled in a course on U.S. Diversity at a large mid-western university." Unless this course is required of all students, the subjects cannot be considered a random sample even from this campus. Students were placed in the two groups on the basis of a questionnaire, 39 in the "no service" group and 71 in the "service" group. The data were gathered from a follow-up survey two years later; 17 of the 39 "no service" students responded (44%), compared with 80% response (57 of 71) in the "service" group. Nonresponse is confounded with group: students who had done community service were much more likely to respond. Finally, 75% of the "service" respondents were women, compared with 47% of the "no service" respondents. Gender, which can strongly affect attachment, is badly confounded with the presence or absence of community service. The data are so far from meeting the SRS condition for inference that the t test is meaningless.

APPLY YOUR KNOWLEDGE

In exercises that call for two-sample t procedures, use Option 1 if you have technology that implements that method. Otherwise, use Option 2 (degrees of freedom the smaller of $n_1 - 1$ and $n_2 - 1$).

17.5 Logging in the rain forest. "Conservationists have despaired over destruction of tropical rain forest by logging, clearing, and burning." These words begin a report on a statistical study of the effects of logging in Borneo.[4] Here are data on the number of tree species in 12 unlogged forest plots and 9 similar plots logged 8 years earlier:

Unlogged	22	18	22	20	15	21	13	13	19	13	19	15
Logged	17	4	18	14	18	15	15	10	12			

Digital Vision/Getty Images

(a) The study report says, "Loggers were unaware that the effects of logging would be assessed." Why is this important? The report also explains why the plots can be considered to be randomly assigned.

(b) Does logging significantly reduce the mean number of species in a plot after 8 years? Follow the four-step process as illustrated in Examples 17.3 and 17.4.

17.6 Daily activity and obesity. We can conclude from Examples 17.3 and 17.4 that mildly obese people spend less time standing and walking (on the average) than lean people. Is there a significant difference between the mean times the two groups spend lying down? Use the four-step process to answer this question from the data in Table 17.1. Follow the model of Examples 17.3 and 17.4.

17.7 Logging in the rain forest, continued. Use the data in Exercise 17.5 to give a 90% confidence interval for the difference in mean number of species between unlogged and logged plots.

Using technology

Software should use Option 1 for the degrees of freedom to give accurate confidence intervals and P-values. Unfortunately, there is variation in how well software implements Option 1. Figure 17.4 displays output from a graphing calculator, a statistical program, and a spreadsheet program for the test of Example 17.4. All three claim to use Option 1. The two-sample t statistic is exactly as in Example 17.4, $t = 3.808$. You can find this in all three outputs (Minitab rounds to 3.81; Excel and the graphing calculator give additional decimal places). The different technologies use different methods to find the P-value for $t = 3.808$.

- The calculator gets Option 1 completely right. The accurate approximation uses the t distribution with approximately 15.174 degrees of freedom. The P-value is $P = 0.0008$.

- Minitab uses Option 1, but it *truncates* the exact degrees of freedom to the next smaller whole number to get critical values and P-values. In this example, the exact df = 15.174 is truncated to df = 15, so that Minitab's results are slightly conservative. That is, Minitab's P-value (rounded to $P = 0.001$ in the output) is slightly larger than the full Option 1 P-value.

- Excel *rounds* the exact degrees of freedom to the nearest whole number, so that df = 15.174 becomes df = 15. Excel's method agrees with Minitab's in this example. But when rounding moves the degrees of freedom up to the next higher whole number, Excel's P-values are slightly smaller than is correct. This is misleading.

The two-sample *t* procedures applied to the data on activity and obesity: output from a graphing calculator, a statistical program, and a spreadsheet program.

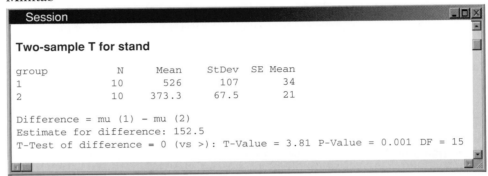

Texas Instruments Graphing Calculator

```
2-SampTTest
 μ1>μ2
 t=3.808375604
 p=8.4101904E-4
 df=15.17355038
 x̄1=525.7513
↓x̄2=373.2692
```

Minitab

Session

Two-sample T for stand

group	N	Mean	StDev	SE Mean
1	10	526	107	34
2	10	373.3	67.5	21

Difference = mu (1) − mu (2)
Estimate for difference: 152.5
T-Test of difference = 0 (vs >): T-Value = 3.81 P-Value = 0.001 DF = 15

Microsoft Excel

Excel

	A	B	C
1	t-Test: Two-Sample Assuming Unequal Variances		
2			
3		*Lean*	*Obese*
4	Mean	525.7513	373.2692
5	Variance	11474.8903	4556.019849
6	Observations	10	10
7	Hypothesized Mean	0	
8	df	15	
9	t Stat	3.808375604	
10	P(T<=t) one-tail	0.000856818	
11	t Critical one-tail	1.753051038	
12	P(T<=t) two-tail	0.001713635	
13	P(T<t) two-tail	2.131450856	
14			

Sheet4

Excel's label for the test, "Two-Sample Assuming Unequal Variances," is seriously misleading. *The two-sample t procedures we have described work whether or not the two populations have the same variance.* There is an old-fashioned special procedure that works only when the two variances are equal. We won't discuss this method because you should never use it.

Although different calculators and software give slightly different *P*-values, in practice you can just accept what your technology says. The small differences in *P* don't affect the conclusion. Even "between 0.001 and 0.0025" from Option 2 (Example 17.4) is close enough for practical purposes.

17.8 Does polyester decay? How quickly do synthetic fabrics such as polyester decay in landfills? A researcher buried 10 strips of polyester fabric in well-drained soil in the summer. Five of the strips, chosen at random, were dug up after 2 weeks; the other 5 were dug up after 16 weeks. Breaking strength is easy to measure and is a good indicator of decay. Lower strength means the fabric has decayed. Here are the breaking strengths in pounds:[5]

Sample 1 (2 weeks)	118	126	126	120	129
Sample 2 (16 weeks)	124	98	110	140	110

Figure 17.5 shows output for the two-sample t test using Option 1. (This output is from software that does Option 1 without rounding or truncating the degrees of freedom.) Do polyester strips buried for 16 weeks have significantly lower mean breaking strength than those buried for 2 weeks? Using the output in Figure 17.5, write a summary in a sentence or two, including t, df, P, and a conclusion.

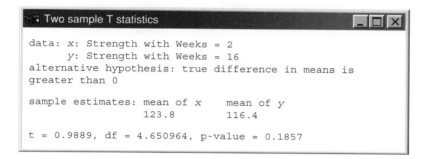

```
Two sample T statistics                               _ □ X

data: x: Strength with Weeks = 2
      y: Strength with Weeks = 16
alternative hypothesis: true difference in means is
greater than 0

sample estimates: mean of x    mean of y
                     123.8         116.4

t = 0.9889, df = 4.650964, p-value = 0.1857
```

FIGURE 17.5
Two-sample t software output for Exercise 17.8.

Robustness again

The two-sample t procedures are even more robust than the one-sample t methods, particularly when the distributions are not symmetric. When the sizes of the two samples are equal and the two populations being compared have distributions with similar shapes, probability values from the t table are quite accurate for a broad range of distributions when the sample sizes are as small as $n_1 = n_2 = 5$.[6] When the two population distributions have different shapes, larger samples are needed.

As a guide to practice, adapt the guidelines given on page 298 for the use of one-sample t procedures to two-sample procedures by replacing "sample size" with the "sum of the sample sizes," $n_1 + n_2$. These guidelines err on the side of safety, especially when the two samples are of equal size. *In planning a two-sample study, choose equal sample sizes whenever possible. The two-sample t procedures are most robust against non-Normality in this case, and the conservative Option 2 probability values are most accurate.*

17.9 Do good smells bring good business? Businesses know that customers often respond to background music. Do they also respond to odors? Spread a relaxing lavender odor through a small restaurant on one Saturday evening and do nothing on another evening.

TABLE 17.2 Time (minutes) and spending (euros) by restaurant customers

NO ODOR		LAVENDER	
MINUTES	EUROS SPENT	MINUTES	EUROS SPENT
103	15.9	92	21.9
68	18.5	126	18.5
79	15.9	114	22.3
106	18.5	106	21.9
72	18.5	89	18.5
121	21.9	137	24.9
92	15.9	93	18.5
84	15.9	76	22.5
72	15.9	98	21.5
92	15.9	108	21.9
85	15.9	124	21.5
69	18.5	105	18.5
73	18.5	129	25.5
87	18.5	103	18.5
109	20.5	107	18.5
115	18.5	109	21.9
91	18.5	94	18.5
84	15.9	105	18.5
76	15.9	102	24.9
96	15.9	108	21.9
107	18.5	95	25.9
98	18.5	121	21.9
92	15.9	109	18.5
107	18.5	104	18.5
93	15.9	116	22.8
118	18.5	88	18.5
87	15.9	109	21.9
101	25.5	97	20.7
75	12.9	101	21.9
86	15.9	106	22.5

Table 17.2 gives the time (minutes) that samples of 30 customers spent in the restaurant and the amount they spent (in euros).[7] The two evenings were comparable in many ways (weather, customer count, and so on), so we are willing to regard the data as independent SRSs from spring Saturday evenings at this restaurant.

(a) Does a lavender odor encourage customers to stay longer in the restaurant? Examine the time data and explain why they are suitable for two-sample t procedures. Use the two-sample t test to answer the question posed.

(b) Does a lavender odor encourage customers to spend more while in the restaurant? Examine the spending data. In what ways do these data deviate from Normality? With 30 observations, the t procedures are nonetheless reasonably accurate. Use the two-sample t test to answer the question posed.

17.10 Compressing soil. Farmers know that driving heavy equipment on wet soil compresses the soil and injures future crops. Here are data on the "penetrability" of the same type of soil at two levels of compression.[8] Penetrability is a measure of how much resistance plant roots will meet when they try to grow through the soil.

Compressed soil									
2.86	2.68	2.92	2.82	2.76	2.81	2.78	3.08	2.94	2.86
3.08	2.82	2.78	2.98	3.00	2.78	2.96	2.90	3.18	3.16

Intermediate soil									
3.14	3.38	3.10	3.40	3.38	3.14	3.18	3.26	2.96	3.02
3.54	3.36	3.18	3.12	3.86	2.92	3.46	3.44	3.62	4.26

(a) Make stemplots to investigate the shape of the distributions. The penetrabilities for intermediate soil are skewed to the right and have a high outlier. Returning to the source of the data shows that the outlying sample had unusually low soil density, so that it belongs in the "loose soil" class. We are justified in removing the outlier.

(b) We suspect that the penetrability of compressed soil is less than that of intermediate soil. Do the data (with the outlier removed) support this suspicion?

17.11 Weeds among the corn. Exercise 6.30 (page 121) gives these corn yields (bushels per acre) for experimental plots controlled to have 1 weed per meter of row and 3 weeds per meter of row:

1 weed/meter	166.2	157.3	166.7	161.1
3 weeds/meter	158.6	176.4	153.1	156.0

Explain carefully why a two-sample t confidence interval for the difference in mean yields may not be accurate.

17.12 Compressing soil, continued. Use the data in Exercise 17.10, omitting the outlier, to give a 95% confidence interval for the decrease in penetrability of compressed soil relative to intermediate soil.

CHAPTER 17 SUMMARY

■ The data in a **two-sample problem** are two independent SRSs, each drawn from a separate population.

■ Tests and confidence intervals for the difference between the means μ_1 and μ_2 of two Normal populations start from the difference $\overline{x}_1 - \overline{x}_2$ between the two sample means. Because of the central limit theorem, the resulting procedures are approximately correct for other population distributions when the sample sizes are large.

■ Draw independent SRSs of sizes n_1 and n_2 from two Normal populations. Estimate the standard deviation of $\overline{x}_1 - \overline{x}_2$ by the **standard error**

$$\sqrt{\frac{s_1^2}{n_1} + \frac{s_2^2}{n_2}}$$

to get the **two-sample t statistic**

$$t = \frac{\overline{x}_1 - \overline{x}_2}{\sqrt{\dfrac{s_1^2}{n_1} + \dfrac{s_2^2}{n_2}}}$$

The statistic t has approximately a t distribution.

■ There are two choices for the **degrees of freedom** of the two-sample t statistic. Option 1: software produces accurate probability values using degrees of freedom calculated from the data. Option 2: for conservative inference procedures, use degrees of freedom equal to the smaller of $n_1 - 1$ and $n_2 - 1$.

■ The **confidence interval for $\mu_1 - \mu_2$** is

$$(\bar{x}_1 - \bar{x}_2) \pm t^* \sqrt{\frac{s_1^2}{n_1} + \frac{s_2^2}{n_2}}$$

The critical value t^* from Option 1 gives a confidence level very close to the desired level C. Option 2 produces a margin of error at least as wide as is needed for the desired level C.

■ **Significance tests for H_0: $\mu_1 = \mu_2$** are based on the two-sample t statistic. P-values calculated from Option 1 are very accurate. Option 2 P-values are always at least as large as the true P.

■ The two-sample t procedures are quite **robust** against departures from Normality. Guidelines for practical use are similar to those for one-sample t procedures. Equal sample sizes are recommended.

CHECK YOUR SKILLS

17.13 The National Assessment of Educational Progress (NAEP) gave a mathematics test to a random sample of eighth-graders in Texas. The mean score was 281 out of 500. To give a confidence interval for the mean score of all Texas eighth-graders, you would use
(a) the one-sample t interval.
(b) the matched pairs t interval.
(c) the two-sample t interval.

17.14 In the NAEP sample of Texas eighth-graders, the mean mathematics scores were 279 for female students and 283 for male students. To see if this difference is statistically significant, you would use
(a) the one-sample t test.
(b) the matched pairs t test.
(c) the two-sample t test.

17.15 A study of the effects of exercise used rats bred to have high or low capacity for exercise. There were 8 high-capacity and 8 low-capacity rats. To compare the mean blood pressure of the two types of rats using the two-sample t procedures with the conservative Option 2, the correct degrees of freedom is
(a) 7.   (b) 14.   (c) 15.

17.16 The 8 high-capacity rats had mean blood pressure 89 with standard deviation 9; the 8 low-capacity rats had mean blood pressure 105 with standard deviation 13. (Blood pressure is measured in millimeters of mercury.) The two-sample t statistic for comparing the population means has value
(a) 0.5.   (b) 2.86.   (c) 9.65.

17.17 A study of road rage asked samples of 596 men and 523 women about their behavior while driving. Based on their answers, each subject was assigned a road rage score on a scale of 0 to 20. The subjects were chosen by random digit dialing of telephone numbers. Are the conditions for two-sample t inference satisfied?
(a) Maybe: the SRS condition is OK but we need to look at the data to check Normality.
(b) No: scores in a range between 0 and 20 can't be Normal.
(c) Yes: the SRS condition is OK and large sample sizes make the Normality condition unnecessary.

17.18 We suspect that men are more prone to road rage than women. To see if this is true, test these hypotheses for the mean road rage scores of all male and female drivers:
(a) H_0: $\mu_M = \mu_F$ versus H_a: $\mu_M > \mu_F$.
(b) H_0: $\mu_M = \mu_F$ versus H_a: $\mu_M \neq \mu_F$.
(c) H_0: $\mu_M = \mu_F$ versus H_a: $\mu_M < \mu_F$.

17.19 The two-sample t statistic for the road rage study (male mean minus female mean) is $t = 3.18$. The P-value for testing the hypotheses from the previous exercise satisfies
(a) $0.001 < P < 0.005$.   (b) $0.0005 < P < 0.001$.
(c) $0.001 < P < 0.002$.

CHAPTER 17 EXERCISES

Exercises 17.20 to 17.27 are based on summary statistics rather than raw data. This information is typically all that is presented in published reports. You can calculate inference procedures by hand from the summaries. Use the conservative Option 2 (degrees of freedom the smaller of n_1-1 and n_2-1) for two-sample t confidence intervals and P-values. You must trust that the authors understood the conditions for inference and verified that they apply. This isn't always true.

17.20 Do women talk more than men? Equip male and female students with a small device that secretly records sound for a random 30 seconds during each 12.5-minute period over two days. Count the words each subject speaks during each recording period, and from this, estimate how many words per day each subject speaks. The published report includes a table summarizing six such studies.[9] Here are two of the six:

	Sample Size		Estimated Average Number (SD) of Words/Day	
Study	Women	Men	Women	Men
1	56	56	16,177 (7520)	16,569 (9108)
2	27	20	16,496 (7914)	12,867 (8343)

Readers are supposed to understand that, for example, the 56 women in the first study had $\bar{x} = 16{,}177$ and $s = 7520$. It is commonly thought that women talk more than men. Does either of the two samples support this idea? For each study:
(a) State hypotheses in terms of the population means for men (μ_M) and women (μ_F).
(b) Find the two-sample t statistic.
(c) What degrees of freedom does Option 2 use to get a conservative P-value?
(d) Compare your value of t with the critical values in Table C. What can you say about the P-value of the test?
(e) What do you conclude from the results of these two studies?

17.21 Eating potato chips. Give healthy women aged 18 to 40 bags of potato chips and bottled water and invite them to snack freely. Some women were trying to restrain their diet out of concern about their weight. How much effect did these good intentions have on their eating habits? The table below summarizes data on grams of potato chips consumed.[10] (The study report gave the standard error of the mean $s/\sqrt{n}$, abbreviated as SEM, rather than the standard deviation s.)

Group	n	$\bar{x}$	SEM
Unrestrained	9	59	7
Restrained	11	32	10

(a) What are the two sample standard deviations?
(b) What degrees of freedom does the conservative Option 2 use for two-sample t procedures for these samples?
(c) Using Option 2, give a 90% confidence interval for the mean difference between the two populations of women.

17.22 Ginkgo extract and the post-lunch dip. The post-lunch dip is the drop in mental alertness after a midday meal. Does an extract of the leaves of the ginkgo tree reduce the post-lunch dip? Assign healthy people aged 18 to 40 to take either ginkgo extract or a placebo pill. After lunch, ask them to read seven pages of random letters and place an X over every e. Count the number of misses per line read.[11]
(a) What is a placebo and why was one group given a placebo?
(b) What is the double-blind method and why was it used in this experiment?
(c) Here are summaries of performance after 13 weeks of either ginkgo extract or placebo:

Group	Group size	Mean	Std. dev.
Ginkgo	21	0.06383	0.01462
Placebo	18	0.05342	0.01549

Is there a significant difference between the two groups? What do these data show about the effect of ginkgo extract?

17.23 Hispanic customers and Anglo customers. As the presence of Hispanics in the United States has grown, businesses try to understand what Hispanics like. One study sampled customers leaving a bank. Customers were classified as Hispanic if they preferred to be interviewed in Spanish or as Anglo if they preferred English. Each customer rated the importance of several aspects of bank service on a 10-point scale.[12] Here are summary results for the importance of "reliability" (the accuracy of account records and so on):

Group	n	$\bar{x}$	s
Anglo	92	6.37	0.60
Hispanic	86	5.91	0.93

Another aspect of service quality is "empathy," the relationship that bank employees have with customers. The summary data are

Group	n	$\bar{x}$	s
Anglo	92	6.00	0.89
Hispanic	86	6.43	0.70

Do Hispanic and Anglo bank customers differ in the importance they place on either or both of these qualities? Write a one-sentence description of the differences in what the two groups find important.

17.24 Cholesterol in Canadian young adults. A random sample of 2053 Canadian women aged 18 to 34 found mean blood cholesterol level $\bar{x} = 4.5$ millimoles per liter (mmol/l), with standard deviation $s = 0.8$ mmol/l. A sample of 1990 Canadian young men in the same study had $\bar{x} = 4.6$ mmol/l and $s = 0.9$ mmol/l.[13]
(a) We know that even small differences can be statistically significant if the samples are large. Is there a significant difference between the mean blood cholesterol levels of Canadian young women and young men?
(b) We also know that estimating the size of a difference helps us decide whether it is large enough to be important. Give a 95% confidence interval for the difference between female and male mean cholesterol.

17.25 Coaching and SAT scores. Coaching companies claim that their courses can raise the SAT scores of high school students. Of course, students who retake the SAT without coaching generally raise their scores. A random sample of students who took the SAT twice found 427 who were coached and 2733 who were uncoached.[14] Starting with their verbal scores on the first and second tries, we have these summary statistics:

	n	$\bar{x}$	s	$\bar{x}$	s	$\bar{x}$	s
		Try 1		**Try 2**		**Gain**	
Coached	427	500	92	529	97	29	59
Uncoached	2733	506	101	527	101	21	52

Let's first ask if students who are coached significantly increased their scores.
(a) You could use the information on the Coached line to carry out either a two-sample *t* test comparing Try 1 with Try 2 for coached students or a matched pairs *t* test using Gain. Which is the correct test? Why?
(b) Carry out the proper test. What do you conclude?
(c) Give a 99% confidence interval for the mean gain of all students who are coached.

17.26 Coaching and SAT scores, continued. What we really want to know is whether coached students improve more than uncoached students, and whether any advantage is large enough to be worth paying for. Use the information in the previous exercise to answer these questions:
(a) Is there good evidence that coached students gained more on the average than uncoached students?
(b) How much more do coached students gain on the average? Give a 99% confidence interval.

(c) Based on your work, what is your opinion: do you think coaching courses are worth paying for?

17.27 Coaching and SAT scores: critique. The data you used in the previous two problems came from a random sample of students who took the SAT twice. The response rate was 63%, which is pretty good for nongovernment surveys, so let's accept that the respondents do represent all students who took the exam twice. Nonetheless, we can't be sure that coaching actually *caused* the coached students to gain more than the uncoached students. Explain briefly but clearly why this is so.

Exercises 17.28 to 17.34 include the actual data. To apply the two-sample t procedures, use Option 1 if you have technology that implements that method. Otherwise, use Option 2.

17.28 IQ scores for boys and girls. Here are the IQ test scores of 31 seventh-grade girls in a Midwest school district:[15]

114	100	104	89	102	91	114	114	103	105
108	130	120	132	111	128	118	119	86	72
111	103	74	112	107	103	98	96	112	112	93

The IQ test scores of 47 seventh-grade boys in the same district are

111	107	100	107	115	111	97	112	104	106	113
109	113	128	128	118	113	124	127	136	106	123
124	126	116	127	119	97	102	110	120	103	115
93	123	79	119	110	110	107	105	105	110	77
90	114	106

(a) Make stemplots or histograms of both sets of data. Because the distributions are reasonably symmetric with no extreme outliers, the *t* procedures will work well.
(b) Treat these data as SRSs from all seventh-grade students in the district. Is there good evidence that girls and boys differ in their mean IQ scores? State hypotheses, carry out a two-sample *t* test, and report your conclusions.

17.29 Do good smells bring good business, continued. In Exercise 17.9 (page 317) you examined the effects of a lavender odor on customer behavior in a small restaurant. Lavender is a relaxing odor. The researchers also looked at the effects of lemon, a stimulating odor. Here are the times in minutes that customers spent in the restaurant when no odor was present:

103	68	79	106	72	121	92	84	72	92
85	69	73	87	109	115	91	84	76	96
107	98	92	107	93	118	87	101	75	86

When a lemon odor was present, customers lingered for these times:

78	104	74	75	112	88	105	97	101	89
88	73	94	63	83	108	91	88	83	106
108	60	96	94	56	90	113	97		

(a) Examine both samples. Does it appear that use of two-sample t procedures is justified? Do the sample means suggest that a lemon odor changes the average length of stay?

(b) Does a lemon odor influence the length of time customers stay in the restaurant? State hypotheses, carry out a t test, and report your conclusions.

17.30 IQ scores for boys and girls, continued. Use the data in Exercise 17.28 to give a 95% confidence interval for the difference between the mean IQ scores of all boys and girls in the district.

17.31 How strong are durable press fabrics? "Durable press" cotton fabrics are treated to improve their recovery from wrinkles after washing. Unfortunately, the treatment also reduces the strength of the fabric. A study compared the breaking strength of fabrics treated by two commercial durable press processes. Five swatches of the same fabric were assigned at random to each process. Here are the data, in pounds of pull needed to tear the fabric:[16]

Permafresh	29.9	30.7	30.0	29.5	27.6
Hylite	28.8	23.9	27.0	22.1	24.2

Is there good evidence that the two processes result in different mean breaking strengths?

(a) Do the sample means suggest that one of the processes is superior in breaking strength?

(b) Make stemplots for both samples. The Permafresh sample contains a mild outlier. With just 5 observations per group, we worry that this outlier will affect our conclusions.

(c) Test the hypothesis $H_0: \mu_1 = \mu_2$ against the two-sided alternative twice: once using all the data and again without the outlier in the Permafresh sample. Do the two tests lead to similar conclusions? Can we safely conclude that one treatment has significantly higher mean breaking strength than the other?

17.32 Reducing wrinkles. Of course, the reason for durable press treatment is to reduce wrinkling. "Wrinkle recovery angle" measures how well a fabric recovers from wrinkles. Higher is better. Here are data on the wrinkle recovery angle (in degrees) for the same fabric swatches discussed in the previous exercise:

Permafresh	136	135	132	137	134
Hylite	143	141	146	141	145

Is there a significant difference in wrinkle resistance?

(a) Do the sample means suggest that one process has better wrinkle resistance?

(b) Make stemplots for both samples. There are no obvious deviations from Normality.

(c) Test the hypothesis $H_0: \mu_1 = \mu_2$ against the two-sided alternative. What do you conclude from part (a) and from the result of your test?

17.33 How much stronger? Continue your work from Exercise 17.31. A fabric manufacturer wants to know how large an advantage in strength fabrics treated by the Permafresh method have over fabrics treated by the Hylite process. Give a 90% confidence interval for the difference in mean breaking strengths. (Use all 5 fabric swatches.)

17.34 How much less wrinkling? In Exercise 17.32, you found that the Hylite process results in significantly greater wrinkle resistance than the Permafresh process. How large is the difference in mean wrinkle recovery angle? Give a 90% confidence interval.

Do birds learn to time their breeding? *Blue titmice eat caterpillars. The birds would like lots of caterpillars around when they have young to feed, but they breed earlier than peak caterpillar season. Do the birds learn from one year's experience when they time their breeding the next year? Researchers randomly assigned 7 pairs of birds to have the natural caterpillar supply supplemented while feeding their young and another 6 pairs to serve as a control group relying on natural food supply. The next year, they measured how many days after the caterpillar peak the birds produced their nestlings.[17] Exercises 17.35 to 17.37 are based on this experiment.*

17.35 Did the randomization produce similar groups? First, compare the two groups in the first year. The only difference should be the chance effect of the random assignment. The study report says: "In the experimental year, the degree of synchronization did not differ between food-supplemented and control females." For this comparison, the report gives $t = -1.05$. What type of t statistic (paired or two-sample) is this? What are the degrees of freedom for this statistic? Show that this t leads to the quoted conclusion.

17.36 Did the treatment have an effect? The investigators expected the control group to adjust their breeding date the next year, whereas the well-fed supplemented group had no reason to change. The report continues: "but in the following year food-supplemented females were more out of synchrony with the caterpillar peak than the controls." Here are the data (days behind the caterpillar peak):

Control	4.6	2.3	7.7	6.0	4.6	−1.2	
Supplemented	15.5	11.3	5.4	16.5	11.3	11.4	7.7

Carry out a t test and show that it leads to the quoted conclusion.

17.37 Year-to-year comparison. Rather than comparing the two groups in each year, we could compare the behavior of each group in the first and second years. The study report says: "Our main prediction was that females receiving additional food in the nestling period should not change laying date the next year, whereas controls, which (in our area) breed too late in their first year, were expected to advance their laying date in the second year."

Comparing days behind the caterpillar peak in Years 1 and 2 gave $t = 0.63$ for the control group and $t = −2.63$ for the supplemented group. Are these paired or two-sample t statistics? What are the degrees of freedom for each t? Show that these t-values do *not* agree with the prediction.

The remaining exercises ask you to answer questions from data without having the details outlined for you. The exercise statements give you the **State** *step of the four-step process. Follow the* **Plan, Solve,** *and* **Conclude** *steps as illustrated in Examples 17.3 and 17.4 for tests and Example 17.5 for confidence intervals. Remember that examining the data and discussing the conditions for inference are part of the* **Solve** *step.*

17.38 Thinking about money changes behavior. Kathleen Vohs of the University of Minnesota and her coworkers carried out several randomized comparative experiments on the effects of thinking about money. Here's part of one such experiment.[18] Ask student subjects to unscramble 30 sets of five words to make a meaningful phrase from four of the five words. The control group unscrambled phrases like "cold it desk outside is" into "it is cold outside." The treatment group unscrambled phrases that lead to thinking about money, turning "high a salary desk paying" into "a high-paying salary." Then each subject worked a hard puzzle, knowing that they could ask for help. Here are the times in seconds until subjects asked for help, for the treatment group,

609	444	242	199	174	55	251	466	443
531	135	241	476	482	362	69	160	

and for the control group,

118	272	413	291	140	104	55	189	126
400	92	64	88	142	141	373	156	

The researchers suspected that money is connected with self-sufficiency, so that the treatment group would ask for help less quickly on the average. Do the data support this idea?

17.39 Active versus passive learning. A study of computer-assisted learning examined the learning of "Blissymbols" by children. Blissymbols are pictographs (think of Egyptian hieroglyphs) that are sometimes used to help learning-impaired children communicate. The researcher designed two computer lessons that taught the same content using the same examples. One lesson required the children to interact with the material, while in the other the children controlled only the pace of the lesson. Call these two styles "Active" and "Passive." Children were assigned at random to Active and Passive groups. After the lesson, the computer presented a quiz that asked the children to identify 56 Blissymbols. Here are the numbers of correct identifications by the 24 children in the Active group:[19]

29	28	24	31	15	24	27	23	20	22	23	21
24	35	21	24	44	28	17	21	21	20	28	16

The 24 children in the Passive group had these counts of correct identifications:

16	14	17	15	26	17	12	25	21	20	18	21
20	16	18	15	26	15	13	17	21	19	15	12

Is there good evidence that active learning is superior to passive learning?

17.40 Each day I am getting better in math. A "subliminal" message is one that we can't perceive but that may nonetheless influence us. Can subliminal messages help students learn math? A group of students who had failed the mathematics part of the City University of New York Skills Assessment Test agreed to participate in a study to find out.

All received a daily subliminal message, flashed on a screen too rapidly to be consciously read. The treatment group of 10 students (chosen at random) was exposed to "Each day I am getting better in math." The control group of 8 students was exposed to "People are walking on the street." All students participated in a summer program designed to raise their math skills, and all took the assessment test again at the end of the program. Table 17.3 gives data on the subjects' scores before and after the program.[20] Is there good evidence that the treatment brought about a greater improvement in math scores than the control message? How large is the mean difference in gains between treatment and control? (Use 90% confidence.)

17.41 Active versus passive learning, continued.
(a) Use the data in Exercise 17.39 to give a 90% confidence interval for the difference in mean number of Blissymbols identified correctly by children after active and passive lessons.
(b) Give a 90% confidence interval for the mean number of Blissymbols identified correctly by children after the active lesson.

TABLE 17.3 Mathematics skills scores before and after a subliminal message

TREATMENT GROUP		CONTROL GROUP	
BEFORE	AFTER	BEFORE	AFTER
18	24	18	29
18	25	24	29
21	33	20	24
18	29	18	26
18	33	24	38
20	36	22	27
23	34	15	22
23	36	19	31
21	34		
17	27		

17.42 Tropical flowers. Different varieties of the tropical flower *Heliconia* are fertilized by different species of hummingbirds. Over time, the lengths of the flowers and the forms of the hummingbirds' beaks have evolved to match each other. Here are data on the lengths in millimeters of two color varieties of the same species of flower on the island of Dominica:[21]

H. caribaea red

41.90	42.01	41.93	43.09	41.47	41.69	39.78	40.57
39.63	42.18	40.66	37.87	39.16	37.40	38.20	38.07
38.10	37.97	38.79	38.23	38.87	37.78	38.01	

H. caribaea yellow

36.78	37.02	36.52	36.11	36.03	35.45	38.13	37.10
35.17	36.82	36.66	35.68	36.03	34.57	34.63	

Is there good evidence that the mean lengths of the two varieties differ? Estimate the difference between the population means. (Use 95% confidence.)

17.43 Student drinking. A professor asked her sophomore students, "How many drinks do you typically have per session? (A drink is defined as one 12 oz beer, one 4 oz glass of wine, or one 1 oz shot of liquor.)" Some of the students didn't drink. Table 17.4 gives the responses of the female and male students who did drink.[22] It is likely that some of the students exaggerated a bit. The sample is all students in one large sophomore-level class. The class is popular, so we are tentatively willing to regard its members as an SRS of sophomore students at this college. Do a complete analysis that reports on
(a) the drinking behavior claimed by sophomore women.
(b) the drinking behavior claimed by sophomore men.
(c) a comparison of the behavior of women and men.

TABLE 17.4 Drinks per session claimed by female and male students

					FEMALE STUDENTS							
2.5	9	1	3.5	2.5	3	1	3	3	3	3	2.5	2.5
5	3.5	5	1	2	1	7	3	7	4	4	6.5	4
3	6	5	3	8	6	6	3	6	8	3	4	7
4	5	3.5	4	2	1	5	5	3	3	6	4	2
7	7	7	3.5	3	2.5	10	5	4	9	8	1	6
2	5	2.5	3	4.5	9	5	4	4	3	4	6	7
4	5	1	5	3	4	10	7	3	4	4	4	4
2	1	2.5	2.5									

					MALE STUDENTS							
7	7.5	8	15	3	4	1	5	11	4.5	6	4	10
16	4	8	5	9	7	7	3	5	6.5	1	12	4
6	8	8	4.5	10.5	8	6	10	1	9	8	7	8
15	3	10	7	4	6	5	2	10	7	9	5	8
7	3	7	6	4	5	2	5	5.5	9	10	10	4
8	4	2	4	12.5	3	15	2	6	3	4	3	10
6	4.5	5										

Is it really true that newborn babies are more likely to be boys than girls? See Example 18.6 for some evidence.

Inference about a Population Proportion

IN THIS CHAPTER
WE COVER...

■ The sample proportion $\hat{p}$

■ Large-sample confidence intervals for a proportion

■ Choosing the sample size

■ Significance tests for a proportion

Our discussion of statistical inference to this point has concerned making inferences about population *means*. Now we turn to questions about the *proportion* of some outcome in a population. Here are some examples that call for inference about population proportions.

EXAMPLE 18.1 Risky behavior in the age of AIDS

How common is behavior that puts people at risk of AIDS? The National AIDS Behavioral Surveys interviewed a random sample of 2673 adult heterosexuals. Of these, 170 had more than one sexual partner in the past year. That's 6.36% of the sample.[1] Based on these data, what can we say about the percent of all adult heterosexuals who have multiple partners? We want to *estimate a single population proportion*. This chapter concerns inference about one proportion. ■

EXAMPLE 18.2 Young adults living with their parents

A surprising number of young adults (ages 19 to 25) still live with their parents. A random sample of 2253 men and 2629 women in this age group found that 44% of the men but only 35% of the women lived at home. Is this significant evidence that the proportions living at home differ in the populations of all young men and all young women? We want to *compare two population proportions*. This is the topic of Chapter 19. ■

To do inference about a population mean μ, we use the mean $\overline{x}$ of a random sample from the population. The reasoning of inference starts with the sampling distribution of $\overline{x}$. Now we follow the same pattern, replacing means by proportions.

The sample proportion $\hat{p}$

We are interested in the unknown proportion p of a population that has some outcome. For convenience, call the outcome we are looking for a "success." In Example 18.1, the population is adult heterosexuals, and the parameter p is the proportion who have had more than one sexual partner in the past year. To estimate p, the National AIDS Behavioral Surveys used random dialing of telephone numbers to contact a sample of 2673 people. Of these, 170 said they had multiple sexual partners. The statistic that estimates the parameter p is the **sample proportion**

sample proportion

$$\hat{p} = \frac{\text{number of successes in the sample}}{\text{total number of individuals in the sample}}$$

$$= \frac{170}{2673} = 0.0636$$

Read the sample proportion $\hat{p}$ as "p-hat."

How good is the statistic $\hat{p}$ as an estimate of the parameter p? To find out, we ask, "What would happen if we took many samples?" The sampling distribution of $\hat{p}$ answers this question. Here are the facts.[2]

SAMPLING DISTRIBUTION OF A SAMPLE PROPORTION

Draw an SRS of size n from a large population that contains proportion p of successes. Let $\hat{p}$ be the **sample proportion** of successes,

$$\hat{p} = \frac{\text{number of successes in the sample}}{n}$$

Then:

■ The **mean** of the sampling distribution of $\hat{p}$ is p.
■ The **standard deviation** of the sampling distribution is

$$\sqrt{\frac{p(1-p)}{n}}$$

■ As the sample size increases, the sampling distribution of $\hat{p}$ becomes **approximately Normal**. That is, for large n, $\hat{p}$ has approximately the $N(p, \sqrt{p(1-p)/n})$ distribution.

Figure 18.1 summarizes these facts in a form that helps you recall the big idea of a sampling distribution. The mean of the sampling distribution of $\hat{p}$ is the true value of the population proportion p. That is, $\hat{p}$ is an unbiased estimator of p. The standard deviation of $\hat{p}$ gets smaller as the sample size n gets larger, so that estimation is likely to be more accurate when the sample is larger. As is the case for $\overline{x}$, the standard deviation gets smaller only at the rate $\sqrt{n}$. We need four times as many observations to cut the standard deviation in half.

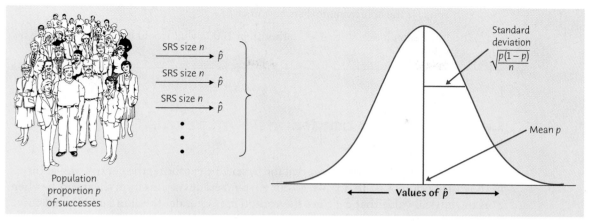

FIGURE 18.1

Select a large SRS from a population in which the proportion p are successes. The sampling distribution of the proportion $\hat{p}$ of successes in the sample is approximately Normal. The mean is p and the standard deviation is $\sqrt{p(1-p)/n}$.

EXAMPLE 18.3 Asking about risky behavior

Suppose that in fact 6% of all adult heterosexuals had more than one sexual partner in the past year (and would admit it when asked). The National AIDS Behavioral Surveys interviewed a random sample of 2673 people from this population. In many such samples, the proportion $\hat{p}$ of the 2673 people in the sample who had more than one partner would vary according to (approximately) the Normal distribution with mean 0.06 and standard deviation

$$\sqrt{\frac{p(1-p)}{n}} = \sqrt{\frac{(0.06)(0.94)}{2673}}$$

$$= \sqrt{0.0000211} = 0.00459 \;\blacksquare$$

APPLY YOUR KNOWLEDGE

18.1 Do college students pray? A study of religious practices among college students interviewed a sample of 127 students; 107 of the students said that they prayed at least once in a while.

(a) Describe the population and explain in words what the parameter p is.

(b) Give the numerical value of the statistic $\hat{p}$ that estimates p.

18.2 Spam. Are you getting more spam in your personal email account? Suppose that 40% of adult email users would say "Yes." A polling firm contacts an SRS of 1500 people chosen from this population. If the sample were repeated many times, what would be the range of sample proportions who say "Yes," according to the 99.7 part of the 68–95–99.7 rule?

18.3 Watching online video. About 75% of young adult Internet users (ages 18 to 29) watch online video. Suppose that a sample survey contacts an SRS of 1000 young adult Internet users and calculates the proportion $\hat{p}$ in this sample who watch online video.

(a) What is the approximate distribution of $\hat{p}$?

(b) If the sample size were 4000 rather than 1000, what would be the approximate distribution of $\hat{p}$?

Large-sample confidence intervals for a proportion

To obtain a level C confidence interval for p, start by capturing the central probability C in the distribution of $\hat{p}$. To do this, go out z^* standard deviations from the mean p, where z^* is the critical value that captures the central area C under the standard Normal curve. Figure 18.2 shows the result. The confidence interval is

$$\hat{p} \pm z^* \sqrt{\frac{p(1-p)}{n}}$$

This won't do, because we don't know the value of p. So we replace the standard deviation by the **standard error of $\hat{p}$**

standard error of $\hat{p}$

$$\sqrt{\frac{\hat{p}(1-\hat{p})}{n}}$$

to get the confidence interval

$$\hat{p} \pm z^* \sqrt{\frac{\hat{p}(1-\hat{p})}{n}}$$

Because the sampling distribution of $\hat{p}$ is only approximately Normal, we can trust this confidence interval only for large samples.

FIGURE 18.2
With probability C, $\hat{p}$ lies within $\pm z^* \sqrt{p(1-p)/n}$ of the unknown population proportion p. That is to say that in these samples p lies within $\pm z^* \sqrt{p(1-p)/n}$ of $\hat{p}$.

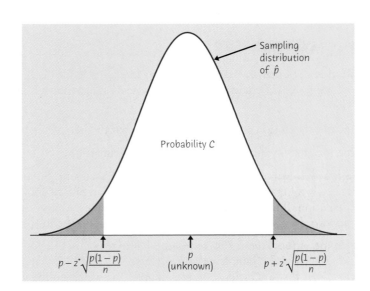

Sampling distribution of $\hat{p}$

Probability C

$$p - z^* \sqrt{\frac{p(1-p)}{n}} \qquad \begin{array}{c} p \\ \text{(unknown)} \end{array} \qquad p + z^* \sqrt{\frac{p(1-p)}{n}}$$

LARGE-SAMPLE CONFIDENCE INTERVAL FOR A
POPULATION PROPORTION

Draw an SRS of size n from a large population that contains an unknown proportion p of successes. An approximate level C **confidence interval for p** is

$$\hat{p} \pm z^* \sqrt{\frac{\hat{p}(1 - \hat{p})}{n}}$$

where z^* is the critical value for the standard Normal density curve with area C between $-z^*$ and z^*.

Use this interval only when the numbers of successes and failures in the sample are both 15 or greater.

EXAMPLE 18.4   **Estimating risky behavior**

The four-step process for any confidence interval is outlined on page 236.

STATE: The National AIDS Behavioral Surveys found that 170 of a sample of 2673 adult heterosexuals had multiple partners. That is,

$$\hat{p} = \frac{170}{2673} = 0.0636$$

What can we say about the population of all adult heterosexuals?

PLAN: We will give a 99% confidence interval to estimate the proportion p of all adult heterosexuals who have multiple partners.

SOLVE: First verify the conditions for inference:

- The sampling design was a complex random sample, and the survey used inference procedures for that design. The overall effect is close to an SRS, however.
- The sample is large enough: the numbers of successes (170) and failures (2503) in the sample are both much larger than 15.

The sample size condition is easily satisfied. The condition that the sample be an SRS is only approximately met.

A 99% confidence interval for the proportion p of all adult heterosexuals with multiple partners uses the standard Normal critical value $z^* = 2.576$. The confidence interval is

$$\hat{p} \pm z^* \sqrt{\frac{\hat{p}(1 - \hat{p})}{n}} = 0.0636 \pm 2.576 \sqrt{\frac{(0.0636)(0.9364)}{2673}}$$

$$= 0.0636 \pm 0.0122$$

$$= 0.0514 \text{ to } 0.0758$$

CONCLUDE: We are 99% confident that the percent of adult heterosexuals who have had more than one sexual partner in the past year lies between about 5.1% and 7.6%. ■

As usual, the practical problems of a large sample survey weaken our confidence in the AIDS survey's conclusions. Only households with landline telephones were contacted. About

30% of the people reached refused to cooperate. Some respondents may not have told the truth when asked about their sexual behavior. The survey report says that some response bias is probably present:

> It is more likely that the present figures are underestimates; some respondents may underreport their numbers of sexual partners and intravenous drug use because of embarrassment and fear of reprisal, or they may forget or not know details of their own or of their partner's HIV risk and their antibody testing history.[3]

Reading the report of a large study like the National AIDS Behavioral Surveys reminds us that statistics in practice involves much more than formulas for inference.

APPLY YOUR KNOWLEDGE

18.4 Teens' MySpace profiles. Over half of all American teens (ages 12 to 17 years) have an online profile, mainly on MySpace. A random sample of 487 teens with profiles found that 385 included photos of themselves.[4] Give a 95% confidence interval for the proportion p of all teens with profiles who include photos of themselves. Follow the four-step process as illustrated in Example 18.4.

18.5 How common is SAT coaching? A random sample of students who took the SAT college entrance examination twice found that 427 of the respondents had paid for coaching courses and that the remaining 2733 had not.[5] Give a 99% confidence interval for the proportion of coaching among students who retake the SAT. Follow the four-step process as illustrated in Example 18.4.

18.6 Canadian attitudes toward guns. Canadians support gun control more strongly than do Americans. A sample survey asked a random sample of 1505 adult Canadians, "Do you agree or disagree that all firearms should be registered?" Of the 1505 people in the sample, 1288 answered either "Agree strongly" or "Agree somewhat."[6]

(a) The survey dialed residential telephone numbers at random in all ten Canadian provinces (omitting the sparsely populated northern territories). Based on what you know about sample surveys, what is likely to be the biggest weakness in this survey?

(b) Nonetheless, act as if we have an SRS from adults in the Canadian provinces. Give a 95% confidence interval for the proportion who support registration of all firearms.

18.7 No confidence interval. In the National AIDS Behavioral Surveys sample of 2673 adult heterosexuals, 0.2% (that's 0.002 as a decimal fraction) had both received a blood transfusion and had a sexual partner from a group at high risk of AIDS. Explain why we can't use the large-sample confidence interval to estimate the proportion p in the population who share these two risk factors.

Choosing the sample size

In planning a study, we may want to choose a sample size that will allow us to estimate the parameter within a given margin of error. The margin of error in the large-sample confidence interval for p is

$$m = z^* \sqrt{\frac{\hat{p}(1 - \hat{p})}{n}}$$

Here z^* is the standard Normal critical value for the level of confidence we want. Because the margin of error involves the sample proportion of successes $\hat{p}$, we need to guess this value when choosing n. Call our guess p^*. There are two ways to get p^*:

1. Use a guess p^* based on a pilot study or on past experience with similar studies. You can do several calculations to cover the range of values of $\hat{p}$ you might get.
2. Use $p^* = 0.5$ as the guess. The margin of error m is largest when $\hat{p} = 0.5$, so this guess is conservative in the sense that, if we get any other $\hat{p}$ when we do our study, we will get a margin of error smaller than planned.

Once you have a guess p^*, the recipe for the margin of error can be solved to give the sample size n needed. Here is the result.

SAMPLE SIZE FOR DESIRED MARGIN OF ERROR

The level C confidence interval for a population proportion p will have margin of error approximately equal to a specified value m when the sample size is

$$n = \left(\frac{z^*}{m}\right)^2 p^*(1 - p^*)$$

where p^* is a guessed value for the sample proportion. The margin of error will always be less than or equal to m if you take the guess p^* to be 0.5.

You can use the conservative guess $p^* = 0.5$ if you expect the true $\hat{p}$ to be roughly between 0.3 and 0.7. If the true $\hat{p}$ is close to 0 or 1, using $p^* = 0.5$ as your guess will give a sample much larger than you need. Try to use a better guess from a pilot study when you suspect that $\hat{p}$ will be less than 0.3 or greater than 0.7.

EXAMPLE 18.5   **Planning a poll**

STATE: Gloria Chavez and Ronald Flynn are the candidates for mayor in a large city. You are planning a sample survey to determine what percent of the voters intend to vote for Chavez. You will contact an SRS of registered voters in the city. You want to estimate the proportion p of Chavez voters with 95% confidence and a margin of error no greater than 3%, or 0.03. How large a sample do you need?

PLAN: Find the sample size n needed for margin of error $m = 0.03$ and 95% confidence. The winner's share in all but the most lopsided elections is between 30% and 70% of the vote. You can use the guess $p^* = 0.5$.

SOLVE: The sample size you need is

$$n = \left(\frac{1.96}{0.03}\right)^2 (0.5)(1 - 0.5) = 1067.1$$

Round the result up to $n = 1068$. (Rounding down would give a margin of error slightly greater than 0.03.)

CONCLUDE: An SRS of 1068 registered voters is adequate for margin of error ±3%. ∎

As usual, a smaller margin of error calls for a larger sample. If you want a 2.5% margin of error rather than 3%, then (after rounding up)

$$n = \left(\frac{1.96}{0.025}\right)^2 (0.5)(1 - 0.5) = 1537$$

APPLY YOUR KNOWLEDGE

18.8 Canadians and doctor-assisted suicide. A Gallup Poll asked a sample of Canadian adults if they thought the law should allow doctors to end the life of a patient who is in great pain and near death if the patient makes a request in writing. The poll included 270 people in Québec, 221 of whom agreed that doctor-assisted suicide should be allowed.[7]

(a) What is the margin of error of the large-sample 95% confidence interval for the proportion of all Québec adults who would allow doctor-assisted suicide?

(b) How large a sample is needed to get the common ±3 percentage point margin of error? Use the previous sample as a pilot study to get p^*.

18.9 Can you taste PTC? PTC is a substance that has a strong bitter taste for some people and is tasteless for others. The ability to taste PTC is inherited. About 75% of Italians can taste PTC, for example. You want to estimate the proportion of Americans with at least one Italian grandparent who can taste PTC. Starting with the 75% estimate for Italians, how large a sample must you collect in order to estimate the proportion of PTC tasters within ±0.04 with 90% confidence?

Significance tests for a proportion

The test statistic for the null hypothesis H_0: $p = p_0$ is the sample proportion $\hat{p}$ standardized using the value p_0 specified by H_0,

$$z = \frac{\hat{p} - p_0}{\sqrt{\dfrac{p_0(1 - p_0)}{n}}}$$

This z statistic has approximately the standard Normal distribution when H_0 is true. P-values therefore come from the standard Normal distribution. Here is the procedure for tests.

SIGNIFICANCE TESTS FOR A PROPORTION

Draw an SRS of size n from a large population that contains an unknown proportion p of successes. To **test the hypothesis** H_0: $p = p_0$, compute the z statistic

$$z = \frac{\hat{p} - p_0}{\sqrt{\dfrac{p_0(1 - p_0)}{n}}}$$

Find P-values from the standard Normal distribution.

Use this test when the sample size n is so large that both np_0 and $n(1 - p_0)$ are 10 or more.[8]

EXAMPLE 18.6 **Are boys more likely?**

The four-step process for any significance test is outlined on page 246.

Blaine Harrington III/CORBIS

STATE: We hear that newborn babies are more likely to be boys than girls. Is this true? A random sample found 13,173 boys among 25,468 children.[9] The sample proportion of boys was

$$\hat{p} = \frac{13{,}173}{25{,}468} = 0.5172$$

Boys do make up more than half of the sample, but of course we don't expect a perfect 50-50 split in a random sample. Is this sample evidence that boys are more common than girls in the entire population?

PLAN: Take p to be the proportion of boys among all children of American mothers. We want to test the hypotheses

$$H_0: p = 0.5$$
$$H_a: p > 0.5$$

SOLVE: The conditions for inference are met, so we can go on to the z test statistic:

$$z = \frac{\hat{p} - p_0}{\sqrt{\dfrac{p_0(1 - p_0)}{n}}}$$

$$= \frac{0.5172 - 0.5}{\sqrt{\dfrac{(0.5)(0.5)}{25{,}468}}} = 5.49$$

The P-value is the area under the standard Normal curve to the right of $z = 5.49$. Figure 18.3 reminds us that this area is very small. Table C shows that $P < 0.0005$ and software says that P is about 0.00000002.

CONCLUDE: There is very strong evidence that more than half of newborns are boys ($P < 0.0005$). ∎

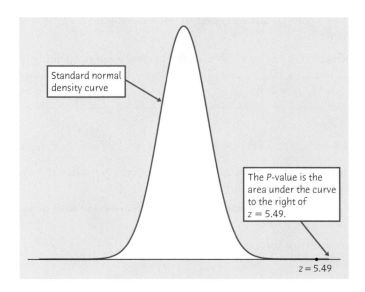

Standard normal density curve

The P-value is the area under the curve to the right of $z = 5.49$.

$z = 5.49$

FIGURE 18.3
The one-sided P-value for Example 18.6 is the area under the standard Normal curve to the right of $z = 5.49$.

EXAMPLE 18.7 **Estimating the chance of a boy**

A 99% confidence interval for the proportion p of boys in the population of all newborns is

$$\hat{p} \pm z^* \sqrt{\frac{\hat{p}(1-\hat{p})}{n}} = 0.5172 \pm 2.576 \sqrt{\frac{(0.5172)(0.4828)}{25,468}}$$

$$= 0.5172 \pm 0.0081$$

$$= 0.5091 \text{ to } 0.5253$$

We are 99% confident that between about 51% and 52.5% of children are boys. The confidence interval is more informative than the test in Example 18.6, which tells us only that more than half are boys. ■

APPLY YOUR KNOWLEDGE

18.10 Spinning pennies. Spinning a coin, unlike tossing it, may not give heads and tails equal probabilities. I spun a penny 200 times and got 83 heads. How significant is this evidence against equal probabilities? Follow the four-step process as illustrated in Example 18.6.

18.11 Vote for the best face? We often judge other people by their faces. It appears that some people judge candidates for elected office by their faces. Psychologists showed head-and-shoulders photos of the two main candidates in 32 races for the U.S. Senate to many subjects (dropping subjects who recognized one of the candidates) to see which candidate was rated "more competent" based on nothing but the photos. On election day, the candidates whose faces looked more competent won 22 of the 32 contests.[10] If faces don't influence voting, half of all races in the long run should be won by the candidate with the better face. Is there evidence that the candidate with the better face wins more than half the time? Follow the four-step process as illustrated in Example 18.6.

18.12 No test. Explain why we can't use the z test for a proportion in these situations:

(a) You toss a coin 10 times in order to test the hypothesis $H_0: p = 0.5$ that the coin is balanced.

(b) A college president says, "99% of the alumni support my firing of Coach Boggs." You contact an SRS of 200 of the college's 15,000 living alumni to test the hypothesis $H_0: p = 0.99$.

CHAPTER 18 SUMMARY

■ Tests and confidence intervals for a population proportion p when the data are an SRS of size n are based on the **sample proportion** $\hat{p}$.

■ When n is large, $\hat{p}$ has approximately the Normal distribution with mean p and standard deviation $\sqrt{p(1-p)/n}$.

■ The level C **confidence interval for** p is

$$\hat{p} \pm z^* \sqrt{\frac{\hat{p}(1-\hat{p})}{n}}$$

where z^* is the critical value for the standard Normal curve with area C between $-z^*$ and z^*. Use this interval only when the sample is so large that the counts of successes and failures are both 15 or greater.

- The **sample size** needed to obtain a confidence interval with approximate margin of error m for a population proportion is

$$n = \left(\frac{z^*}{m}\right)^2 p^*(1 - p^*)$$

where p^* is a guessed value for the sample proportion $\hat{p}$, and z^* is the standard Normal critical point for the level of confidence you want. If you use $p^* = 0.5$ in this formula, the margin of error of the interval will be less than or equal to m no matter what the value of $\hat{p}$ is.

- **Significance tests for H_0: $p = p_0$** are based on the z statistic

$$z = \frac{\hat{p} - p_0}{\sqrt{\dfrac{p_0(1 - p_0)}{n}}}$$

with P-values calculated from the standard Normal distribution. Use this test in practice when $np_0 \geq 10$ and $n(1 - p_0) \geq 10$.

CHECK YOUR SKILLS

18.13 An opinion poll asks an SRS of 100 college seniors how they view their job prospects. In all, 53 say "Good." The sample proportion $\hat{p}$ who said "Good" is
(a) 53.   (b) 1.89.   (c) 0.53.

18.14 Based on the sample in Exercise 18.13, the 95% confidence interval for estimating the proportion of all college seniors who think their job prospects are good is
(a) 0.53 ± 0.0049.   (b) 0.53 ± 0.050.   (c) 0.53 ± 0.098.

18.15 The sample survey in Exercise 18.13 actually called 130 seniors, but 30 of the seniors refused to answer. This nonresponse could cause the survey result to be in error. The error due to nonresponse
(a) is in addition to the margin of error found in Exercise 18.14.
(b) is included in the margin of error found in Exercise 18.14.
(c) can be ignored because it isn't random.

18.16 Does the poll in Exercise 18.13 give reason to conclude that more than half of all seniors think their job prospects are good? The hypotheses for a test to answer this question are
(a) H_0: $p = 0.5$, H_a: $p > 0.5$.
(b) H_0: $p > 0.5$, H_a: $p = 0.5$.
(c) H_0: $p = 0.5$, H_a: $p \neq 0.5$.

18.17 The value of the z statistic for the test of the previous exercise is about
(a) $z = 12$.   (b) $z = 6$.   (c) $z = 0.6$.

18.18 *Sports Illustrated* once asked a random sample of Division I college athletes, "Do you believe performance-enhancing drugs are a problem in college sports?" How many athletes must be interviewed to estimate the proportion concerned about use of drugs within ± 0.02 with 95% confidence? Use 0.5 as the conservative guess for p.
(a) $n = 25$ (b) $n = 1225$ (c) $n = 2401$

18.19 A Gallup Poll found that 28% of American adults expect to inherit money or valuable possessions from a relative. The poll's margin of error was 3%. This means that
(a) the poll used a method that gets an answer within 3% of the truth about the population 95% of the time.
(b) we can be sure that the percent of all adults who expect an inheritance is between 25% and 31%.
(c) if Gallup takes another poll using the same method, the results of the second poll will lie between 25% and 31%.

CHAPTER 18 EXERCISES

18.20 Reporting cheating. Students are reluctant to report cheating by other students. A student project put this question to an SRS of 172 undergraduates at a large university: "You witness two students cheating on a quiz. Do you go to the professor?" Only 19 answered "Yes."[11] Give a 95% confidence interval for the proportion of all undergraduates at this university who would report cheating.

18.21 Do smokers know that smoking is bad for them? The Harris Poll asked a sample of smokers, "Do you believe that smoking will probably shorten your life, or not?" Of the 1010 people in the sample, 848 said "Yes."

(a) Harris called residential telephone numbers at random in an attempt to contact an SRS of smokers. Based on what you know about national sample surveys, what is likely to be the biggest weakness in the survey?

(b) We will nonetheless act as if the people interviewed are an SRS of smokers. Give a 95% confidence interval for the percent of smokers who agree that smoking will probably shorten their lives.

18.22 Do college students pray? Social scientists asked 127 undergraduate students "from courses in psychology and communications" about prayer and found that 107 prayed at least a few times a year.[12]

(a) To use any inference procedure, we must be willing to regard these 127 students, as far as their religious behavior goes, as an SRS from the population of all undergraduate students. Do you think it is reasonable to do this? Why or why not?

(b) Does the sample size meet the conditions for using the large-sample confidence interval?

(c) If we act as if the sample is an SRS, what is the 99% confidence interval for the proportion p of all students who pray?

18.23 Harris announces a margin of error. Exercise 18.21 describes a Harris Poll survey of 1010 smokers. Harris announces a margin of error of ±3 percentage points for all samples of about this size. Opinion polls announce the margin of error for 95% confidence.

(a) What is the actual margin of error (in percent) for the confidence interval from this sample?

(b) The margin of error is largest when $\hat{p} = 0.5$. What would the margin of error (in percent) be if the sample had resulted in $\hat{p} = 0.5$?

(c) Why do you think that Harris announces a ±3% margin of error for all samples of about this size?

18.24 Canadian TV for Canadians? During hearings on the regulation of cable and satellite TV in Canada, the polling firm Pollara contacted a sample of 1200 Canadian adults who subscribe to a cable or satellite TV service. When asked whether they agreed that less regulation would probably reduce Canadian programming, 888 of the respondents agreed. (American programming would be less expensive for the cable companies.) Give a 90% confidence interval for the proportion p of all Canadian cable/satellite subscribers who think that deregulation would reduce Canadian programming.

18.25 Detecting genetically modified soybeans. Most soybeans grown in the United States and Canada are genetically modified (GM). Because some nations do not accept

Wesley Hitt/Alamy

GM foods, grain-handling facilities routinely test soybean shipments for the presence of GM beans. In a study of the accuracy of these tests, researchers submitted shipments of soybeans containing 1% of GM beans to 23 randomly selected facilities. Eighteen detected the GM beans.[13] Explain why we can't use the large-sample confidence interval to estimate the percent of all grain-handling facilities that will correctly detect 1% of GM beans in a shipment.

18.26 Shrubs that survive fires. Some shrubs have the useful ability to resprout from their roots after their tops are destroyed. One study of resprouting took place in a dry area of Mexico.[14] The investigators clipped the tops of samples of several species of shrubs. In some cases, they also applied a propane torch to the stumps to simulate a fire. Of 12 specimens of the shrub *Krameria cytisoides*, 5 resprouted after fire. Explain why we can't use the large-sample confidence interval to estimate the proportion of all shrubs of this species that would resprout.

18.27 Running red lights. A random digit dialing telephone survey of 880 drivers asked, "Recalling the last ten traffic lights you drove through, how many of them were red when you entered the intersections?" Of the 880 respondents, 171 admitted that at least one light had been red.[15]

(a) Give a 95% confidence interval for the proportion of all drivers who ran one or more of the last ten red lights they met.

(b) Nonresponse is a practical problem for this survey—only 21.6% of calls that reached a live person were completed. Another practical problem is that people may not give truthful answers. What is the likely direction of the bias: do you think more or fewer than 171 of the 880 respondents really ran a red light? Why?

18.28 The IRS plans an SRS. The Internal Revenue Service plans to examine an SRS of individual federal income tax returns from each state. One variable of interest is the proportion of returns claiming itemized deductions. The total number of tax returns in a state varies from more than 15 million in California to fewer than 250,000 in Wyoming.

(a) Will the margin of error for estimating the population proportion change from state to state if an SRS of 2000 tax returns is selected in each state? Explain your answer.

(b) Will the margin of error change from state to state if an SRS of 1% of all tax returns is selected in each state? Explain your answer.

18.29 Customer satisfaction. An automobile manufacturer would like to know what proportion of its customers are not satisfied with the service provided by the local dealer. The customer relations department will survey a random sample of customers and compute a 99% confidence interval for the proportion who are not satisfied.
(a) Past studies suggest that this proportion will be about 0.2. Find the sample size needed if the margin of error of the confidence interval is to be about 0.015.
(b) When the sample is actually contacted, 10% of the sample say they are not satisfied. What is the margin of error of the 99% confidence interval?

18.30 Surveying students. You are planning a survey of students at a large university to determine what proportion favor an increase in student fees to support an expansion of the student newspaper. Using records provided by the registrar, you can select a random sample of students. You will ask each student in the sample whether he or she is in favor of the proposed increase. Your budget will allow a sample of 100 students.
(a) For a sample of size 100, construct a table of the margins of error for 95% confidence intervals when $\hat{p}$ takes the values 0.1, 0.2, 0.3, 0.4, 0.5, 0.6, 0.7, 0.8, and 0.9.
(b) A former editor of the student newspaper offers to provide funds for a sample of size 500. Repeat the margin of error calculations in (a) for the larger sample size. Then write a short thank-you note to the former editor describing how the larger sample size will improve the results of the survey.

In responding to Exercises 18.31 to 18.36, follow the **Plan, Solve,** *and* **Conclude** *steps of the four-step process.*

18.31 Student drinking. The College Alcohol Study interviewed a sample of 14,941 college students about their drinking habits. The overall effect of the sample design is close to an SRS of students. The response rate was more than 60%. This is quite good for a national sample, though nonresponse is as usual the biggest weakness of this survey. Of the students in the sample, 10,010 supported cracking down on underage drinking.[16] Estimate with 99% confidence the proportion of all college students who feel this way.

18.32 Condom usage. The National AIDS Behavioral Surveys (Example 18.1) also interviewed a sample of adults in the cities where AIDS is most common. This sample included 803 heterosexuals who reported having more than one sexual partner in the past year. We can consider this an SRS of size 803 from the population of all heterosexuals in high-risk cities who have multiple partners. These people risk infection with the AIDS virus. Yet 304 of the respondents said they never use condoms. Is this strong evidence that more than one-third of this population never use condoms?

18.33 Opinions about evolution. A sample survey funded by the National Science Foundation asked a random sample of American adults about biological evolution.[17] One question asked subjects to answer "True," "False," or "Not sure" to the statement "Human beings, as we know them today, developed from earlier species of animals." Of the 1484 respondents, 594 said "True." What can you say with 95% confidence about the percent of all American adults who think that humans developed from earlier species of animals?

18.34 Seat belt use. The proportion of drivers who use seat belts depends on things like age, gender, ethnicity, and local law. As part of a broader study, investigators observed a random sample of 117 female Hispanic drivers in Boston; 68 of these drivers were wearing seat belts.[18] Give a 95% confidence interval for the proportion of all female Hispanic drivers in Boston who wear seat belts.

18.35 Opinions about evolution, continued. Does the sample in Exercise 18.33 give good evidence to support the claim that "Fewer than half of American adults think that humans developed from earlier species of animals"?

18.36 Seat belt use, continued. Do the data in Exercise 18.34 give good reason to conclude that more than half of Hispanic female drivers in Boston wear seat belts?

18.37 Seat belt use: planning a study. How large a sample would be needed to obtain margin of error ±0.05 in the study of seat belt use among Hispanic females? Use the $\hat{p}$ from Exercise 18.34 as your guess for the unknown p.

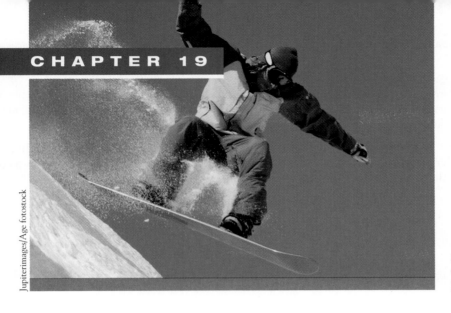

Jupiterimages/Age fotostock

Skiers and snowboarders should wear helmets. The data in Exercise 19.5 show why.

CHAPTER 19

Comparing Two Proportions

In a **two-sample problem,** we want to compare two populations or the responses to two treatments based on two independent samples. When the comparison involves the *means* of two populations, we use the two-sample *t* methods of Chapter 17. Now we turn to methods to compare the *proportions* of successes in two populations.

Two-sample problems: proportions

We will use notation similar to that used in our study of two-sample *t* statistics. The groups we want to compare are Population 1 and Population 2. We have a separate SRS from each population or responses from two treatments in a randomized comparative experiment. A subscript shows which group a parameter or statistic describes. Here is our notation:

Population	Population proportion	Sample size	Sample proportion
1	p_1	n_1	$\hat{p}_1$
2	p_2	n_2	$\hat{p}_2$

We compare the populations by doing inference about the difference $p_1 - p_2$ between the population proportions. The statistic that estimates this difference is the difference between the two sample proportions, $\hat{p}_1 - \hat{p}_2$.

EXAMPLE 19.1 **Young adults living with their parents**

STATE: A surprising number of young adults (ages 19 to 25) still live in their parents' home. A random sample by the National Institutes of Health included 2253 men and

IN THIS CHAPTER
WE COVER...

- Two-sample problems: proportions

- The sampling distribution of a difference between proportions

- Large-sample confidence intervals for comparing proportions

- Using technology

- Significance tests for comparing proportions

2629 women in this age group.[1] The survey found that 986 of the men and 923 of the women lived with their parents. How large is the difference between the proportions of young men and young women who live with their parents?

PLAN: Take young men to be Population 1 and young women to be Population 2. The population proportions who live in their parents' home are p_1 for men and p_2 for women. We will use a confidence interval to estimate the difference $p_1 - p_2$.

SOLVE: Inference about population proportions is based on the sample proportions

$$\hat{p}_1 = \frac{986}{2253} = 0.4376 \quad \text{(men)}$$

$$\hat{p}_2 = \frac{923}{2629} = 0.3511 \quad \text{(women)}$$

We see that about 44% of the men but only about 35% of the women lived with their parents. To estimate $p_1 - p_2$, start from the difference of sample proportions

$$\hat{p}_1 - \hat{p}_2 = 0.4376 - 0.3511 = 0.0865$$

To complete the *Solve* step, we must know how this difference behaves. ■

The sampling distribution of a difference between proportions

To use $\hat{p}_1 - \hat{p}_2$ for inference, we must know its sampling distribution. Here are the facts we need.

SAMPLING DISTRIBUTION OF A DIFFERENCE BETWEEN PROPORTIONS

Draw an SRS of size n_1 from a large population having proportion p_1 of successes, and draw an independent SRS of size n_2 from another large population having proportion p_2 of successes. For the difference $\hat{p}_1 - \hat{p}_2$ between the proportions of successes in the two samples,

- The **mean** of the sampling distribution is $p_1 - p_2$.
- The **standard deviation** of the sampling distribution is

$$\sqrt{\frac{p_1(1 - p_1)}{n_1} + \frac{p_2(1 - p_2)}{n_2}}$$

- When the samples are large, the distribution of $\hat{p}_1 - \hat{p}_2$ is **approximately Normal.**

Figure 19.1 displays the distribution of $\hat{p}_1 - \hat{p}_2$. The difference of sample proportions is an unbiased estimator of the difference of population proportions. The standard deviation of $\hat{p}_1 - \hat{p}_2$ involves the unknown parameters p_1 and p_2. Just as in the previous chapter, we must replace these by estimates in order to do inference.

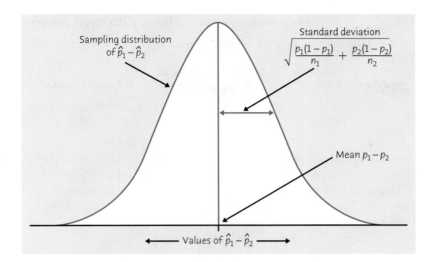

FIGURE 19.1
Select independent SRSs from two populations having proportions of successes p_1 and p_2. The proportions of successes in the two samples are $\hat{p}_1$ and $\hat{p}_2$. When the samples are large, the sampling distribution of the difference $\hat{p}_1 - \hat{p}_2$ is approximately Normal.

Large-sample confidence intervals for comparing proportions

To obtain a confidence interval, replace the population proportions p_1 and p_2 in the standard deviation by the sample proportions. The result is the **standard error** of the statistic $\hat{p}_1 - \hat{p}_2$:   *standard error*

$$SE = \sqrt{\frac{\hat{p}_1(1 - \hat{p}_1)}{n_1} + \frac{\hat{p}_2(1 - \hat{p}_2)}{n_2}}$$

The confidence interval has the same form we met in the previous chapter:

$$\text{estimate} \pm z^* SE_{\text{estimate}}$$

LARGE-SAMPLE CONFIDENCE INTERVAL FOR COMPARING TWO PROPORTIONS

Draw an SRS of size n_1 from a large population having proportion p_1 of successes and draw an independent SRS of size n_2 from another large population having proportion p_2 of successes. When n_1 and n_2 are large, an approximate level C **confidence interval for $p_1 - p_2$** is

$$(\hat{p}_1 - \hat{p}_2) \pm z^* SE$$

In this formula the standard error SE of $\hat{p}_1 - \hat{p}_2$ is

$$SE = \sqrt{\frac{\hat{p}_1(1 - \hat{p}_1)}{n_1} + \frac{\hat{p}_2(1 - \hat{p}_2)}{n_2}}$$

and z^* is the critical value for the standard Normal density curve with area C between $-z^*$ and z^*.

Use this interval only when the numbers of successes and failures are each 10 or more in both samples.

EXAMPLE 19.2 **Men versus women living with their parents**

We can now complete Example 19.1. Here is a summary of the basic information:

Population	Population description	Sample size	Number of successes	Sample proportion
1	men	$n_1 = 2253$	986	$\hat{p}_1 = 986/2253 = 0.4376$
2	women	$n_2 = 2629$	923	$\hat{p}_2 = 923/2629 = 0.3511$

SOLVE: We will give a 95% confidence interval for $p_1 - p_2$, the difference between the proportions of young men and young women who live with their parents. To check that the large-sample confidence interval is safe, look at the counts of successes and failures in the two samples. All of these four counts are much larger than 10, so the large-sample method will be accurate. The standard error is

$$SE = \sqrt{\frac{\hat{p}_1(1 - \hat{p}_1)}{n_1} + \frac{\hat{p}_2(1 - \hat{p}_2)}{n_2}}$$

$$= \sqrt{\frac{(0.4376)(0.5624)}{2253} + \frac{(0.3511)(0.6489)}{2629}}$$

$$= \sqrt{0.0001959} = 0.01400$$

The 95% confidence interval is

$$(\hat{p}_1 - \hat{p}_2) \pm z^*SE = (0.4376 - 0.3511) \pm (1.960)(0.01400)$$

$$= 0.0865 \pm 0.0274$$

$$= 0.059 \text{ to } 0.114$$

CONCLUDE: We are 95% confident that the percent of young men living with their parents is between 5.9 and 11.4 percentage points higher than the percent of young women who live with their parents. ■

The sample survey in this example selected a single random sample of young adults, not two separate random samples of young men and young women. To get two samples, we divided the single sample by sex. This means that we did not know the two sample sizes n_1 and n_2 until after the data were in hand. The two-sample z procedures for comparing proportions are valid in such situations. This is an important fact about these methods.

Using technology

Figure 19.2 displays output for Example 19.2 from a graphing calculator and a statistical software program. As usual, you can understand the output even without knowledge of the program that produced it. Minitab gives the test as well as the confidence interval, confirming that the difference between men and women is highly significant. Excel spreadsheet output is not shown because Excel lacks menu items for inference about proportions. You must use the spreadsheet's formula capability to program the confidence interval or test statistic and then to find the P-value of a test.

Texas Instruments Graphing Calculator

```
2-PropZInt
 (.05912,.11399)
 p̂1=.437638704
 p̂2=.3510840624
 n1=2253
 n2=2629
```

Minitab

```
 Session                                        _ □ ✕

 Test and CI for Two Proportions

 Sample    X     N    Sample p
 1        986   2253   0.437639
 2        923   2629   0.351084

 Difference = p (1) - p (2)
 Estimate for difference: 0.0865546
 95% CI for difference: (0.0591225, 0.113987)
 Test for difference = 0 (vs not = 0): Z = 6.18   P-Value = 0.000
```

FIGURE 19.2
Output from a graphing calculator and Minitab for the 95% confidence interval of Example 19.2.

APPLY YOUR KNOWLEDGE

19.1 Who uses instant messaging? Younger people use online instant messaging (IM) more often than older people. A random sample of IM users found that 73 of the 158 people in the sample aged 18 to 27 said they used IM more often than email. In the 28 to 39 age group, 26 of 143 people used IM more often than email.[2] Give a 95% confidence interval for the difference between the proportions of IM users in these age groups who use IM more often than email. Follow the four-step process as illustrated in Examples 19.1 and 19.2.

19.2 Listening to rap. Rap music is more popular among young blacks than among young whites. A sample survey compared 634 randomly chosen blacks aged 15 to 25 with 567 randomly selected whites in the same age group. It found that 368 of the blacks and 130 of the whites listened to rap music every day.[3] Give a 90% confidence interval for the difference between the proportions of black and white young people who listen to rap every day. Follow the four-step process as illustrated in Examples 19.1 and 19.2.

19.3 High school students in action. A government survey randomly selected 6889 female high school students and 7028 male high school students.[4] Of these students, 1915 females and 3078 males met recommended levels of physical activity. (These levels are quite high: at least 60 minutes of activity that makes you breathe hard on at least 5 of the past 7 days.) Give a 99% confidence interval for the difference between the proportions of all female and male high school students who meet the recommended levels of activity.

Significance tests for comparing proportions

An observed difference between two sample proportions can reflect an actual difference between the populations, or it may just be due to chance variation in random sampling. Significance tests help us decide if the effect we see in the samples is really there in the populations. The null hypothesis says that there is no difference between the two populations:

$$H_0: p_1 = p_2$$

The alternative hypothesis says what kind of difference we expect.

EXAMPLE 19.3 Choosing a mate

STATE: "Would you marry a person from a lower social class than your own?" Researchers asked this question of a sample of 385 black, never-married students at two historically black colleges in the South. We will consider this to be an SRS of black students at historically black colleges. Of the 149 men in the sample, 91 said "Yes." Among the 236 women, 117 said "Yes."[5] Is there reason to think that different proportions of men and women in this student population would be willing to marry beneath their class?

PLAN: Call the population proportions p_1 for men and p_2 for women. We had no direction for the difference in mind before looking at the data, so we have a two-sided alternative:

$$H_0: p_1 = p_2$$
$$H_a: p_1 \neq p_2$$

SOLVE: The men and women in a single SRS can be treated as if they were separate SRSs of men and women students. The sample proportions who would marry someone from a lower social class are

$$\hat{p}_1 = \frac{91}{149} = 0.611 \quad \text{(men)}$$

$$\hat{p}_2 = \frac{117}{236} = 0.496 \quad \text{(women)}$$

That is, about 61% of the men but only about 50% of the women would marry beneath their class. Is this apparent difference statistically significant? To continue the solution, we must learn the proper test. ■

To do a test, standardize the difference between the sample proportions $\hat{p}_1 - \hat{p}_2$ to get a z statistic. If H_0 is true, both samples come from populations in which the same unknown proportion p would marry someone from a lower social class. We therefore combine the two samples to estimate this single p, rather than estimating p_1 and p_2 separately. Call *pooled sample proportion* this the **pooled sample proportion.** It is

$$\hat{p} = \frac{\text{number of successes in both samples combined}}{\text{number of individuals in both samples combined}}$$

Use $\hat{p}$ in place of both $\hat{p}_1$ and $\hat{p}_2$ in the expression for the standard error SE of $\hat{p}_1 - \hat{p}_2$ to get a z statistic that has the standard Normal distribution when H_0 is true. Here is the test.

Draw an SRS of size n_1 from a large population having proportion p_1 of successes, and draw an independent SRS of size n_2 from another large population having proportion p_2 of successes. To **test the hypothesis H_0: $p_1 = p_2$**, first find the pooled proportion $\hat{p}$ of successes in both samples combined. Then compute the z statistic

$$z = \frac{\hat{p}_1 - \hat{p}_2}{\sqrt{\hat{p}(1 - \hat{p})\left(\dfrac{1}{n_1} + \dfrac{1}{n_2}\right)}}$$

Find P-values from the standard Normal distribution.

Use this test when the counts of successes and failures are each 5 or more in both samples.[6]

EXAMPLE 19.4 **Choosing a mate, continued**

SOLVE: The data come from an SRS and the counts of successes and failures are all much larger than 5. The pooled proportion of students who would marry beneath their own social class is

$$\hat{p} = \frac{\text{number of "Yes" responses among men and women combined}}{\text{number of men and women combined}}$$

$$= \frac{91 + 117}{149 + 236}$$

$$= \frac{208}{385} = 0.5403$$

The z test statistic is

$$z = \frac{\hat{p}_1 - \hat{p}_2}{\sqrt{\hat{p}(1 - \hat{p})\left(\dfrac{1}{n_1} + \dfrac{1}{n_2}\right)}}$$

$$= \frac{0.611 - 0.496}{\sqrt{(0.5403)(0.4597)\left(\dfrac{1}{149} + \dfrac{1}{236}\right)}}$$

$$= \frac{0.115}{0.05215} = 2.205$$

The two-sided P-value is the area under the standard Normal curve more than 2.205 distant from 0. Figure 19.3 shows this area. Software tells us that $P = 0.0275$.

Without software, you can compare $z = 2.205$ with the bottom row of Table C (standard Normal critical values) to approximate P. It lies between the critical values 2.054 and 2.326 for two-sided P-values 0.04 and 0.02.

z^*	2.054	2.326
Two-sided P	.04	.02

CONCLUDE: There is good evidence ($P < 0.04$) that men are more likely than women to say they will marry someone from a lower social class. ■

FIGURE 19.3

The *P*-value for the two-sided test of Example 19.4.

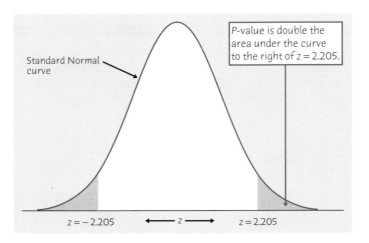

Standard Normal curve

P-value is double the area under the curve to the right of $z = 2.205$.

$z = -2.205$ ← z → $z = 2.205$

APPLY YOUR KNOWLEDGE

19.4 Did the random assignment work? A large clinical trial of the effect of diet on breast cancer assigned women at random to either a normal diet or a low-fat diet. To check that the random assignment did produce comparable groups, we can compare the two groups at the start of the study. Ask if there is a family history of breast cancer: 3396 of the 19,541 women in the low-fat group and 4929 of the 29,294 women in the control group said "Yes."[7] If the random assignment worked well, there should *not* be a significant difference in the proportions with a family history of breast cancer. How significant is the observed difference? Follow the four-step process as illustrated in Examples 19.3 and 19.4.

19.5 Protecting skiers and snowboarders. Most alpine skiers and snowboarders do not use helmets. Do helmets reduce the risk of head injuries? A study in Norway compared skiers and snowboarders who suffered head injuries with a control group who were not injured. Of 578 injured subjects, 96 had worn a helmet. Of the 2992 in the control group, 656 wore helmets.[8] Is helmet use less common among skiers and snowboarders who have head injuries? (Note that this is an observational study that compares injured and uninjured subjects. An experiment that assigned subjects to helmet and no-helmet groups would be more convincing.)

Jupiterimages/Age fotostock

19.6 Canada versus the United States: health care. The Joint Canada/United States Survey of Health asked the same questions of random samples of American and Canadian adults. Respondents who had received health care services within the past 12 months were asked, "Overall, how satisfied were you with the way health care services were provided?" Here are some data from the survey:[9]

	Canada	United States
Complete sample	3505	5183
Health care in past 12 months	2618	3980
Very satisfied with care	1144	2120

Is there a significant difference between the proportions of Americans and Canadians who are very satisfied with health care they have recently received?

CHAPTER 19 SUMMARY

- The data in a **two-sample problem** are two independent SRSs, each drawn from a separate population.

- Tests and confidence intervals to compare the proportions p_1 and p_2 of successes in the two populations are based on the difference $\hat{p}_1 - \hat{p}_2$ between the sample proportions of successes in the two SRSs.

- When the sample sizes n_1 and n_2 are large, the sampling distribution of $\hat{p}_1 - \hat{p}_2$ is close to Normal with mean $p_1 - p_2$.

- The level C **large-sample confidence interval for $p_1 - p_2$** is

$$(\hat{p}_1 - \hat{p}_2) \pm z^* SE$$

where the **standard error** of $\hat{p}_1 - \hat{p}_2$ is

$$SE = \sqrt{\frac{\hat{p}_1(1 - \hat{p}_1)}{n_1} + \frac{\hat{p}_2(1 - \hat{p}_2)}{n_2}}$$

and z^* is a standard Normal critical value. Use this interval only if the counts of successes and failures in both samples are 10 or greater.

- **Significance tests for $H_0: p_1 = p_2$** use the **pooled sample proportion**

$$\hat{p} = \frac{\text{number of successes in both samples combined}}{\text{number of individuals in both samples combined}}$$

and the z statistic

$$z = \frac{\hat{p}_1 - \hat{p}_2}{\sqrt{\hat{p}(1 - \hat{p})\left(\frac{1}{n_1} + \frac{1}{n_2}\right)}}$$

P-values come from the standard Normal distribution. Use this test when there are 5 or more successes and 5 or more failures in both samples.

CHECK YOUR SKILLS

A sample survey interviews SRSs of 500 female college students and 550 male college students. Each student is asked if he or she worked for pay last summer. In all, 410 of the women and 484 of the men say "Yes." Exercises 19.7 to 19.11 are based on this survey.

19.7 Take p_M and p_F to be the proportions of all college males and females who worked last summer. We conjectured before seeing the data that men are more likely to work. The hypotheses to be tested are
(a) $H_0: p_M = p_F$ versus $H_a: p_M \neq p_F$.
(b) $H_0: p_M = p_F$ versus $H_a: p_M > p_F$.
(c) $H_0: p_M = p_F$ versus $H_a: p_M < p_F$.

19.8 The sample proportions of college males and females who worked last summer are about
(a) $\hat{p}_M = 0.88$ and $\hat{p}_F = 0.82$.

(b) $\hat{p}_M = 0.82$ and $\hat{p}_F = 0.88$.
(c) $\hat{p}_M = 0.75$ and $\hat{p}_F = 0.97$.

19.9 The pooled sample proportion who worked last summer is about
(a) $\hat{p} = 1.70$. (b) $\hat{p} = 0.89$. (c) $\hat{p} = 0.85$.

19.10 The z statistic for a test comparing the proportions of college men and women who worked last summer is about
(a) $z = 2.66$. (b) $z = 2.72$. (c) $z = 3.10$.

19.11 The 95% large-sample confidence interval for the difference $p_M - p_F$ in the proportions of college men and women who worked last summer is about
(a) 0.06 ± 0.00095. (b) 0.06 ± 0.043. (c) 0.06 ± 0.036.

19.12 In an experiment to learn if substance M can help restore memory, the brains of 20 rats were treated to damage their memories. The rats were trained to run a maze. After a day, 10 rats were given M and 7 of them succeeded in the maze; only 2 of the 10 control rats were successful. The z test for "no difference" against "a higher proportion of the M group succeeds" has

(a) $z = 2.25$, $P < 0.02$.
(b) $z = 2.60$, $P < 0.005$.
(c) $z = 2.25$, $P < 0.04$ but not < 0.02.

19.13 The z test in the previous exercise
(a) may be inaccurate because the populations are too small.
(b) may be inaccurate because some counts of successes and failures are too small.
(c) is reasonably accurate because the conditions for inference are met.

CHAPTER 19 EXERCISES

19.14 Truthfulness in online profiles. Many teens have posted profiles on sites such as MySpace. A sample survey asked random samples of teens with online profiles if they included false information in their profiles. Of 170 younger teens (ages 12 to 14), 117 said "Yes." Of 317 older teens (ages 15 to 17), 152 said "Yes."[10]
(a) Do these samples satisfy the guidelines for the large-sample confidence interval?
(b) Give a 95% confidence interval for the difference between the proportions of younger and older teens who include false information in their online profiles.

19.15 Drug testing in schools. Does drug testing reduce use of illegal drugs by high school athletes? A study compared two similar high schools in Oregon. Wahtonka High School tested athletes at random and Warrenton High School did not. In a confidential survey, 7 of 135 athletes at Wahtonka and 27 of 141 athletes at Warrenton said they were using drugs.[11] Regard these athletes as SRSs from the populations of athletes at similar schools with and without drug testing.
(a) Do the data give good reason to think that drug use among athletes is lower in schools that test for drugs? State hypotheses, find the test statistic, and use either software or the bottom row of Table C for the P-value. Be sure to state your conclusion.
(b) You should not use the large-sample confidence interval for the difference between the proportions of athletes using drugs at schools with and without testing. Why not?

Call a statistician. *Does involving a statistician to help with statistical methods improve the chance that a medical research paper will be published? A study of papers submitted to two medical journals found that 135 of 190 papers that lacked statistical assistance were rejected without even being reviewed in detail. In contrast, 293 of*

the 514 papers with statistical help were sent back without review.[12] *Exercises 19.16 to 19.18 are based on this study.*

19.16 Does statistical help make a difference? Is there a significant difference in the proportions of papers with and without statistical help that are rejected without review? State hypotheses, find the test statistic, use software or the bottom row of Table C to get a P-value, and give your conclusion. (This observational study does not establish causation, because studies that include statistical help may also be better in other ways than those that do not.)

19.17 How often are statisticians involved? Give a 95% confidence interval for the proportion of papers submitted to these journals that include help from a statistician.

19.18 How big a difference? Give a 95% confidence interval for the difference between the proportions of papers rejected without review when a statistician is and is not involved in the research.

19.19 Significant does not mean important. Never forget that even small effects can be statistically significant if the samples are large. To illustrate this fact, consider a sample of 148 small businesses. During a three-year period, 15 of the 106 headed by men and 7 of the 42 headed by women failed.[13]
(a) Find the proportions of failures for businesses headed by women and businesses headed by men. These sample proportions are quite close to each other. Give the P-value for the z test of the hypothesis that the same proportion of women's and men's businesses fail. (Use the two-sided alternative.) The test is very far from being significant.
(b) Now suppose that the same sample proportions came from a sample 30 times as large. That is, 210 out of 1260 businesses headed by women and 450 out of 3180 businesses headed by men fail. Verify that the proportions of failures are exactly the same as in (a). Repeat the z test for the new data, and show that it is now significant at the $\alpha = 0.05$ level.
(c) It is wise to use a confidence interval to estimate the size of an effect, rather than just giving a P-value. Give 95% confidence intervals for the difference between the proportions of women's and men's businesses that fail for the settings of both (a) and (b). What is the effect of larger samples on the confidence interval? (In practice, the large-sample confidence interval can't be trusted in setting (a).)

19.20 No inference: sample size. One of the processes that turn genes on or off (so to speak) is called "DNA methylation." Do low levels of this process help cause tumors? Compare mice altered to have low levels with normal mice. Of 33 mice with lowered levels of DNA methylation, 23 developed tumors. None of the control group of 18 normal mice developed tumors in the same time period.[14] Explain why we cannot safely use either the large-sample confidence interval or the test for comparing the proportions of normal and altered mice that develop tumors.

19.21 No inference: study design. Grain-handling facilities test for the presence of genetically modified (GM) soybeans in shipments to countries that do not allow GM beans. Batches of soybeans containing some genetically modified (GM) beans were submitted to 23 grain-handling facilities. When batches contained 1% of GM beans, 18 of the facilities detected the presence of GM beans. Only 7 of the same facilities detected GM beans when they made up one-tenth of 1% of the beans in the batches.[15] Explain why the study design does not allow us to use the methods of this chapter to compare the proportions of facilities that will detect the two levels of GM soybeans, even for large sample sizes.

In responding to Exercises 19.22 to 19.31, follow the **Plan, Solve,** *and* **Conclude** *steps of the four-step process.*

19.22 Are urban students more successful? North Carolina State University looked at the factors that affect whether students get a C or better in a required chemical engineering course. There were 65 students from urban or suburban backgrounds, and 52 of these students succeeded. Another 55 students were from rural or small-town backgrounds; 30 of these students succeeded in the course.[16] Is there good evidence that the proportion of students who succeed is different for urban/suburban versus rural/small-town backgrounds?

19.23 Female and male students. The North Carolina State University study in the previous exercise also compared the proportions of female and male students who succeeded in the course. They found that 23 of the 34 women and 60 of the 89 men succeeded. Is there evidence of a difference between the proportions of women and men who succeed?

19.24 Are urban students more successful, continued. Continue your work from Exercise 19.22. Estimate the difference between the success rates for all urban/suburban and rural/small-town students who plan to study chemical engineering at North Carolina State. (Use 90% confidence.)

19.25 How to quit smoking. Nicotine patches are often used to help smokers quit. Does giving medicine to fight depression help? A randomized double-blind experiment assigned 244 smokers who wanted to stop to receive nicotine patches and another 245 to receive both a patch and the antidepression drug bupropion. After a year, 40 subjects in the nicotine patch group and 87 in the patch-plus-drug group had abstained from smoking.[17] Give a 99% confidence interval for the difference (treatment minus control) in the proportions of smokers who quit.

19.26 The Gold Coast. An historian examining British colonial records for the Gold Coast in Africa suspects that the death rate was higher among African miners than among European miners. In the year 1936, there were 223 deaths among 33,809 African miners and 7 deaths among 1541 European miners on the Gold Coast.[18] (The Gold Coast became the independent nation of Ghana in 1957.)

Consider this year as a random sample from the colonial era in West Africa. Is there good evidence that the proportion of African miners who died was higher than the proportion of European miners who died?

19.27 The ultimatum game. In the "ultimatum game," your partner gets $10, on the condition that it be shared with you. The partner makes you an offer. If you refuse, neither of you gets anything. So it's to your advantage to accept even the unfair offer of $2 out of the $10. But many people refuse unfair offers anyway. This is evidence that our emotions can influence our economic decisions. Here are data on the responses of 76 subjects randomly assigned to receive an offer of $2 from either a person they were introduced to or a computer:[19]

	Accept	Reject
Human offers	20	18
Computer offers	32	6

We suspect that emotion will lead to offers from another person being rejected more often than offers from an impersonal computer. Do a test to assess the evidence for this conjecture.

19.28 Seat belt use. The proportion of drivers who use seat belts depends on local law. In New York City, police can stop a driver who is not belted. In Boston at the time of the survey, police could cite a driver for not wearing a seat belt only if the driver had been stopped for some other violation. Here are data from observing random samples of female Hispanic drivers in these two cities:[20]

City	Drivers	Belted
New York	220	183
Boston	117	68

(a) Is this an experiment or an observational study? Why?
(b) Comparing local laws suggests the hypothesis that a smaller proportion of drivers wear seat belts in Boston than in New York. Do the data give good evidence that this is true for female Hispanic drivers?

19.29 Acorns and mice. The mouse population in wooded areas rises and falls with the abundance of acorns, their favored food. Experimenters studied two similar forest areas in a year when the acorn crop failed. They added hundreds of thousands of acorns to one area to imitate an abundant acorn crop, while leaving the other area untouched. The next spring, 54 of the 72 mice trapped in the first area were in breeding condition, versus 10 of the 17 mice trapped in the second area.[21] Is there a significant difference between the proportions of mice ready to breed in good acorn years and bad acorn years?

19.30 Does preschool help? What are the long-term effects of preschool programs for poor children? To find out, investigators followed two groups of Michigan children from early childhood.[22] One group of 62 attended preschool as 3- and 4-year-olds. A control group of 61 children from the same area and similar backgrounds did not attend preschool. Over a ten-year period as adults, 38 of the preschool sample and 49 of the control sample needed social services (mainly welfare). Does the study provide significant evidence that children who attend preschool have less need for social services as adults? How large is the difference between the proportions of the preschool and no-preschool populations that require social services? Do inference to answer both questions. Be sure to explain exactly what inference you choose to do.

19.31 Using credit cards. Are shoppers more or less likely to use credit cards for "impulse purchases" that they

decide to make on the spot, as opposed to purchases that they had in mind when they went to the store? Stop every third person leaving a department store with a purchase. (This is in effect a random sample of people who buy at that store.) A few questions allow us to classify the purchase as impulse or not. Here are the data on how the customer paid:[23]

	Credit Card?	
	Yes	No
Impulse purchases	13	18
Planned purchases	35	31

Estimate with 95% confidence the percent of all customers at this store who use a credit card. Give numerical summaries to describe the difference in credit card use between impulse and planned purchases. Is this difference statistically significant?

19.32 Study design. The study in Exercise 19.30 randomly assigned 123 children to the two groups. The same data could have come from a study that followed children whose parents did or did not enroll them in preschool. Explain carefully how the conclusions we can draw depend on which design was used.

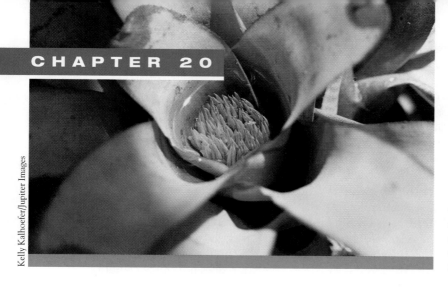

Kelly Kalhoefer/Jupiter Images

CHAPTER 20

Bromeliads are tropical plants whose leaf bases form cups that collect water. Exercise 20.38 describes an experiment on the effect of adding nitrogen fertilizer to bromeliad cups.

Inference about Variables: Part III Review

IN THIS CHAPTER WE COVER...

- Statistics in Outline
- Part III Summary
- Review Exercises
- Supplementary Exercises

The procedures of Chapters 16, 17, 18, and 19 are among the most common statistical inference methods. Now that you have mastered important ideas and practical methods for inference, it's time to review the big ideas of statistics in outline form. Here is a summary of Parts I and II of this book, leading up to Part III. The outline contains some important warnings: look for the word "Beware."

Statistics in Outline

DATA PRODUCTION

- Data basics:

    Individuals (subjects).

    Variables: categorical versus quantitative, units of measurement, explanatory versus response.

- Data production basics:

    Observation versus experiment.

    Simple random samples.

    Completely randomized experiments.

- *Beware:* really bad data production (voluntary response, confounding) can make inference impossible.

- *Beware:* weaknesses in data production (for example, sampling students at only one campus) can make inference to a wider population dubious.

DATA ANALYSIS

- Plot your data. Look for overall pattern and striking deviations.

- Add numerical descriptions based on what you see.

- One quantitative variable:
    Graphs: stemplot, histogram, boxplot.
    Pattern: distribution shape, center, spread. Outliers?
    Density curves (such as Normal curves) to describe overall pattern.
    Numerical descriptions: five-number summary or $\bar{x}$ and s.
    Beware: averages and other simple descriptions can miss the real story.
- Relationships between two quantitative variables:
    Graph: scatterplot.
    Pattern: relationship form, direction, strength. Outliers? Influential observations?
    Numerical description for linear relationships: correlation, regression line.
    Beware the effects of outliers and influential observations.
    Beware the lurking variable: correlation does not imply causation.

THE REASONING OF INFERENCE

- Inference uses data to infer conclusions about a wider population.
- When you do inference, you are acting as if your data come from random samples or randomized comparative experiments. *Beware*: if they don't, you may have "garbage in, garbage out."
- Always examine your data before doing inference. Inference often requires a regular pattern, such as roughly Normal with no strong outliers.
- Key idea: "What would happen if we did this many times?"
- Confidence intervals: estimate a population parameter.
    95% confidence: I used a method that captures the true parameter 95% of the time in repeated use.
    Beware: the margin of error of a confidence interval does not include the effects of practical errors such as undercoverage and nonresponse.
- Significance tests: assess evidence against H_0 in favor of H_a.
    P-value: If H_0 were true, how often would I get an outcome favoring the alternative this strongly? Smaller P = stronger evidence against H_0.
    Statistical significance at the 5% level, $P < 0.05$, means that an outcome this extreme would occur less than 5% of the time if H_0 were true.
    Beware: $P < 0.05$ is not sacred.
    Beware: statistical significance is not the same as practical importance. Large samples can make small effects significant. Small samples can fail to declare large effects significant.
    Always try to estimate the size of an effect (for example, with a confidence interval), not just its significance.

PART III SUMMARY

Part III of this book picks up at the end of this outline, introducing practical methods of inference. The Statistics in Summary flowchart on the next page offers a brief guide to choosing the right inference procedure. It is important to do some of the review exercises because now, for the first time, you must decide which of several inference procedures to use. Learning to recognize problem settings in order to choose the right type of inference is a key step in advancing your mastery of statistics. This is the *Plan* step in the four-step process, in which you translate the real-world problem from the *State* step into a specific inference procedure.

STATISTICS IN SUMMARY

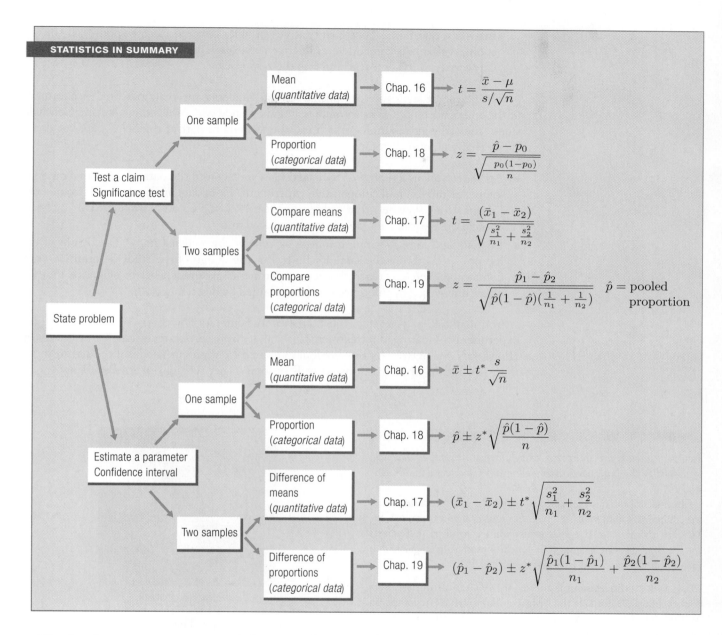

The flowchart organizes one way of planning inference problems. Let's go through it from left to right.

1. *Do you want to test a claim or estimate an unknown quantity?* That is, will you need a test of significance or a confidence interval?

2. *Are your data a single sample representing one population or two samples chosen to compare two populations or responses to two treatments in an experiment?* Remember that to work with *matched pairs* data you form one sample from the differences within pairs.

3. *Is the response variable quantitative or categorical?* Quantitative variables take numerical values with some unit of measurement such as inches or grams. The most common

inference questions about quantitative variables concern *mean* responses. If the response variable is categorical, inference most often concerns the *proportion* of some category (call it a "success") among the responses.

The flowchart leads you to a specific test or confidence interval, indicated by a formula at the end of each path. The formula is an aid to guide you toward the *Solve* and *Conclude* steps. You (or your technology) will use the formula as part of the *Solve* step, but don't forget that you must do more:

- *Are the conditions for this procedure met?* Can you act as if the data come from a random sample or randomized comparative experiment? Does data analysis show extreme outliers or strong skewness that forbid use of inference based on Normality? Do you have enough observations for your intended procedure?
- *Do your data come from an experiment or from an observational study?* The details of inference methods are the same for both. But the design of the study determines what conclusions you can reach, because experiments give much better evidence that an effect uncovered by inference can be explained by direct causation.

You may ask, as you study the Statistics in Summary flowchart, "What if I have an experiment comparing four treatments, or samples from three populations?" The flowchart allows only one or two, not three or four or more. Be patient: methods for comparing more than two means or proportions, as well as some other settings for inference, appear in Part IV.

REVIEW EXERCISES

Review exercises are short and straightforward exercises that help you solidify the basic ideas and skills from Chapters 16, 17, 18, and 19.

In review exercises that call for inference, you can assume that the conditions for inference are met. For tests of significance, use Table C to approximate P-values unless you use software that reports the P-value. Be sure to state your conclusions in plain language that identifies the populations to which they apply.

20.1 Wikipedia. A sample survey of 1497 adult Internet users found that 36% consult the online collaborative encyclopedia Wikipedia.[1] Give a 95% confidence interval for the proportion of all adult Internet users who refer to Wikipedia.

20.2 Game players. A government survey randomly selected 6889 female high school students and 7028 male high school students.[2] Of these students, 1020 females and 1926 males played video or computer games for 3 or more hours a day. Use a 99% confidence interval to estimate the proportion of all male high school students who play games at least 3 hours a day.

20.3 Spinning euros. When the new euro coins were introduced throughout Europe in 2002, two Polish mathematicians spun a Belgian euro (one side of the coin has a different design

Matthias Kulka/CORBIS

for each country) 250 times. They got 140 heads. Is it significant evidence that the coin is not balanced when spun?

20.4 Game players, female and male. Use the information in Exercise 20.2 to answer these questions.
(a) What are the sample proportions of females and males who played games at least 3 hours a day?
(b) The samples are large and the sample proportions are quite different, so the difference is sure to be highly significant. Give a 99% confidence interval for the difference between the proportions of all male and female high school students who play games at least 3 hours a day.

20.5 Men and muscle. Ask young men to estimate their own degree of body muscle by choosing from a set of 100 photos. Then ask them to choose what they think women prefer. The researchers know the actual degree of muscle, measured as kilograms per square meter of fat-free mass, for each of the photos. They can therefore measure the difference between what a subject thinks women prefer and the subject's own self-image. Call this difference the "muscle gap." Here are summary statistics for the muscle gap from two samples, one of American and European young men and the other of Chinese young men from Taiwan:[3]

Group	n	$\bar{x}$	s
American/European	200	2.35	2.5
Chinese	55	1.20	3.2

Give a 95% confidence interval for the mean size of the muscle gap for all American and European young men. On the average, men think they need this much more muscle to match what women prefer.

20.6 Are Chinese men different? Continue to use the data in Exercise 20.5. Is there a significant difference between the mean size of the muscle gap for American/European men and Chinese men?

20.7 Butterflies mating. Here's how butterflies mate: a male passes to a female a packet of sperm called a spermatophore. Females may mate several times. Will they remate sooner if the first spermatophore they receive is small? Among 20 females who received a large spermatophore (greater than 25 milligrams), the mean time to the next mating was 5.15 days, with standard deviation 0.18 day. For 21 females who received a small spermatophore (about 7 milligrams), the mean was 4.33 days and the standard deviation was 0.31 day.[4] Is the observed difference in means statistically significant?

Listening to rap. *The Black Youth Project of the University of Chicago interviewed random samples of 634 blacks, 314 Hispanics, and 567 whites aged 15 to 25. The survey found that 58% of black youth listen to rap music every day, compared with 45% of Hispanics and 23% of whites. But attitudes were quite similar in the three groups. For example, 72% of blacks, 72% of Hispanics, and 68% of whites agreed that "rap music videos contain too many references to sex."[5] Exercises 20.8 to 20.10 are based on this study.*

20.8 Black young people listening to rap. Give a 90% confidence interval for the proportion of all black young people who listen to rap every day.

20.9 Listening to rap: Hispanics and whites. Give a 90% confidence interval for the difference between the proportions of all Hispanic and all white young people who listen to rap every day.

20.10 Too much sex in rap music? Is there a significant difference between the proportions of black and white young people who think that rap videos contain too much sex?

20.11 Mouse endurance. To test the endurance of a mouse, make it swim in a bucket with a weight attached to its tail. (Rescue the mouse when it is exhausted.) Here are data on endurance in minutes for female and male mice:[6]

Group	n	Mean	Standard deviation
Female	162	11.4	26.09
Male	135	6.7	6.69

(a) Both sets of endurance data are skewed to the right. Why are *t* procedures nonetheless reasonably accurate for these data?
(b) Do the data show that female mice have significantly higher endurance on the average than male mice?

20.12 Female mouse endurance. Use the information in the previous exercise to give a 95% confidence interval for the mean endurance of female mice swimming.

20.13 More on mouse endurance. Use the information in Exercise 20.11 to give a 95% confidence interval for the mean difference (female minus male) in endurance times.

The National Assessment of Educational Progress (NAEP) includes a "long-term trend" study that tracks reading and mathematics skills over time in a way that allows comparisons between results from different years. Exercises 20.14 to 20.18 are based on information on 17-year-old students from the report on the latest long-term trend study, carried out in 2004.[7] The NAEP sample used a multistage design, but the overall effect is quite similar to an SRS of 17-year-olds who are still in school.

20.14 Better-educated parents. In the 1978 sample of 17,554 students, 5617 had at least one parent who was a college graduate. In the 2004 sample of 2158 students, 1014 had at least one college graduate parent. Give a 99% confidence interval for the increase in the proportion of students with a college graduate parent between 1978 and 2004.

20.15 College-educated parents. Use the information in the previous exercise to give a 99% confidence interval for the proportion of all students in 2004 who had at least one parent who graduated from college. (The sample excludes 17-year-olds who had dropped out of school, so your estimate is valid for students but is probably too high for all 17-year-olds.)

20.16 The effect of parents' education. The mean NAEP mathematics score (on a scale of 0 to 500) for the 1014 students in the 2004 sample with at least one parent who graduated from college was 317, with standard deviation 28.6. The 2004 sample contained 410 students whose parents' highest level of education was high school graduate. The mean score for these students was 295, with standard deviation 22.3. Is there a significant difference in mean score between these two groups of students? Estimate the size of the difference in the entire student population (use 95% confidence).

20.17 Students with college-educated parents. Use the information in the previous exercise to give a 95% confidence interval for the mean NAEP mathematics score of all 17-year-old students with at least one parent who graduated from college.

20.18 Men versus women. The 2004 NAEP sample contained 1122 female students and 1036 male students. The women had a mean mathematics score (on a scale of 0 to 500) of 305, with standard error 0.9. The male mean was 308, with standard error 1.0. Is there evidence that the mean mathematics scores of men and women differ in the population of all 17-year-old students?

20.19 Very-low-birth-weight babies. Starting in the 1970s, medical technology allowed babies with very low birth weight (VLBW, less than 1500 grams, about 3.3 pounds) to survive without major handicaps. It was noticed that these children nonetheless had difficulties in school and as adults. A long-term study has followed 242 VLBW babies to age 20 years, along with a control group of 233 babies from the same population who had normal birth weight.[8]
(a) Is this an experiment or an observational study? Why?
(b) At age 20, 179 of the VLBW group and 193 of the control group had graduated from high school. Is the graduation rate among the VLBW group significantly lower than for the normal-birth-weight controls?

20.20 Very low birth weight and IQ. IQ scores were available for 113 men in the VLBW group. The mean IQ was 87.6, and the standard deviation was 15.1. The 106 men in the control group had mean IQ 94.7, with standard deviation 14.9. Is there good evidence that mean IQ is lower among VLBW men than among controls from similar backgrounds?

20.21 Very low birth weight, drug use, and IQ. Of the 126 women in the VLBW group, 37 said they had used illegal drugs; 52 of the 124 control group women had done so. The IQ scores for the VLBW women had mean 86.2 (standard deviation 13.4), and the normal-birth-weight controls had mean IQ 89.8 (standard deviation 14.0). Is there a statistically significant difference between the two groups in either proportion using drugs or mean IQ?

20.22 Smoking in Canada and the United States. The Joint Canada/United States Survey of Health interviewed a random sample of 3505 Canadian adults and a separate random sample of 5183 American adults. The survey found that 736 of the Canadians and 974 of the Americans were daily smokers.[9] Give a 95% confidence interval for the percent of all Canadian adults who are daily smokers.

20.23 Smoking in Canada and the United States. Is there good evidence that the percent of daily smokers is higher in Canada than in the United States? Use the survey information in the previous exercise.

20.24 Cholesterol in dogs. Because a diet rich in saturated fats raises the level of cholesterol in the blood, it is plausible that dogs owned as pets have higher cholesterol levels than dogs owned by a veterinary research clinic. A clinic compared healthy dogs it owned with healthy pets brought to the clinic to be neutered. The summary statistics for blood cholesterol levels (milligrams per deciliter of blood) appear below.[10]

Group	n	$\bar{x}$	s
Pets	26	193	68
Clinic	23	174	44

Is there strong evidence that pets have a higher mean cholesterol level than clinic dogs?

20.25 Pets versus clinic dogs. Using the information in the previous exercise, give a 95% confidence interval for the difference in mean cholesterol levels between pets and clinic dogs.

20.26 Cholesterol in pets. Continue your work with the information in Exercise 20.24. Give a 95% confidence interval for the mean cholesterol level in pets.

20.27 Conditions for inference. What conditions must be satisfied to justify the procedures you used in Exercise 20.24? In Exercise 20.25? In Exercise 20.26? Assuming that the cholesterol measurements have no outliers and are not strongly skewed, what is the chief threat to the validity of the results of this study?

Choosing an inference procedure. *In each of Exercises 20.28 to 20.34, say which type of inference procedure from the Statistics in Summary flowchart (page 355) you would use, or explain why none of these procedures fits the problem. You do not need to carry out any procedures.*

20.28 Driving too fast. How seriously do people view speeding in comparison with other annoying behaviors? A large random sample of adults was asked to rate a number of behaviors on a scale of 1 (no problem at all) to 5 (very severe problem). Do speeding drivers get a higher average rating than noisy neighbors?

20.29 Preventing drowning. Drowning in bathtubs is a major cause of death in children less than 5 years old. A random sample of parents was asked many questions related to bathtub safety. Overall, 85% of the sample said they used baby bathtubs for infants. Estimate the percent of all parents of young children who use baby bathtubs.

20.30 Acid rain? You have data on rainwater collected at 16 locations in the Adirondack Mountains of New York State. One measurement is the acidity of the water, measured by pH on a scale of 0 to 14 (the pH of distilled water is 7.0). Estimate the average acidity of rainwater in the Adirondacks.

20.31 Athletes' salaries. Looking online, you find the salaries of the 27 players on the roster of the Chicago Cubs as of opening day of the 2008 baseball season. The team total was $118.6 million, seventh highest in the major leagues. Estimate the average salary of the Cubs players.

20.32 Looking back on love. How do young adults look back on adolescent romance? Investigators interviewed 40 couples in their midtwenties. The female and male partners were interviewed separately. Each was asked about his or her current relationship and also about a romantic relationship that lasted at least two months when they were aged 15 or 16. One response variable was a measure on a numerical scale of how much the attractiveness of the adolescent partner mattered. You want to compare the men and women on this measure.

20.33 Dropping out. You have data from interviews with a random sample of students who failed to graduate from your university in 7 years and also from a random sample of students who entered at the same time and did graduate. You will use these data to
(a) estimate the percent of dropouts who transferred to another school.
(b) compare the first-year grade point averages of dropouts and graduates.
(c) compare the percents of students from rural backgrounds among dropouts and graduates.

20.34 Preventing AIDS through education. The Multisite HIV Prevention Trial was a randomized comparative experiment to compare the effects of twice-weekly small-group AIDS discussion sessions (the treatment) with a single one-hour session (the control). Compare the effects of treatment and control on each of the following response variables:
(a) A subject does or does not use condoms 6 months after the education sessions.

(b) The number of unprotected intercourse acts by a subject between 4 and 8 months after the sessions.
(c) A subject is or is not infected with a sexually transmitted disease 6 months after the sessions.

SUPPLEMENTARY EXERCISES

*Supplementary exercises apply the skills you have learned in ways that require more thought or more use of technology. Some of these exercises start from actual data rather than from data summaries. Many of these exercises ask you to follow the **Plan, Solve,** and **Conclude** steps of the four-step process. Remember that the **Solve** step includes checking the conditions for the inference you plan.*

20.35 Do you have confidence? A report of a survey distributed to randomly selected email addresses at a large university says: "We have collected 427 responses from our sample of 2,100 as of April 30, 2004. This number of responses is large enough to achieve a 95% confidence interval with ±5% margin of sampling error in generalizing the results to our study population."[11] Why would you be reluctant to trust a confidence interval based on these data?

20.36 Monkeys and music. Humans generally prefer music to silence. What about monkeys? Allow a tamarin monkey to enter a V-shaped cage with food in both arms of the V. In one arm, it hears a lullaby played by a flute; in the other arm, silence. After the monkey eats the food, it can choose to stay in either arm. Each of 4 monkeys was tested 6 times. The monkeys chose silence for about 65% of their time in the cage. The researchers reported a one-sample t test for the mean percent of time spent in the music arm, $H_0: \mu = 50\%$ against the two-sided alternative, $t = -5.26$, df = 23, $P < 0.0001$.[12]

Although the result is interesting, the statistical analysis is not correct. The degrees of freedom df = 23 show that the researchers assumed that they had 24 independent observations. Explain why the results of the 24 trials are not independent.

20.37 Starting to talk. At what age do infants speak their first word of English? Here are data (ages in months) for 20 normally developing children:[13]

| 15 | 26 | 10 | 9 | 15 | 20 | 18 | 11 | 8 | 20 |
| 7 | 9 | 10 | 11 | 11 | 10 | 12 | 17 | 11 | 10 |

Is there good evidence that the mean age at first word among all normal children is greater than one year?

20.38 Fertilizing a tropical plant. Bromeliads are tropical flowering plants. Many are epiphytes that attach to trees and obtain moisture and nutrients from air and rain. Their leaf bases form cups that collect water and are home to the larvae of many insects. Jacqueline Ngai and Diane Srivastava randomly assigned bromeliad plants to treatment (add nitrogen to the cups) or control groups. Here are data on the number of new leaves produced over a 7-month period:[14]

Control	11	13	16	15	15	11	12	
Treatment	15	14	15	16	17	18	17	13

Is there evidence that adding nitrogen increases the mean number of new leaves formed?

20.39 Starting to talk, continued. Use the data in Exercise 20.37 to give a 90% confidence interval for the mean age at which children speak their first word.

20.40 Dyeing fabrics. Different fabrics respond differently when dyed. This matters to clothing manufacturers, who want the color of the fabric to be just right. A researcher dyed fabrics made of cotton and of ramie with the same "procion blue" dye applied in the same way. Then she used a colorimeter to measure the lightness of the color on a scale in which black is 0 and white is 100. Here are the data for 8 pieces of each fabric:[15]

Cotton	48.82	48.88	48.98	49.04	48.68	49.34	48.75	49.12
Ramie	41.72	41.83	42.05	41.44	41.27	42.27	41.12	41.49

Is there a significant difference between the fabrics? Which fabric is darker when dyed in this way?

20.41 More on dyeing fabrics. The color of a fabric depends on the dye used and also on how the dye is applied. The study discussed in the previous exercise went on to dye fabric made of ramie with the same "procion blue" dye applied in two different ways. The chart gives the lightness scores for 8 pieces of identical fabric dyed in each way.

Method B	40.98	40.88	41.30	41.28	41.66	41.50	41.39	41.27
Method C	42.30	42.20	42.65	42.43	42.50	42.28	43.13	42.45

(a) This is a randomized comparative experiment. Outline the design.

(b) A clothing manufacturer wants to know which method gives the darker color (lower lightness score). Use sample means to answer this question. Is the difference between the two sample means statistically significant? Can you tell from just the P-value whether the difference is large enough to be important in practice?

20.42 Do parents matter? A professor asked her sophomore students, "Does either of your parents allow you to drink alcohol around him or her?" and "How many drinks do you typically have per session?" (A drink is defined as one 12 oz beer, one 4 oz glass of wine, or one 1 oz shot of liquor.) Table 20.1 contains the responses of the female students who are not abstainers.[16] The sample is all students in one large sophomore-level class. The class is popular, so we are tentatively willing to regard its members as an SRS of sophomore students at this college. Does the behavior of parents make a significant difference in how many drinks students have on the average?

20.43 Parents' behavior. We wonder what proportion of female students have at least one parent who allows them to drink around him or her. Table 20.1 contains information about a sample of 94 students. Use this sample to give a 95% confidence interval for this proportion.

20.44 Diabetic mice. The body's natural electrical field helps wounds heal. If diabetes changes this field, that might explain why people with diabetes heal slowly. A study of this idea compared normal mice and mice bred to

TABLE 20.1 Drinks per session by female students

Parent Allows Student to Drink												
2.5	1	2.5	3	1	3	3	3	2.5	2.5	3.5	5	2
7	7	6.5	4	8	6	6	3	6	3	4	7	5
3.5	2	1	5	3	3	6	4	2	7	5	8	1
6	5	2.5	3	4.5	9	5	4	4	3	4	6	4
5	1	5	3	10	7	4	4	4	4	2	2.5	2.5
Parent Does Not Allow Student to Drink												
9	3.5	3	5	1	1	3	4	4	3	6	5	3
8	4	4	5	7	7	3.5	3	10	4	9	2	7
4	3	1										

spontaneously develop diabetes. The investigators attached sensors to the right hip and front feet of the mice and measured the difference in electrical potential (millivolts) between these locations. Here are the data:[17]

		Diabetic Mice			
14.70	13.60	7.40	1.05	10.55	16.40
10.00	22.60	15.20	19.60	17.25	18.40
9.80	11.70	14.85	14.45	18.25	10.15
10.85	10.30	10.45	8.55	8.85	19.20

		Normal Mice			
13.80	9.10	4.95	7.70	9.40	7.20
10.00	14.55	13.30	6.65	9.50	10.40
7.75	8.70	8.85	8.40	8.55	12.60

(a) Make a stemplot of each sample of potentials. There is a low outlier in the diabetic group. Does it appear that potentials in the two groups differ in a systematic way?

(b) Is there significant evidence of a difference in mean potentials between the two groups?

(c) Repeat your inference without the outlier. Does the outlier affect your conclusion?

20.45 Keeping crackers from breaking. We don't like to find broken crackers when we open the package. How can makers reduce breaking? One idea is to microwave the crackers for 30 seconds right after baking them. Randomly assign 20 crackers to be microwaved and another 20 to a control group. After 14 days, break the crackers. Here are summaries of the pressure needed to break them, in pounds per square inch:[18]

	Microwave	Control
Mean	139.6	77.0
Standard deviation	33.6	22.6

What do you conclude about the idea of microwaving crackers?

20.46 Falling through the ice. Table 6.3 (page 123) gives the dates on which a wooden tripod fell through the ice of the Tanana River in Alaska, thus deciding the winner of the Nenana Ice Classic contest, for the years 1917 to 2008. Give a 95% confidence interval for the mean date on which the tripod falls through the ice. After calculating the interval in the scale used in the table (days from April 20, which is Day 1), translate your result into calendar dates and hours within the dates. (Each hour is 1/24, or 0.042, of a day.)

20.47 A case for the Supreme Court. In 1986, a Texas jury found a black man guilty of murder. The prosecutors had used "peremptory challenges" to remove 10 of the 11 blacks and 4 of the 31 whites in the pool from which the jury was chosen.[19] The law says that there must be a plausible reason (that is, a reason other than race) for different treatment of blacks and whites in the jury pool. When the case reached the Supreme Court 17 years later, the Court said that "happenstance is unlikely to produce this disparity." Explain why the methods we know can't be safely used to do the inference that lies behind the Court's finding that chance is unlikely to produce so large a black-white difference.

Inference about Relationships

PART IV

INFERENCE ABOUT RELATIONSHIPS

CHAPTER 21 Two Categorical Variables: The Chi-Square Test

CHAPTER 22 Inference for Regression

CHAPTER 23 One-Way Analysis of Variance: Comparing Several Means

Statistical inference offers more methods than anyone can know well, as a glance at the offerings of any large statistical software package demonstrates. In an introductory text, we must be selective. Parts I to III have laid a foundation for understanding statistics:

- The nature and purpose of data analysis.
- The central ideas of designs for data production.
- The reasoning behind confidence intervals and significance tests.
- Experience applying these ideas in practice.

Each of the three chapters of Part IV offers an introduction to a more advanced topic in statistical inference. You may choose to read any or all of them, in any order.

What makes a statistical method "more advanced"? More complex data, for one thing. In Part III, we looked only at methods for inference about a single population parameter and for comparing two parameters. All of the chapters in Part IV present methods for studying relationships between two variables. In Chapter 21, both variables are categorical, with data given as a two-way table of counts of outcomes. Chapter 22 considers inference in the setting of regressing a response variable on an explanatory variable. This is an important type of relationship between two quantitative variables. In Chapter 23 we meet methods for comparing the mean response in more than two groups. Here, the explanatory variable (group) is categorical and the response variable is quantitative.

With greater complexity comes greater reliance on technology. In these final three chapters you will more often be interpreting the output of statistical software or using software yourself. With effort, you can do the calculations needed in Chapter 21 with a basic calculator. In Chapters 22 and 23, the pain is too great and the contribution to learning too small. Fortunately, you can grasp the ideas without step-by-step arithmetic.

Another aspect of "more advanced" methods is new concepts and ideas. This is where we draw the line in deciding what statistical topics we can master in a first course. Part IV builds elaborate methods on the foundation we have laid without introducing fundamentally new concepts. Statistical practice does need additional big ideas, but the ideas you already know place you among the world's statistical sophisticates.

AB/Getty Images

Many young people use a cell phone as their only phone. How do the opinions of cell-only users differ from those of people who have landline telephones? See Example 21.8 for some data.

Two Categorical Variables: The Chi-Square Test

IN THIS CHAPTER WE COVER...

- Two-way tables

- Is there a relationship? Expected cell counts

- The chi-square test

- Data analysis for chi-square

- Another use of the chi-square test

- The chi-square distributions*

- The chi-square test for goodness of fit*

Correlation and regression describe relationships between quantitative variables. Now we will describe relationships between two categorical variables. Some variables—such as sex, race, and occupation—are categorical by nature. Other categorical variables are created by grouping values of a quantitative variable into classes. Published data often appear in grouped form to save space. As usual, we are interested in both data analysis (describe the relationship) and inference (is the relationship statistically significant).

Two-way tables

To analyze categorical data, we use the *counts* or *percents* of individuals that fall into various categories. Data on two categorical variables are most often presented in a **two-way table** of counts.

EXAMPLE 21.1 Where do young people live?

A sample survey asked a random sample of young adults, "Where do you live now? That is, where do you stay most often?" Table 21.1 is a two-way table of the 2984 people in the sample, classified by their age and by where they lived.[1] Living arrangement is a categorical variable. Even though age is quantitative, the two-way table treats age as dividing young adults into four categories. Table 21.1 gives the counts for all 20 combinations of age and living arrangement. Each of the 20 counts occupies a **cell** of the table. ■

How can we best grasp the information contained in Table 21.1? *First, look at the distribution of each variable separately.* The distribution of a categorical variable says how

TABLE 21.1 Young adults by age and living arrangement

	AGE 19	AGE 20	AGE 21	AGE 22	TOTAL
Parents' home	324	378	337	318	1357
Another person's home	37	47	40	38	162
Your own place	116	279	372	487	1254
Group quarters	58	60	49	25	192
Other	5	2	3	9	19
Total	540	766	801	877	2984

marginal distribution

often each outcome occurred. The distributions of living arrangements alone and age alone are called **marginal distributions** because they appear at the right and bottom margins of the two-way table.

The "Total" column at the right of the table displays the marginal distribution of living arrangements, found by adding each row in the table. Percents are often more informative than counts. We can display the marginal distribution in percents by dividing each row total by the table total and converting to a percent.

EXAMPLE 21.2 Calculating a marginal distribution

The percent of young adults who live in their parents' home is

$$\frac{\text{parent's home total}}{\text{table total}} = \frac{1357}{2984} = 0.455 = 45.5\%$$

Do four more such calculations to obtain the marginal distribution of living arrangements. Here is the complete distribution:

Live in:	Percent
Parents' home	$\frac{1357}{2984} = 45.5\%$
Another person's home	$\frac{162}{2984} = 5.4\%$
Your own place	$\frac{1254}{2984} = 42.0\%$
Group quarters	$\frac{192}{2984} = 6.4\%$
Other	$\frac{19}{2984} = 0.6\%$

The total should be 100% because all young adults live in one of these locations. In fact, the percents add to 99.9% because we rounded each one to the nearest tenth. We see that more than 87% of young adults live either with their parents or in their own place. ■

Table 21.1 contains much more information than the two marginal distributions of living arrangements and age. We would like to know how living arrangements are related to age. *Marginal distributions tell us nothing about the relationship between two variables.* To describe a relationship between two categorical variables, we must calculate some well-chosen percents from the counts given in the body of the table. Here is a hint on how to proceed: *if there is an explanatory-response relationship, compare the distributions of the response variable for the separate values of the explanatory variable.* These are called **conditional dis-tributions.**

conditional distribution

EXAMPLE 21.3 **Calculating a conditional distribution**

Because we think that age helps explain where young people live, look at each age group separately. For each age group, find the percents of people who have each living arrangement. For example, to explore the living arrangements of 19-year-olds, look only at the "Age 19" column in Table 21.1. The percent *of 19-year-olds* who live with their parents is

$$\frac{\text{19-year-olds in parents' home}}{\text{age 19 column total}} = \frac{324}{540} = 0.600 = 60.0\%$$

Doing this for all five entries in the "Age 19" column gives the *conditional distribution* of living arrangements among 19-year-olds:

Live in:	Percent
Parents' home	$\frac{324}{540} = 60.0\%$
Another person's home	$\frac{37}{540} = 6.9\%$
Your own place	$\frac{116}{540} = 21.5\%$
Group quarters	$\frac{58}{540} = 10.7\%$
Other	$\frac{5}{540} = 0.9\%$

This distribution is quite different from the marginal distribution of living arrangements for all young adults aged 19 to 22 years. We use the term "conditional" because this distribution describes only young adults who satisfy the condition that they are age 19. ■

MARGINAL AND CONDITIONAL DISTRIBUTIONS

The **marginal distribution** of one of the categorical variables in a two-way table of counts is the distribution of values of that variable among all individuals described by the table.

A **conditional distribution** of a variable is the distribution of values of that variable among only individuals who have a given value of the other variable. There is a separate conditional distribution for each value of the other variable.

EXAMPLE 21.4 **Age and living arrangements**

STATE: Describe the relationship between living arrangements and age for young adults.

PLAN: Make a two-way table of living arrangement by age. Find and compare the conditional distributions of living arrangements for the four age groups.

SOLVE: Table 21.1 is the two-way table we need. We found one of the conditional distributions in Example 21.3. Software speeds the job of finding the four conditional distributions. Figure 21.1 shows Minitab's output. The percents in each column show the four conditional distributions of living arrangements given a specific age and, at the right, the marginal distribution of living arrangements. Each column adds to 100% because each displays a separate distribution. The "Age 19" and "All" columns agree with our work in Examples 21.2 and 21.3, up to roundoff error. Figure 21.2 is Minitab's bar graph comparing the four conditional distributions.

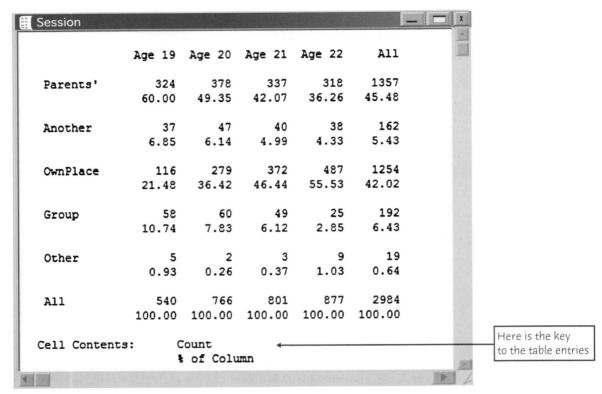

	Age 19	Age 20	Age 21	Age 22	All
Parents'	324	378	337	318	1357
	60.00	49.35	42.07	36.26	45.48
Another	37	47	40	38	162
	6.85	6.14	4.99	4.33	5.43
OwnPlace	116	279	372	487	1254
	21.48	36.42	46.44	55.53	42.02
Group	58	60	49	25	192
	10.74	7.83	6.12	2.85	6.43
Other	5	2	3	9	19
	0.93	0.26	0.37	1.03	0.64
All	540	766	801	877	2984
	100.00	100.00	100.00	100.00	100.00

Cell Contents: Count
                        % of Column

Here is the key to the table entries

FIGURE 21.1

Minitab output showing the conditional distributions (column percents) of where young people live for each age group, for Example 21.4.

FIGURE 21.2

Minitab bar graph comparing the four conditional distributions of living arrangements given age, for Example 21.4.

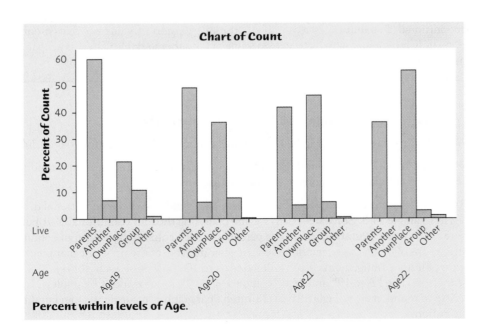

CONCLUDE: There is a strong relationship between age and living arrangement. As young adults age from 19 to 22, the percent living with their parents drops and the percent living in their own place rises. The percent living in group quarters also declines with age as college students move out of dormitories. ■

Now that we understand what the data show, we can turn to inference: *Is the relationship between age and living arrangements statistically significant?*

APPLY YOUR KNOWLEDGE

21.1 Attitudes toward recycled products. Some people think recycled products are lower in quality than other products. Here are data on attitudes toward coffee filters made of recycled paper among people who had bought these filters and people who had not:[2]

	Think the quality of the recycled product is		
	Higher	The same	Lower
Buyers	20	7	9
Nonbuyers	29	25	43

(a) How many people does this table describe? How many of these were buyers of coffee filters made of recycled paper?

(b) Give the marginal distribution of opinion about the quality of recycled filters. What percent of consumers think the quality of the recycled product is the same or higher than the quality of other filters?

(c) It appears that people who have bought the recycled filters have more positive opinions than those who have not. Give percents to back up this claim. Make a bar graph that compares your percents for buyers and nonbuyers.

(d) Association does not prove causation. Explain how buying recycled filters might improve a person's opinion of their quality. Then explain how the opinion a person holds might influence his or her decision to buy or not. You see that the cause-and-effect relationship might go in either direction.

21.2 Facebook at Penn State. The Pennsylvania State University has its main campus in University Park and more than 20 smaller "commonwealth campuses" around the state. The Penn State Division of Student Affairs polled a random sample of undergraduates about their use of online social networking. (The response rate was only about 20%, which casts doubt on the usefulness of the data.) Facebook was the most popular site, with more than 80% of students having an account. Here is a comparison of Facebook use by undergraduates at the University Park and commonwealth campuses:[3]

Courtesy Pennsylvania State University

	University Park	Commonwealth
Do not use Facebook	68	248
Several times a month or less	55	76
At least once a week	215	157
At least once a day	640	394

(a) What percent of University Park students fall in each Facebook category? What percent of commonwealth campus students fall in each category? Each column should add to 100% (up to roundoff error). These are the conditional distributions of Facebook use given campus setting.

(b) Make a bar graph that compares the two conditional distributions. What are the most important differences in Facebook use between the two campus settings?

21.3 Marginal distributions aren't the whole story. Here are the row and column totals for a two-way table with two rows and two columns:

a	b	50
c	d	50
60	40	100

Make up *two different* sets of counts a, b, c, and d for the body of the table that give these same totals. This shows that the relationship between two variables cannot be obtained from the two individual distributions of the variables.

Is there a relationship? Expected cell counts

We want to test the null hypothesis that in the population of all American young adults there is *no difference* among the four distributions of living arrangements for people aged 19, 20, 21, and 22. If the null hypothesis is true, the differences in the sample are just accidents due to random selection of the sample. Put more generally, the null hypothesis is that there is *no relationship* between two categorical variables,

H_0: there is no relationship between age and where young people live

The alternative hypothesis says that there *is* a relationship but does not specify any particular kind of relationship,

H_a: there is some relationship between age and living arrangement

Any difference among the four distributions of living arrangements in the population of all young adults means that the null hypothesis is false and the alternative hypothesis is true. The alternative hypothesis is not one-sided or two-sided. We might call it "many-sided" because it allows any kind of difference.

To assess the significance of the relationship between two categorical variables in a two-way table:

■ Use an *overall test* of the null hypothesis H_0 to see if there is good evidence of *any* relationship between the two variables.

■ Do *data analysis* to describe the nature of the relationship in detail.

The overall test of the null hypothesis H_0 that the row and column variables are not related compares the observed counts in the table with the *expected counts*, the counts we would expect—except for random variation—if H_0 were true. If the observed counts are far from the expected counts, that is evidence against H_0. It is easy to find the expected counts.

EXPECTED COUNTS

The **expected count** in any cell of a two-way table when H_0 is true is

$$\text{expected count} = \frac{\text{row total} \times \text{column total}}{\text{table total}}$$

EXAMPLE 21.5 **Where young people live: expected counts**

Let's find the expected counts for the study of where young people live. Look back at the two-way table of counts, Table 21.1. That table includes the row and column totals. The expected count of 19-year-olds who live in their parents' home is

$$\frac{\text{row 1 total} \times \text{column 1 total}}{\text{table total}} = \frac{(1357)(540)}{2984} = 245.57$$

The expected count of 22-year-olds who live with their parents is

$$\frac{\text{row 1 total} \times \text{column 4 total}}{\text{table total}} = \frac{(1357)(877)}{2984} = 398.82$$

The actual counts are 324 and 318. More younger people and fewer older people live with their parents than we would expect if there were no relationship between age and living arrangement. Table 21.2 shows all 20 expected counts.

As this table shows, *the expected counts have exactly the same row and column totals (up to roundoff error) as the observed counts*. That's a good way to check your work. Comparing the actual counts (Table 21.1) and the expected counts (Table 21.2) shows in what ways the data diverge from the null hypothesis. ■

TABLE 21.2 Young adults by age and living arrangement: expected cell counts

	AGE 19	AGE 20	AGE 21	AGE 22	TOTAL
Parents' home	245.57	348.35	364.26	398.82	1357
Another person's home	29.32	41.59	43.49	47.61	162
Your own place	226.93	321.90	336.61	368.55	1254
Group quarters	34.75	49.29	51.54	56.43	192
Other	3.44	4.88	5.10	5.58	19
Total	540	766	801	877	2984

APPLY YOUR KNOWLEDGE

21.4 Facebook at Penn State. The two-way table in Exercise 21.2 displays data on use of Facebook by two groups of Penn State students. It's clear that nonusers are much more frequent at the commonwealth campuses. Let's look just at students who have Facebook accounts:

Use Facebook	University Park	Commonwealth
Several times a month or less	55	76
At least once a week	215	157
At least once a day	640	394
Total Facebook users	910	627

The null hypothesis is that there is no relationship between campus and Facebook use.

(a) If this hypothesis is true, what are the expected counts for Facebook use among commonwealth campus students? This is one column of the two-way table of expected counts. Find the column total and verify that it agrees with the column total for the observed counts.

(b) Commonwealth campus students as a group are older and more likely to be married and employed than University Park students. What does comparing the observed and expected counts in this column show about Facebook use by these students?

21.5 Attitudes toward recycled products. Exercise 21.1 describes a comparison of the attitudes of people who do and don't buy coffee filters made of recycled paper. The null hypothesis "no relationship" says that in the population of all consumers, the proportions who hold each attitude are the same for buyers and nonbuyers.

(a) Find the expected cell counts if this hypothesis is true and display them in a two-way table. Add the row and column totals to your table and check that they agree with the totals for the observed counts.

(b) Are there any large differences between the observed counts and the expected counts? What kind of relationship between the two variables do these deviations point to?

The chi-square test

To test whether the observed relationship between the row and column variables in a two-way table is statistically significant, we compare the observed and expected counts. The test statistic that makes the comparison is the *chi-square statistic*.

THE CHI-SQUARE TEST

Draw an SRS from a large population and make a two-way table of the sample counts for two categorical variables. To test the null hypothesis H_0 that there is no relationship between the row and column variables in the population, calculate the **chi-square statistic**

$$\chi^2 = \sum \frac{(\text{observed count} - \text{expected count})^2}{\text{expected count}}$$

The sum is over all cells in the table.

The **chi-square test** rejects H_0 when χ^2 is large. Software finds P-values from a **chi-square distribution.**

The symbol χ in the box is the Greek letter chi. Think of χ^2 as a measure of the distance of the observed counts from the expected counts. It is always zero or positive, and it is zero only when the observed counts are exactly equal to the expected counts. Large values of χ^2 are evidence against H_0 because they say that the observed counts are far from what we would expect if H_0 were true. *Although the alternative hypothesis H_a is*

many-sided, the chi-square test is one-sided because any violation of H_0 tends to produce a large value of χ^2. Small values of χ^2 are not evidence against H_0.

EXAMPLE 21.6   Where young people live: the test statistic

In the study of where young people live, 324 19-year-olds lived with their parents. The expected count for this cell is 245.57. So the term of the chi-square statistic from this cell is

$$\frac{(\text{observed count} - \text{expected count})^2}{\text{expected count}} = \frac{(324 - 245.57)^2}{245.57}$$

$$= \frac{6151.26}{245.57} = 25.05$$

The chi-square statistic χ^2 is the sum of 20 terms like this one. Here they are, arranged to match the layout of the two-way table:

$$\chi^2 = 25.05 + 2.53 + 2.04 + 16.38$$
$$+ \ 2.01 + 0.71 + 0.28 + \ 1.94$$
$$+ 54.23 + 5.72 + 3.72 + 38.07$$
$$+ 15.56 + 2.33 + 0.13 + 17.51$$
$$+ \ 0.71 + 1.70 + 0.87 + \ 2.09$$
$$= 193.58$$

Software is very handy in finding χ^2. Figure 21.3 shows Minitab's chi-square output. We see that $\chi^2 = 193.548$ (more accurate than our rounded hand calculation). The P-value is 0 to three decimal places. The relationship between the age of young people and where they live is highly significant. ∎

The chi-square test, like the z procedures for inference about proportions, is an approximate method that becomes more accurate as the counts in the cells of the table get larger. Approximate P-values come from a *chi-square distribution*, usually calculated by software. We must check that the counts are large enough to allow us to trust the P-value. Fortunately, the approximation is accurate for quite modest counts. Here is a practical guideline.[4]

CELL COUNTS REQUIRED FOR THE CHI-SQUARE TEST

You can safely use the chi-square test with P-values from the chi-square distribution when no more than 20% of the expected counts are less than 5 and all individual expected counts are 1 or greater. In particular, all four expected counts in a 2×2 table should be 5 or greater.

Note that the guideline uses *expected* cell counts. The expected counts for the living arrangements study of Example 21.1 appear in Table 21.2 and in the Minitab output in Figure 21.3. Only 2 of the 20 expected counts (that's 10%) are less than 5 and all are greater than 1, so the data meet the guideline for safe use of chi-square.

FIGURE 21.3

Minitab output showing observed and expected cell counts and contributions to chi-square for the study of where young people live, for Examples 21.6 and 21.7.

```
Session                                                              _  □  X

                    Age 19   Age 20   Age 21   Age 22      All

     Parents'          324      378      337      318     1357
                     245.6    348.3    364.3    398.8   1357.0
                    25.049    2.525    2.040   16.379        *

     Another            37       47       40       38      162
                      29.3     41.6     43.5     47.6    162.0
                     2.014    0.705    0.279    1.940        *

     OwnPlace          116      279      372      487     1254
                     226.9    321.9    336.6    368.6   1254.0
                    54.226    5.719    3.720   38.068        *

     Group              58       60       49       25      192
                      34.7     49.3     51.5     56.4    192.0
                    15.564    2.329    0.125   17.505        *

     Other               5        2        3        9       19
                       3.4      4.9      5.1      5.6     19.0
                     0.709    1.697    0.865    2.090        *

     All               540      766      801      877     2984
                     540.0    766.0    801.0    877.0   2984.0
                         *        *        *        *        *

     Cell Contents:        Count
                           Expected count
                           Contribution to Chi-square

     Pearson Chi-Square = 193.548, DF = 12, P-Value = 0.000

     * NOTE * 2 cells with expected counts less than 5
```

Data analysis for chi-square

The chi-square test is an overall test for detecting relationships between two categorical variables. If the test is significant, it is important to look at the data to learn the nature of the relationship. We have three ways to look at the living arrangements data:

- **Compare selected percents:** which living arrangements occur in quite different percents of the four age groups? Example 21.4 illustrates this method.
- **Compare observed and expected cell counts:** which cells have more or fewer observations than we would expect if H_0 were true?
- **Look at the terms of the chi-square statistic:** which cells contribute the most to the value of χ^2?

Statistical software offers this information on request. Figure 21.1 shows Minitab output comparing the conditional distributions of living arrangements for different age groups.

Figure 21.3 includes the observed counts and expected counts and also the term in the chi-square statistic for each cell, called the "contribution to chi-square." For example, the top left cell has expected count 245.57 and contributes 25.049 to the chi-square statistic, as we calculated earlier. (Roundoff errors are smaller with software than in hand calculation.)

EXAMPLE 21.7 **Where young people live: conclusion**

There is very strong evidence ($\chi^2 = 193.548$, $P < 0.001$) that living arrangements of young people are not the same for ages 19, 20, 21, and 22. Comparing selected percents—specifically, the four conditional distributions of living arrangements for each age in Table 21.2 and Figure 21.1—shows how young people become more independent as they grow older.

A quick way to find the most important differences among the age groups is to look for the cells that contribute the most to the chi-square statistic, then compare observed and expected counts in these cells. Just 6 of the 20 cells in Figure 21.3 contribute 166.791 of the total chi-square $\chi^2 = 193.548$. These 6 cells occur in pairs:

- 54.226 and 38.068: fewer 19-year-olds than expected and more 22-year-olds than expected live in their own place.
- 25.049 and 16.379: more 19-year-olds than expected and fewer 22-year-olds than expected live in their parents' home.
- 15.564 and 17.505: more 19-year-olds than expected and fewer 22-year-olds than expected live in group quarters.

These three trends display the increase in independent living between age 19 and age 22. ■

APPLY YOUR KNOWLEDGE

21.6 Facebook at Penn State. Figure 21.4 displays Minitab output for how frequently students at the University Park and commonwealth campuses of Penn State who have Facebook accounts make use of their accounts. The output includes the two-way table of observed counts, the expected counts, and each cell's contribution to the chi-square statistic.

(a) Verify from the output that the data meet the cell count requirement for use of chi-square.

(b) What hypotheses does chi-square test? What are the test statistic and its P-value?

(c) Which cells contribute the most to χ^2? Compare the observed and expected counts in these cells and comment on the most important differences in Facebook use between students at the two locations.

21.7 Attitudes toward recycled products. Your data analysis in Exercise 21.1 found that people who have bought recycled coffee filters tend to have more positive opinions about the filters than those who have not. Figure 21.5 gives Minitab output for the two-way table in Exercise 21.1.

(a) Verify from the output that the data meet the cell count requirement for use of chi-square.

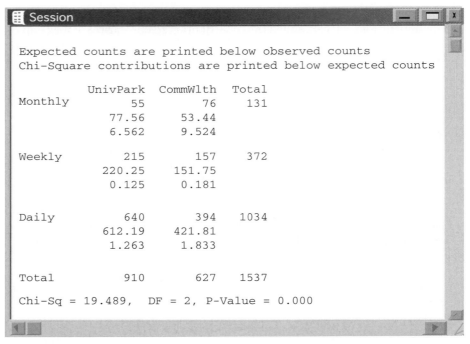

FIGURE 21.4
Minitab output for the two-way table of Facebook use by Penn State campus, for Exercise 21.6.

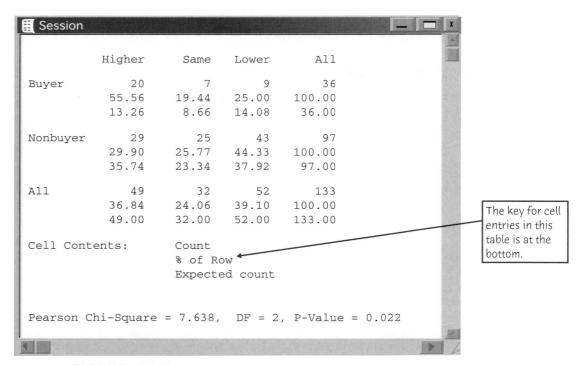

FIGURE 21.5
Minitab output for the study of consumer attitudes toward recycled products, for Exercise 21.7.

(b) What are the chi-square statistic and its P-value? Explain in simple language what it means to reject H_0 in this setting.

(c) Give an overall conclusion that refers to row percents to describe the nature of the relationship between attitude and decision to buy.

21.8 Is astrology scientific? The General Social Survey asked a random sample of adults about their education and about their view of astrology as scientific or not. Here are the data for people with three levels of higher education:[5]

	Degree Held		
	Associate's	Bachelor's	Master's
Not at all scientific	169	256	114
Very or sort of scientific	65	65	18

Figure 21.6 gives Minitab chi-square output for these data. Follow the *Plan, Solve,* and *Conclude* steps of the four-step process using the information in the output to describe how people with these levels of education differ in their opinions about astrology. Be sure that your *Solve* step includes data analysis and checking conditions for inference as well as a formal test.

```
⊞ Session                                        ─ ☐ ✕

                 Associate  Bachelor    Master       All

    NotScience         169       256       114       539
                     72.22     79.75     86.36     78.46
                     183.6     251.8     103.6     539.0
                    1.1594    0.0685    1.0518         *

    Science             65        65        18       148
                     27.78     20.25     13.64     21.54
                      50.4      69.2      28.4     148.0
                    4.2224    0.2494    3.8304         *

    All                234       321       132       687
                    100.00    100.00    100.00    100.00
                     234.0     321.0     132.0     687.0
                         *         *         *         *

    Cell Contents:        Count
                          % of Column
                          Expected count
                          Contribution to Chi-square

    Pearson Chi-Square = 10.582,   DF = 2, P-Value = 0.005
```

FIGURE 21.6

Minitab output for the two-way table of opinion about astrology by degree held, for Exercise 21.8.

Another use of the chi-square test

One of the most useful properties of chi-square is that it tests the null hypothesis "the row and column variables are not related to each other" whenever this hypothesis makes sense for a two-way table. Some two-way tables classify a single sample by two categorical variables. Our earlier examples were of this kind. Other two-way tables compare the values of a categorical response variable in two separate samples. Here is an example of this setting.

EXAMPLE 21.8 Are cell-only telephone users different?

STATE: Random digit dialing telephone surveys do not call cell phone numbers. If the opinions of people who have only cell phones differ from those of people who still have landline service, the poll results may not represent the entire adult population. The Pew Research Center interviewed separate random samples of cell-only and landline telephone users. We will compare the 96 cell-only users and the 104 landline users who were less than 30 years old. Here's what the Pew survey found about how these people describe their political party affiliation:[6]

	Cell-only sample	Landline sample
Democrat or lean Democratic	49	47
Refuse to lean either way	15	27
Republican or lean Republican	32	30
Total	96	104

AB/Getty Images

PLAN: Carry out a chi-square test for

H_0: no relationship; that is, the distribution of party affiliation is the same in both populations

H_a: there is some relationship; that is, the party distribution in the cell-only population differs from that of landline users

Compare column percents or observed versus expected cell counts or terms of chi-square to see the nature of the relationship.

SOLVE: The Minitab output in Figure 21.7 includes the column percents. These give the conditional distributions of party given telephone use. Cell-only users are less likely to have no party affiliation (15.63% versus 25.96% of landline users). The party affiliations among the 158 people who prefer one party are nearly the same in both groups, 60% Democrat for cell-only, 61% Democrat for landline.

To see if the differences are significant, first check the guidelines for use of chi-square. The samples are reasonably close to SRSs, though nonresponse was higher for the cell phone calls. The Minitab output shows that all expected cell counts are greater than 5. The chi-square test shows that there is no significant difference between the party affiliations of the two groups of young adults ($\chi^2 = 3.22$, $P = 0.200$). Comparing observed and expected cell counts again shows that cell-only young adults are less likely to have no party preference than would be expected if there were no relationship, and that landline users are more likely to have no preference. The two "refuse to lean" cells contribute 2.54 of the total chi-square $\chi^2 = 3.22$. But the overall comparison is not significant.

CONCLUDE: There is no significant difference between the political party affiliations of young people who have a landline telephone and those who rely entirely on cell phones. The data

```
┌─────────────────────────────────────────────────────────────────┐
│ ▦ Session                                        ─   □   X        │
├─────────────────────────────────────────────────────────────────┤
│                                                                   │
│                 Cell-only   Landline      All                     │
│                                                                   │
│   Democrat            49          47        96                    │
│                    51.04       45.19     48.00                    │
│                    46.08       49.92     96.00                    │
│                   0.1850      0.1708         *                    │
│                                                                   │
│   RefuseToLean        15          27        42                    │
│                    15.63       25.96     21.00                    │
│                    20.16       21.84     42.00                    │
│                   1.3207      1.2191         *                    │
│                                                                   │
│   Republican          32          30        62                    │
│                    33.33       28.85     31.00                    │
│                    29.76       32.24     62.00                    │
│                   0.1686      0.1556         *                    │
│                                                                   │
│   All                 96         104       200                    │
│                   100.00      100.00    100.00                    │
│                    96.00      104.00    200.00                    │
│                        *           *         *                    │
│                                                                   │
│                                                                   │
│   Cell Contents:      Count                                       │
│                       % of Column                                 │
│                       Expected count                              │
│                       Contribution to Chi-square                  │
│                                                                   │
│   Pearson Chi-Square = 3.220,  DF = 2, P-Value = 0.200            │
│                                                                   │
└─────────────────────────────────────────────────────────────────┘
```

FIGURE 21.7

Minitab output for the two-way table of political party affiliation and telephone use, for Example 21.8.

do suggest that cell-only users are more likely to have some affiliation, so that a larger sample might find a significant difference. The Pew study found "little difference" to be true for all adults and for a variety of political questions. Traditional telephone sample surveys will live on, at least for a while. ■

APPLY YOUR KNOWLEDGE

21.9 Cell-only versus landline users. We suspect that people who rely entirely on cell phones will as a group be younger than those who have a landline telephone. Do data confirm this guess? Here is a two-way table that breaks down both of Pew's samples (see Example 21.8) by age group:

	Landline sample	Cell-only sample
Age 18–29	108	96
Age 30–49	264	70
Age 50–64	202	26
Age 65 or older	178	8
Total	752	200

Do a complete analysis of these data, following the four-step process as illustrated in Example 21.8.

The chi-square distributions*

Software usually finds P-values for us. The P-value for a chi-square test comes from comparing the value of the chi-square statistic with critical values for a *chi-square distribution*.

THE CHI-SQUARE DISTRIBUTIONS

The **chi-square distributions** are a family of distributions that take only positive values and are skewed to the right. A specific chi-square distribution is specified by giving its **degrees of freedom.**

The chi-square test for a two-way table with r rows and c columns uses critical values from the chi-square distribution with $(r-1)(c-1)$ degrees of freedom. The P-value is the area under the density curve of this chi-square distribution to the right of the value of the test statistic.

Figure 21.8 shows the density curves for three members of the chi-square family of distributions. As the degrees of freedom increase, the density curves become less skewed and larger values become more probable. Table D in the back of the book gives critical values for chi-square distributions. You can use Table D if you do not have software that gives you P-values for a chi-square test.

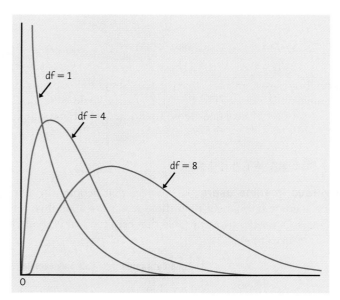

FIGURE 21.8

Density curves for the chi-square distributions with 1, 4, and 8 degrees of freedom. Chi-square distributions take only positive values and are right-skewed.

---

* This short section is optional if you will always use software for the chi-square test.

EXAMPLE 21.9 Using the chi-square table

The two-way table of 5 outcomes by 4 age groups for the living arrangements study (Table 21.1) has 5 rows and 4 columns. That is, $r = 5$ and $c = 4$. The chi-square statistic therefore has degrees of freedom

$$(r - 1)(c - 1) = (5 - 1)(4 - 1) = (4)(3) = 12$$

The output in Figure 21.3 gives 12 as the degrees of freedom.

The observed value of the chi-square statistic is $\chi^2 = 193.548$. Look in the df = 12 row of Table D. The value $\chi^2 = 193.548$ falls above the largest critical value in the table, for $P = 0.0005$. Remember that the chi-square test is always one-sided. So the P-value of $\chi^2 = 193.548$ is less than 0.0005. ■

df = 12

p	.001	.0005
x^*	32.91	34.82

We know that all z and t statistics measure the size of an effect in the standard scale centered at zero. We can roughly assess the size of any z or t statistic by the 68–95–99.7 rule, though this is exact only for z. The chi-square statistic does not have any such natural interpretation. But here is a helpful fact: *the mean of any chi-square distribution is equal to its degrees of freedom.* In Example 21.7, χ^2 would have mean 12 if the null hypothesis were true. The observed value $\chi^2 = 193.55$ is so much larger than 12 that we suspect it is significant even before we look at Table D.

APPLY YOUR KNOWLEDGE

21.10 Facebook at Penn State. The Minitab output in Figure 21.4 gives the degrees of freedom for a table of Facebook use by students at two campus locations as DF = 2.

(a) Show that this is correct for a table with 3 rows and 2 columns.

(b) Minitab gives the chi-square statistic as Chi-Sq = 19.489. Where does this value fall when compared with critical values of the chi-square distribution with 2 degrees of freedom in Table D? How does Minitab's result P-Value = 0.000 compare with the P-value from the table?

(c) The table included only students who have Facebook accounts. The original table in Exercise 21.2 had 4 rows and 2 columns. What is the proper degrees of freedom for that table?

21.11 Attitudes toward recycled products. The Minitab output in Figure 21.5 gives 2 degrees of freedom for the table in Exercise 21.1.

(a) Verify that this is correct.

(b) The computer gives the value of the chi-square statistic as $\chi^2 = 7.638$. Between what two entries in Table D does this value lie? Verify that Minitab's P-value does fall between the tail probabilities p for these two entries.

(c) What is the mean value of the statistic χ^2 if the null hypothesis is true? How does the observed value of χ^2 compare with this mean?

The chi-square test for goodness of fit*

The most common and most important use of the chi-square statistic is to test the hypothesis that there is *no relationship between two categorical variables*. A variation of the statistic can be used to test a different kind of null hypothesis: that *a categorical variable has a specified distribution*. Here is an example that illustrates this use of chi-square.

EXAMPLE 21.10 **Never on Sunday?**

Births are not evenly distributed across the days of the week. Fewer babies are born on Saturday and Sunday than on other days, probably because doctors find weekend births inconvenient.

A random sample of 140 births from local records shows this distribution across the days of the week:

Day	Sun.	Mon.	Tue.	Wed.	Thu.	Fri.	Sat.
Births	13	23	24	20	27	18	15

Sure enough, the two smallest counts of births are on Saturday and Sunday. Do these data give significant evidence that local births are not equally likely on all days of the week? ■

The chi-square test answers the question of Example 21.10 by comparing observed counts with expected counts under the null hypothesis. The null hypothesis for births says that they *are* evenly distributed. To state the hypotheses carefully, write the discrete probability distribution for days of birth:

Day	Sun.	Mon.	Tue.	Wed.	Thu.	Fri.	Sat.
Probability	p_1	p_2	p_3	p_4	p_5	p_6	p_7

The null hypothesis says that the probabilities are the same on all days. In that case, all 7 probabilities must be 1/7. So the null hypothesis is

$$H_0: p_1 = p_2 = p_3 = p_4 = p_5 = p_6 = p_7 = \frac{1}{7}$$

The alternative hypothesis says that days are *not* all equally probable:

$$H_a: \text{ not all } p_i = \frac{1}{7}$$

As usual in chi-square tests, H_a is a "many-sided" hypothesis that simply says that H_0 is not true. The chi-square statistic is also as usual:

$$\chi^2 = \sum \frac{(\text{observed count} - \text{expected count})^2}{\text{expected count}}$$

---

* This special topic is optional.

The expected count for an outcome with probability p is simply np. Under the null hypothesis, all the probabilities p_i are the same, so all 7 expected counts are equal to

$$np_i = 140 \times \frac{1}{7} = 20$$

These expected counts easily satisfy our guidelines for using chi-square. The chi-square statistic is

$$\chi^2 = \sum \frac{(\text{observed count} - 20)^2}{20}$$

$$= \frac{(13 - 20)^2}{20} + \frac{(23 - 20)^2}{20} + \cdots + \frac{(15 - 20)^2}{20}$$

$$= 7.6$$

This new use of χ^2 requires a different degrees of freedom. To find the P-value, compare χ^2 with critical values from the chi-square distribution with degrees of freedom one less than the number of values the birth day can take. That's $7 - 1 = 6$ degrees of freedom. From Table D, we see that $\chi^2 = 7.6$ is smaller than the smallest entry in the df $= 6$ row, which is the critical value for tail area 0.25. The P-value is therefore greater than 0.25 (software gives the more exact value $P = 0.269$). These 140 births don't give convincing evidence that births are not equally likely on all days of the week.

df = 6		
p	.25	.20
x^*	7.84	8.56

The chi-square test applied to the hypothesis that a categorical variable has a specified distribution is called the test for *goodness of fit*. The idea is that the test assesses whether the observed counts "fit" the distribution. The chi-square statistic is the same as for the two-way table test, but the expected counts and degrees of freedom are different. Here are the details.

THE CHI-SQUARE TEST FOR GOODNESS OF FIT

A categorical variable has k possible outcomes, with probabilities $p_1, p_2, p_3, \ldots, p_k$. That is, p_i is the probability of the ith outcome. We have n independent observations from this categorical variable.

To test the null hypothesis that the probabilities have specified values

$$H_0\colon p_1 = p_{10}, \ p_2 = p_{20}, \ \ldots, \ p_k = p_{k0}$$

find the **expected count** for the ith possible outcome as np_{i0} and use the **chi-square statistic**

$$\chi^2 = \sum \frac{(\text{observed count} - \text{expected count})^2}{\text{expected count}}$$

The sum is over all the possible outcomes.

The P-value is the area to the right of χ^2 under the density curve of the chi-square distribution with $k - 1$ degrees of freedom.

In Example 21.10, the outcomes are days of the week, with $k = 7$. The null hypothesis says that the probability of a birth on the ith day is $p_{i0} = 1/7$ for all days. We observe

$n = 140$ births and count how many fall on each day. These are the counts used in the chi-square statistic.

21.12 Saving birds from windows. Many birds are injured or killed by flying into windows. It appears that birds don't see windows. Can tilting windows down so that they reflect earth rather than sky reduce bird strikes? Place six windows at the edge of a woods: two vertical, two tilted 20 degrees, and two tilted 40 degrees. During the next four months, there were 53 bird strikes, 31 on the vertical windows, 14 on the 20-degree windows, and 8 on the 40-degree windows.[7] If the tilt has no effect, we expect strikes on windows with all three tilts to have equal probability. Test this null hypothesis. What do you conclude?

21.13 More on birth days. Births really are not evenly distributed across the days of the week. The data in Example 21.10 failed to reject this null hypothesis because of random variation in a quite small number of births. Here are data on 700 births in the same locale:

Day	Sun.	Mon.	Tue.	Wed.	Thu.	Fri.	Sat.
Births	84	110	124	104	94	112	72

(a) The null hypothesis is that all days are equally probable. What are the probabilities specified by this null hypothesis? What are the expected counts for each day in 700 births?

(b) Calculate the chi-square statistic for goodness of fit.

(c) What are the degrees of freedom for this statistic? Do these 700 births give significant evidence that births are not equally probable on all days of the week?

21.14 Police harassment? Police sometimes use minor violations such as not wearing a seat belt to stop motorists for other reasons. A large study in Michigan first studied the population of drivers not wearing seat belts during daylight hours by observation at more than 400 locations around the state. Here is the population distribution of seat belt violators by age group:[8]

Age group	16 to 29	30 to 59	60 or older
Proportion	0.328	0.594	0.078

The researchers then looked at court records and called a random sample of 803 drivers who had actually been cited by police for not wearing a seat belt. Here are the counts:

Age group	16 to 29	30 to 59	60 or older
Count	401	382	20

Does the age distribution of people cited differ significantly from the distribution of ages of all seat belt violators? Which age groups have the largest contributions to chi-square? Are these age groups cited more or less frequently than is justified? (The study found that males, blacks, and younger drivers were all overcited.)

21.15 Course grades. Most students in a large statistics course are taught by teaching as-sistants (TAs). One section is taught by the course supervisor, a senior professor. The distribution of grades for the hundreds of students taught by TAs this semester was

Grade	A	B	C	D/F
Probability	0.32	0.41	0.20	0.07

The grades assigned by the professor to students in his section were

Grade	A	B	C	D/F
Count	22	38	20	11

(These data are real. We won't say when and where, but the professor was not the author of this book.)

(a) What percents of each grade did students in the professor's section earn? In what ways does this distribution of grades differ from the TA distribution?

(b) Because the TA distribution is based on hundreds of students, we are willing to regard it as a fixed probability distribution. If the professor's grading follows this distribution, what are the expected counts of each grade in his section?

(c) Does the chi-square test for goodness of fit give good evidence that the professor's grades follow a different distribution? (State hypotheses, check the guidelines for using chi-square, give the test statistic and its P-value, and state your conclusion.)

21.16 What's your sign? For reasons known only to social scientists, the General Social Survey (GSS) regularly asks its subjects their astrological sign. Here are the counts of responses for the most recent GSS:

Sign	Aries	Taurus	Gemini	Cancer	Leo	Virgo
Count	321	360	367	374	383	402

Sign	Libra	Scorpio	Sagittarius	Capricorn	Aquarius	Pisces
Count	392	329	331	354	376	355

If births are spread uniformly across the year, we expect all 12 signs to be equally likely. Are they? Follow the four-step process in your answer.

CHAPTER 21 SUMMARY

- A **two-way table** of counts organizes data about two categorical variables. Values of the **row variable** label the rows that run across the table, and values of the **column variable** label the columns that run down the table. Two-way tables are often used to summarize large amounts of information by grouping outcomes into categories.

- The **row totals** and **column totals** in a two-way table give the **marginal distributions** of the two individual variables. It is clearer to present these distributions as percents of the table total. Marginal distributions tell us nothing about the relationship between the variables.

- There are two sets of **conditional distributions** for a two-way table: the distributions of the row variable for each fixed value of the column variable, and the distributions of the column variable for each fixed value of the row variable. Comparing one set of conditional distributions is one way to describe the association between the row and the column variables.

■ To find the **conditional distribution** of the row variable for one specific value of the column variable, look only at that one column in the table. Find each entry in the column as a percent of the column total.

■ The **chi-square test** for a two-way table tests the null hypothesis H_0 that there is no relationship between the row variable and the column variable. The alternative hypothesis H_a says that there is some relationship but does not say what kind.

■ The test compares the observed counts of observations in the cells of the table with the counts that would be expected if H_0 were true. The **expected count** in any cell is

$$\text{expected count} = \frac{\text{row total} \times \text{column total}}{\text{table total}}$$

The **chi-square statistic** is

$$\chi^2 = \sum \frac{(\text{observed count} - \text{expected count})^2}{\text{expected count}}$$

The chi-square test compares the value of the statistic χ^2 with critical values from the **chi-square distribution** with $(r-1)(c-1)$ **degrees of freedom.** Large values of χ^2 are evidence against H_0, so the P-value is the area under the chi-square density curve to the right of χ^2.

■ The chi-square distribution is an approximation to the distribution of the statistic χ^2. You can safely use this approximation when all expected cell counts are at least 1 and no more than 20% are less than 5.

■ If the chi-square test finds a statistically significant relationship between the row and column variables in a two-way table, do data analysis to describe the nature of the relationship. You can do this by comparing well-chosen percents, comparing the observed counts with the expected counts, and looking for the largest **terms of the chi-square statistic.**

CHECK YOUR SKILLS

The National Longitudinal Survey of Adolescent Health interviewed several thousand teens (grades 7 to 12). One question asked was "What do you think are the chances you will be married in the next ten years?" Here is a two-way table of the responses by gender:[9]

	Female	Male
Almost no chance	119	103
Some chance, but probably not	150	171
A 50-50 chance	447	512
A good chance	735	710
Almost certain	1174	756

21.17 The percent of the females in the sample who responded "almost certain" is about
(a) 44.7%.   (b) 39.6%.   (c) 33.6%.

21.18 Your percent from the previous exercise is part of
(a) the marginal distribution of opinion about marriage.
(b) the conditional distribution of opinion among females.
(c) the conditional distribution of gender among adolescents who are almost certain they will be married.

21.19 The expected count of females who respond "almost certain" is about
(a) 464.6.   (b) 891.2.   (c) 1038.8.

21.20 The term in the chi-square statistic for the cell of females who respond "almost certain" is about
(a) 17.6.   (b) 15.6.   (c) 0.1.

21.21 The degrees of freedom for the chi-square test for this two-way table are
(a) 4.   (b) 8.   (c) 20.

21.22 The null hypothesis for the chi-square test for this two-way table is
(a) Equal proportions of female and male teenagers are almost certain they will be married in ten years.
(b) There is no difference between female and male teenagers in their distributions of opinions about marriage.
(c) There are equal numbers of female and male teenagers.

21.23 The alternative hypothesis for the chi-square test for this two-way table is
(a) Female and male teenagers do not have the same distribution of opinions about marriage.
(b) Female teenagers are more likely than male teenagers to think it is almost certain they will be married in ten years.
(c) Female teenagers are less likely than male teenagers to think it is almost certain they will be married in ten years.

21.24 (Optional) Software gives chi-square statistic $\chi^2 = 69.8$ for this table. From the table of critical values, we can say that the P-value is
(a) between 0.0025 and 0.001.
(b) between 0.001 and 0.0005.
(c) less than 0.0005.

CHAPTER 21 EXERCISES

If you have access to software or a graphing calculator, use it to speed your analysis of the data in these exercises. Exercises 21.25 to 21.36 don't require software.

21.25 Got broadband? A sample survey asked a random sample of adults about use of the Internet. One question was whether the subject had a broadband Internet connection at home. Here is a two-way table of home broadband use by type of community:[10]

	Community Type		
	Urban	Suburban	Rural
Have broadband	300	521	174
No broadband	276	542	387

(a) Give a 95% confidence interval for the difference between the proportions of all rural and urban adults who have a home broadband connection.
(b) What proportion of each of the three groups in the sample have home broadband? Are there statistically significant differences among these proportions? State hypotheses and give a test statistic and its P-value.

21.26 Free speech for racists? The General Social Survey (GSS) asked this question: "Consider a person who believes that Blacks are genetically inferior. If such a person wanted to make a speech in your community claiming that Blacks are inferior, should he be allowed to speak, or not?" Here are the responses, broken down by the race of the respondent:

	Black	White	Other
Allowed	140	976	121
Not allowed	129	480	131

(a) Because the GSS is essentially an SRS of all adults, we can combine the races in these data and give a 99% confidence interval for the proportion of all adults who would allow a racist to speak. Do this.
(b) Find the column percents and use them to compare the attitudes of the three racial groups. How significant are the differences found in the sample?

21.27 Do you use cocaine? Sample surveys on sensitive issues can give different results depending on how the question is asked. A University of Wisconsin study divided 2400 respondents into 3 groups at random. All were asked if they had ever used cocaine. One group of 800 was interviewed by phone; 21% said they had used cocaine. Another 800 people were asked the question in a one-on-one personal interview; 25% said "Yes." The remaining 800 were allowed to make an anonymous written response; 28% said "Yes."[11] Are there statistically significant differences among these proportions? State the hypotheses, convert the information given into a two-way table of counts, give the test statistic and its P-value, and state your conclusions.

21.28 Did the randomization work? After randomly assigning subjects to treatments in a randomized comparative experiment, we can compare the treatment groups to see how well the randomization worked. We hope to find no significant differences among the groups. A study of how to provide premature infants with a substance essential to their development assigned infants at random to receive one of four types of supplement, called PBM, NLCP, PL-LCP, and TG-LCP.[12]
(a) The subjects were 77 premature infants. Outline the design of the experiment if 20 are assigned to the PBM group and 19 to each of the other treatments.
(b) The random assignment resulted in 9 females in the TG-LCP group and 11 females in each of the other groups. Make a two-way table of group by gender and do a chi-square test to see if there are significant differences among the groups. What do you find?

21.29 Opinions about the death penalty. The data for comparing two sample proportions can be presented in a two-way table containing the counts of successes and failures in both samples, with two rows and two columns. Here is an example from the General Social Survey. The question was "Do you favor or oppose the death penalty for persons convicted of murder?" The table gives the responses of people whose highest education was a high school degree and of people with a bachelor's degree.

	Favor	Oppose
High school	1010	369
Bachelor's	319	185

(a) Is there evidence that the proportions of all people at these levels of education who favor the death penalty differ? Find the two sample proportions, the z statistic, and its P-value.

(b) Is there evidence that the opinions of all people at these levels of education differ? Find the chi-square statistic χ^2 and its P-value.

(c) Show that (up to roundoff error) your χ^2 is the same as z^2. The two P-values are also the same. These facts are always true, so you will often see chi-square for 2×2 tables used to compare two proportions.

21.30 Unhappy rats and tumors. Some people think that the attitude of cancer patients can influence the progress of their disease. We can't experiment with humans, but here is a rat experiment on this theme. Inject 60 rats with tumor cells and then divide them at random into two groups of 30. All the rats receive electric shocks, but rats in Group 1 can end the shock by pressing a lever. (Rats learn this sort of thing quickly.) The rats in Group 2 cannot control the shocks, which presumably makes them feel helpless and unhappy. We suspect that the rats in Group 1 will develop fewer tumors. The results: 11 of the Group 1 rats and 22 of the Group 2 rats developed tumors.[13]

(a) Make a two-way table of tumors by group. State the null and alternative hypotheses for this investigation.

(b) Although we have a two-way table, the chi-square test can't test a one-sided alternative. Carry out the z test and report your conclusion.

21.31 I think I'll be rich by age 30. A sample survey asked young adults (aged 19 to 25), "What do you think are the chances you will have much more than a middle-class income at age 30?" The Minitab output in Figure 21.9 shows the two-way table and related information, omitting a few subjects who refused to respond or who said they were already rich.[14] Use the output as the basis for a discussion of the differences between young men and young women in assessing their chances of being rich by age 30.

```
 Session                                         _ □ x

                                  Female      Male

A: Almost no chance                   96        98
                                    95.2      98.8
                                  0.0076    0.0073

B: Some chance but probably not      426       286
                                   349.2     362.8
                                 16.8842   16.2525

C: A 50 50 chance                    696       720
                                   694.5     721.5
                                  0.0032    0.0031

D: A good chance                     663       758
                                   697.0     724.0
                                  1.6543    1.5924

E: Almost certain                    486       597
                                   531.2     551.8
                                  3.8424    3.6986

Cell Contents:        Count
                      Expected count
                      Contribution to Chi-square

Pearson Chi-Square = 43.946,  DF = 4, P-Value = 0.000
```

FIGURE 21.9

Minitab output for the sample survey responses of Exercise 21.31.

21.32 Sexy magazine ads? Look at full-page ads in magazines with a young adult readership. Classify ads that show a model as "not sexual" or "sexual" depending on how the model is dressed. Here are data on 1509 ads in magazines aimed at young men, at young women, or at young adults in general:[15]

	Readers		
	Men	**Women**	**General**
Sexual	105	225	66
Not sexual	514	351	248

Figure 21.10 displays Minitab chi-square output. Use the information in the output to describe the relationship between the target audience and the sexual content of ads in magazines for young adults.

Mistakes in using the chi-square test are unusually common. Exercises 21.33 to 21.36 illustrate several kinds of mistake.

21.33 Sorry, no chi-square. Are preschool children affected by how knowledgeable they think teachers are? Assign 48 three- and four-year-olds at random to be taught the name of a

FIGURE 21.10

Minitab output for a study of ads in magazines, for Exercise 21.32.

new toy by either an adult who claims to know about the toy or an adult who claims not to know about it. Then ask the children to pick out a picture of the new toy in a set of pictures of other toys and say its name. The response variable is the count of right answers in four tries. Here are the data:[16]

	Correct Answers				
	0	1	2	3	4
Knowledgeable teacher	5	1	6	3	9
Ignorant teacher	20	0	3	0	1

The researchers report that children taught by the teacher who claimed to be knowledgeable did significantly better ($\chi^2 = 20.4$, $P < 0.05$).

(a) The data do show that children taught by the knowledgeable teacher did better. Show this by comparing suitable percents.

(b) Why can't the chi-square test be trusted to assess significance for these data?

(c) If you use software, does the chi-square output for these data warn you against using the test?

21.34 Sorry, no chi-square. How do U.S. residents who travel overseas for leisure differ from those who travel for business? Here is the breakdown by occupation:[17]

	Leisure travelers	Business travelers
Professional/technical	36%	39%
Manager/executive	23%	48%
Retired	14%	3%
Student	7%	3%
Other	20%	7%
Total	100%	100%

Explain why we don't have enough information to use the chi-square test to learn whether these two distributions differ significantly.

21.35 Sorry, no chi-square. Here (see page 390) is more information about Internet use by students at Penn State, based on a random sample of 1852 undergraduates. Explain why it is not correct to use a chi-square test on this table to compare the University Park and commonwealth campuses.

	University Park	Commonwealth
Viewed a video on YouTube or similar site	875	700
Legally purchased music or videos online	514	348
Downloaded a podcast	235	145
Participated in Internet gambling	114	93

21.36 Sorry, no chi-square. Does eating chocolate trigger headaches? To find out, women with chronic headaches followed the same diet except for eating chocolate bars and carob bars that looked and tasted the same. Each subject ate both chocolate and carob bars in random order with at least three days between. Each woman then reported whether or not she had a headache within 12 hours of eating the bar. Here is a two-way table of the results for the 64 subjects:[18]

	No headache	Headache
Chocolate	53	11
Carob (placebo)	38	26

The researchers carried out a chi-square test on this table to see if the two types of bar differ in triggering headaches. Explain why this test is incorrect. (*Hint:* There are 64 subjects. How many observations appear in the two-way table?)

The remaining exercises concern larger tables that require software for easy analysis. In many cases, you should follow the **Plan, Solve,** *and* **Conclude** *steps of the four-step process in your answers.*

21.37 Animal testing. "It is right to use animals for medical testing if it might save human lives." The General Social Survey asked 1152 adults to react to this statement. Here is the two-way table of their responses:

	Male	Female
Strongly agree	76	59
Agree	270	247
Neither agree nor disagree	87	139
Disagree	61	123
Strongly disagree	22	68

(a) Compare the conditional distributions of opinion among men and among women. What are the most important differences?
(b) Carry out the chi-square test for the hypothesis of no difference between the opinions of men and women. What is the *P*-value?
(c) Look at the terms of the chi-square statistic and compare observed and expected counts in the cells that contribute the most to chi-square. Based on this and your findings in part (a), write a short comparison of the opinions of men and women about animal testing.

21.38 Smoking among French men. In the United States, there is a strong relationship between education and smoking: well-educated people are less likely to smoke. Does a similar relationship hold in France? Here is a two-way table of the level of education and smoking status (nonsmoker, former smoker, moderate smoker, heavy smoker) of a sample of 459 French men aged 20 to 60 years.[19] The subjects are a random sample of men who visited a health center for a routine checkup. We are willing to consider them an SRS of men from their region of France.

Education	Smoking Status			
	Nonsmoker	Former	Moderate	Heavy
Primary school	56	54	41	36
Secondary school	37	43	27	32
University	53	28	36	16

(a) Find the conditional distributions of smoking status for each education level. Make a graph that compares the three conditional distributions. Use your work to describe the overall relationship between education and smoking in this sample.
(b) Do French men with different levels of education differ significantly in their smoking status? State hypotheses, give the chi-square statistic and its *P*-value, and state your conclusion.

21.39 Canada versus the United States: health care. The Joint Canada/United States Survey of Health asked the same questions of random samples of American and Canadian adults. Respondents who had received health care services within the past 12 months were asked, "Overall, how satisfied were you with the way health care services were provided?" Here are the results:[20]

	Canada	United States
Very satisfied	1144	2120
Somewhat satisfied	1134	1460
Neither satisfied nor dissatisfied	128	139
Somewhat dissatisfied	144	186
Very dissatisfied	68	75
Total	2618	3980

Describe the most important differences between the opinions of Canadian and American patients. Is there a significant overall difference between the two distributions of responses?

21.40 How are schools doing? A nonprofit group conducted telephone interviews with random samples of 202 black parents of high school children, 202 Hispanic parents, and 201 white parents. One question asked was "Are the high schools in your state doing an excellent, good, fair or poor job, or don't you know enough to say?" Here are the survey results:[21]

	Black parents	Hispanic parents	White parents
Excellent	12	34	22
Good	69	55	81
Fair	75	61	60
Poor	24	24	24
Don't know	22	28	14
Total	202	202	201

Are the differences in the distributions of responses for the three groups of parents statistically significant? What departures from the null hypothesis "no relationship between group and response" contribute most to the value of the chi-square statistic? Write a brief conclusion based on your analysis.

21.41 The Mediterranean diet. Cancer of the colon and rectum is less common in the Mediterranean region than in other Western countries. The Mediterranean diet contains little animal fat and lots of olive oil. Italian researchers compared 1953 patients with colon or rectal cancer with a control group of 4154 patients admitted to the same hospitals for unrelated reasons. They estimated consumption of various foods from a detailed interview, then divided the patients into three groups according to their consumption of olive oil. Here are some of the data:[22]

	Olive Oil			
	Low	Medium	High	Total
Colon cancer	398	397	430	1225
Rectal cancer	250	241	237	728
Controls	1368	1377	1409	4154

(a) Is this study an experiment? Explain your answer.

(b) The investigators report that "less than 4% of cases or controls refused to participate." Why does this fact strengthen our confidence in the results?

(c) The researchers conjectured that high olive oil consumption would be more common among patients without cancer than among patients with colon cancer or rectal cancer. What do the data say?

21.42 Market research. Before bringing a new product to market, firms carry out extensive studies to learn how consumers react to the product. Here are data from a study of a new laundry detergent.[23] The subjects are people who don't currently use the established brand that the new product will compete with. Give subjects free samples of both detergents. After they have tried both for a while, ask which they prefer. The answers may depend on other facts about how people do laundry.

	Laundry Practices			
	Soft water, warm wash	Soft water, hot wash	Hard water, warm wash	Hard water, hot wash
Prefer established brand	53	27	42	30
Prefer new product	63	29	68	42

How do water hardness and wash temperature influence the choice of detergent? In which settings does the new detergent do best? Are the differences between the detergents statistically significant?

Babies cry when a rubber band snaps their feet. What's surprising is that those who cry more intensely tend to score higher on an IQ test given years later. See Example 22.1.

Inference for Regression

When a scatterplot shows a linear relationship between a quantitative explanatory variable x and a quantitative response variable y, we can use the least-squares line fitted to the data to predict y for a given value of x. When the data are a sample from a larger population, we need statistical inference to answer questions like these about the population:

■ Is there really a linear relationship between x and y in the population, or might the pattern we see in the scatterplot plausibly arise just by chance?

■ What is the slope (rate of change) that relates y to x in the population, including a margin of error for our estimate of the slope?

■ If we use the least-squares line to predict y for a given value of x, how accurate is our prediction (again, with a margin of error)?

This chapter shows you how to answer these questions. Here is an example we will explore.

IN THIS CHAPTER WE COVER...

■ Conditions for regression inference

■ Estimating the parameters

■ Using technology

■ Testing the hypothesis of no linear relationship

■ Testing lack of correlation

■ Confidence intervals for the regression slope

■ Inference about prediction

■ Checking the conditions for inference

EXAMPLE 22.1 Crying and IQ

STATE: Infants who cry easily may be more easily stimulated than others. This may be a sign of higher IQ. Child development researchers explored the relationship between the crying of infants four to ten days old and their later IQ test scores. A snap of a rubber band on the sole of the foot caused the infants to cry. The researchers recorded the crying and measured its intensity by the number of peaks in the most active 20 seconds. They later measured the children's IQ at age three years. Table 22.1 contains data on 38 infants.[1] Do children with higher crying counts tend to have higher IQ?

TABLE 22.1 Infants' crying and IQ scores

CRYING	IQ	CRYING	IQ	CRYING	IQ	CRYING	IQ
10	87	20	90	17	94	12	94
12	97	16	100	19	103	12	103
9	103	23	103	13	104	14	106
16	106	27	108	18	109	10	109
18	109	15	112	18	112	23	113
15	114	21	114	16	118	9	119
12	119	12	120	19	120	16	124
20	132	15	133	22	135	31	135
16	136	17	141	30	155	22	157
33	159	13	162				

Benelux Press/Index Stock
Imagery/PictureQuest

scatterplot

correlation

least-squares line

PLAN: Make a scatterplot. If the relationship appears linear, use correlation and regression to describe it. Finally, ask whether there is a *statistically significant* linear relationship between crying and IQ.

SOLVE (first steps): Figure 22.1 is a **scatterplot** of the crying data. Plot the explanatory variable (count of crying peaks) horizontally and the response variable (IQ) vertically. Look for the form, direction, and strength of the relationship as well as for outliers or other deviations. There is a moderate positive linear relationship, with no extreme outliers or potentially influential observations.

Because the scatterplot shows a roughly linear (straight-line) pattern, the **correlation** describes the direction and strength of the relationship. The correlation between crying and IQ is $r = 0.455$. We are interested in predicting the response from information about the explanatory variable. So we find the **least-squares regression line** for predicting IQ from crying. The equation of the regression line is

$$\hat{y} = a + bx$$
$$= 91.27 + 1.493x$$

FIGURE 22.1

Scatterplot of the IQ scores of infants at age three years against the intensity of their crying soon after birth, with the least-squares regression line, for Example 22.1.

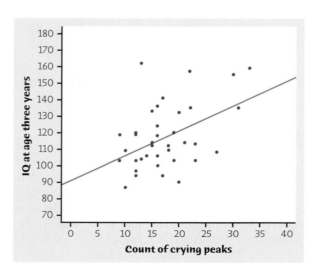

CONCLUDE (first steps):   Children who cry more vigorously do tend to have higher IQs. Because $r^2 = 0.207$, only about 21% of the variation in IQ scores is explained by crying intensity. Prediction of IQ will not be very accurate. It is nonetheless impressive that behavior soon after birth can even partly predict IQ three years later. Is this observed relationship statistically significant? We must now develop tools for inference in the regression setting. ■

Conditions for regression inference

We can fit a regression line to *any* data relating two quantitative variables, though the results are useful only if the scatterplot shows a linear pattern. Statistical inference requires more detailed conditions. Because the conclusions of inference always concern some *population*, the conditions describe the population and how the data are produced from it. The slope b and intercept a of the least-squares line are *statistics* calculated from the sample data. These statistics would take somewhat different values if we repeated the study with different infants. To do inference, think of a and b as estimates of unknown *parameters* that describe the population of all infants.

CONDITIONS FOR REGRESSION INFERENCE

We have n observations on an explanatory variable x and a response variable y. Our goal is to study or predict the behavior of y for given values of x.

■ For any fixed value of x, the response y varies according to a **Normal distribution.** Repeated responses y are **independent** of each other.

■ The mean response μ_y has a **straight-line relationship** with x given by a **population regression line**

$$\mu_y = \alpha + \beta x$$

The slope β and intercept α are unknown parameters.

■ The **standard deviation** of y (call it σ) is the same for all values of x. The value of σ is unknown.

There are thus three population parameters that we must estimate from the data: α, β, and σ.

These conditions say that in the population there is an "on the average" straight-line relationship between y and x. The population regression line $\mu_y = \alpha + \beta x$ says that the *mean* response μ_y moves along a straight line as the explanatory variable x changes. We can't observe the population regression line. The values of y that we do observe vary about their means according to a Normal distribution. In practice, we observe y for many different values of x, so that we see an overall linear pattern formed by points scattered about the population line. The standard deviation σ determines whether the points fall close to the population regression line (small σ) or are widely scattered (large σ).

Figure 22.2 shows the conditions for regression inference in picture form. The line in the figure is the population regression line. The mean response μ_y moves along this line as the explanatory variable x takes different values. The Normal curves show how y will

The conditions for regression inference in a picture. The line is the population regression line, which shows how the mean response μ_y changes as the explanatory variable x changes. For any fixed value of x, the observed response y varies according to a Normal distribution having mean μ_y and standard deviation σ.

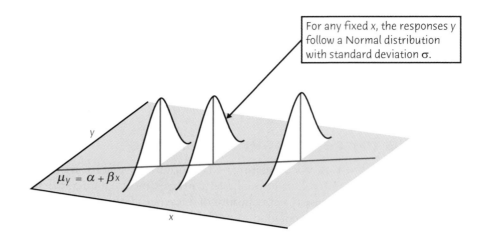

For any fixed x, the responses y follow a Normal distribution with standard deviation σ.

$$\mu_y = \alpha + \beta x$$

vary when x is held fixed at different values. The mean depends on x, but the standard deviation is always the same. You must check the conditions for inference when you do inference about regression. We will see later how to do that.

Estimating the parameters

The first step in inference is to estimate the unknown parameters α, β, and σ.

> **ESTIMATING THE POPULATION REGRESSION LINE**
>
> When the conditions for regression are met and we calculate the least-squares line $\hat{y} = a + bx$, the slope b of the least-squares line is an unbiased estimator of the population slope β, and the intercept a of the least-squares line is an unbiased estimator of the population intercept α.

EXAMPLE 22.2 **Crying and IQ: slope and intercept**

The data in Figure 22.1 satisfy the condition of scatter about an invisible population regression line reasonably well. The least-squares line is $\hat{y} = 91.27 + 1.493x$. The slope is particularly important. A *slope is a rate of change*. The population slope β says how much higher average IQ is for children with one more peak in their crying measurement. Because $b = 1.493$ estimates the unknown β, we estimate that, on the average, IQ is about 1.5 points higher for each added crying peak.

We need the intercept $a = 91.27$ to draw the line, but it has no statistical meaning in this example. No child had fewer than 9 crying peaks, so we have no data near $x = 0$. We suspect that all normal children would cry when snapped with a rubber band, so that we will never observe $x = 0$. ■

The remaining parameter is the standard deviation σ, which describes the variability of the response y about the population regression line. The least-squares line estimates the population regression line. So the ***residuals*** estimate how much y varies about the population line. Recall that the residuals are the vertical deviations of the data points

residuals

from the least-squares line:

$$\text{residual} = \text{observed } y - \text{predicted } y$$
$$= y - \hat{y}$$

There are n residuals, one for each data point. Because σ is the standard deviation of responses about the population regression line, we estimate it by a sample standard deviation of the residuals. We call this sample standard deviation the *regression standard error* to emphasize that it is estimated from data. The residuals from a least-squares line always have mean zero. That simplifies their standard error.

REGRESSION STANDARD ERROR

The **regression standard error** is

$$s = \sqrt{\frac{1}{n-2}\sum \text{residual}^2}$$

$$= \sqrt{\frac{1}{n-2}\sum (y - \hat{y})^2}$$

Use s to estimate the standard deviation σ of responses about the mean given by the population regression line.

Because we use the regression standard error so often, we just call it s. The quantity $\sum (y - \hat{y})^2$ is the sum of the squared deviations of the data points from the line. We average the squared deviations by dividing by $n-2$, the number of data points less 2. It turns out that if we know $n-2$ of the n residuals, the other two are determined. That is, $n-2$ are the **degrees of freedom** of s. We first met the idea of degrees of freedom in the case of the ordinary sample standard deviation of n observations, which has $n-1$ degrees of freedom. Now we observe two variables rather than one, and the proper degrees of freedom are $n-2$ rather than $n-1$.

degrees of freedom

Calculating s is unpleasant. You must find the predicted response for each x in your data set, then the residuals, and then s. In practice you will use software that does this arithmetic instantly. Nonetheless, here is an example to help you understand the standard error s.

EXAMPLE 22.3 **Crying and IQ: residuals and standard error**

Table 22.1 shows that the first infant studied had 10 crying peaks and a later IQ of 87. The predicted IQ for $x = 10$ is

$$\hat{y} = 91.27 + 1.493x$$
$$= 91.27 + 1.493(10) = 106.2$$

The residual for this observation is

$$\text{residual} = y - \hat{y}$$
$$= 87 - 106.2 = -19.2$$

That is, the observed IQ for this infant lies 19.2 points below the least-squares line on the scatterplot.

Repeat this calculation 37 more times, once for each subject. The 38 residuals are

−19.20	−31.13	−22.65	−15.18	−12.18	−15.15	−16.63	−6.18
−1.70	−22.60	−6.68	−6.17	−9.15	−23.58	−9.14	2.80
−9.14	−1.66	−6.14	−12.60	0.34	−8.62	2.85	14.30
9.82	10.82	0.37	8.85	10.87	19.34	10.89	−2.55
20.85	24.35	18.94	32.89	18.47	51.32		

Check the calculations by verifying that the sum of the residuals is zero. It is 0.04, not quite zero, because of roundoff error. Another reason to use software in regression is that roundoff errors in hand calculation can accumulate to make the results inaccurate.

The variance about the line is

$$s^2 = \frac{1}{n-2} \sum \text{residual}^2$$

$$= \frac{1}{38-2}[(-19.20)^2 + (-31.13)^2 + \cdots + (51.32)^2]$$

$$= \frac{1}{36}(11023.3) = 306.20$$

Finally, the regression standard error is

$$s = \sqrt{306.20} = 17.50 \quad \blacksquare$$

We will study several kinds of inference in the regression setting. The regression standard error s is the key measure of the variability of the responses in regression. It is part of the standard error of all the statistics we will use for inference.

APPLY YOUR KNOWLEDGE

22.1 Ebola and gorillas. An outbreak of the deadly Ebola virus in 2002 and 2003 killed 91 of the 95 gorillas in 7 home ranges in the Congo. To study the spread of the virus, measure "distance" by the number of home ranges separating a group of gorillas from the first group infected. Here are data on distance and number of days until deaths began in each later group:[2]

Distance x	1	3	4	4	4	5
Days y	4	21	33	41	43	46

(a) Examine the data. Make a scatterplot with distance as the explanatory variable and find the correlation. There is a strong linear relationship.

(b) Explain in words what the slope β of the population regression line would tell us if we knew it. Based on the data, what are the estimates of β and the intercept α of the population regression line?

(c) Calculate by hand the residuals for the six data points. Check that their sum is 0 (up to roundoff error). Use the residuals to estimate the standard deviation σ that measures variation in the responses (days) about the means given by the population regression line. You have now estimated all three parameters.

Using technology

Inference about regression requires the regression standard error *s* and other calculations that are unpleasant with a basic calculator. Software or a graphing calculator that includes procedures for regression inference is almost essential for practical work.

Figure 22.3 shows regression output for the data of Table 22.1 from a graphing calculator, a statistical program, and a spreadsheet program. When we entered the data into the programs, we called the explanatory variable "Crycount." The software outputs use that

Texas Instruments Graphing Calculator

FIGURE 22.3

Regression of IQ on crying peaks: output from a graphing calculator, a statistical program, and a spreadsheet program.

Minitab

Regression Analysis: IQ versus Crycount

The regression equation is
IQ = 91.3 + 1.49 Crycount

Predictor	Coef	SE Coef	T	P
Constant	91.268	8.934	10.22	0.000
Crycount	1.4929	0.4870	3.07	0.004

S = 17.50   R-Sq = 20.7%   R-Sq(adj) = 18.5%

Excel

	A	B	C	D	E	F	G
1	SUMMARY OUTPUT						
2							
3	*Regression statistics*						
4	Multiple R	0.4550					
5	R Square	0.2070					
6	Adjusted R Square	0.1850					
7	Standard Error	17.4987					
8	Observations	38					
9							
10		Coefficients	Standard Error	t Stat	P-value	Lower 95%	Upper 95%
11	Intercept	91.2683	8.9342	10.2156	3.5E-12	73.1489	109.3877
12	Crycount	1.4929	0.4870	3.0655	0.004105	0.5052	2.4806
13							

label. The graphing calculator just uses "x" and "y" to label the explanatory and response variables. You can locate the basic information in all of the outputs. The regression slope is $b = 1.4929$ and the regression intercept is $a = 91.268$. The equation of the least-squares line is therefore (after rounding) just as given in Example 22.1. The regression standard error is $s = 17.4987$ and the squared correlation is $r^2 = 0.207$. Both of these results reflect the rather wide scatter of the points in Figure 22.1 about the least-squares line.

Each output contains other information, some of which we will need shortly and some of which we don't need. Once you know what to look for, you can find what you want in almost any output and ignore what doesn't interest you.

APPLY YOUR KNOWLEDGE

Kristjan Fridriksson/Getty Images

22.2 How fast do icicles grow? The rate at which an icicle grows depends on temperature, water flow, and wind. The data below are for an icicle grown in a cold chamber at $-11°C$ with no wind and a water flow of 11.9 milligrams per second.[3]

Time (min)	10	20	30	40	50	60	70	80	90
Length (cm)	0.6	1.8	2.9	4.0	5.0	6.1	7.9	10.1	10.9

Time (min)	100	110	120	130	140	150	160	170	180
Length (cm)	12.7	14.4	16.6	18.1	19.9	21.0	23.4	24.7	27.8

We want to predict length from time. Figure 22.4 shows Minitab regression output for these data.

(a) Make a scatterplot suitable for predicting length from time. The pattern is very linear. What is the squared correlation r^2? Time explains almost all of the change in length.

(b) For regression inference, we must estimate the three parameters α, β, and σ. From the output, what are the estimates of these parameters?

(c) What is the equation of the least-squares regression line of length on time? Add this line to your plot. We will continue the analysis of these data in later exercises.

FIGURE 22.4

Minitab output for the icicle growth data, for Exercise 22.2.

```
Session                                                        _ □ ×

Regression Analysis: Length versus Time

The regression equation is
Length = -2.39 + 0.158 Time

Predictor        Coef       SE Coef           T          P
Constant      -2.3948        0.3963       -6.04      0.000
Time         0.158483       0.003661       43.29      0.000

S = 0.8059    R-Sq = 99.2%        R-Sq(adj) = 99.1%
```

22.3 Great Arctic rivers. One effect of global warming is to increase the flow of water into the Arctic Ocean from rivers. Such an increase may have major effects on the world's climate. Six rivers (Yenisey, Lena, Ob, Pechora, Kolyma, and Severnaya Dvina) drain two-thirds of the Arctic region in Europe and Asia. Several of these are among the largest rivers on earth. Table 22.2 presents the total discharge from these rivers into the Arctic Ocean each year from 1936 to 1999.[4] Discharge is measured in cubic kilometers of water. Use software to analyze these data.

(a) Make a scatterplot of river discharge against time. Is there a clear increasing trend? Calculate r^2 and briefly interpret its value. There is considerable year-to-year variation, so we wonder if the trend is statistically significant.

(b) As a first step, find the least-squares line and draw it on your plot. Then find the regression standard error s, which measures scatter about this line. We will continue the analysis in later exercises.

TABLE 22.2 Arctic river discharge (cubic kilometers), 1936 to 1999

YEAR	DISCHARGE	YEAR	DISCHARGE	YEAR	DISCHARGE	YEAR	DISCHARGE
1936	1721	1952	1829	1968	1713	1984	1823
1937	1713	1953	1652	1969	1742	1985	1822
1938	1860	1954	1589	1970	1751	1986	1860
1939	1739	1955	1656	1971	1879	1987	1732
1940	1615	1956	1721	1972	1736	1988	1906
1941	1838	1957	1762	1973	1861	1989	1932
1942	1762	1958	1936	1974	2000	1990	1861
1943	1709	1959	1906	1975	1928	1991	1801
1944	1921	1960	1736	1976	1653	1992	1793
1945	1581	1961	1970	1977	1698	1993	1845
1946	1834	1962	1849	1978	2008	1994	1902
1947	1890	1963	1774	1979	1970	1995	1842
1948	1898	1964	1606	1980	1758	1996	1849
1949	1958	1965	1735	1981	1774	1997	2007
1950	1830	1966	1883	1982	1728	1998	1903
1951	1864	1967	1642	1983	1920	1999	1970

Testing the hypothesis of no linear relationship

Example 22.1 asked, "Do children with higher crying counts tend to have higher IQ?" Data analysis supports this conjecture. But is the positive association statistically significant? That is, is it too strong to be likely to occur just by chance? To answer this question, test hypotheses about the slope β of the population regression line:

$$H_0: \beta = 0$$
$$H_a: \beta > 0$$

A regression line with slope 0 is horizontal. That is, the mean of y does not change at all when x changes. So H_0 says that there is *no linear relationship* between x and y in the population. Put another way, H_0 says that *linear regression of y on x is of no value for predicting y*.

The test statistic is just the standardized version of the least-squares slope b, using the hypothesized value $\beta = 0$ for the mean of b. It is another t statistic. Here are the details.

SIGNIFICANCE TEST FOR REGRESSION SLOPE

To **test the hypothesis H_0: $\beta = 0$,** compute the t statistic

$$t = \frac{b}{SE_b}$$

In this formula, the standard error of the least-squares slope b is

$$SE_b = \frac{s}{\sqrt{\sum(x - \bar{x})^2}}$$

The sum runs over all observations on the explanatory variable x.

Find P-values from the t distribution with $n - 2$ degrees of freedom.

The standard error of b is a multiple of the regression standard error s. The degrees of freedom $n - 2$ are the degrees of freedom of s. Although we give the formula for this standard error, you should not try to calculate it by hand. Regression software gives the standard error SE_b along with b itself.

EXAMPLE 22.4 **Crying and IQ: is the relationship significant?**

The hypothesis H_0: $\beta = 0$ says that crying has no straight-line relationship with IQ. We conjecture that there is a positive relationship, so we use the one-sided alternative H_a: $\beta > 0$.

Figure 22.1 shows that there is a positive relationship, so it is not surprising that all of the outputs in Figure 22.3 give $t = 3.07$ with two-sided P-value 0.004. The P-value for the one-sided test is half of this, $P = 0.002$. There is very strong evidence that IQ increases as the intensity of crying increases. ■

APPLY YOUR KNOWLEDGE

22.4 Ebola and gorillas: testing. Exercise 22.1 gives data on the distance of gorilla groups from the origin of an Ebola outbreak and the number of days until deaths from Ebola began. Software tells us that the least-squares slope is $b = 11.263$ with standard error $SE_b = 1.591$.

(a) What is the t statistic for testing H_0: $\beta = 0$?

(b) How many degrees of freedom does t have? Use Table C to approximate the P-value of t against the one-sided alternative H_a: $\beta > 0$. What do you conclude?

22.5 Great Arctic rivers: testing. The most important question we ask of the data in Table 22.2 is this: is the increasing trend visible in your plot (Exercise 22.3) statistically significant? If so, changes in the Arctic may already be affecting the earth's climate. Use software to answer this question. Give a test statistic, its P-value, and the conclusion you draw from the test.

Testing lack of correlation

The slope β of the population regression line is 0 exactly when the population correlation between x and y is 0. Testing the null hypothesis $H_0: \beta = 0$ is therefore exactly the same as testing that there is *no correlation* between x and y in the population from which we drew our data. You can use the test for zero slope to test the hypothesis of zero correlation between any two quantitative variables. That's a useful trick. It works even when there is no explanatory-response distinction, so that regression itself is not useful.

EXAMPLE 22.5 Testing lack of correlation

The left scatterplot in Figure 22.5 displays data from an experiment on the healing of cuts in the limbs of newts. The data are the healing rates (micrometers per hour) for the two front limbs of 18 newts. The right-hand scatterplot shows the first- and second-round scores for the 96 golfers in the 2007 Masters Tournament. (There are fewer than 96 points because of duplicate scores.)

We will test the hypotheses

$$H_0: \text{population correlation} = 0$$
$$H_a: \text{population correlation} \neq 0$$

for both sets of data. (The Masters scores are all whole numbers, but with $n = 96$ the robustness of the t procedures allows their use.) Software gives

```
newts      r=0.3581     t=1.5342     P=0.1445
masters    r=0.1924     t=1.9010     P=0.0604
```

The two-sided P-values for the t statistic for testing slope 0 are also the two-sided P-values for testing correlation 0. ■

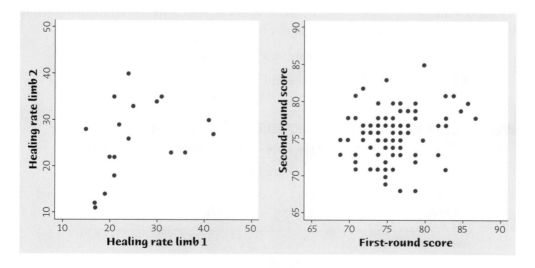

FIGURE 22.5
Two scatterplots for inference about the population correlation, for Example 22.5. (a) Healing rates for the two front limbs of 18 newts. (b) Scores on the first two rounds of the 2007 Masters Tournament.

Although the evidence for nonzero correlation is not strong for either set of data, it is stronger for Masters scores ($t = 1.9$, $P = 0.06$) than for newts ($t = 1.5$, $P = 0.14$). Yet the correlation for the newts is almost double that for the Masters, and the scatterplots suggest a stronger linear relationship for the newts. What happened? The larger sample size for the Masters data is largely responsible. The same r will have a smaller P-value for $n = 96$ than for $n = 18$. Our eyeball impression, even aided by calculating r, can't assess significance. We need the P-value from a formal test to guide us.

22.6 Ebola and gorillas: testing correlation. Exercise 22.1 gives data showing that the delay in deaths from an Ebola outbreak in groups of gorillas increases linearly with distance from the origin of the outbreak. There are only 6 observations, so we worry that the apparent relationship may be just chance. Is the correlation significantly greater than 0? Return to your t statistic from Exercise 22.4. What is the one-sided P-value for this t? Apply your result to test the correlation.

22.7 Does social rejection hurt? Exercise 4.37 (page 89) gives data from a study of whether social rejection causes activity in areas of the brain that are known to be activated by physical pain. The explanatory variable is a subject's score on a test of "social distress" after being excluded from an activity. The response variable is activity in an area of the brain that responds to physical pain. Your scatterplot (Exercise 4.37) shows a positive linear relationship. The research report gives the correlation r and the P-value for a test that r is greater than 0. Calculate r and the P-value? What do you conclude about the relationship?

Confidence intervals for the regression slope

The slope β of the population regression line is usually the most important parameter in a regression problem. The slope is the rate of change of the mean response as the explanatory variable increases. The slope b of the least-squares line is an unbiased estimator of β. A confidence interval is more useful because it shows how accurate the estimate b is likely to be. The confidence interval for β has the familiar form

$$\text{estimate} \pm t^*\text{SE}_\text{estimate}$$

Because b is our estimate, the confidence interval is $b \pm t^*\text{SE}_b$.

> **CONFIDENCE INTERVAL FOR REGRESSION SLOPE**
>
> A level C **confidence interval for the slope β** of the population regression line is
>
> $$b \pm t^*\text{SE}_b$$
>
> Here t^* is the critical value for the $t(n-2)$ density curve with area C between $-t^*$ and t^*. The formula for SE_b appears in the box on page 402.

EXAMPLE 22.6 Crying and IQ: estimating the slope

The two software outputs in Figure 22.3 give the slope $b = 1.4929$ and also the standard error $\text{SE}_b = 0.4870$. The outputs use a similar arrangement, a table in which each regression coefficient is followed by its standard error. Excel also gives the lower and upper endpoints of the 95% confidence interval for the population slope β, 0.505 and 2.481.

Once we know b and SE_b, it is easy to find the confidence interval. There are 38 data points, so the degrees of freedom are $n - 2 = 36$. Because Table C does not have a row for $df = 36$, we must use either software or the next smaller degrees of freedom in the table, $df = 30$. To use software, enter 36 degrees of freedom. For 95% confidence, enter the cumulative proportion 0.975 that corresponds to upper tail area 0.025. Minitab gives

```
Student's t distribution with 36 DF
P(X<=x)          x
  0.975    2.02809
```

The 95% confidence interval for the population slope β is

$$b \pm t^*SE_b = 1.4929 \pm (2.02809)(0.4870)$$
$$= 1.4929 \pm 0.9877$$
$$= 0.505 \text{ to } 2.481$$

This agrees with Excel's result. We are 95% confident that mean IQ increases by between about 0.5 and 2.5 points for each additional peak in crying. ∎

APPLY YOUR KNOWLEDGE

22.8 Ebola and gorillas: estimating slope. Exercise 22.1 presents data on distance and days until an Ebola outbreak reached six groups of gorillas. Software tells us that the least-squares slope is $b = 11.263$ with standard error $SE_b = 1.591$. Because there are only 6 observations, the observed slope b may not be an accurate estimate of the population slope β. Give a 90% confidence interval for β.

22.9 Growth of icicles: estimating slope. Exercise 22.2 gives data on the growth of an icicle. We want a 95% confidence interval for the slope of the population regression line. Starting from the information in the Minitab output in Figure 22.4, find this interval. Say in words what the slope of the population regression line tells us about the growth of icicles under the conditions of this experiment.

22.10 Great Arctic rivers: estimating slope. Use the data in Table 22.2 to give a 90% confidence interval for the slope of the population regression line of Arctic river discharge on year. Does this interval convince you that discharge is actually increasing over time? Explain your answer.

Inference about prediction

One of the most common reasons to fit a line to data is to predict the response to a particular value of the explanatory variable. We want a prediction with a margin of error that describes how accurate the prediction is likely to be.

EXAMPLE 22.7 **Beer and blood alcohol**

STATE: The EESEE story "Blood Alcohol Content" describes a study in which 16 student volunteers at the Ohio State University drank a randomly assigned number of cans of beer. Thirty minutes later, a police officer measured their blood alcohol content (BAC) in grams of alcohol per deciliter of blood. Here are the data:[5]

Student	1	2	3	4	5	6	7	8
Beers	5	2	9	8	3	7	3	5
BAC	0.10	0.03	0.19	0.12	0.04	0.095	0.07	0.06

Student	9	10	11	12	13	14	15	16
Beers	3	5	4	6	5	7	1	4
BAC	0.02	0.05	0.07	0.10	0.085	0.09	0.01	0.05

The students were equally divided between men and women and differed in weight and usual drinking habits. Because of these differences, many students don't believe that number of drinks predicts blood alcohol well. Steve thinks he can drive legally 30 minutes after he finishes drinking 5 beers. The legal limit for driving is BAC 0.08 in all states. We want to predict Steve's blood alcohol content, using no information except that he drinks 5 beers.

PLAN: Regress BAC on number of beers. Use the regression line to predict Steve's BAC. Give a margin of error that allows us to have 95% confidence in our prediction.

SOLVE: The scatterplot in Figure 22.6 and the regression output in Figure 22.7 show that number of beers predicts blood alcohol content quite well. In fact, $r^2 = 0.80$, so that number of beers explains 80% of the observed variation in BAC. To predict Steve's BAC after 5 beers, use the equation of the regression line:

$$\hat{y} = -0.0127 + 0.0180x$$
$$= -0.0127 + 0.0180(5) = 0.077$$

That's dangerously close to the legal limit 0.08. What about 95% confidence? The "Predicted Values" part of the output in Figure 22.7 shows *two* 95% intervals. Which should we use? ■

FIGURE 22.6

Scatterplot of students' blood alcohol content against the number of cans of beer consumed, with the least-squares regression line, for Example 22.7.

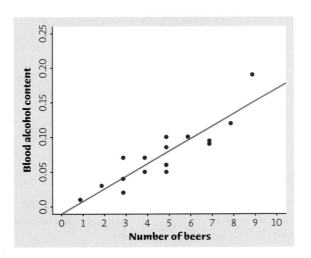

The two intervals answer two different questions:

■ To predict the *mean BAC for all students* who drink 5 beers, use a *confidence interval* for the mean response when $x = 5$. This mean is a parameter, a fixed number whose value we don't know.

- To predict *Steve's individual BAC* after 5 beers, use a **prediction interval.** A prediction interval estimates a single random response y rather than a parameter like the mean response.

prediction interval

The actual prediction is the same, $\hat{y} = 0.077$. But the margin of error is different for the two kinds of prediction. Individual students who drink 5 beers don't all have the same BAC. So we need a larger margin of error to pin down Steve's result than to estimate the mean BAC for all students who have 5 beers.

> ### EXAMPLE 22.8 Beer and blood alcohol: conclusion
>
> Steve is one individual, so we must use the prediction interval. The output in Figure 22.7 helpfully labels the confidence interval as "95% CI" and the prediction interval as "95% PI." We are 95% confident that Steve's BAC after 5 beers will lie between 0.032 and 0.122. The upper part of that range will get him arrested if he drives. The 95% confidence interval for the mean BAC of all students who drink 5 beers is much narrower, 0.066 to 0.088. ■

The confidence interval for a mean response and the prediction interval for an individual response have similar forms,

$$\hat{y} \pm t^*\mathrm{SE}$$

The standard error SE for estimating an individual response is larger than the standard error SE needed to estimate a mean response. The formulas for the standard errors are a bit messy, so we rely on software for confidence and prediction intervals.

The interpretation of confidence intervals and prediction intervals is also similar: both give correct answers 95% of the time in repeated use. "Repeated use" for a prediction interval means that we measure BAC for 16 students who drink the same numbers of beers as in Example 22.7, calculate the prediction interval for 5 beers, then have one more student drink 5 beers. The interval covers the last student's BAC in 95% of all repetitions.

22.11 Ebola and gorillas: prediction. Exercise 22.1 presents data on distance and days until an Ebola outbreak reached six groups of gorillas. If another group were located 2 ranges from the original outbreak, predict the number of days until deaths begin in this group.

(a) Figure 22.8 is part of the output from Minitab for prediction when $x^* = 2$. Which interval in the output is the proper 95% interval for predicting the number of days until deaths begin in this group?

(b) Minitab gives only one of the two standard errors used in prediction. It is the standard error for estimating the mean response. Use this fact along with the output to give a 90% confidence interval for the mean number of days the Ebola outbreak takes to reach gorilla groups 2 ranges from the origin.

FIGURE 22.8
Partial Minitab output for regressing days until Ebola outbreak on distance (number of ranges) from initial outbreak, for Exercise 22.11.

```
Session

Predictor      Coef    SE Coef        T        P
Constant     -8.088      5.917    -1.37    0.243
Ranges       11.263      1.591     7.08    0.002

Predicted Values for New Observations

New
Obs        Fit     SE Fit        95% CI              95% PI
  1      14.44       3.11    (5.79, 23.09)     (-1.69, 30.57)
```

22.12 Growth of icicles: prediction. Analysis of the data in Exercise 22.2 shows that growth of icicles is very linear. We might want to predict the mean length of icicles after 200 minutes under the same conditions of temperature, wind, and water flow. Here is the Minitab output for prediction when $x^* = 200$ minutes:

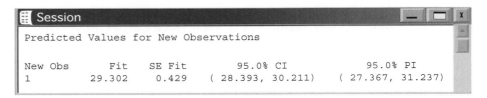

```
Session

Predicted Values for New Observations

New Obs      Fit    SE Fit       95.0% CI            95.0% PI
1         29.302     0.429   ( 28.393, 30.211)   ( 27.367, 31.237)
```

(a) Use the regression line from Figure 22.4 to verify that "Fit" is the predicted value for $x^* = 200$. (Start with the results in the "Coef" column of Figure 22.4 to reduce roundoff error.)

(b) What is the 95% interval we want?

Checking the conditions for inference

You can fit a least-squares line to any set of explanatory-response data when both variables are quantitative, though the line is useful only when the scatterplot shows a roughly linear pattern. To use regression inference, however, the data must satisfy additional conditions. *Before you can trust the results of inference, you must check the conditions for inference one by one.*

The conditions involve the population regression line and the deviations of responses from this line. We can't observe the population line, but the least-squares line estimates it, and the residuals estimate the deviations from the population line. *To check the conditions for regression inference, look at graphs of the residuals.* Regression software will calculate and save the residuals for you. Make a stemplot or histogram of the residuals and also a **residual plot,** a plot of the residuals against the explanatory variable x, with a horizontal line at the "residual = 0" position. The "residual = 0" line represents the position of the least-squares line in the scatterplot of y against x. Let's look at each condition in turn.

residual plot

- **The relationship is linear in the population.** Look for curved patterns or other departures from a straight-line overall pattern in the residual plot. You can also use the original scatterplot, but the residual plot magnifies any effects.

- **The response varies Normally about the population regression line.** Because different y-values usually come from different x-values, the responses themselves need not be Normal. It is the deviations from the population line—estimated by the residuals—that must be Normal. Check for clear skewness or other major departures from Normality in your stemplot or histogram of the residuals.

- **Observations are independent.** In particular, repeated observations on the same individual are not allowed. You should not use ordinary regression to make inferences about the growth of a single child over time, for example. Signs of dependence in the residual plot are a bit subtle, so we usually rely on common sense.

- **The standard deviation of the responses is the same for all values of x.** Look at the scatter of the residuals above and below the "residual = 0" line in the residual plot. The scatter should be roughly the same from one end to the other. You will sometimes find that, as the response y gets larger, so does the scatter of the residuals. Rather than remaining fixed, the standard deviation σ about the line changes with x as the mean response changes with x. There is no fixed σ for s to estimate. You cannot trust the results of inference when this happens.

You will always see some irregularity when you look for Normality and fixed standard deviation in the residuals, especially when you have few observations. Don't overreact to minor violations of the conditions. Like other t procedures, inference for regression is (with one exception) not very sensitive to lack of Normality, especially when we have many observations. Do beware of influential observations, which can greatly affect the results of inference.

The exception is the prediction interval for a single response y. This interval relies on Normality of individual observations, not just on the approximate Normality of statistics like the slope a and intercept b of the least-squares line. The statistics a and b become more Normal as we take more observations. This contributes to the robustness of regression inference, but it isn't enough for the prediction interval. We will not study methods that carefully check Normality of the residuals, so *you should regard prediction intervals as rough approximations*.

EXAMPLE 22.9 **Climate change chases fish north**

STATE: As the climate grows warmer, many animal species may move toward the poles to maintain their preferred temperature range. Do data on fish in the North Sea show this effect? Table 22.3 gives data for 25 years on mean winter temperatures at the bottom of the North Sea (degrees Celsius) and the center of the distribution of anglerfish in degrees of north latitude.[6]

TABLE 22.3 Winter temperature (degrees Celsius) and anglerfish latitude, 1977 to 2001

YEAR	TEMP.	LATITUDE	YEAR	TEMP.	LATITUDE	YEAR	TEMP.	LATITUDE
1977	6.26	57.20	1986	6.52	57.72	1994	7.02	58.71
1978	6.26	57.96	1987	6.68	57.83	1995	7.09	58.07
1979	6.27	57.65	1988	6.76	57.87	1996	7.13	58.49
1980	6.31	57.59	1989	6.78	57.48	1997	7.15	58.28
1981	6.34	58.01	1990	6.89	58.13	1998	7.29	58.49
1982	6.32	59.06	1991	6.90	58.52	1999	7.34	58.01
1983	6.37	56.85	1992	6.93	58.48	2000	7.57	58.57
1984	6.39	56.87	1993	6.98	57.89	2001	7.65	58.90
1985	6.42	57.43						

PLAN: Regress latitude on temperature. Look for a positive linear relationship and assess its significance. Be sure to check the conditions for regression inference.

SOLVE: The scatterplot in Figure 22.9 shows a clear positive linear relationship. The solid line in the plot is the least-squares regression line of the center of the fish distribution (north latitude) on winter ocean temperature. Software shows that the slope is $b = 0.818$. That is, each degree of ocean warming moves the fish about 0.8 degree of latitude farther north. The t statistic for testing $H_0: \beta = 0$ is $t = 3.6287$ with one-sided P-value $P = 0.0007$. There is very strong evidence that the population slope is positive, $\beta > 0$.

Dave Harasti

FIGURE 22.9
Plot of the latitude of the center of the distribution of anglerfish in the North Sea against mean winter temperature at the bottom of the sea, for Example 22.9. The two regression lines are for the data with (solid) and without (dashed) Observation 6.

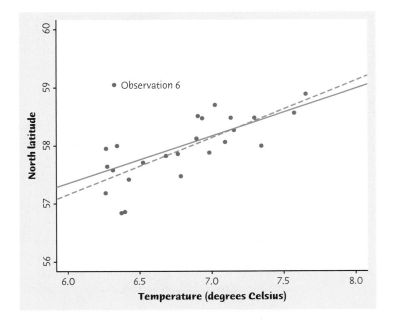

CONCLUDE: The data give highly significant evidence that anglerfish have moved north as the ocean has grown warmer. Before relying on this conclusion, we must check the conditions for inference. ■

The software that did the regression calculations also finds the 25 residuals. In the same order as the observations in Example 22.9, they are

```
-0.3731   0.3869   0.0687  -0.0240   0.3714   1.4378  -0.8131
-0.8095  -0.2740  -0.0658  -0.0867  -0.1121  -0.5185   0.0415
 0.4234   0.3588  -0.2721   0.5152  -0.1821   0.2052  -0.0211
 0.0743  -0.4466  -0.0747   0.1899
```

Begin by making two graphs of the residuals. Figure 22.10 is a histogram of the residuals. Figure 22.11 is the residual plot, a plot of the residuals against the explanatory variable, sea-bottom temperature. The "residual = 0" line marks the position of the regression line. Notice that the vertical scale in Figure 22.11 is expanded beyond what is necessary to simply show the points. Patterns in residual plots are often easier to see if you use a wider vertical scale than your software's default plot. Both graphs show that Observation 6 is a high outlier. Let's check the conditions for regression inference.

- **Linear relationship.** The scatterplot in Figure 22.9 and the residual plot in Figure 22.11 both show a linear relationship except for the outlier.
- **Normal residuals.** The histogram in Figure 22.10 is roughly symmetric and single-peaked. There are no important departures from Normality except for the outlier.
- **Independent observations.** The observations were taken a year apart, so we are willing to regard them as close to independent. The residual plot shows no obvious pattern of dependence, such as runs of points all above or all below the line.
- **Constant standard deviation.** Again excepting the outlier, the residual plot shows no unusual variation in the scatter of the residuals above and below the line as x varies.

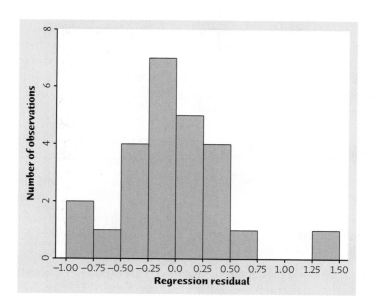

FIGURE 22.10
Histogram of the residuals from the regression of latitude on temperature in Example 22.9.

FIGURE 22.11

Residual plot for the regression of latitude on temperature in Example 22.9.

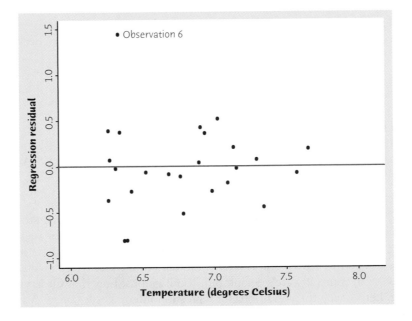

The outlier is the only serious violation of the conditions for inference. How influential is the outlier? The dashed line in Figure 22.9 is the regression line without Observation 6. Because there are several other observations with similar values of temperature, dropping Observation 6 does not move the regression line very much. *Even though the outlier is not very influential for the regression line, it influences regression inference because of its effect on the regression standard error.* The standard error is $s = 0.4734$ with Observation 6 and $s = 0.3622$ without it. When we omit the outlier, the t statistic changes from $t = 3.6287$ to $t = 5.5599$, and the one-sided P-value changes from $P = 0.0007$ to $P < 0.00001$. Fortunately, the outlier does not affect the conclusion we drew from the data. Dropping Observation 6 makes the test for the population slope *more* significant and *increases* the percent of variation in fish location explained by ocean temperature.

One more caution about inference in this example: as usual in an observational study, the possibility of lurking variables makes us hesitant to conclude that rising temperature is *causing* anglerfish to move north. Ocean temperature was steadily rising during these years. The effect on fish latitude of any lurking variable that increased over time—perhaps increased commercial fishing—is confounded with the effect of temperature.

APPLY YOUR KNOWLEDGE

22.13 Crying and IQ: residuals. The residuals for the study of crying and IQ appear in Example 22.3.

(a) Make a stemplot to display the distribution of the residuals (round to the nearest whole number). Are there strong outliers or other signs of departures from Normality?

(b) Make a residual plot, residuals against crying peaks. Try a vertical scale of −60 to 60 to show patterns more clearly. Draw the "residual = 0" line. Does the residual plot show clear deviations from a linear pattern or clearly unequal spread about the line?

(c) Using the information given in Example 22.1, explain why the 38 observations are independent.

22.14 Growth of icicles: residuals. Figure 22.4 gives part of the Minitab output for the data on growth of icicles in Exercise 22.2. Figure 22.12 comes from another part of the output. It gives x, y, the predicted response $\hat{y}$, the residual $y - \hat{y}$, and related quantities for each of the 18 observations. This table is stored in the data file *ex22-14.dat* on the text CD and Web site. Most statistical software provides similar output. Examine the conditions for regression inference one by one. This example illustrates mild violations of the conditions that did not prevent the researchers from doing inference.

(a) **Linear relationship.** Your scatterplot and r^2 from Exercise 22.2 show that the relationship is very linear. Residual plots magnify effects. Plot the residuals against time. What kind of deviation from a straight line is now visible? (The deviation is clear in the residual plot, but it is very small in the original scale.)

(b) **Normal variation about the line.** Make a stemplot of the residuals (round to the nearest tenth, use split stems, and don't forget that −0 and 0 are separate stems). With only 18 observations, the small right skew is not disturbing. Minitab suggests that Observation 18 may be an outlier. Does your plot confirm or refute this suggestion?

(c) **Independent observations.** The data come from the growth of a single icicle, not from a different icicle at each time. Explain why this would violate the independence condition if we had data on the growth of a child rather than of an icicle.

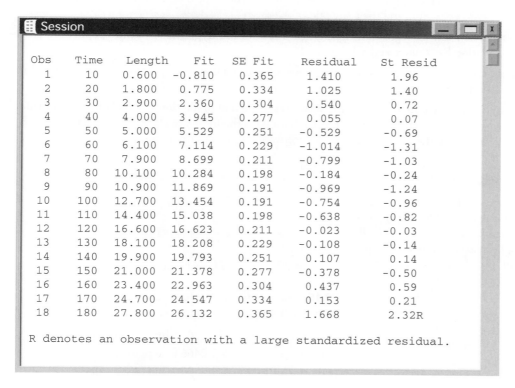

```
 Session                                                    _ □ X

 Obs   Time   Length    Fit    SE Fit    Residual    St Resid
  1     10    0.600   -0.810    0.365      1.410        1.96
  2     20    1.800    0.775    0.334      1.025        1.40
  3     30    2.900    2.360    0.304      0.540        0.72
  4     40    4.000    3.945    0.277      0.055        0.07
  5     50    5.000    5.529    0.251     -0.529       -0.69
  6     60    6.100    7.114    0.229     -1.014       -1.31
  7     70    7.900    8.699    0.211     -0.799       -1.03
  8     80   10.100   10.284    0.198     -0.184       -0.24
  9     90   10.900   11.869    0.191     -0.969       -1.24
 10    100   12.700   13.454    0.191     -0.754       -0.96
 11    110   14.400   15.038    0.198     -0.638       -0.82
 12    120   16.600   16.623    0.211     -0.023       -0.03
 13    130   18.100   18.208    0.229     -0.108       -0.14
 14    140   19.900   19.793    0.251      0.107        0.14
 15    150   21.000   21.378    0.277     -0.378       -0.50
 16    160   23.400   22.963    0.304      0.437        0.59
 17    170   24.700   24.547    0.334      0.153        0.21
 18    180   27.800   26.132    0.365      1.668        2.32R

 R denotes an observation with a large standardized residual.
```

FIGURE 22.12
Residuals from Minitab for Exercise 22.14. The table gives the predicted value ("Fit") and the residual for each observation.

(The researchers decided that all icicles, unlike all children, grow at the same rate if the conditions are held fixed. So one icicle can stand in for a separate icicle at each time.)

(d) **Spread about the line stays the same.** Your plot in (a) suggests that spread may be higher at both ends. (Once again, the plot greatly magnifies small deviations.)

CHAPTER 22 SUMMARY

■ **Least-squares regression** fits a straight line to data in order to predict a response variable y from an explanatory variable x. Inference about regression requires more conditions.

■ The **conditions for regression inference** say that there is a **population regression line** $\mu_y = \alpha + \beta x$ that describes how the mean response varies as x changes. The observed response y for any x has a Normal distribution with mean given by the population regression line and with the same standard deviation σ for any value of x. Observations on y are independent.

■ The **parameters to be estimated** are the intercept α and the slope β of the population regression line, and also the standard deviation σ. The slope a and intercept b of the least-squares line estimate α and β. Use the **regression standard error s** to estimate σ.

■ The regression standard error s has $n - 2$ **degrees of freedom.** All t procedures in regression inference have $n - 2$ degrees of freedom.

■ To test **the hypothesis that the slope is zero in the population,** use the t statistic $t = b/SE_b$. This null hypothesis says that straight-line dependence on x has no value for predicting y. In practice, use software to find the slope b of the least-squares line, its standard error SE_b, and the t statistic.

■ The t test for regression slope is also a test for **the hypothesis that the population correlation between x and y is zero.**

■ **Confidence intervals for the slope** of the population regression line have the form $b \pm t^*SE_b$.

■ **Confidence intervals for the mean response** and **prediction intervals for an individual response** when x has a given value both have the form $\hat{y} \pm t^*SE$. The standard error SE is larger for the prediction interval. Software often gives these intervals.

CHECK YOUR SKILLS

Florida reappraises real estate every year, so the county appraiser's Web site lists the current "fair market value" of each piece of property. Table 22.4 gives the appraised market values and actual selling prices (in thousands of dollars) of condominium units sold in a beachfront building over a 19-month period.[7] Here is part of the Minitab output for regressing selling price on appraised value, along with prediction for a unit with appraised value $802,600:

```
Predictor   Coef   SE Coef    T      P
Constant   127.27   79.49   1.60   0.132
appraisal  1.0466  0.1126   9.29   0.000

S = 69.7299   R-Sq = 86.1%   R-Sq(adj) = 85.1%
```

Predicted Values for New Observations

```
New
Obs   Fit   SE Fit      95% CI            95% PI
  1  967.3   21.6  (920.9, 1013.7)  (810.7, 1123.9)
```

Exercises 22.15 to 22.21 are based on this information.

22.15 The equation of the least-squares regression line for predicting selling price from appraised value is

(a) price = 79.49 + 0.1126 × appraised value.

(b) price = 127.27 + 1.0466 × appraised value.

(c) price = 1.0466 + 127.27 × appraised value.

TABLE 22.4 Appraised value and selling price (in thousands of dollars) for condominium units

SELLING PRICE	APPRAISED VALUE	MONTH	SELLING PRICE	APPRAISED VALUE	MONTH
850	758.0	0	790	605.9	13
900	812.7	1	700	483.8	14
625	504.0	2	715	585.8	14
1075	956.7	2	825	707.6	14
890	747.9	8	675	493.9	17
810	717.7	8	1050	802.6	17
650	576.6	9	1325	1031.8	18
845	648.3	12	845	586.7	19

22.16 The slope β of the population regression line describes
(a) the exact increase in the selling price of an individual unit when its appraised value increases by $1000.
(b) the average increase in selling price in a population of units when appraised value increases by $1000.
(c) the average selling price in a population of units when a unit's appraised value is 0.

22.17 Is there significant evidence that selling price increases as appraised value increases? Minitab shows that the P-value for the test that answers this question is
(a) 0.132.   (b) less than 0.001.   (c) 0.861.

22.18 The regression standard error for these data is
(a) 0.1126.   (b) 69.7299.   (c) 79.49.

22.19 Confidence intervals and tests for these data use the t distribution with degrees of freedom
(a) 14.   (b) 15.   (c) 16.

22.20 A 95% confidence interval for the population slope β is
(a) 1.0466 ± 0.2415.   (b) 1.0466 ± 149.5706.
(c) 1.0466 ± 0.2387.

22.21 Hamada owns a unit in this building appraised at $802,600. The Minitab output includes prediction for this appraised value. She can be 95% confident that her unit would sell for between
(a) $920,900 and $1,013,700.
(b) $810,700 and $1,123,900.
(c) $945,700 and $988,900.

CHAPTER 22 EXERCISES

22.22 Too much nitrogen? Burning fossil fuels deposits extra nitrogen on the land. Too much nitrogen can reduce the variety of plants by favoring rapid growth of some species. A study of 68 grassland sites in Britain measured nitrogen deposited (kilo-grams of nitrogen per hectare of land area per year) and also the "richness" of plant species (based on number of species and how abundant each species is). The authors reported a regression analysis as follows:[8]

$$\text{plant species richness} = 23.3 - 0.408 \times \text{nitrogen deposited}$$
$$r^2 = 0.55 \quad P < 0.0001$$

(a) What does the slope $b = -0.408$ say about the effect of increased nitrogen deposits on species richness?
(b) What does $r^2 = 0.55$ add to the information given by the equation of the least-squares line?
(c) What null and alternative hypotheses do you think the P-value refers to? What does this P-value tell you?

Exercise 6.43 (page 124) gives data from a study of the "gate velocity" of molten metal that experienced foundry workers choose based on the thickness of the aluminum piston being cast. Gate velocity is measured in feet per second, and the piston wall thickness is in inches. A scatterplot (you need not make one) shows a moderate positive linear relationship. Figure 22.13 displays part of the Minitab regression output. Exercises 22.23 to 22.25 analyze these data.

22.23 Casting aluminum: is there a relationship? Figure 22.13 leaves out the t statistics and their P-values. Based on the information in the output, test the hypothesis that there is no straight-line relationship between thickness and gate velocity. State hypotheses, give a test statistic and its approximate P-value, and state your conclusion.

22.24 Casting aluminum: intervals. The output in Figure 22.13 includes prediction for piston wall thickness $x^* = 0.5$ inch. Use the output to give 90% intervals for
(a) the slope of the population regression line of gate velocity on piston thickness.
(b) the average gate velocity for a type of piston with thickness 0.5 inch.

FIGURE 22.13
Minitab output for the regression of gate velocity on piston thickness in casting aluminum parts, for Exercises 22.23 to 22.25.

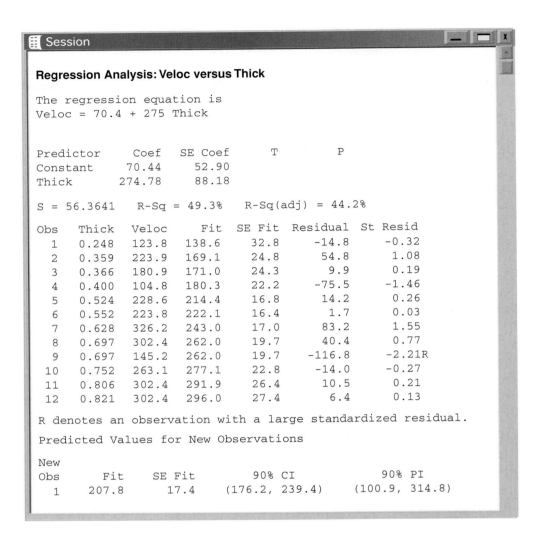

```
☰ Session                                                    ─ ☐ x

Regression Analysis: Veloc versus Thick

The regression equation is
Veloc = 70.4 + 275 Thick


Predictor       Coef    SE Coef        T         P
Constant       70.44      52.90
Thick         274.78      88.18

S = 56.3641    R-Sq = 49.3%    R-Sq(adj) = 44.2%

Obs    Thick    Veloc      Fit   SE Fit   Residual  St Resid
  1    0.248    123.8    138.6     32.8      -14.8     -0.32
  2    0.359    223.9    169.1     24.8       54.8      1.08
  3    0.366    180.9    171.0     24.3        9.9      0.19
  4    0.400    104.8    180.3     22.2      -75.5     -1.46
  5    0.524    228.6    214.4     16.8       14.2      0.26
  6    0.552    223.8    222.1     16.4        1.7      0.03
  7    0.628    326.2    243.0     17.0       83.2      1.55
  8    0.697    302.4    262.0     19.7       40.4      0.77
  9    0.697    145.2    262.0     19.7     -116.8     -2.21R
 10    0.752    263.1    277.1     22.8      -14.0     -0.27
 11    0.806    302.4    291.9     26.4       10.5      0.21
 12    0.821    302.4    296.0     27.4        6.4      0.13

R denotes an observation with a large standardized residual.

Predicted Values for New Observations

New
Obs      Fit    SE Fit        90% CI              90% PI
  1    207.8      17.4    (176.2, 239.4)      (100.9, 314.8)
```

22.25 Casting aluminum: residuals. The output in Figure 22.13 includes a table of the x and y variables, the fitted values $\hat{y}$ for each x, the residuals, and some related quantities. (This table is stored as *ex22-25.dat* on the text CD and Web site.)
(a) Plot the residuals against thickness (the explanatory variable). Use vertical scale −200 to 200 so that the pattern is clearer. Add the "residual = 0" line. Does your plot show a systematically nonlinear relationship? Does it show systematic change in the spread about the regression line?
(b) Make a histogram of the residuals. Minitab identifies the residual for Observation 9 as a suspected outlier. Does your histogram agree?
(c) Redoing the regression without Observation 9 gives regression standard error $s = 42.4725$ and predicted mean velocity 216 feet per second (90% confidence interval 191.4 to 240.6) for piston walls 0.5 inch thick. Compare these values with those in Figure 22.13. Is Observation 9 influential for inference?

Table 4.1 gives 31 years' data on boats registered in Florida and manatees killed by boats. Figure 4.2 (page 78) shows a strong linear relationship. The correlation is $r = 0.947$. Figure 22.14 shows part of the Minitab regression output. Exercises 22.26 to 22.28 analyze the manatee data.

22.26 Manatees: conditions for inference. We know that there is a strong linear relationship. Let's check the other conditions for inference. Figure 22.14 includes a table of the two variables, the predicted values $\hat{y}$ for each x in the data, the residuals, and related quantities. (This table is stored as *ex22-26.dat* on the text CD and Web site.)

```
┌─ Session ──────────────────────────────────────── _ □ x ─┐

  Regression Analysis: Kills versus Boats

  The regression equation is
  Kills = - 40.6 + 0.125 Boats

  Predictor      Coef    SE Coef      T        P
  Constant    -40.641     5.840
  Boats       0.125006  0.007867

  S = 7.87985   R-Sq = 89.7%   R-Sq(adj) = 89.3%

  Analysis of Variance

  Source          DF      SS      MS       F       P
  Regression       1   15677   15677  252.48   0.000
  Residual Error  29    1801      62
  Total           30   17477

  Obs  Boats  Kills    Fit  SE Fit  Residual  St Resid
    1    447  13.00  15.24    2.57     -2.24     -0.30
    2    460  21.00  16.86    2.49      4.14      0.55
    3    481  24.00  19.49    2.35      4.51      0.60
    4    498  16.00  21.61    2.25     -5.61     -0.74
    5    513  24.00  23.49    2.16      0.51      0.07
    6    512  20.00  23.36    2.16     -3.36     -0.44
    7    526  15.00  25.11    2.08    -10.11     -1.33
    8    559  34.00  29.24    1.90      4.76      0.62
    9    585  33.00  32.49    1.77      0.51      0.07
   10    614  33.00  36.11    1.64     -3.11     -0.40
   11    645  39.00  39.99    1.53     -0.99     -0.13
   12    675  43.00  43.74    1.46     -0.74     -0.10
   13    711  50.00  48.24    1.42      1.76      0.23
   14    719  47.00  49.24    1.42     -2.24     -0.29
   15    681  53.00  44.49    1.45      8.51      1.10
   16    679  38.00  44.24    1.45     -6.24     -0.81
   17    678  35.00  44.11    1.45     -9.11     -1.18
   18    696  49.00  46.36    1.43      2.64      0.34
   19    713  42.00  48.49    1.42     -6.49     -0.84
   20    732  60.00  50.86    1.42      9.14      1.18
   21    755  54.00  53.74    1.44      0.26      0.03
   22    809  66.00  60.49    1.58      5.51      0.71
   23    830  82.00  63.11    1.66     18.89      2.45R
   24    880  78.00  69.36    1.89      8.64      1.13
   25    944  81.00  77.36    2.26      3.64      0.48
   26    962  95.00  79.61    2.37     15.39      2.05R
   27    978  73.00  81.61    2.47     -8.61     -1.15
   28    983  69.00  82.24    2.51    -13.24     -1.77
   29   1010  79.00  85.61    2.68     -6.61     -0.89
   30   1024  92.00  87.36    2.78      4.64      0.63
   31   1027  73.00  87.74    2.80    -14.74     -2.00R

  R denotes an observation with a large standardized residual.

  Predicted Values for New Observations

  New
  Obs    Fit  SE Fit      95% CI            95% PI
    1  96.87    3.31  (90.10, 103.63)  (79.39, 114.34)
```

FIGURE 22.14
Minitab output for the regression of number of manatees killed by boats on the number of boats (in thousands) registered in Florida, for Exercises 22.26 to 22.28.

(a) Round the residuals to the nearest whole number and make a stemplot. The distribution is single-peaked and symmetric and appears close to Normal.
(b) Make a residual plot, residuals against boats registered. Use a vertical scale from -25 to 25 to show the pattern more clearly. Add the "residual = 0" line. There is no clearly nonlinear pattern. The spread about the line may be a bit greater for larger values of the explanatory variable, but the effect is not large.
(c) It is reasonable to regard the number of manatees killed by boats in successive years as independent. The number of boats grew over time. Someone says that pollution also grew over time and may explain more manatee deaths. How would you respond to this idea?

22.27 Manatees: do more boats bring more kills? The output in Figure 22.14 omits the t statistics and their P-values. Based on the information in the output, is there good evidence that the number of manatees killed increases as the number of boats registered increases? State hypotheses and give a test statistic and its approximate P-value. What do you conclude?

22.28 Manatees: estimation. The output in Figure 22.14 includes prediction of manatees killed when there are 1,100,000 boats registered in Florida. Give 95% intervals for
(a) the increase in manatees killed for each additional 1000 boats registered.
(b) the number of manatees that will be killed next year if there are 1,100,000 boats registered next year.

22.29 Fidgeting keeps you slim: inference. Our first example of regression (Example 5.1, page 91) presented data showing that people who increased their nonexercise activity (NEA) when they were deliberately overfed gained less fat than other people. Use software to add formal inference to the data analysis for these data.
(a) Based on 16 subjects, the correlation between NEA increase and fat gain was $r = -0.7786$. Is this significant evidence that people with higher NEA increase gain less fat? (Report a t statistic from regression output and give the one-sided P-value.)
(b) The slope of the least-squares regression line was $b = -0.00344$, so that fat gain decreased by 0.00344 kilogram for each added calorie of NEA. Give a 90% confidence interval for the slope of the population regression line. This rate of change is the most important parameter to be estimated.
(c) Sam's NEA increases by 400 calories. His predicted fat gain is 2.13 kilograms. Give a 95% interval for predicting Sam's fat gain.

22.30 Predicting tropical storms. Exercise 5.44 (page 113) gives data on William Gray's predictions of the number of named tropical storms in Atlantic hurricane seasons from 1984 to 2007. Use these data for regression inference as follows.
(a) Does Professor Gray do better than random guessing? That is, is there a significantly positive correlation between his forecasts and the actual number of storms? (Report a t statistic from regression output and give the one-sided P-value.)
(b) Give a 95% confidence interval for the mean number of storms in years when Professor Gray forecasts 16 storms.

22.31 Sparrowhawk colonies. One of nature's patterns connects the percent of adult birds in a colony that return from the previous year and the number of new adults that join the colony. Exercise 4.23 (page 86) gives data for 13 colonies of sparrowhawks. In Exercises 4.23 and 5.31 (page 111), you showed that there is a moderately strong linear relationship.
(a) Biologists conjecture that the number of new adults joining colonies goes down as higher percents of adults return from the previous year. Do the data show this effect? Is it statistically significant?
(b) Use the data to predict with 95% confidence the average number of new birds in colonies to which 60% of the past year's adults return.

22.32 Predicting tropical storms: residuals. Make a stemplot of the residuals (round to the nearest tenth) from your regression in Exercise 22.30. Explain why your plot suggests that we should not use these data to get a prediction interval for the number of storms in a single year.

22.33 Sparrowhawk colonies: residuals. The regression of number of new birds that join a sparrowhawk colony on the percent of adult birds in the colony that return from the previous year is an example of data that satisfy the conditions for regression inference well. Here are the residuals for the 13 colonies in Exercise 22.31:

Percent return	74	66	81	52	73	62	52
Residual	-4.44	-5.87	0.69	-5.13	2.26	1.92	-0.13

Percent return	45	62	46	60	46	38
Residual	-1.25	4.92	0.05	5.31	2.05	-0.38

(a) **Linear relationship.** A plot of the residuals against the explanatory variable x magnifies the deviations from the least-squares line. Does the plot show any systematic deviation from a roughly linear pattern?
(b) **Normal variation about the line.** Make a histogram of the residuals. With only 13 observations, no clear shape emerges. Do strong skewness or outliers suggest lack of Normality?
(c) **Independent observations.** Why are the 13 observations independent?

(d) **Spread about the line stays the same.** Does your plot in (a) show any systematic change in spread as x changes?

22.34 Our brains don't like losses. Exercise 4.24 (page 86) describes an experiment that showed a linear relationship between how sensitive people are to monetary losses ("behavioral loss aversion") and activity in one part of their brains ("neural loss aversion").

(a) Make a scatterplot with neural loss aversion as x and behavioral loss aversion as y. One point is a high outlier in both the x and y directions. In Exercise 5.32 (page 111) you found that this outlier is not influential for the least-squares line.

(b) The research report says that $r = 0.85$ and that the test for regression slope has $P < 0.001$. Verify these results, using all of the observations.

(c) The report recognizes the outlier and says, "However, this regression also remained highly significant ($P = 0.004$) when the extreme data point (top right corner) was removed from the analysis." Repeat your analysis omitting the outlier. Show that the outlier influences regression inference by comparing the t statistic for testing slope with and without the outlier. Then verify the report's claim about the P-value of this test.

22.35 Time at the table. Does how long young children remain at the lunch table help predict how much they eat? Here are data on 20 toddlers observed over several months at a nursery school.[9] "Time" is the average number of minutes a child spent at the table when lunch was served. "Calories" is the average number of calories the child consumed during lunch.

Time	21.4	30.8	37.7	33.5	32.8	39.5	22.8	34.1	33.9	43.8
Calories	472	498	465	456	423	437	508	431	479	454
Time	42.4	43.1	29.2	31.3	28.6	32.9	30.6	35.1	33.0	43.7
Calories	450	410	504	437	489	436	480	439	444	408

(a) Make a scatterplot. Find the correlation and the least-squares regression line. (Be sure to save the regression residuals.) Based on your work, describe the direction, form, and strength of the relationship.

(b) Check the conditions for regression inference. Parts (a) to (d) of Exercise 22.33 provide a handy outline. Use vertical limits -100 to 100 in your plot of the residuals against time to help you see the pattern. What do you conclude?

(c) Is there significant evidence that more time at the table is associated with more calories consumed? Give a 95% confidence interval to estimate how rapidly calories consumed changes as time at the table increases.

22.36 DNA on the ocean floor. We think of DNA as the stuff that stores the genetic code. It turns out that DNA occurs, mainly outside living cells, on the ocean floor. Scientists think that this DNA comes from organic matter that settles to the bottom from the top layers of the ocean. "Phytopigments," which come mainly from algae, are a measure of the amount of organic matter that has settled to the bottom. The data file *ex22-36.dat* on the text CD and Web site contains data on concentrations of DNA and phytopigments (both in grams per square meter) in 116 ocean locations around the world.[10] Look first at DNA alone. Describe the distribution of DNA concentration and give a confidence interval for the mean concentration. Be sure to explain why your confidence interval is trustworthy in the light of the shape of the distribution. The data show surprisingly high DNA concentration, and this by itself was an important finding.

22.37 Time at the table: prediction. Rachel is another child at the nursery school of Exercise 22.35. Over several months, Rachel averages 40 minutes at the lunch table. Give a 95% interval to predict Rachel's average calorie consumption at lunch.

*Exercises 22.38 to 22.42 ask practical questions of regression inference without step-by-step instructions. Do complete regression analyses, using the **Plan, Solve,** and **Conclude** steps of the four-step process to organize your answers. Follow the model of Example 22.9 and the following discussion, with checking the conditions as part of the **Solve** step.*

22.38 DNA on the ocean floor. Another conclusion of the study introduced in Exercise 22.36 was that organic matter settling down from the top layers of the ocean is the main source of DNA on the seafloor. An important piece of evidence is the relationship between DNA and phytopigments. Do the data in the file *ex22-36.dat* give good reason to think that phytopigment concentration helps explain DNA concentration? (Try vertical limits -1 to 1 to make the pattern of your residual plot clearer.)

22.39 Squirrels and their food supply. Exercise 6.23 (page 120) gives data on the abundance of the pine cones that red squirrels feed on and the mean number of offspring per female squirrel over 16 years. The strength of the relationship is remarkable because females produce young before the food is available. How significant is the evidence that more cones leads to more offspring? (Use a vertical scale from -2 to 2 in your residual plot to show the pattern more clearly.)

22.40 A big toe problem. Table 6.4 (page 124) and Exercises 6.39 and 6.41 describe the relationship between two deformities of the feet in young patients. Metatarsus abductus (MA) may help predict the severity of hallux abducto valgus (HAV). The paper that reports this study says, "Linear regression analysis, using the hallux abductus angle as the response variable, demonstrated a significant correlation between the metatarsus abductus and hallux abductus angles."[11] Do a suitable analysis to verify this finding. The study authors note that the scatterplot suggests that the variation in y may change as x changes, so they offer a more elaborate analysis as well.

22.41 Beavers and beetles. Exercise 5.42 (page 113) describes a study that found that the number of stumps from trees felled by beavers predicts the abundance of beetle larvae. Is there good evidence that more beetle larvae clusters are present when beavers have left more tree stumps? Estimate how many more clusters accompany each additional stump, with 95% confidence.

22.42 Sulfur, the ocean, and the sun. Sulfur in the atmosphere affects climate by influencing formation of clouds. The main natural source of sulfur is dimethyl sulfide (DMS) produced by small organisms in the upper layers of the oceans. DMS production is in turn influenced by the amount of energy the upper ocean receives from sunlight. Exercise 4.25 (page 86) gives monthly data on solar radiation dose (SRD, in watts per square meter) and surface DMS concentration (in nanomolars) for a region in the Mediterranean. Do the data provide convincing evidence that DMS increases as SRD increases? We also want to estimate the rate of increase, with 90% confidence.

22.43 Tests for the intercept (optional). Figure 22.7 (page 407) gives Minitab output for the regression of blood alcohol content (BAC) on number of beers consumed. The t test for the hypothesis that the population regression line has *slope* $\beta = 0$ has $P < 0.001$. The data show a positive linear relationship between BAC and beers. We might expect the *intercept* α of the population regression line to be 0, because no beers ($x = 0$) should produce no alcohol in the blood ($y = 0$). To test

$$H_0: \alpha = 0$$
$$H_a: \alpha \neq 0$$

we use a t statistic formed by dividing the least-squares intercept a by its standard error SE_a. Locate this statistic in the output of Figure 22.7 and verify that it is in fact a divided by its standard error. What is the P-value? Do the data suggest that the intercept is not 0?

22.44 Confidence intervals for the intercept (optional). The output in Figure 22.7 allows you to calculate confidence intervals for both the slope β and the intercept α of the population regression line of BAC on beers in the population of all students. Confidence intervals for the intercept α have the familiar form $a \pm t^*SE_a$ with degrees of freedom $n - 2$. What is the 95% confidence interval for the intercept? Does it contain 0, the value we might guess for α?

The music on your iPod is yours alone, but Exercise 23.11 shows that the music you play for a group may depend on the makeup of the group.

One-Way Analysis of Variance: Comparing Several Means

IN THIS CHAPTER WE COVER...

- The analysis of variance *F* test
- Using technology
- The idea of analysis of variance
- Conditions for ANOVA
- *F* distributions and degrees of freedom*

The two-sample *t* procedures of Chapter 17 compare the means of two populations or the mean responses to two treatments in an experiment. Of course, studies don't always compare just two groups. We need a method for comparing any number of means.

EXAMPLE 23.1 Comparing tropical flowers

STATE: Ethan Temeles and W. John Kress of Amherst College studied the relationship between varieties of the tropical flower *Heliconia* and the hummingbirds that fertilize the flowers.[1] The researchers conjecture that flower varieties fertilized by different hummingbird species should have distinct distributions of length.

Table 23.1 gives length measurements (in millimeters) for samples of three varieties of *Heliconia*, each fertilized by a different species of hummingbird. Do the three varieties display distinct distributions of length? In particular, are the mean lengths of their flowers different?

PLAN: Use graphs and numerical descriptions to describe and compare the three distributions of flower length. Finally, ask whether the differences among the mean lengths of the three varieties are *statistically significant*.

SOLVE (first steps): We first met these data in Chapter 2 (page 42), where we compared the distributions. Figure 23.1 repeats side-by-side stemplots from Chapter 2. The lengths have been rounded to the nearest tenth of a millimeter. Here are the summary measures we will use in further analysis:

TABLE 23.1 Flower lengths (millimeters) for three *Heliconia* varieties

			H. bihai				
47.12	46.75	46.81	47.12	46.67	47.43	46.44	46.64
48.07	48.34	48.15	50.26	50.12	46.34	46.94	48.36

			H. caribaea red				
41.90	42.01	41.93	43.09	41.47	41.69	39.78	40.57
39.63	42.18	40.66	37.87	39.16	37.40	38.20	38.07
38.10	37.97	38.79	38.23	38.87	37.78	38.01	

			H. caribaea yellow				
36.78	37.02	36.52	36.11	36.03	35.45	38.13	37.10
35.17	36.82	36.66	35.68	36.03	34.57	34.63	

Sample	Variety	Sample size	Mean length	Standard deviation
1	*bihai*	16	47.60	1.213
2	red	23	39.71	1.799
3	yellow	15	36.18	0.975

CONCLUDE (first steps): The three varieties differ so much in flower length that there is little overlap among them. In particular, the flowers of *bihai* are longer than either red or yellow. The mean lengths are 47.6 mm for *H. bihai*, 39.7 mm for *H. caribaea* red, and 36.2 mm for *H. caribaea* yellow. Are these observed differences in sample means statistically significant? We must develop a test for comparing more than two population means. ■

```
        bihai              red               yellow
    34 |              34 |              34 | 6 6
    35 |              35 |              35 | 2 5 7
    36 |              36 |              36 | 0 0 1 5 7 8 8
    37 |              37 | 4 8 9        37 | 0 1
    38 |              38 | 0 0 1 1 2 2 8 9   38 | 1
    39 |              39 | 2 6 8        39 |
    40 |              40 | 6 7          40 |
    41 |              41 | 5 7 9 9      41 |
    42 |              42 | 0 2          42 |
    43 |              43 | 1            43 |
    44 |              44 |              44 |
    45 |              45 |              45 |
    46 | 3 4 6 7 8 8 9  46 |           46 |
    47 | 1 1 4        47 |             47 |
    48 | 1 2 3 4      48 |             48 |
    49 |              49 |             49 |
    50 | 1 3          50 |             50 |
```

FIGURE 23.1

Side-by-side stemplots comparing the lengths in millimeters of samples of flowers from three varieties of *Heliconia*, from Table 23.1.

The analysis of variance *F* test

Call the mean lengths for the three populations of flowers μ_1 for *bihai*, μ_2 for red, and μ_3 for yellow. The subscript reminds us which group a parameter or statistic describes. To compare these three population means, we might use the two-sample *t* test three times:

- Test H_0: $\mu_1 = \mu_2$ to see if the mean length for *bihai* differs from the mean for red.
- Test H_0: $\mu_1 = \mu_3$ to see if *bihai* differs from yellow.
- Test H_0: $\mu_2 = \mu_3$ to see if red differs from yellow.

If we do three tests, we get three *P*-values, one for each test alone. That doesn't tell us how likely it is that *three* sample means are spread apart as far as these are. It may be that $\overline{x}_1 = 47.60$ and $\overline{x}_3 = 36.18$ are significantly different if we look at just two groups but not significantly different if we know that they are the largest and the smallest means in three groups. As we look at more groups, we expect the gap between the largest and smallest sample mean to get larger. (Think of comparing the tallest and shortest person in larger and larger groups of people.) *We can't safely compare many means by doing tests or confidence intervals for two means at a time.* Instead, we will use a single test to see if there is good evidence of *any* differences among the means that we want to compare.

The basic *conditions for inference* (more detail later) are that we have random samples from the three populations and that flower lengths are Normally distributed in each population and have the same standard deviation σ in each population. The three population means μ_1, μ_2, μ_3 and the common population standard deviation σ are all unknown.

We want to test the null hypothesis that there are *no differences* among the mean lengths for the three populations of flowers:

$$H_0: \mu_1 = \mu_2 = \mu_3$$

The alternative hypothesis is that there is *some difference*. That is, not all three population means are equal:

$$H_a: \text{not all of } \mu_1, \ \mu_2, \text{ and } \mu_3 \text{ are equal}$$

The alternative hypothesis is no longer one-sided or two-sided. It is "many-sided," because it allows any relationship other than "all three equal." For example, H_a includes the case in which $\mu_2 = \mu_3$ but μ_1 has a different value. The test of H_0 against H_a is called the **analysis of variance *F* test.** Analysis of variance is usually abbreviated as ANOVA. The ANOVA *F* test is almost always carried out by software that reports the test statistic and its *P*-value.

analysis of variance F test

 Comparing tropical flowers: ANOVA

SOLVE (inference): Software tells us that for the flower length data in Table 23.1, the test statistic is $F = 259.12$ with *P*-value $P < 0.0001$. There is very strong evidence that the three varieties of flowers do not all have the same mean length.

The *F* test does not say *which* of the three means are significantly different. It appears from our preliminary data analysis that *bihai* flowers are distinctly longer than either red or yellow. Red and yellow are closer together, but the red flowers tend to be longer.

CONCLUDE: There is strong evidence ($P < 0.0001$) that the population means are not all equal. The most important difference among the means is that the *bihai* variety has longer flowers than the red and yellow varieties. ∎

Example 23.2 illustrates our approach to comparing means. The ANOVA *F* test (done by software) assesses the evidence for *some* difference among the population means. We rely on examination of the data to show what specific differences are present and whether they are large enough to be interesting.

23.1 Choose your parents wisely. To live long, it helps to have long-lived parents. One study of this "inheritance of longevity" looked at records of families in a small mountain valley in France where the style of life changed little over time. Married couples in which both husband and wife were born between 1745 and 1849 were divided into four groups as follows:

	Short-lived wife	Long-lived wife
Short-lived husband	Group A	Group C
Long-lived husband	Group B	Group D

"Long-lived" parents were in the top 70% of the distribution of age at death, "short-lived" parents were in the bottom 30%. To examine extended life, the investigators looked at the ages at death of the children of these parents who lived to at least age 55. The report includes a graph like Figure 23.2 and concludes: "The mean life spans varied significantly among the four groups, indicating an influence of parental phenotype on offspring longevity (ANOVA, $F = 9.2$, d.f. $= 3, 1085$, $P = 0.0001$)."[2]

(a) What are the null and alternative hypotheses for the ANOVA *F* test? Be sure to explain what means the test compares.

(b) Based on the graph and the *F* test, what do you conclude?

FIGURE 23.2

Bar graph comparing the longevity of children from four groups of parents, for Exercise 23.1.

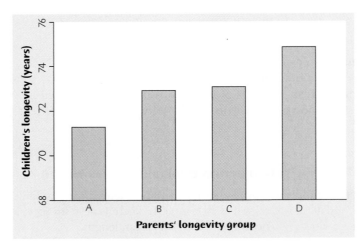

23.2 Road rage. "The phenomenon of road rage has been frequently discussed but infrequently examined." So begins a report based on interviews with 1382 randomly selected drivers.[3] The respondents' answers to interview questions produced scores on an "angry/threatening driving scale" with values between 0 and 19. What driver characteristics go with road rage? There were no significant differences among races or levels of education. What about the effect of the driver's age? Here are the mean responses for three age groups:

< 30 yr	30–55 yr	> 55 yr
2.22	1.33	0.66

The report says that $F = 34.96$, with $P < 0.01$.

(a) What are the null and alternative hypotheses for the ANOVA F test? Be sure to explain what means the test compares.

(b) Based on the sample means and the F test, what do you conclude?

Using technology

Any technology used for statistics should perform analysis of variance. Figure 23.3 displays ANOVA output for the data of Table 23.1 from a graphing calculator, a statistical program, and a spreadsheet program.

The two software outputs give the sizes of the three samples and their means. These agree with those in Example 23.1. Minitab also gives the standard deviations and Excel gives the variances. All three outputs report the F test statistic, $F = 259.12$, and its P-value. Minitab sensibly reports the P-value as 0 to three decimal places, which is all we need to know in practice. Excel and the graphing calculator offer the specific value 1.92×10^{-27}. This would be correct if the population distributions were exactly Normal. In practice, read such values simply as "P is very small." There is very strong evidence that the three varieties of flowers do not all have the same mean length.

All three outputs report degrees of freedom (df), sums of squares (SS), and mean squares (MS). We don't need this information now. Minitab also gives confidence intervals for all three means that help us see which means differ and by how much. None of the intervals overlap, and *bihai* is much above the other two. These are 95% confidence intervals for each mean separately. We are *not* 95% confident that *all three* intervals cover the three means.

APPLY YOUR KNOWLEDGE

23.3 Logging in the rain forest. How does logging in a tropical rain forest affect the forest in later years? Researchers compared forest plots in Borneo that had never been logged (Group 1) with similar plots nearby that had been logged 1 year earlier (Group 2) and 8 years earlier (Group 3). The authors explain why we can consider the plots to be randomly selected. The data appear in Table 23.2 (page 427). The variable Trees is the count of trees in a plot; Species is the count of tree species in a plot. The variable Richness is the number of species divided by the number of individual trees.[4]

(a) Make side-by-side stemplots of Trees for the three groups. Use stems 0, 1, 2, and 3 and split the stems. What effects of logging are visible?

Texas Instruments Graphing Calculator

Minitab

Excel

FIGURE 23.3

ANOVA for the flower length data: output from a graphing calculator, a statistical program, and a spreadsheet program.

TABLE 23.2 Data from a study of logging in Borneo

GROUP	TREES	SPECIES	RICHNESS	GROUP	TREES	SPECIES	RICHNESS
1	27	22	0.81481	2	18	15	0.83333
1	22	18	0.81818	2	17	15	0.88235
1	29	22	0.75862	2	14	12	0.85714
1	21	20	0.95238	2	14	13	0.92857
1	19	15	0.78947	2	2	2	1.00000
1	33	21	0.63636	2	17	15	0.88235
1	16	13	0.81250	2	19	8	0.42105
1	20	13	0.65000	3	18	17	0.94444
1	24	19	0.79167	3	4	4	1.00000
1	27	13	0.48148	3	22	18	0.81818
1	28	19	0.67857	3	15	14	0.93333
1	19	15	0.78947	3	18	18	1.00000
2	12	11	0.91667	3	19	15	0.78947
2	12	11	0.91667	3	22	15	0.68182
2	15	14	0.93333	3	12	10	0.83333
2	9	7	0.77778	3	12	12	1.00000
2	20	18	0.90000				

(b) Figure 23.4 shows Excel ANOVA output for Trees. What do the group means show about the effects of logging?

(c) What are the values of the ANOVA F statistic and its P-value? What hypotheses does F test? What conclusions about the effects of logging on number of trees do the data lead to?

	A	B	C	D	E	F	G
1	Anova: Single Factor						
2							
3	SUMMARY						
4	Groups	Count	Sum	Average	Variance		
5	Group 1	12	285	23.75	25.6591		
6	Group 2	12	169	14.0833	24.8106		
7	Group 3	9	142	15.7778	33.1944		
8							
9							
10	ANOVA						
11	Source of variation	SS	df	MS	F	P-value	F crit
12	Between Groups	625.1566	2	312.57828	11.4257	0.000205	3.31583
13	Within Groups	820.7222	30	27.3574			
14							
15	Total	1445.879	32				

Microsoft Excel Book 1

FIGURE 23.4

Excel output for analysis of variance on the number of trees in forest plots, for Exercise 23.3.

23.4 Do good smells bring good business? Businesses know that customers often respond to background music. Do they also respond to odors? Nicolas Guéguen and his colleagues studied this question in a small pizza restaurant in France on Saturday evenings in May. On one evening, a relaxing lavender odor was spread through the restaurant; on another evening, a stimulating lemon odor; a third evening served as a control, with no odor. The three evenings were comparable in many ways (weather, customer count, and so on), so

TABLE 23.3 Time (minutes) that customers remain in a restaurant when exposed to odors

				LAVENDER ODOR					
92	126	114	106	89	137	93	76	98	108
124	105	129	103	107	109	94	105	102	108
95	121	109	104	116	88	109	97	101	106
				LEMON ODOR					
78	104	74	75	112	88	105	97	101	89
88	73	94	63	83	108	91	88	83	106
108	60	96	94	56	90	113	97		
				NO ODOR					
103	68	79	106	72	121	92	84	72	92
85	69	73	87	109	115	91	84	76	96
107	98	92	107	93	118	87	101	75	86

we are willing to regard the data as independent SRSs from spring Saturday evenings at this restaurant. Table 23.3 contains data on how long (in minutes) customers stayed in the restaurant on each of the three evenings.[5]

(a) Make stemplots of the customer times for each evening. Do any of the distributions show outliers, strong skewness, or other clear deviations from Normality?

(b) Figure 23.5 gives the Minitab ANOVA output for these data. What do the mean times in the restaurant say about the effects of the two odors?

(c) What are the values of the ANOVA F statistic and its P-value? What hypotheses does F test? Briefly describe the conclusions you draw from these data. Did you find anything surprising?

FIGURE 23.5

Minitab output for the data in Table 23.3 on time in minutes that customers spend in a restaurant, for Exercise 23.4.

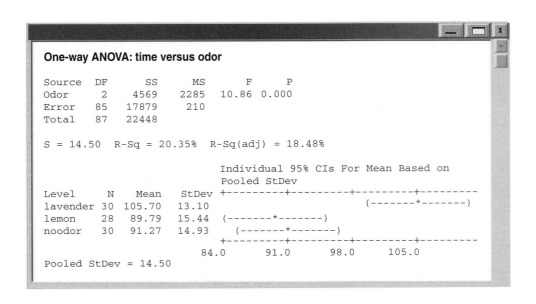

```
One-way ANOVA: time versus odor

Source  DF      SS      MS      F      P
Odor     2    4569    2285   10.86  0.000
Error   85   17879     210
Total   87   22448


S = 14.50   R-Sq = 20.35%   R-Sq(adj) = 18.48%


                              Individual 95% CIs For Mean Based on
                              Pooled StDev
Level      N    Mean   StDev  +---------+---------+---------+---------
lavender  30  105.70   13.10                        (-------*-------)
lemon     28   89.79   15.44  (-------*-------)
noodor    30   91.27   14.93     (-------*-------)
                              +---------+---------+---------+---------
                             84.0      91.0      98.0     105.0
Pooled StDev = 14.50
```

The idea of analysis of variance

The details of calculating ANOVA are a bit daunting. The main idea of ANOVA is much more important. Here it is: when we ask if a set of sample means gives evidence for differences among the population means, what matters is not how far apart the sample means are but how far apart they are *relative to the variability of individual observations*.

Look at the two sets of boxplots in Figure 23.6. For simplicity, these distributions are all symmetric, so that the mean and median are the same. The center line in each boxplot is therefore the sample mean. Both sets of boxplots compare three samples with the same three means. Could differences this large easily arise just due to chance, or are they statistically significant?

- The boxplots in Figure 23.6(a) have tall boxes, which show lots of variation among the individuals in each group. With this much variation among individuals, we would not be surprised if another set of samples gave quite different sample means. The observed differences among the sample means could easily happen just by chance.
- The boxplots in Figure 23.6(b) have the same centers as those in Figure 23.6(a), but the boxes are much shorter. There is much less variation among the individuals in each group. It is unlikely that any sample from the first group would have a mean as small as the mean of the second group. Because means as far apart as those observed would rarely arise just by chance in repeated sampling, they are good evidence of real differences among the means of the three populations we are sampling from.

 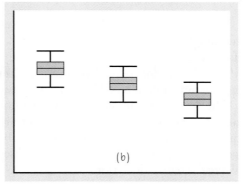

FIGURE 23.6

Boxplots for two sets of three samples each. The sample means are the same in (a) and (b). Analysis of variance will find a more significant difference among the means in (b) because there is less variation among the individuals within those samples.

This comparison of the two parts of Figure 23.6 is too simple in one way. It ignores the effect of the sample sizes, an effect that boxplots do not show. *Small differences among sample means can be significant if the samples are large. Large differences among sample means can fail to be significant if the samples are small.* All we can be sure of is that for the same sample size, Figure 23.6(b) will give a much smaller P-value than Figure 23.6(a). Despite this qualification, the big idea remains: if sample means are far apart relative to the variation among individuals in the same groups, that's evidence that something other than chance is at work.

> **THE ANALYSIS OF VARIANCE IDEA**
>
> **Analysis of variance** compares the variation due to specific sources with the variation among individuals who should be similar. In particular, ANOVA tests whether several populations have the same mean by comparing how far apart the sample means are with how much variation there is within the samples.

It is one of the oddities of statistical language that methods for comparing means are named after the variance. The reason is that the test works by comparing two kinds of variation. Analysis of variance is a general method for studying sources of variation in responses. Comparing several means is the simplest form of ANOVA, called **one-way ANOVA**.

one-way ANOVA

> **THE ANOVA _F_ STATISTIC**
>
> The **analysis of variance _F_ statistic** for testing the equality of several means has this form:
>
> $$F = \frac{\text{variation among the sample means}}{\text{variation among individuals in the same sample}}$$

The F statistic can take only values that are zero or positive. It is zero only when all the sample means are identical and gets larger as they move farther apart. Large values of F are evidence against the null hypothesis H_0 that all population means are the same. Although the alternative hypothesis H_a is many-sided, the ANOVA F test is one-sided because any violation of H_0 tends to produce a large value of F.

The "variation" terms in the numerator and denominator of the F statistic are the *mean squares* **mean squares** that appear in the outputs in Figure 23.3. Roughly speaking, a mean square is similar to a variance. Recall that the variance of a set of data is an average of the squared deviations of the observations from their mean. Mean squares are average squared deviations that measure specific kinds of variation in the ANOVA setting.

APPLY YOUR KNOWLEDGE

23.5 ANOVA calculation basics. Look at the Minitab output in Figure 23.3.

(a) Verify that the F statistic is the "Variety" mean square (MS) divided by the "Error" mean square. Although we don't show the details of the algebra, the "Variety" mean square measures variation among the sample mean lengths for the three flower varieties. The "Error" mean square measures variation among individual flowers of the same variety.

(b) Verify that the quantity s is the square root of the "Error" mean square. In fact, s is the *pooled standard deviation,* which uses data from all three flower varieties to estimate the common population standard deviation σ.

23.6 The idea of ANOVA. Here is a simplified set of flower lengths similar to those in Table 23.1:

bihai	red	yellow
48	39	37
52	40	34
50	41	38
49	38	36
46	37	40

(a) Using software, do ANOVA to compare the mean lengths. Report the sample mean and standard deviation for each variety, the mean squares for variety and error, the F statistic and its P-value, and the pooled standard deviation s. The differences among sample means are highly significant.

(b) Now modify the data by subtracting 10 from each *bihai* length and adding 1 to each yellow length (leave the red lengths unchanged). Do ANOVA and report the same statistics as in (a). The means of the new data are closer together, but the standard deviations are the same as in (a). Because ANOVA compares variation among the sample means with variation among individuals in the same sample, F is now much smaller and is not significant.

(c) The mean square for variety measures variation among the sample means. The mean square for error measures variation among flowers of the same variety. How are these mean squares affected by the change in the data from (a) to (b)?

Conditions for ANOVA

Like all inference procedures, ANOVA is valid only in some circumstances. Here are the conditions under which we can use ANOVA to compare population means.

> **CONDITIONS FOR ANOVA INFERENCE**
>
> - We have *I* **independent SRSs,** one from each of *I* populations. We measure the same response variable for each sample.
> - The *i*th population has a **Normal distribution** with unknown mean μ_i. One-way ANOVA tests the null hypothesis that all the population means are the same.
> - All of the populations have the **same standard deviation** σ, whose value is unknown.

The first two conditions are familiar from our study of the two-sample t procedures for comparing two means. As usual, the design of the data production is the most important condition for inference. Biased sampling or confounding can make any inference meaningless. ANOVA, like other inference procedures, is often used when random samples are not available. You must judge each use on its merits, a judgment that usually requires some knowledge of the subject of the study in addition to some knowledge of statistics.

No real population has exactly a Normal distribution. Fortunately, procedures for comparing means are not very sensitive to lack of Normality. The ANOVA F test, like the *robustness*   *t* procedures, is **robust.** What matters is Normality of the sample means, so ANOVA becomes safer as the sample sizes get larger, because of the central limit theorem effect. Remember to check for outliers that change the value of sample means and for extreme skewness. When there are no outliers and the distributions are roughly symmetric, you can safely use ANOVA for sample sizes as small as 4 or 5.

The third condition is annoying: unlike the *t* test for comparing two means (Chapter 17), ANOVA assumes that the variability of observations, measured by the standard deviation, is the same in all populations. It is not easy to check the condition that the populations have equal standard deviations. Statistical tests for equality of standard deviations are very sensitive to lack of Normality, so much so that they are of little practical value. You must either seek expert advice or rely on the robustness of ANOVA.

How serious are unequal standard deviations? ANOVA is not too sensitive to violations of the condition, especially when all samples have the same or similar sizes and no sample is very small. When designing a study, try to take samples of about the same size from all the groups you want to compare. The sample standard deviations estimate the population standard deviations, so check before doing ANOVA that the sample standard deviations are similar to each other. We expect some variation among them due to chance. Here is a rule of thumb that is safe in almost all situations.

CHECKING STANDARD DEVIATIONS IN ANOVA

The results of the ANOVA *F* test are approximately correct when the largest sample standard deviation is no more than twice as large as the smallest sample standard deviation.

EXAMPLE 23.3 Comparing tropical flowers: conditions for ANOVA

The study of *Heliconia* blossoms is based on three independent samples that the researchers consider to be random samples from all flowers of these varieties in Dominica. The stemplots in Figure 23.1 show that the *bihai* and red varieties have slightly skewed distributions, but the sample means of samples of sizes 16 and 23 will have distributions that are close to Normal. The sample standard deviations for the three varieties are

$$s_1 = 1.213 \quad s_2 = 1.799 \quad s_3 = 0.975$$

These standard deviations satisfy our rule of thumb:

$$\frac{\text{largest } s}{\text{smallest } s} = \frac{1.799}{0.975} = 1.85 \quad \text{(less than 2)}$$

We can safely use ANOVA to compare the mean lengths for the three populations. ■

EXAMPLE 23.4 Thinking about money changes behavior

STATE: Kathleen Vohs of the University of Minnesota and her coworkers carried out several randomized comparative experiments on the effects of thinking about money. Here's an outline of one of the experiments. Ask student subjects to unscramble 30 sets of five words to make a meaningful phrase from four of the five. The control group unscrambled phrases like "cold it desk outside is" into "it is cold outside." The "play money" group unscrambled similar sets of words, but a stack of Monopoly money was placed nearby. The "money prime"

TABLE 23.4 Time (seconds) until subjects ask for help with a puzzle

GROUP	TIME	GROUP	TIME	GROUP	TIME
Prime	609	Play	455	Control	118
Prime	444	Play	100	Control	272
Prime	242	Play	238	Control	413
Prime	199	Play	243	Control	291
Prime	174	Play	500	Control	140
Prime	55	Play	570	Control	104
Prime	251	Play	231	Control	55
Prime	466	Play	380	Control	189
Prime	443	Play	222	Control	126
Prime	531	Play	71	Control	400
Prime	135	Play	232	Control	92
Prime	241	Play	219	Control	64
Prime	476	Play	320	Control	88
Prime	482	Play	261	Control	142
Prime	362	Play	290	Control	141
Prime	69	Play	495	Control	373
Prime	160	Play	600	Control	156
		Play	67		

group unscrambled phrases that lead to thinking about money, turning "high a salary desk paying" into "a high-paying salary." Then each subject worked a hard puzzle, knowing that they could ask for help. Table 23.4 shows the time in seconds that each subject worked on the puzzle before asking for help.[6] Psychologists think that money tends to make people self-sufficient. If so, the two groups that were encouraged in different ways to think about money should take longer on the average to ask for help. Do the data support this idea?

PLAN: Examine the data to compare the effect of the treatments and check that we can safely use ANOVA. If the data allow ANOVA, assess the significance of observed differences in mean times to ask for help.

SOLVE: Figure 23.7 shows side-by-side stemplots of the data in the three groups. We expect some irregularity in small samples, but there are no outliers or strong skewness that would hinder use of ANOVA. The Minitab ANOVA output in Figure 23.8 shows that the group standard deviations easily satisfy our rule of thumb. The control group subjects asked for help much sooner (mean 186.1 seconds) than did subjects in the two money groups (means 305.2 seconds and 314.1 seconds). The three means are significantly different ($F = 3.73$, $P = 0.031$).

```
    Prime           Play            Control
 0 | 6 7        0 | 7 7         0 | 6 6 9 9
 1 | 4 6 7      1 | 0           1 | 0 2 3 4 4 4 6 9
 2 | 0 4 4 5    2 | 2 2 3 3 4 6 9   2 | 7 9
 3 | 6          3 | 2 8         3 | 7
 4 | 4 4 7 8 8  4 | 6           4 | 0 1
 5 | 3          5 | 0 0 7       5 |
 6 | 1          6 | 0           6 |
```

FIGURE 23.7
Side-by-side stemplots comparing the time until subjects asked for help with a puzzle, for Example 23.4.

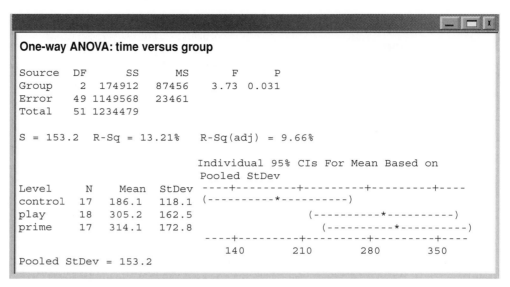

One-way ANOVA: time versus group

```
Source  DF       SS      MS      F      P
Group    2   174912   87456   3.73  0.031
Error   49  1149568   23461
Total   51  1234479

S = 153.2   R-Sq = 13.21%    R-Sq(adj) = 9.66%


                            Individual 95% CIs For Mean Based on
                            Pooled StDev
Level     N    Mean   StDev  ----+---------+---------+---------+----
control  17   186.1   118.1  (----------*----------)
play     18   305.2   162.5                 (----------*----------)
prime    17   314.1   172.8                    (---------*----------)
                             ----+---------+---------+---------+----
                             140       210       280       350

Pooled StDev = 153.2
```

FIGURE 23.8

Minitab ANOVA output for comparing the three treatments in Example 23.4.

CONCLUDE: The experiment gives good evidence that reminding people of money in either of two ways does make them less willing to ask others for help. This is consistent with the idea that money makes people feel more self-sufficient. ▪

APPLY YOUR KNOWLEDGE

23.7 Checking standard deviations. Verify that the sample standard deviations for these sets of data do allow use of ANOVA to compare the population means.

(a) The counts of trees in Exercise 23.3 and Figure 23.4.

(b) The restaurant times of Exercise 23.4 and Figure 23.5.

23.8 Species richness after logging. Table 23.2 gives data on the species richness in rain forest plots, defined as the number of tree species in a plot divided by the number of trees in the plot. ANOVA may not be trustworthy for the richness data. Do data analysis: make side-by-side stemplots to examine the distributions of the response variable in the three groups, and also compare the standard deviations. What characteristic of the data makes ANOVA risky?

23.9 Fertilizing bromeliads. Bromeliads are tropical flowering plants. Many are epiphytes that attach to trees and obtain moisture and nutrients from air and rain. Their leaf bases form cups that collect water and are home to the larvae of many insects. Jacqueline Ngai and Diane Srivastava examined the effects of adding nitrogen, phosphorus, or both to the cups. They randomly assigned 8 bromeliads to each of four treatment groups, including an unfertilized control group. A monkey destroyed one of the plants in the control group, leaving 7 bromeliads in that group. Here are the numbers of new leaves on each plant over the 7 months following fertilization:[7]

Nitrogen	Phosphorus	Both	Neither
15	14	14	11
14	14	16	13
15	14	15	16
16	11	14	15
17	13	14	15
18	12	13	11
17	15	17	12
13	15	14	

Analyze these data and discuss the results. Does nitrogen or phosphorus have a greater effect on the growth of bromeliads? Follow the four-step process as illustrated in Example 23.4.

F distributions and degrees of freedom*

The ANOVA *F* statistic is

$$F = \frac{\text{variation among the sample means}}{\text{variation among individuals in the same sample}}$$

To find the *P*-value for this statistic, software uses the sampling distribution of *F* when the null hypothesis (all population means equal) is true. This sampling distribution is an **F distribution.**

    F distribution

The *F* distributions are a family of right-skewed distributions that take only values greater than 0. The density curves in Figure 23.9 illustrate their shapes. A specific *F* distribution is determined by the **degrees of freedom** of the numerator and denominator of the *F* statistic. When describing an *F* distribution, always give the numerator degrees of freedom first. Our brief notation will be *F*(df1, df2) for the *F* distribution with df1 degrees of freedom in the numerator and df2 in the denominator. *Interchanging the degrees*

    degrees of freedom

FIGURE 23.9

Density curves for two *F* distributions. Both are right-skewed and take only positive values. The upper 5% critical values are marked under the curves.

---
* This section is not required to do ANOVA with software.

of freedom changes the distribution, so the order is important. Tables of F critical points are awkward, because we need a separate table for every pair of degrees of freedom df1 and df2. Fortunately, software gives you P-values for the ANOVA F test without the need for a table.

EXAMPLE 23.5 **Comparing flowers: the *F* distribution**

Look again at the software output in Figure 23.3 for the flower length data. All three outputs give the degrees of freedom for the F test, labeled "df" or "DF." There are 2 degrees of freedom in the numerator and 51 in the denominator. P-values for the F test therefore come from the F distribution $F(2, 51)$ with 2 and 51 degrees of freedom. The right-hand curve in Figure 23.9 is the density curve of this distribution. The 5% critical value marked on that curve is 3.18, and the 1% critical value is 5.05. The observed value $F = 259.12$ of the ANOVA F statistic lies far to the right of these values, so the P-value is extremely small. ▪

Even without software, it is easy to find the proper degrees of freedom:

- The numerator degrees of freedom are 1 fewer than the number of groups the F statistic compares.
- The denominator degrees of freedom are the total number of observations in all groups, less the number of groups.

EXAMPLE 23.6 **Degrees of freedom for *F***

In Examples 23.1 and 23.2, we compared the mean lengths for 3 varieties of flowers. The three sample sizes are $n_1 = 16, n_2 = 23, n_3 = 15$, so that the total number of observations is

$$n_1 + n_2 + n_3 = 16 + 23 + 15 = 54$$

The ANOVA F test has numerator degrees of freedom 2 (1 less than the number of groups) and denominator degrees of freedom 51 (number of observations minus number of groups, $54 - 3$). These are the degrees of freedom given in the outputs in Figure 23.3. ▪

APPLY YOUR KNOWLEDGE

23.10 Logging in the rain forest, continued. Exercise 23.3 compares the number of tree species in rain forest plots that had never been logged (Group 1) with similar plots nearby that had been logged 1 year earlier (Group 2) and 8 years earlier (Group 3). What are the sample sizes in the three groups? Find the degrees of freedom for the ANOVA F statistic. Check your work against the Excel output in Figure 23.4.

23.11 What music will you play? People often match their behavior to their social environment. One study of this idea first established that the type of music most preferred by black college students is R&B and that whites' most preferred music is rock. Will students hosting a small group of other students choose music that matches the makeup of the people attending? Assign 90 black business students at random to three equal-sized groups. Do the same for 96 white students. Each student sees a picture of the people he or she will host. Group 1 sees 6 blacks, Group 2 sees 3 whites and 3 blacks, and Group 3 sees 6 whites. Ask how likely the host is to play the type of music preferred by the other race. Use ANOVA to compare the three groups to see whether the racial mix of the gathering affects the choice of music.[8]

(a) For the white subjects, $F = 16.48$. What are the degrees of freedom?

(b) For the black subjects, $F = 2.47$. What are the degrees of freedom?

CHAPTER 23 SUMMARY

- **One-way analysis of variance (ANOVA)** compares the means of several populations. The **ANOVA F test** tests the null hypothesis that all the populations have the same mean. If the F test shows significant differences, examine the data to see where the differences lie and whether they are large enough to be important.

- The **conditions for ANOVA** state that we have an **independent SRS** from each population; that each population has a **Normal distribution**; and that all populations have the **same standard deviation.**

- In practice, ANOVA inference is relatively **robust** when the populations are non-Normal, especially when the samples are large. Before doing the F test, check the observations in each sample for outliers or strong skewness. Also verify that the largest sample standard deviation is no more than twice as large as the smallest standard deviation.

- When the null hypothesis is true, the **ANOVA F statistic** for comparing I means from a total of N observations in all samples combined has the **F distribution** with $I - 1$ and $N - I$ degrees of freedom.

CHECK YOUR SKILLS

23.12 A study of the effects of smoking classifies subjects as nonsmokers, moderate smokers, or heavy smokers. The investigators interview a sample of 200 people from each group. Among the questions is "How many hours do you sleep on a typical night?" The null hypothesis for the ANOVA F test is
(a) the mean hours of sleep in the groups are all the same.
(b) the three groups all have the same standard deviation.
(c) hours of sleep follows a Normal distribution in each group.

23.13 The alternative hypothesis for the ANOVA F test in the previous exercise is
(a) the mean hours of sleep in the groups are all the same.
(b) the mean hours of sleep in the groups are all different.
(c) the mean hours of sleep in the groups are not all the same.

Fungus spores in the air in poultry-processing plants can affect the health of workers. To measure the presence of spores, air samples are pumped to an agar plate and "colony-forming units (CFUs)" are counted after an incubation period. Here are data from the "kill room" of a plant that slaughters 37,000 turkeys per day, taken

at four seasons of the year. Each observation was made on a different day. The units are CFUs per cubic meter of air.[9]

Fall	Winter	Spring	Summer
1231	384	2105	3175
1254	104	701	2526
752	251	2947	1763
1088	97	842	1090

Here is Minitab output for ANOVA to compare mean CFUs in the four seasons:

```
Source   DF        SS       MS      F      P
Season    3   8236359  2745453   5.38  0.014
Error    12   6124211   510351
Total    15  14360570
```

```
                 Individual 95% CIs For Mean Based on
                 Pooled StDev
Level   N    Mean    StDev  ------+---------+---------+---------+---
Fall    4  1081.3    231.5            (-------*-------)
Spring  4  1648.8   1071.2                  (------*-------)
Summer  4  2138.5    906.4                      (------*-------)
Winter  4   209.0    136.6  (-------*-------)
                            ------+---------+---------+---------+---
                                0      1000      2000      3000
```

Exercises 23.14 to 23.18 are based on this study.

23.14 The most striking conclusion from the numerical summaries for the turkey processing plant is that
(a) there appears to be little difference among the seasons.
(b) on the average, CFUs are much lower in winter than in other seasons.
(c) the air in the plant is clearly unhealthy.

23.15 We might use the two-sample t procedures to compare summer and winter. The conservative 90% confidence interval for the difference in the two population means is
(a) 1929.5 ± 458.3.   (b) 1929.5 ± 1078.4.
(c) 1929.5 ± 1458.4.

23.16 In all, we would have to give 6 two-sample confidence intervals to compare all pairs of seasons. The weakness of doing this is that
(a) we don't know how confident we can be that all 6 intervals cover the true differences in means.
(b) 90% confidence is OK for one comparison, but it isn't high enough for 6 comparisons done at once.
(c) the conditions for two-sample t inference are not met for all 6 pairs of seasons.

23.17 The conclusion of the ANOVA test is that
(a) there is quite strong evidence ($P = 0.014$) that the mean CFUs are not the same in all four seasons.
(b) there is quite strong evidence ($P = 0.014$) that the mean CFUs are much lower in winter than in any other season.
(c) the data give no evidence ($P = 0.014$) to suggest that mean CFUs differ from season to season.

23.18 The P-value 0.014 in the output may not be accurate because the conditions for ANOVA are not satisfied. The most serious violation of the conditions is that
(a) the sample standard deviations are too different.
(b) there is an extreme outlier in the data.
(c) the data can't be regarded as random samples.

CHAPTER 23 EXERCISES

Exercises 23.19 to 23.22 describe situations in which we want to compare the mean responses in several populations. For each setting, identify the populations and the response variable and give the null and alternative hypotheses for the ANOVA F statistic.

23.19 Morning or evening? Are you a morning person, an evening person, or neither? Does this personality trait affect how well you perform? A sample of 100 students took a psychological test that found 16 morning people, 30 evening people, and 54 who were neither. All the students then took a test of their ability to memorize at 8 A.M. and again at 9 P.M. The response variable is the score at 8 A.M. minus the score at 9 P.M.

23.20 Writing essays. Do strategies such as preparing a written outline help students write better essays? College students were divided at random into four groups of 20 students each, then asked to write an essay on an assigned topic. Group A (the control group) received no additional instruction. Group B was required to prepare a written outline. Group C was given 15 ideas that might be relevant to the essay topic. Group D was given the ideas and also required to prepare an outline. An expert scored the quality of the essays on a scale of 1 to 7.

23.21 Test accommodations. Many states require schoolchildren to take regular statewide tests to assess their progress. Children with learning disabilities who read poorly may not do well on mathematics tests because they can't read the problems. Most states allow "accommodations" for learning-disabled children. Randomly assign 100 learning-disabled children in equal numbers to three types of accommodation and a control group: math problems are read by a teacher; by a computer; by a computer that also shows a video; and standard test conditions. Compare the mean scores on the state mathematics assessment.

23.22 A medical study. The Québec (Canada) Cardiovascular Study recruited men aged 34 to 64 at random from towns in the Québec City metropolitan area. Of these, 1824 met the criteria (no diabetes, free of heart disease, and so on) for a study of the relationship between being overweight and medical risks. The 719 normal-weight men had mean triglyceride level 1.5 millimoles per liter (mmol/l); the 885 overweight men had mean 1.7 mmol/l; and the 220 obese men had mean 1.9 mmol/l.[10]

23.23 Plants defend themselves. When some plants are attacked by leaf-eating insects, they release chemical compounds that attract other insects that prey on the leaf-eaters. A study carried out on plants growing naturally in the Utah desert studied the release of these compounds.[11] The investigators chose 8 plants attacked by each of three leaf-eaters and 8 more that were undamaged, 32 plants of the same species in all. They then measured emissions of several compounds during seven hours. Here are data (mean ± standard error of the mean for eight plants) for one compound. The emission rate is measured in nanograms (ng) per hour.

Group	Emission rate (ng/hr)
Control	9.22 ± 5.93
Hornworm	31.03 ± 8.75
Leaf bug	18.97 ± 6.64
Flea beetle	27.12 ± 8.62

(a) Make a graph that compares the mean emission rates for the four groups. Does it appear that emissions increase when the plant is attacked?

(b) What hypotheses does ANOVA test in this setting?

(c) We do not have the full data. What would you look for in deciding whether you can safely use ANOVA?

(d) What is the relationship between the standard error of the mean (SEM) and the standard deviation for a sample? What are the four sample standard deviations? Do they satisfy our rule of thumb for safe use of ANOVA?

23.24 Can you hear these words? Hearing tests often ask subjects to try to repeat words played at low volume. There are several different lists of words that are supposed to be equally difficult. Are the lists equally difficult when there is background noise? To find out, an experimenter had subjects with normal hearing listen to four lists with a noisy background. The response variable was the percent of the 50 words in a list that the subject repeated correctly. The data set contains 96 responses.[12] Here are two study designs that could produce these data:

> **Design A.** The experimenter assigns 96 subjects to 4 groups at random. Each group of 24 subjects listens to one of the lists. All individuals listen and respond separately.

> **Design B.** The experimenter has 24 subjects. Each subject listens to all four lists in random order. All individuals listen and respond separately.

Does Design A allow use of one-way ANOVA to compare the lists? Does Design B allow use of one-way ANOVA to compare the lists? Briefly explain your answers.

23.25 More rain for California? The changing climate will probably bring more rain to California, but we don't know whether the additional rain will come during the winter wet season or extend into the long dry season in spring and summer. Kenwyn Suttle of the University of California at Berkeley and his coworkers randomly assigned plots of open grassland to three treatments: added water equal to 20% of annual rainfall either during January to March (winter) or during April to June (spring), and no added water (control). Here are some of the data, for plant biomass (in grams per square meter) produced by each plot in 2003:[13]

Winter	Spring	Control
264.1514	318.4182	129.0538
187.7312	281.6830	144.6578
291.1431	288.8433	172.7772
176.2879	382.6673	113.2813
141.7525	326.8877	142.1562
169.9737	293.8502	117.9808

Figure 23.10 shows Minitab ANOVA output for these data.

(a) Make side-by-side stemplots of plant biomass for the three treatments, as well as a table of the sample means and standard deviations. What do the data appear to show about the effect of extra water in winter and in spring on biomass? Do these data satisfy the conditions for ANOVA?

(b) State H_0 and H_a for the ANOVA F test, and explain in words what ANOVA tests in this setting.

(c) Report your overall conclusions about the effect of added water on plant growth in California.

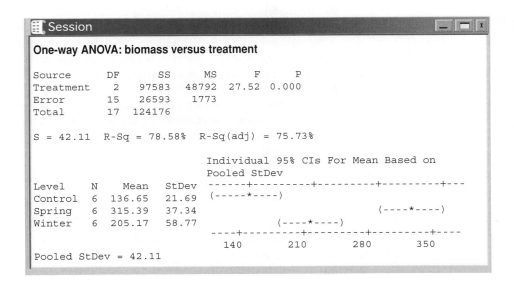

```
Session                                              _ □ x

One-way ANOVA: biomass versus treatment

Source      DF     SS     MS     F      P
Treatment    2   97583  48792  27.52  0.000
Error       15   26593   1773
Total       17  124176

S = 42.11  R-Sq = 78.58%  R-Sq(adj) = 75.73%

                          Individual 95% CIs For Mean Based on
                          Pooled StDev
Level     N    Mean   StDev  ------+---------+---------+---------+---
Control   6  136.65   21.69  (-----*----)
Spring    6  315.39   37.34                        (----*----)
Winter    6  205.17   58.77            (----*----)
                             ----+---------+---------+---------+----
                             140       210       280       350
Pooled StDev = 42.11
```

FIGURE 23.10

Minitab ANOVA output for comparing the total plant biomass of grassland plots under different water conditions, for Exercise 23.25.

FIGURE 23.11

Minitab ANOVA output for comparing the percents heard correctly in four lists of words, for Exercise 23.26.

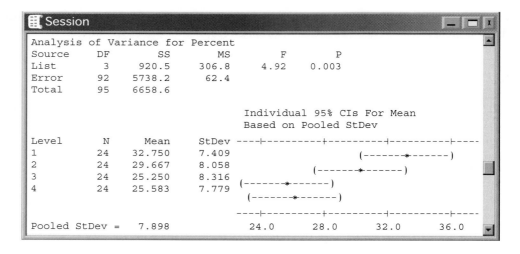

```
Session                                                                    _  □  x

Analysis of Variance for Percent
Source    DF       SS       MS        F        P
List       3    920.5    306.8     4.92    0.003
Error     92   5738.2     62.4
Total     95   6658.6

                                    Individual 95% CIs For Mean
                                    Based on Pooled StDev
Level      N     Mean    StDev  ----+---------+---------+---------+-----
1         24   32.750    7.409                      (------*------)
2         24   29.667    8.058                 (------*------)
3         24   25.250    8.316        (------*------)
4         24   25.583    7.779          (------*------)
                                   ---+---------+---------+---------+-----
Pooled StDev =    7.898            24.0      28.0      32.0      36.0
```

23.26 Can you hear these words? Figure 23.11 displays the Minitab output for one-way ANOVA applied to the hearing data described in Exercise 23.24. The response variable is "Percent," and "List" identifies the four lists of words. Based on this analysis, is there good reason to think that the four lists are not all equally difficult? Write a brief summary of the study findings.

23.27 Which blue is most blue? The color of a fabric depends on the dye used and also on how the dye is applied. This matters to clothing manufacturers, who want the color of the fabric to be just right. Treat fabric made of ramie with the same "procion blue" dye applied in four different ways. Then use a colorimeter to measure the lightness of the color on a scale in which black is 0 and white is 100. Here are the data for 8 pieces of fabric dyed in each way:[14]

```
Method A   41.72  41.83  42.05  41.44  41.27  42.27  41.12  41.49
Method B   40.98  40.88  41.30  41.28  41.66  41.50  41.39  41.27
Method C   42.30  42.20  42.65  42.43  42.50  42.28  43.13  42.45
Method D   41.68  41.65  42.30  42.04  42.25  41.99  41.72  41.97
```

(a) This is a randomized comparative experiment. Outline the design.

(b) A clothing manufacturer wants to know which method gives the darkest color. Follow the four-step process in answering this question.

23.28 Does nature heal best? Our bodies have a natural electrical field that helps wounds heal. Might higher or lower levels speed healing? An experiment with newts investigated this question. Newts were randomly assigned to five groups. In four of the groups, an electrode applied to one hind limb (chosen at random) changed the natural field, while the other hind limb was not manipulated. Both limbs in the fifth (control) group remained in their natural state.[15]

Table 23.5 gives data from this experiment. The "Group" variable shows the field applied as a multiple of the natural field for each newt. For example, "0.5" is half the natural field, "1" is the natural level (the control group), and "1.5" indicates a field 1.5 times natural. "Diff" is the response variable, the difference in the healing rate (in micrometers per hour) of cuts made in the experimental and control limbs of that newt. Negative values mean that the experimental limb healed more slowly. The investigators conjectured that nature heals best, so that changing the field from the natural state (the "1" group) will slow healing.

Do a complete analysis to see whether the groups differ in the effect of the electrical field level on healing. Follow the four-step process in your work.

23.29 Does polyester decay? How quickly do synthetic fabrics such as polyester decay in landfills? A researcher buried polyester strips in the soil for different lengths of time, then dug up the strips and measured the force required to break them. Breaking strength is easy to measure and is a good indicator of decay; lower strength means the fabric has decayed.

Part of the study buried 20 polyester strips in well-drained soil in the summer. Five of the strips, chosen at random, were dug up after each of 2 weeks, 4 weeks, and 8 weeks. Here are the breaking strengths in pounds:[16]

2 weeks	118	126	126	120	129
4 weeks	130	120	114	126	128
8 weeks	122	136	128	146	140

The investigator conjectured that buried polyester loses strength over time. Do the data support this conjecture? Follow the four-step process in data analysis and ANOVA. Be sure to check the conditions for ANOVA.

TABLE 23.5 Effect of electrical field on healing rate in newts

GROUP	DIFF	GROUP	DIFF	GROUP	DIFF	GROUP	DIFF	GROUP	DIFF
0	−10	0.5	−1	1	−7	1.25	1	1.5	−13
0	−12	0.5	10	1	15	1.25	8	1.5	−49
0	−9	0.5	3	1	−4	1.25	−15	1.5	−16
0	−11	0.5	−3	1	−16	1.25	14	1.5	−8
0	−1	0.5	−31	1	−2	1.25	−7	1.5	−2
0	6	0.5	4	1	−13	1.25	−1	1.5	−35
0	−31	0.5	−12	1	5	1.25	11	1.5	−11
0	−5	0.5	−3	1	−4	1.25	8	1.5	−46
0	13	0.5	−7	1	−2	1.25	11	1.5	−22
0	−2	0.5	−10	1	−14	1.25	−4	1.5	2
0	−7	0.5	−22	1	5	1.25	7	1.5	10
0	−8	0.5	−4	1	11	1.25	−14	1.5	−4
		0.5	−1	1	10	1.25	0	1.5	−10
		0.5	−3	1	3	1.25	5	1.5	2
				1	6	1.25	−2	1.5	−5
				1	−1				
				1	13				
				1	−8				

23.30 Durable press fabrics are weaker. "Durable press" cotton fabrics are treated to improve their recovery from wrinkles after washing. Unfortunately, the treatment also reduces the strength of the fabric. A study compared the breaking strength of untreated fabric with that of fabrics treated by three commercial durable press processes. Five specimens of the same fabric were assigned at random to each group. Here are the data, in pounds of pull needed to tear the fabric:[17]

Untreated	60.1	56.7	61.5	55.1	59.4
Permafresh 55	29.9	30.7	30.0	29.5	27.6
Permafresh 48	24.8	24.6	27.3	28.1	30.3
Hylite LF	28.8	23.9	27.0	22.1	24.2

The untreated fabric is clearly much stronger than any of the treated fabrics. We want to know if there is a significant difference in breaking strength among the three durable press treatments. Analyze the data for the three processes and write a clear summary of your findings. Which process do you recommend if breaking strength is a main concern? Use the four-step process to guide your discussion. (Although the standard deviations do not quite satisfy our rule of thumb, that rule is conservative and many statisticians would use ANOVA for these data.)

23.31 Durable press fabrics wrinkle less. The data in Exercise 23.30 show that durable press treatment greatly reduces the breaking strength of cotton fabric. Of course, durable press treatment also reduces wrinkling. "Wrinkle recovery angle" measures how well a fabric recovers from wrinkles. Higher is better. Here are data on the wrinkle recovery angle (in degrees) for the same fabric specimens discussed in the previous exercise:

Untreated	79	80	78	80	78
Permafresh 55	136	135	132	137	134
Permafresh 48	125	131	125	145	145
Hylite LF	143	141	146	141	145

The untreated fabric once again stands out, this time as inferior to the treated fabrics in wrinkle resistance. Examine the data for the three durable press processes and summarize your findings. How does the ranking of the three processes by wrinkle resistance compare with their ranking by breaking strength in Exercise 23.30? Explain why we can't trust the ANOVA F test.

23.32 Logging in the rain forest: species counts. Table 23.2 gives data on the number of trees per forest plot, the number of species per plot, and species richness. Exercise 23.3 analyzed the effect of logging on number of trees. Exercise 23.8 concludes that it would be risky to use ANOVA to analyze richness. Use software to analyze the effect of logging on the number of species.

(a) Make a table of the group means and standard deviations. Do the standard deviations satisfy our rule of thumb for safe use of ANOVA? What do the means suggest about the effect of logging on the number of species?

(b) Carry out the ANOVA. Report the F statistic and its P-value and state your conclusion.

TABLE 23.6 Plant biomass (g/m^2) for three water conditions over five years

TREATMENT	PLOT	YEAR				
		2001	2002	2003	2004	2005
Winter	3	136.8358	228.0717	264.1514	254.6453	344.3933
Winter	8	151.4154	189.9505	187.7312	233.8155	203.3908
Winter	14	136.1536	209.0485	291.1431	253.4506	331.9724
Winter	20	121.6323	189.6755	176.2879	228.5882	388.1056
Winter	27	124.1459	188.0090	141.7525	158.6675	382.8617
Winter	32	125.2986	215.2174	169.9737	212.3232	346.3042
Spring	4	338.1301	422.7411	318.4182	517.6650	344.0489
Spring	11	291.8597	339.8243	281.6830	342.2825	261.8016
Spring	18	244.8727	398.7296	288.8433	270.5785	262.7238
Spring	22	234.6599	400.6878	382.6673	212.5324	316.9683
Spring	25	197.5830	326.9497	326.8877	213.9879	224.1109
Spring	35	239.0122	444.1556	293.8502	240.1927	328.2783
Control	6	73.4288	148.8907	129.0538	178.9988	237.6596
Control	7	110.6306	182.6762	144.6578	205.5165	281.1442
Control	17	95.3405	196.8303	172.7772	242.6795	313.7242
Control	24	83.0584	186.1953	113.2813	231.7639	258.3631
Control	28	30.5886	154.0401	142.1562	134.9847	235.8320
Control	33	96.9709	213.2537	117.9808	212.4862	217.5060

More rain for California? *Exercise 23.25 describes a randomized experiment carried out by Kenwyn Suttle and his coworkers to examine the effects of additional water on California grassland. The experimental units are 18 plots of grassland, assigned at random among three treatments: added water in the winter wet season, added water in the spring dry season, and no added water (control group). Field experiments, unlike laboratory experiments, are exposed to variations in the natural environment. The experiment therefore continued over 5 years, 2001 to 2005. Table 23.6 gives data on the total plant biomass (grams per square meter) that grew on each plot during each year.*[18] *The "Plot" column shows how the random assignment of 18 of the 36 available plots worked. Exercises 23.33 to 23.35 are based on this information.*

23.33 Plot the means. Starting from the data in Table 23.6, you can calculate the mean plant biomass for each treatment in each year as follows:

	Year				
	2001	2002	2003	2004	2005
Winter	132.58	203.33	205.17	223.58	332.84
Spring	257.69	388.85	315.39	299.54	289.66
Control	81.67	180.31	136.65	201.07	257.37

Plot the means for each of the three treatments against year, connecting the yearly means for each treatment by lines to show the pattern over time. Use the same plot for all three treatments, with a different color for each treatment. From this plot, you can get an overall picture of the experiment's results.
(a) Across all 5 years, does more water in the wet season increase plant growth? What about more water in the dry season? Which seasonal addition of water has the larger effect?
(b) One-way ANOVAs comparing the mean plant biomass separately in each year find significant differences in 3 years and no significant difference in 2 years. Based on your plot, in which three years do you think the treatment means differ significantly?
(c) In 2005, there were unusual late rains during the spring. How does the effect of this natural rainfall show up in your plot? (You see that it would not be wise to do an experiment like this in just one year.)

23.34 The results for 2001. Your work in Exercise 23.25 shows that there were significant differences in mean plant biomass among the three treatments in 2003. Do a complete analysis of the data for 2001 and report your conclusions.

23.35 Conditions for ANOVA. Examine the data for the year 2004. The conditions for ANOVA inference are not met. In what way do these data fail to meet the conditions? (It is not very surprising that in 5 ANOVAs one will fail to satisfy our quite conservative conditions.)

23.36 Which test? Example 23.4 describes one of the experiments done by Kathleen Vohs and her coworkers to demonstrate that even being reminded of money makes people more self-sufficient and less involved with other people. Here are three more of these experiments. For each experiment, which statistical test from Chapters 16 to 23 would you use, and why?

(a) Randomly assign student subjects to money and control groups. The control group unscrambles neutral phrases, and the money group unscrambles money-oriented phrases, as described in Example 23.4. Then ask the subjects to volunteer to help the experimenter by coding data sheets, about 5 minutes per sheet. Subjects said how many sheets they would volunteer to code. "Participants in the money condition volunteered to help code fewer data sheets than did participants in the control condition."

(b) Randomly assign student subjects to high-money, low-money, and control groups. After playing Monopoly for a short time, the high-money group is left with $4000 in Monopoly money, the low-money group with $200, and the control group with no money. Each subject is asked to imagine a future with lots of money (high-money group), a little money (low-money group), or just their future plans (control group). Another student walks in and spills a box of 27 pencils. How many pencils does the subject pick up? "Participants in the high-money condition gathered fewer pencils" than subjects in the other two groups.

(c) Randomly assign student subjects to three groups. All do paperwork while a computer on the desk shows a screensaver of currency floating underwater (Group 1), a screensaver of fish swimming underwater (Group 2), or a blank screen (Group 3). Each subject must now develop an advertisement and can choose whether to work alone or with a partner. Count how many in each group work alone. "Choosing to perform the task with a coworker was reduced among money condition participants."

Chapter 1

1. Data for 2005 from the 2007 *Statistical Abstract of the United States* at the Census Bureau Web site, www.census.gov.

2. *Arbitron Internet and Media 2006,* at www.arbitron.com.

3. *Arbitron Radio Today 2007 Edition,* at www.arbitron.com.

4. "2008 Student surveys: complete results," *Macleans.ca,* February 19, 2008, at oncampus.macleans.ca.

5. Centers for Disease Control and Prevention, *Births: Final Data for 2005,* National Vital Statistics Reports, 56, No. 6, 2007, at www.cdc.gov. These are the most recent data available as of early 2008, but the numbers change only slightly from year to year.

6. From the 2006 American Community Survey, at factfinder.census.gov.

7. Our eyes do respond to area, but not quite linearly. It appears that we perceive the ratio of two bars to be about the 0.7 power of the ratio of their actual areas. See W. S. Cleveland, *The Elements of Graphing Data,* Wadsworth, 1985, pp. 278–284.

8. See Note 6.

9. From the Gary Community School Corporation, courtesy of Celeste Foster, Purdue University.

10. From the College Board Web site, www.collegeboard.com.

11. United Nations data, at hdr.undp.org/en/statistics. All amounts are in U.S. dollars at purchasing power parity. That is, the exchange rate between each currency and the dollar is set not at the fluctuating market rate but at the rate that gives a dollar the same buying power in each country.

12. Raymond W. Schaffranek and Ami L. Riscassi, *Flow Velocity, Water Temperature, and Conductivity at Selected Locations in Shark River Slough, Everglades National Park, Florida; July 1999–July 2003,* Data Series 110, U.S. Geological Survey, 2004, at water.usgs.gov.

13. College Entrance Examination Board, *Trends in College Pricing, 2007,* at www.collegeboard.com. The averages are "enrollment weighted," so that they give average tuition over *students* rather than over *colleges.* Data for years before 1997 are from past editions, updated to June 2007 price levels by the Consumer Price Index.

14. *DuPont 2007 Color Popularity Report,* at www2.dupont.com.

15. See Note 2.

16. National Center for Health Statistics, *Deaths: Preliminary Data for 2005,* at www.cdc.gov/nchs.

17. Found at spam-filter-review.topten-reviews.com, which claims to have compiled data "from a number of different reputable sources."

18. Tom Lloyd et al., "Fruit consumption, fitness, and cardiovascular health in female adolescents: the Penn State Young Women's Health Study," *American Journal of Clinical Nutrition,* 67 (1998), pp. 624–630.

19. Data provided by Darlene Gordon from her PhD thesis, "Relationships among academic self-concept, academic achievement, and persistence with self-attribution, study habits, and perceived school environment," Purdue University, 1997.

20. National Institutes of Health, Essential Fatty Acids Education site, efaeducation.nih.gov.

21. 2007 *Statistical Abstract of the United States,* Table 154, at www.census.gov.

22. International Energy Agency, *Key World Energy Statistics 2007,* at www.iea.org.

23. National Oceanic and Atmospheric Administration, at www.noaa.gov.

24. David M. Fergusson and L. John Horwood, "Cannabis use and traffic accidents in a birth cohort of young adults," *Accident Analysis and Prevention,* 33 (2001), pp. 703–711.

25. From a plot in K. Krishna Kumar et al., "Unraveling the mystery of Indian monsoon failure during El Niño," *Science,* 314 (2006), pp. 115–119.

26. Census Bureau, New Residential Construction page, at www.census.gov. These are monthly data not seasonally adjusted.

27. Florida Fish and Wildlife Conservation Commission, at myfwc.com/gators.

Chapter 2

1. From the 2003 American Community Survey, at the Census Bureau Web site, www.census.gov. The data are a subsample of the 13,194 individuals in the ACS North Carolina sample who had travel times greater than zero.

2. This isn't a mathematical theorem. The mean can be less than the median in right-skewed distributions that take only a few values, many of which lie exactly at the median. The rule almost never fails for distributions taking many values, and most counterexamples don't appear clearly skewed in graphs even though they may be slightly skewed according to technical measures of skewness. See Paul T. von Hippel, "Mean, median, and skew: correcting a textbook rule," *Journal of Statistics Education*, 13, No. 2 (2005), at www.amstat.org/publications/jse.

3. National Association of College and University Business Officers, 2007 Endowment Study, at www.nacubo.org.

4. From the National Association of Realtors, www.realtor.org.

5. U.S. Census Bureau, *Income, Poverty, and Health Insurance Coverage in the United States: 2007*, August 2008, at www.census.org.

6. Figure 2.2 displays the daily returns for the year ending November 8, 2007, for the CREF Equity Index Fund and the TIAA Real Estate Fund. Daily price data for these funds are at www.tiaa-cref.org. Returns can be easily calculated because dividends are incorporated in the daily prices rather than given separately.

7. Michael W. Peugh, "Field investigation of ventilation and air quality in duck and turkey slaughter plants," MS thesis, Purdue University, 1996.

8. Ethan J. Temeles and W. John Kress, "Adaptation in a plant-hummingbird association," *Science*, 300 (2003), pp. 630–633. I thank Ethan J. Temeles for providing the data.

9. C. H. Cannon, D. R. Peart, and M. Leighton, "Tree species diversity in commercially logged Bornean rainforest," *Science*, 281 (1998), pp. 1366–1367. I thank Charles Cannon for providing the data.

10. Raymond Fisman and Edward Miguel, "Cultures of corruption: evidence from diplomatic parking tickets," National Bureau of Economic Research working paper 12312, June 2006, at www.nber.org.

11. Patrick J. Purcell, *Retirement Savings and Household Wealth: A Survey of Recent Data*, Congressional Research Service, 2004, available at several online repositories. The data are for 2001. To make the amounts more realistic, I have updated them to 2007 dollars using the Consumer Price Index.

12. See Note 5 for Chapter 1.

13. T. Bjerkedal, "Acquisition of resistance in guinea pigs infected with different doses of virulent tubercle bacilli," *American Journal of Hygiene*, 72 (1960), pp. 130–148.

14. Data for 1986 from David Brillinger, University of California, Berkeley. See David R. Brillinger, "Mapping aggregate birth data," in A. C. Singh and P. Whitridge (eds.), *Analysis of Data in Time*, Statistics Canada, 1990, pp. 77–83. A boxplot similar to Figure 2.6 appears in David R. Brillinger, "Some examples of random process environmental data analysis," in P. K. Sen and C. R. Rao (eds.), *Handbook of Statistics*, Vol. 18, *Bioenvironmental and Public Health Statistics*, North Holland, 2000.

15. Nicolas Guéguen and Christine Petr, "Odors and consumer behavior in a restaurant," *Journal of Hospitality Management*, 25 (2006), pp. 335–339. I thank Nicolas Guéguen for providing the data.

16. James A. Levine et al., "Inter-individual variation in posture allocation: possible role in human obesity," *Science*, 307 (2005), pp. 584–586. I thank James Levine for providing the data.

17. Parmeshwar S. Gupta, "Reaction of plants to the density of soil," *Journal of Ecology*, 21 (1933), pp. 452–474.

18. M. Ann Laskey et al., "Bone changes after 3 mo of lactation: influence of calcium intake, breast-milk output, and vitamin D–receptor genotype," *American Journal of Clinical Nutrition*, 67 (1998), pp. 685–692.

19. A sample of responses to the 1901 Census of Canada is available at the Canadian Families Project of the University of Victoria Web site, web.uvic.ca/hrd/

cfp/data. The sample and the data are described in Canadian Families Project, *The National Sample of the 1901 Census of Canada,* 2002, on this Web site. Table 2.6 is a random sample of the 47,417 positive incomes in the census sample. The information on bread and beef prices (for 1900) comes from James Powell, *A History of the Canadian Dollar,* Bank of Canada, no date, at www.bank-canada.ca/en/d.

Chapter 3

1. See Note 9 for Chapter 1.

2. Thomas K. Cureton et al., *Endurance of Young Men,* Monographs of the Society for Research in Child Development, Vol. 10, No. 1, 1945.

3. Monsoon rainfall from B. Parthasarathy, Indian Institute of Tropical Meteorology, at www.iges.org. The data cover the years 1871 to 2000.

4. Based on the National Health and Nutrition Examination Surveys, 1988–1994. From the Web site of the National Center for Health Statistics, www.cdc.gov/nchs.

5. Detailed data appear in P. S. Levy et al., *Total Serum Cholesterol Values for Youths 12–17 Years,* Vital and Health Statistics, Series 11, No. 155, National Center for Health Statistics, 1976.

6. See Note 16 for Chapter 2.

7. All ACT facts are from the ACT Web site, www.act.org.

8. All SAT facts are from the College Board Web site, www.collegeboard.com.

9. See Note 19 for Chapter 1.

10. The data were provided by Nicolas Fisher.

11. From a graph in L. Partridge and M. Farquhar, "Sexual activity reduces lifespan of male fruitflies," *Nature,* 294 (1981), pp. 580–582. Provided by Brigitte Baldi.

12. See Note 3.

Chapter 4

1. Data for 2007 graduates from the College Board Web site, www.collegeboard.com.

2. Government data for 2005, presented in "An accident waiting to happen?" *Consumer Reports,* March 2007, pp. 16–19.

3. The Florida Boating Accident Statistical Report for each year (at myfwc.com/law/boating) gives the number of registered vessels. The Florida Wildlife Commission maintains a manatee death data base at research.myfwc.com/manatees.

4. From a graph in Magdalena Bermejo et al., "Ebola outbreak killed 5000 gorillas," *Science,* 314 (2006), p. 1564.

5. Data for Figure 4.4(b) come from William Gray's Web site, at hurricane.atmos.colostate.edu. Data for Figure 4.4(c) were provided by Drina Iglesia, Purdue University, from a study reported in D. D. S. Iglesia, E. J. Cragoe, Jr., and J. W. Vanable, "Electric field strength and epithelization in the newt (*Notophthalmus viridescens*)," *Journal of Experimental Zoology,* 274 (1996), pp. 56–62. Data for Figure 4.4(d) are for the Wilshire 5000 stock index. As a fine point, plots (b), (c), and (d) are square with the same scales on both axes because both variables measure similar quantities in the same units.

6. This exercise is motivated by Scott Berry, "Statistical fallacies in sports," *Chance,* 19, No. 4 (2006), pp. 50–56, where scores from the 2006 Masters are analyzed.

7. James T. Fleming, "The measurement of children's perception of difficulty in reading materials," *Research in the Teaching of English,* 1 (1967), pp. 136–156.

8. From a graph in Timothy G. O'Brien and Margaret F. Kinnaird, "Caffeine and conservation," *Science,* 300 (2003), p. 587.

9. From a graph in Bernt-Erik Saether, Steiner Engen, and Erik Mattysen, "Demographic characteristics and population dynamical patterns of solitary birds," *Science,* 295 (2002), pp. 2070–2073.

10. From a graph in Sabrina M. Tom et al., "The neural basis of loss aversion in decision-making under risk," *Science,* 315 (2007), pp. 515–518.

11. From a graph in Sergio M. Vallina and Rafel Simó, "Strong relationship between DMS and the solar radiation dose over the global surface ocean," *Science,* 315 (2007), pp. 506–508.

12. N. Maeno et al., "Growth rates of icicles," *Journal of Glaciology,* 40 (1994), pp. 319–326.

13. Simplified from W. L. Colville and D. P. McGill, "Effect of rate and method of planting on several plant characters and yield of irrigated corn," *Agronomy Journal*, 54 (1962), pp. 235–238.

14. Modified from M. C. Wilson and R. E. Shade, "Relative attractiveness of various luminescent colors to the cereal leaf beetle and the meadow spittlebug," *Journal of Economic Entomology*, 60 (1967), pp. 578–580.

15. From a graph in Martin Wild et al., "From dimming to brightening: decadal changes in solar radiation at Earth's surface," *Science*, 308 (2005), pp. 847–850.

16. Data provided by Robert Dale, Purdue University.

17. From a graph in Christer G. Wiklund, "Food as a mechanism of density-dependent regulation of breeding numbers in the merlin *Falco columbarius*," *Ecology*, 82 (2001), pp. 860–867.

18. From a graph in Naomi I. Eisenberger, Matthew D. Lieberman, and Kipling D. Williams, "Does rejection hurt? An fMRI study of social exclusion," *Science*, 302 (2003), pp. 290–292.

Chapter 5

1. From a graph in James A. Levine, Norman L. Eberhardt, and Michael D. Jensen, "Role of nonexercise activity thermogenesis in resistance to fat gain in humans," *Science*, 283 (1999), pp. 212–214.

2. See Note 4 for Chapter 4.

3. From a graph in Tania Singer et al., "Empathy for pain involves the affective but not sensory components of pain," *Science*, 303 (2004), pp. 1157–1162. Data for other brain regions showed a stronger correlation and no outliers.

4. Contributed by Marigene Arnold, Kalamazoo College.

5. Gannett News Service article appearing in the *Lafayette (Ind.) Journal and Courier*, April 23, 1994.

6. P. Goldblatt (ed.), *Longitudinal Study: Mortality and Social Organization*, Her Majesty's Stationery Office, 1990. At least, so claims Richard Conniff, *The Natural History of the Rich*, Norton, 2002, p. 45. The Goldblatt report is not available to me.

7. Laura L. Calderon et al., "Risk factors for obesity in Mexican-American girls: dietary factors, anthropometric factors, physical activity, and hours of television viewing," *Journal of the American Dietetic Association*, 96 (1996), pp. 1177–1179.

8. *The Health Consequences of Smoking: 1983*, Public Health Service, Washington, D.C., 1983.

9. A. K. Yousafzai et al., "Comparison of armspan, arm length and tibia length as predictors of actual height of disabled and nondisabled children in Dharavi, Mumbai, India," *European Journal of Clinical Nutrition*, 57 (2003), pp. 1230–1234. In fact, $r^2 = 0.93$. I changed the value in Exercise 5.18 to avoid confusion with $b = 0.93$.

10. G. L. Kooyman et al., "Diving behavior and energetics during foraging cycles in king penguins," *Ecological Monographs*, 62 (1992), pp. 143–163.

11. T. Constable and E. McBean, "BOD/TOC correlations and their application to water quality evaluation," *Water, Air, and Soil Pollution*, 11 (1979), pp. 363–375.

12. Karl Pearson and A. Lee, "On the laws of inheritance in man," *Biometrika*, 2 (1902), p. 357. These data also appear in D. J. Hand et al., *A Handbook of Small Data Sets*, Chapman & Hall, 1994. This book offers more than 500 data sets that can be used in statistical exercises.

13. See Note 9 for Chapter 4.

14. From a presentation by Charles Knauf, Monroe County (N.Y.) Environmental Health Laboratory.

15. Frank J. Anscombe, "Graphs in statistical analysis," *The American Statistician*, 27 (1973), pp. 17–21.

16. Debora L. Arsenau, "Comparison of diet management instruction for patients with non-insulin dependent diabetes mellitus: learning activity package vs. group instruction," MS thesis, Purdue University, 1993.

17. From a graph in G. D. Martinsen, E. M. Driebe, and T. G. Whitham, "Indirect interactions mediated by changing plant chemistry: beaver browsing benefits beetles," *Ecology*, 79 (1998), pp. 192–200.

18. P. Velleman, *ActivStats 2.0*, Addison Wesley Interactive, 1997.

19. From the Web site of the Tropical Meteorology Project, `hurricane.atmos.colostate.edu`.

20. From a graph in Joaquim I. Goes et al., "Warming of the Eurasian landmass is making the Arabian Sea more productive," *Science*, 308 (2005), pp. 545–547.

21. See Note 11 for Chapter 1.

Chapter 6

1. Pew Research Center for the People and the Press, *Trends in Political Values and Core Attitudes: 1987–2007*, March 2007, at `people-press.org`.

2. See Note 1.

3. Table 1 of E. Thomassot et al., "Methane-related diamond crystallization in the earth's mantle: stable isotopes evidence from a single diamond-bearing xenolith," *Earth and Planetary Science Letters*, 257 (2007), pp. 362–371.

4. Environmental Protection Agency, *Municipal Solid Waste Generation, Recycling, and Disposal in the United States: Facts and Figures for 2006*, November 2007, at `www.epa.gov`.

5. Data provided by Brigitte Baldi, University of California at Irvine.

6. Data for Cohort 2 in Richard A. Morgan et al., "Cancer regression in patients after transfer of genetically engineered lymphocytes," *Science*, 314 (2006), pp. 126–129. The doubling time data are given in the paper and the immune response data appear in the supplementary online material.

7. Margaret A. McDowell et al., "Anthropometric reference data for children and adults: U.S. population, 1999–2002," National Center for Health Statistics, Advance Data from Vital and Health Statistics, No. 361, 2005, at `www.cdc.gov/nchs`.

8. From the MCAT Web site, `www.aamc.org/students/mcat`.

9. From a plot in Jon J. Ramsey et al., "Energy expenditure, body composition, and glucose metabolism in lean and obese rhesus monkeys treated with ephedrine and caffeine," *American Journal of Clinical Nutrition*, 68 (1998), pp. 42–51.

10. Centers for Disease Control and Prevention, *Cigarette Smoking among Adults—United States, 2006*, and related publications at `www.cdc.gov`.

11. From a graph in Stan Boutin et al., "Anticipatory reproduction and population growth in seed predators," *Science*, 314 (2006), pp. 1928–1930.

12. Data from a plot in Josef P. Rauschecker, Biao Tian, and Marc Hauser, "Processing of complex sounds in the macaque nonprimary auditory cortex," *Science*, 268 (1995), pp. 111–114. The paper states that there are $n = 41$ observations, but only $n = 37$ can be read accurately from the plot.

13. J. T. Dwyer et al., "Memory of food intake in the distant past," *American Journal of Epidemiology*, 130 (1989), pp. 1033–1046.

14. "Dancing in step," *Economist*, March 22, 2001.

15. Data provided by Samuel Phillips, Purdue University.

16. From a graph in Peter A. Raymond and Jonathan J. Cole, "Increase in the export of alkalinity from North America's largest river," *Science*, 301 (2003), pp. 88–91.

17. From the Nenana Ice Classic Web site, `www.nenanaakiceclassic.com`. See Raphael Sagarin and Fiorenza Micheli, "Climate change in nontraditional data sets," *Science*, 294 (2001), p. 811, for a careful discussion.

18. Data for 2004 from Alan Heston, Robert Summers, and Bettina Aten, *Penn World Table Version 6.2*, Center for International Comparisons of Production, Income, and Prices at the University of Pennsylvania, September 2006, at `pwt.econ.upenn.edu`.

19. Louie H. Yang, "Periodical cicadas as resource pulses in North American forests," *Science*, 306 (2004), pp. 1565–1567. The data are simulated Normal values that match the means and standard deviations reported in this article.

20. Alan S. Banks et al., "Juvenile hallux abducto valgus association with metatarsus adductus," *Journal of the American Podiatric Medical Association*, 84 (1994), pp. 219–224.

21. Todd W. Anderson, "Predator responses, prey refuges, and density-dependent mortality of a marine fish," *Ecology*, 81 (2001), pp. 245–257.

22. From a graph in Craig Packer et al., "Ecological change, group territoriality, and population dynamics in Serengeti lions," *Science*, 307 (2005), pp. 390–393.

23. Peter H. Chen, Neftali Herrera, and Darren Christiansen, "Relationships between gate velocity and casting features among aluminum round castings," no date. Provided by Darren Christiansen.

24. G. Adams et al., "A study of differences in Canadian university students' gambling and proximity to a casino," *Journal of Gambling Issues*, Issue 19 (January 2007), pp. 9–17, at `www.camh.net/egambling`.

Chapter 7

1. From the index of recent *New York Times* surveys at `nytimes.com/polls`. The methodological statement is similar for most polls listed.

2. Gary S. Foster and Craig M. Eckert, "Up from the grave: a sociohistorical reconstruction of an African American community from cemetary data in the rural Midwest," *Journal of Black Studies*, 33 (2003), pp. 468–489.

3. Pew Forum on Religion and Public Life, *Spirit and Power: A 10-Country Survey of Pentecostals*, October 2006, at `www.pewforum.org`.

4. For information about the 2006 American Community Survey of households (there is a separate sample of group quarters), go to `www.census.gov/acs`.

5. The Pew press release and the full report "Polls face growing resistance, but still representative" (dated April 20, 2004) are at `people-press.org/reports`. Following the standards of the American Association for Public Opinion Research, the report gives contact rate 75.5%, cooperation rate 38.2%, and overall response rate 26.6%.

6. For more detail on the limits of memory in surveys, see N. M. Bradburn, L. J. Rips, and S. K. Shevell, "Answering autobiographical questions: the impact of memory and inference on surveys," *Science*, 236 (1987), pp. 157–161.

7. The immigration questions are from the *New York Times*/CBS News Poll taken May 18 to 23, 2007, found at `www.pollingreport.com`. The responses on welfare are from a *New York Times*/CBS News Poll reported in the *New York Times*, July 5, 1992. Many other examples appear in T. W. Smith, "That which we call welfare by any other name would smell sweeter," *Public Opinion Quarterly*, 51 (1987), pp. 75–83. The example on the effect of question order is cited in Daniel Kahnemann et al., "Would you be happier if you were richer? A focusing illusion," *Science*, 312 (2006), pp. 1908–1910.

8. Giuliana Coccia, "An overview of non-response in Italian telephone surveys," *Proceedings of the 99th Session of the International Statistical Institute*, 1993, Book 3, pp. 271–272.

9. From the Web site of the Gallup Organization, `www.gallup.com`. Individual poll reports remain on this site for only a limited time.

10. Robert C. Parker and Patrick A. Glass, "Preliminary results of double-sample forest inventory of pine and mixed stands with high- and low-density LiDAR," in Kristina F. Connoe (ed.), *Proceedings of the 12th Biennial Southern Silvicultural Research Conference*, U.S. Department of Agriculture, Forest Service, Southern Research Station, 2004. The researchers actually sampled every 10th plot. This is a systematic sample; see Exercise 7.36.

11. Bryan E. Porter and Thomas D. Berry, "A nationwide survey of self-reported red light running: measuring prevalence, predictors, and perceived consequences," *Accident Analysis and Prevention*, 33 (2001), pp. 735–741.

12. Mario A. Parada et al., "The validity of self-reported seatbelt use: Hispanic and non-Hispanic drivers in El Paso," *Accident Analysis and Prevention*, 33 (2001), pp. 139–143.

13. Clyde O. McDaniel, Jr., "Dating roles and reasons for dating," *Journal of Marriage and the Family*, 31 (1969), pp. 97–107.

14. Susan B. Sorenson, "Regulating firearms as a consumer product," *Science*, 286 (1999), pp. 1481–1482.

15. Information from Warren McIsaac and Vivek Goel, "Is access to physician services in Ontario equitable?" Institute for Clinical Evaluative Sciences in Ontario, October 18, 1993.

16. Adam Nagourney and Janet Elder, "New York Times CBS Poll: what Hispanics believe," at `www.Hispanic.cc`.

Chapter 8

1. I. J. Goldberg et al., "Wine and your heart: a science advisory for healthcare professionals from the Nutrition Committee, Council on Epidemiology and Prevention, and Council on Cardiovascular Nursing of the American Heart Association," *Circulation*, 103 (2001), pp. 472–475.

2. J. E. Muscat et al., "Handheld cellular telephone use and risk of brain cancer," *Journal of the American Medical Association*, 284 (2000), pp. 3001–3007.

3. Charles A. Nelson III et al., "Cognitive recovery in socially deprived young children: the Bucharest Early Intervention Project," *Science*, 318 (2007), pp. 1937–1940.

4. Martin J. Bergee and Lecia Cecconi-Roberts, "Effects of small-group peer interaction on self-evaluation of music performance," *Journal of Research in Music Education*, 50 (2002), pp. 256–268.

5. K. B. Suttle, Meredith A. Thomsen, and Mary E. Power, "Species interactions reverse grassland responses to changing climate," *Science*, 315 (2007), pp. 640–642. See Chapter 23 for an analysis of some data from this experiment.

6. How-Ran Guo, "Arsenic level in drinking water and mortality of lung cancer (Taiwan)," *Cancer Causes and Control*, 15 (2004), pp. 171–177.

7. Marielle H. Emmelot-Vonk et al., "Effect of testosterone supplementation on functional mobility, cognition, and other parameters in older men," *Journal of the American Medical Association*, 299 (2008), pp. 39–52.

8. David L. Strayer, Frank A. Drews, and William A. Johnston, "Cell phone–induced failures of visual attention during simulated driving," *Journal of Experimental Psychology: Applied*, 9 (2003), pp. 23–32.

9. K. J. Mukamal et al., "Prior alcohol consumption and mortality following acute myocardial infarction," *Journal of the American Medical Association*, 285 (2001), pp. 1965–1970.

10. Rita F. Redburg, "Vitamin E and cardiovascular health," *Journal of the American Medical Association*, 294 (2005), pp. 107–109.

11. Jo Phelan et al., "The stigma of homelessness: the impact of the label 'homeless' on attitudes towards poor persons," *Social Psychology Quarterly*, 60 (1997), pp. 323–337.

12. Esther Duflo, Rema Hanna, and Stephan Ryan, "Monitoring works: getting teachers to come to school," report dated November 21, 2007, at econ-mit.edu/files/2066.

13. John H. Kagel, Raymond C. Battalio, and C. G. Miles, "Marijuana and work performance: results from an experiment," *Journal of Human Resources*, 15 (1980), pp. 373–395.

14. Shailja V. Nigdikar et al., "Consumption of red wine polyphenols reduces the susceptibility of low-density lipoproteins to oxidation in vivo," *American Journal of Clinical Nutrition*, 68 (1998), pp. 258–265. (There were in fact only 30 subjects, some of whom received more than one treatment with a four-week period intervening.)

15. Ian G. Williamson et al., "Antibiotics and topical nasal steroid for treatment of acute maxillary sinusitis," *Journal of the American Medical Association*, 298 (2007), pp. 2487–2496.

16. Based on Evan H. DeLucia et al., "Net primary production of a forest ecosystem with experimental CO_2 enhancement," *Science*, 284 (1999), pp. 1177–1179. The investigators used the block design.

17. The study is described in Gina Kolata, "New study finds vitamins are not cancer preventers," *New York Times*, July 21, 1994. Look in the *Journal of the American Medical Association* of the same date for the details.

18. R. C. Shelton et al., "Effectiveness of St. John's wort in major depression," *Journal of the American Medical Association*, 285 (2001), pp. 1978–1986.

Chapter 9

1. Note that pennies have rims that make spinning more stable. The probability of a head in spinning a coin depends on the type of coin and also on the surface. See Exercise 20.3 for an account of 56% heads in spinning a Belgian 1-euro coin. *Chance News 11.02* at www.dartmouth.edu/~chance reports about 45% heads in more than 20,000 spins of American pennies by Robin Lock's students at Saint Lawrence University.

2. Data for 2006 from the Web site of Statistics Canada, www.statcan.ca.

3. You can find a mathematical explanation of Benford's law in Ted Hill, "The first-digit phenomenon," *American Scientist*, 86 (1996), pp. 358–363; and Ted Hill, "The difficulty of faking data," *Chance*, 12, No. 3 (1999), pp. 27–31. Applications in fraud detection are discussed in the second paper by Hill and in Mark A. Nigrini, "I've got your number," *Journal of Accountancy*, May 1999, available online at www.aicpa.org/pubs/jofa/joaiss.htm.

4. The National Longitudinal Study of Adolescent Health interviewed a stratified random sample of 27,000 adolescents, then reinterviewed many of the subjects six years later, when most were aged 19 to 25. Data from the Wave III reinterviews in 2000 and 2001 can be found at the Web site of the Carolina Population Center, www.cpc.unc.edu.

5. Information from www-records.ncsu.edu/cgi-bin/grddist.pl.

6. See Note 2 for Chapter 3.

7. See Note 14 for Chapter 1.

8. National population estimates for July 1, 2006, at the Census Bureau Web site, www.census.gov. The table omits people who consider themselves to belong to more than one race.

9. See Note 4.

Chapter 10

1. See Note 5 for Chapter 2.

2. Strictly speaking, the formula $\sigma/\sqrt{n}$ for the standard deviation of $\overline{x}$ assumes that we draw an SRS of size n from an *infinite* population. If the population has finite size N, this standard deviation is multiplied by $\sqrt{1 - (n-1)/(N-1)}$. This "finite population correction" approaches 1 as N increases. When the population is at least 20 times as large as the sample, the correction factor is between about 0.97 and 1. It is reasonable to use the simpler form $\sigma/\sqrt{n}$ in these settings.

3. Sherri A. Buzinski, "The effect of position of methylation on the performance properties of durable press treated fabrics," CSR490 honors paper, Purdue University, 1985.

4. Elroy Dimson, Paul Marsh, and Mike Staunton, *Triumph of the Optimists: 101 Years of Global Investment Returns*, Princeton University Press, 2002. Sophisticates will note that for compounding over several years we want the geometric mean return, which was 6.7%.

Chapter 11

1. This is one of several tests discussed in Bernard M. Branson, "Rapid HIV testing: 2005 update," a presentation by the Centers for Disease Control and Prevention, at www.cdc.gov. The Malawi clinic result is reported by Bernard M. Branson, "Point-of-care rapid tests for HIV antibody," *Journal of Laboratory Medicine*, 27 (2003), pp. 288–295.

2. Robert P. Dellavalle et al., "Going, going, gone: lost Internet references," *Science*, 302 (2003), pp. 787–788.

3. Ward's Automotive, *U.S. Light Vehicle Sales Summary*, December 2007, at wardsauto.com.

4. Information about Internet users comes from sample surveys carried out by the Pew Internet and American Life Project, at www.pewinternet.org.

5. S. H. Sicherer, "Prevalence of peanut and tree nut allergy in the US determined by random digit dial telephone survey," *Journal of Allergy and Clinical Immunology*, 103 (1999), pp. 559–562.

6. Probabilities from trials with 2897 people known to be free of HIV antibodies and 673 people known to be infected, reported in J. Richard George, "Alternative specimen sources: methods for confirming positives," 1998 Conference on the Laboratory Science of HIV, found online at the Centers for Disease Control and Prevention, www.cdc.gov.

7. Sales in 2006 from the Web site of the Entertainment Software Association, at www.theesa.com.

8. Projections from U.S. Department of Education, *Projections of Education Statistics to 2016*, December 2007, at nces.ed.gov.

9. Data from by Patricia Heithaus and the Department of Biology at Kenyon College. Provided by Brad Hartlaub.

10. F. J. G. M. Klaassen and J. R. Magnus, "How to reduce the service dominance in tennis? Empirical results from four years at Wimbledon," in S. J. Haake and A. O. Coe (eds.), *Tennis Science and Technology*, Blackwell, 2000, pp. 277–284.

11. From the National Institutes of Health's National Digestive Diseases Information Clearinghouse, found at wrongdiagnosis.com.

12. The probabilities given are realistic, according to the fundraising firm SCM Associates, at scmassoc.com.

Chapter 12

1. From a Gallup Poll taken in 2003, www.gallup.com.

2. The survey question is reported in Trish Hall, "Shop? Many say 'Only if I must,'" *New York Times*, November 28, 1990. In fact, 66% (1650 of 2500) in the sample said "Agree."

3. John Schwartz, "Leisure pursuits of today's young men," *New York Times*, March 29, 2004. The source cited is comScore Media Matrix.

4. N. Ranjit et al., "Contraceptive failure in the first two years of use: differences across socioeconomic subgroups," *Family Planning Perspectives*, 33 (2001), pp. 19–27.

5. Results for the full 2007 season, at www.pgatour.com.

6. Mélanie Raymond, *High School Dropouts Returning to School*, Statistics Canada 81-595-MIE2008055, April 2008, at www.statcan.ca.

7. Associated Press news item dated December 9, 2007, found at www.msnbc.msn.com.

Chapter 13

1. See Note 7 for Chapter 6.

2. Francisco L. Rivera-Batiz, "Quantitative literacy and the likelihood of employment among young adults," *Journal of Human Resources*, 27 (1992), pp. 313–328.

3. Data provided by Drina Iglesia, Purdue University. The data are part of a larger study reported in D. D. S. Iglesia, E. J. Cragoe, Jr., and J. W. Vanable, "Electric field strength and epithelization in the newt (*Notophthalmus viridescens*)," *Journal of Experimental Zoology*, 274 (1996), pp. 56–62.

4. See Note 19 for Chapter 1.

5. Data simulated from a Normal distribution with the mean and standard deviation reported by Sarah Morrison and Jan Noyes, "A comparison of two computer fonts: serif versus ornate sans serif," *Usability News*, 5.2 (2003), at psychology.wichita.edu/surl/usability_news.html.

6. E. M. Peters et al., "Vitamin C supplementation reduces the incidence of postrace symptoms of upper-respiratory tract infection in ultramarathon runners," *American Journal of Clinical Nutrition*, 57 (1993), pp. 170–174.

7. Chi-Fu Jeffrey Yang, Peter Gray, and Harrison G. Pope, Jr., "Male body image in Taiwan versus the West," *American Journal of Psychiatry*, 162 (2005), pp. 263–269.

8. Ajay Ghei, "An empirical analysis of psychological androgeny in the personality profile of the successful hotel manager," MS thesis, Purdue University, 1992.

9. Seung-Ok Kim, "Burials, pigs, and political prestige in Neolithic China," *Current Anthropology*, 35 (1994), pp. 119–141.

10. Louie H. Yang, "Periodical cicadas as resource pulses in North American forests," *Science*, 306 (2004), pp. 1565–1567.

11. Sara L. Webb and Sara E. Scanga, "Windstorm disturbance without patch dynamics: twelve years of change in a Minnesota forest," *Ecology*, 82 (2001), pp. 893–897.

12. See Note 12 for Chapter 7.

13. See Note 18 for Chapter 2.

14. Data simulated from a Normal distribution based on information in Brian M. DeBroff and Patricia J. Pahk, "The ability of periorbitally applied antiglare products to improve contrast sensitivity in conditions of sunlight exposure," *Archives of Ophthamology*, 121 (2003), pp. 997–1001.

Chapter 14

1. See www.cdc.gov/nchs/tutorials/currentnhanes/SurveyDesign/Sample-Design/sample_intro.htm.

2. See Note 11 for Chapter 7.

3. From the Gallup Web site, www.gallup.com. The poll was taken in December 2006.

4. For a discussion of statistical significance in the legal setting, see D. H. Kaye, "Is proof of statistical significance relevant?" *Washington Law Review*, 61 (1986), pp. 1333–1365.

5. Warren E. Leary, "Cell phones: questions but no answers," *New York Times*, October 26, 1999.

6. Poll for June 7, 2007, at retention.harrisblackintl.com/harris_poll. A note at the bottom of the page says: "Because the sample is based on those who agreed to participate in the Harris Interactive panel, no estimates of theoretical sampling error can be calculated."

7. Justin S. Brashares et al., "Bushmeat hunting, wildlife declines, and fish supply in West Africa," *Science*, 306 (2004), pp. 1180–1183. The data used here (and in Figure 1B of the article) are found in the online supplementary material.

8. Gabriel Gregoratos et al., "ACC/AHA guidelines for implantation of cardiac pacemakers and antiarrhythmia devices: executive summary," *Circulation*, 97 (1998), pp. 1325–1335.

Chapter 15

1. Based on a news item "Bee off with you," *Economist*, November 2, 2002, p. 78.

2. Simplified from D. A. Marcus et al., "A double-blind provocative study of chocolate as a trigger of headache," *Cephalalgia*, 17 (1997), pp. 855–862.

3. Based on Stephen A. Woodbury and Robert G. Spiegelman, "Bonuses to workers and employers to reduce unemployment: randomized trials in Illinois," *American Economic Review*, 77 (1987), pp. 513–530.

4. Votes as of June 27, 2007, at www.pbs.org/wgbh/nova/sciencenow.

5. See Note 24 for Chapter 1.

6. World Health Organization Global InfoBase: Canada, at www.who.int/infobase.

7. K. E. Hobbs et al., "Levels and patterns of persistent organochlorines in minke whale (*Balaenoptera acutorostrata*) stocks from the North Atlantic and European Arctic," *Environmental Pollution*, 121 (2003), pp. 239–252.

8. Maureen Hack et al., "Outcomes in young adulthood for very-low-birth-weight infants," *New England Journal of Medicine*, 346 (2002), pp. 149–157.

9. Data for U.S. searches in February 2008 from Hitwise, at www.hitwise.com.

10. U.S. Census Bureau, *Fertility of American Women: June 2004*, at www.census.gov.

11. Aaron S. Hervey et al., "Reaction time distribution analysis of neuropsychological performance in an ADHD sample," *Child Neuropsychology*, 12 (2006), pp. 125–140.

12. Mikyoung Park et al., "Recycling endosomes supply AMPA receptors for LTP," *Science*, 305 (2004), pp. 1972–1975.

13. Simplified from Sanjay K. Dhar, Claudia González-Vallejo, and Dilip Soman, "Modeling the effects of advertised price claims: tensile versus precise pricing," *Marketing Science*, 18 (1999), pp. 154–177.

14. Charles S. Fuchs et al., "Alcohol consumption and mortality among women," *New England Journal of Medicine*, 332 (1995), pp. 1245–1250.

15. See Note 15 for Chapter 2. Later chapters will suggest more suitable analyses.

16. Data simulated from a Normal distribution with $\mu = 98.2$ and $\sigma = 0.7$. These values are based on P. A. Mackowiak, S. S. Wasserman, and M. M. Levine, "A critical appraisal of 98.6 degrees F, the upper limit of the normal body temperature, and other legacies of Carl Reinhold August Wunderlich," *Journal of the American Medical Association*, 268 (1992), pp. 1578–1580.

17. Research by Louis Chan et al., reported by Robert Schiller, *Irrational Exuberance*, Broadway Books, 2001, p. 253.

18. Amanda Lenhart and Mary Madden, "Music downloading, file-sharing and copyright," Pew Internet and American Life Project, 2003, at www.pewinternet.org.

19. From the Internal Revenue Service Web site, www.irs.gov/taxstats.

20. Susannah Fox and Gretchen Livingston, "Latinos online," Pew Hispanic Center and Pew Internet Project, 2007, at www.pewinternet.org.

21. Alan Schwarz, "In a game of statistics, some numbers have little meaning," *New York Times*, April 3, 2005.

22. Population base from the 2006 Labor Force Survey, at www.statistics.gov.uk. Smoking data from Action on Smoking and Health, *Smoking and Health Inequality*, at www.ash.org.uk.

23. Based on a study reported by Alan B. Krueger, "Economic scene" column, *New York Times*, November 14, 2002.

Chapter 16

1. Note 2 for Chapter 10 explains the reason for this condition in the case of inference about a population mean.

2. Helen E. Staal and D. C. Donderi, "The effect of sound on visual apparent movement," *American Journal of Psychology*, 96 (1983), pp. 95–105.

3. See Note 3 for Chapter 13.

4. From a graph in Benedetto De Martino et al., "Frames, biases, and rational decision-making in the human

brain," *Science*, 313 (2006), pp. 684–687. I simplified the design a bit for easier comprehension: the starting amounts and gambles offered differed from trial to trial, though still matched in pairs; 32 very unbalanced "catch trials" were mixed with the 64 experimental trials to be sure subjects were paying attention; and all money amounts were in British pounds, not dollars.

5. R. A. Berner and G. P. Landis, "Gas bubbles in fossil amber as possible indicators of the major gas composition of ancient air," *Science*, 239 (1988), pp. 1406–1409. The 95% t confidence interval is 54.78 to 64.40. A bootstrap BCa interval is 55.03 to 62.63. So t is reasonably accurate despite the skew and the small sample.

6. Alice P. Melis, Brian Hare, and Michael Tomasello, "Chimpanzees recruit the best collaborators," *Science*, 311 (2006), pp. 1297–1300. A Normal quantile plot does not show major lack of Normality, and a saddlepoint approximation that allows for skew gives $P = 0.0039$. So the t test is reasonably accurate despite the skew and small sample size.

7. Josef P. Rauschecker, Biao Tian, and Marc Hauser, "Processing of complex sounds in the macaque nonprimary auditory cortex," *Science*, 268 (1995), pp. 111–114.

8. For a qualitative discussion explaining why skewness is the most serious violation of the Normal shape condition, see Dennis D. Boos and Jacqueline M. Hughes-Oliver, "How large does n have to be for the Z and t intervals?" *American Statistician*, 54 (2000), pp. 121–128. Our recommendations are based on extensive computer work. See, for example, Harry O. Posten, "The robustness of the one-sample t-test over the Pearson system," *Journal of Statistical Computation and Simulation*, 9 (1979), pp. 133–149; and E. S. Pearson and N. W. Please, "Relation between the shape of population distribution and the robustness of four simple test statistics," *Biometrika*, 62 (1975), pp. 223–241.

9. For more advanced users, a good way to ascertain if the t procedures are safe is to compare the 95% confidence interval produced by t with the BCa interval from a bootstrap with at least 1000 resamples. For (b) the t interval is 29,428 to 32,254 and a BCa interval is 29,106 to 31,894. For (c), on the other hand, t gives 38.93 to 40.49 and BCa gives 38.97 to 40.44. These results confirm the judgment that t is safe for (c) but not for (b).

10. See Note 3 for Chapter 6.

11. From the online supplement to Tor D. Wager et al., "Placebo-induced changes in fMRI in the anticipation and experience of pain," *Science*, 303 (2004), pp. 1162–1167.

12. TUDA results for 2003 from the National Center for Education Statistics, at nces.ed.gov/nationsreportcard.

13. Raul de la Fuente-Fernandez et al., "Expectation and dopamine release: mechanism of the placebo effect in Parkinson's disease," *Science*, 293 (2001), pp. 1164–1166.

14. From the National Institute of Standards and Technology Web site, www.nist.gov/srd/online.htm.

15. Orit E. Hetzroni, "The effects of active versus passive computer-assisted instruction on the acquisition, retention, and generalization of Blissymbols while using elements for teaching compounds," PhD thesis, Purdue University, 1995.

16. See Note 20 for Chapter 6.

17. See Note 3 for Chapter 13.

18. See Note 6 for Chapter 6.

19. I thank Jason Hamilton, University of Illinois, for providing the data. The study is reported in Evan H. DeLucia et al., "Net primary production of a forest ecosystem with experimental CO_2 enhancement," *Science*, 284 (1999), pp. 1177–1179. No method for inference can be trusted with $n = 3$. In this study, each observation is very costly, so the small n is inevitable.

20. See Note 7 for Chapter 2.

21. Harry B. Meyers, "Investigations of the life history of the velvetleaf seed beetle, *Althaeus folkertsi* Kingsolver," MS thesis, Purdue University, 1996. The 95% t interval is 1227.9 to 2507.6. A 95% bootstrap BCa interval is 1444 to 2718, confirming that t inference is inaccurate for these data.

22. J. Marcus Jobe and Hutch Jobe, "A statistical approach for additional infill development," *Energy Exploration and Exploitation*, 18 (2000), pp. 89–103. The comparison interval is the BCa interval based on 1000 bootstrap resamples.

23. Press releases from Sherwood Copper Corporation during 2008, found at Marketwire, www.marketwire.com. I have included only the first assay result for each hole to improve independence.

24. See Note 3 for Chapter 13.

25. Data provided by Timothy Sturm.

26. Lianng Yuh, "A biopharmaceutical example for undergraduate students," manuscript, no date.

Chapter 17

1. See Note 16 for Chapter 2.

2. Detailed information about the conservative t procedures can be found in Paul Leaverton and John J. Birch, "Small sample power curves for the two sample location problem," *Technometrics*, 11 (1969), pp. 299–307; Henry Scheffé, "Practical solutions of the Behrens-Fisher problem," *Journal of the American Statistical Association*, 65 (1970), pp. 1501–1508; and D. J. Best and J. C. W. Rayner, "Welch's approximate solution for the Behrens-Fisher problem," *Technometrics*, 29 (1987), pp. 205–210.

3. Kathleen G. McKinney, "Engagement in community service among college students: is it affected by significant attachment relationships?" *Journal of Adolescence*, 25 (2002), pp. 139–154.

4. See Note 9 for Chapter 2.

5. Sapna Aneja, "Biodeterioration of textile fibers in soil," MS thesis, Purdue University, 1994.

6. See the extensive simulation studies in Harry O. Posten, "The robustness of the two-sample t-test over the Pearson system," *Journal of Statistical Computation and Simulation*, 6 (1978), pp. 295–311; and Harry O. Posten, H. Yeh, and Donald B. Owen, "Robustness of the two-sample t-test under violations of the homogeneity assumption," *Communications in Statistics*, 11 (1982), pp. 109–126.

7. See Note 15 for Chapter 2. Although the spending data are quite discrete, a bootstrap BCa 95% confidence interval for the difference in means based on 1000 resamples is 2.394 to 4.826, close to the Option 1 95% interval 2.209 to 4.736. So the sample means are sufficiently Normal to allow use of t procedures.

8. See Note 17 for Chapter 2.

9. Matthias R. Mehl et al., "Are women really more talkative than men?" *Science*, 317 (2007), p. 82.

10. Debra L. Miller et al., "Effect of fat-free potato chips with and without nutrition labels on fat and energy intakes," *American Journal of Clinical Nutrition*, 68 (1998), pp. 282–290.

11. Mary K. Pawlik, "The effect of ginkgo biloba on the post-lunch dip and chemosensory function," MS thesis, Purdue University, 2002.

12. Gabriela S. Castellani, "The effect of cultural values on Hispanics' expectations about service quality," MS thesis, Purdue University, 2000.

13. See Note 6 for Chapter 15.

14. Wayne J. Camera and Donald Powers, "Coaching and the SAT I," *TIP*, July 1999, at `www.siop.org/tip`.

15. See Note 19 for Chapter 1.

16. See Note 3 for Chapter 10.

17. Fabrizio Grieco, Arie J. van Noordwijk, and Marcel E. Visser, "Evidence for the effect of learning on timing of reproduction in blue tits," *Science*, 296 (2002), pp. 136–138. The data in Exercise 17.36 are from a graph in this paper.

18. Kathleen D. Vohs, Nicole L. Mead, and Miranda R. Goode, "The psychological consequences of money," *Science*, 314 (2006), pp. 1154–1156. I thank Kathleen Vohs for supplying the data.

19. See Note 15 for Chapter 16.

20. Data provided by Warren Page, New York City Technical College, from a study done by John Hudesman.

21. See Note 8 for Chapter 2.

22. Data provided by Marigene Arnold, Kalamazoo College.

Chapter 18

1. Joseph H. Catania et al., "Prevalence of AIDS-related risk factors and condom use in the United States," *Science*, 258 (1992), pp. 1101–1106.

2. See Note 2 for Chapter 10. The same finite population correction applies here.

3. The quotation is from page 1104 of the article cited in Note 1.

4. Amanda Lenhart and Mary Madden, "Teens, Privacy and Online Social Networks," Pew Internet and American Life Project, 2007, at `www.pewinternet.org`.

5. See Note 14 for Chapter 17.

6. G. A. Mauser and H. Taylor Buckner, "Canadian attitudes toward gun control: the real story," The Mackenzie Institute, 1997, at `teapot.usask.ca/cdn-firearms/Mauser/gunstory.html`.

7. Gary Edwards and Josephine Mazzuca, "Three quarters of Canadians support doctor-assisted suicide," Gallup Poll press release, March 24, 1999, at `www.gallup.com`.

8. In fact, P-values for two-sided tests are more accurate than those for one-sided tests. Our rule of thumb is a compromise to avoid the confusion of too many rules.

9. Matthew A. Carlton and William D. Stansfield, "Making babies by the flip of a coin?" *American Statistician*, 59 (2005), pp. 180–182.

10. Alexander Todorov et al., "Inferences of competence from faces predict election outcomes," *Science*, 308 (2005), pp. 1623–1626.

11. Michele L. Head, "Examining college students' ethical values," Consumer Science and Retailing honors project, Purdue University, 2003.

12. John Paul McKinney and Kathleen G. McKinney, "Prayer in the lives of late adolescents," *Journal of Adolescence*, 22 (1999), pp. 279–290.

13. John Fagan et al., "Performance assessment under field conditions of a rapid immunological test for transgenic soybeans," *International Journal of Food Science and Technology*, 36 (2001), pp. 357–367.

14. Francisco Lloret et al., "Fire and resprouting in Mediterranean ecosystems: insights from an external biogeographical region, the Mexican shrubland," *American Journal of Botany*, 88 (1999), pp. 1655–1661.

15. See Note 11 for Chapter 7.

16. Henry Wechsler et al., *Binge Drinking on America's College Campuses*, Harvard School of Public Health, 2001.

17. Jon D. Miller, Eugenie C. Scott, and Shinji Okamoto, "Public acceptance of evolution," *Science*, 313 (2006), pp. 765–766. The information in the exercise appears in the supplementary online material.

18. JoAnn K. Wells, Allan F. Williams, and Charles M. Farmer, "Seat belt use among African Americans, Hispanics, and whites," *Accident Analysis and Prevention*, 34 (2002), pp. 523–529.

Chapter 19

1. See Note 4 for Chapter 9.

2. Eulynn Shiu and Amanda Lenhart, "How Americans use instant messaging," Pew Internet and American Life Project, 2004, at `www.pewinternet.org`.

3. From the Web site of the Black Youth Project, `blackyouthproject.uchicago.edu`.

4. *Youth Risk Behavior Surveillance–United States 2005*, Centers for Disease Control and Prevention, Morbidity and Mortality Weekly Report, Vol. 55, No. 66-5, 2007, at `www.cdc.gov/mmwr`. The data are from a complex multistage sample, so that acting as if we have SRSs is oversimplified.

5. Louie E. Ross, "Mate selection preferences among African American college students," *Journal of Black Studies*, 27 (1997), pp. 554–569.

6. This rule of thumb is quite conservative. It is in fact safe to arrange the data as a 2 × 2 table and apply the rule of thumb from Chapter 21 that all four *expected* counts must be 5 or greater. I give the conservative rule here because expected counts are messy to explain in the present context.

7. Ross L. Prentice et al., "Low-fat dietary pattern and risk of invasive breast cancer," *Journal of the American Medical Association*, 295 (2006), pp. 629–642.

8. Steiner Sulheim et al., "Helmet use and risk of head injuries in alpine skiers and snowboarders," *Journal of the American Medical Association*, 295 (2006), pp. 919–924.

9. Based on Claudia Sanmartin et al., "Joint Canada/United States Survey of Health, 2002–2003," Statistics Canada catalogue no. 82M0022XIE, at `www.cdc.gov/nchs`. The data in the report are adjusted for age distribution, so that the exercise is somewhat oversimplified.

10. See Note 4 for Chapter 18.

11. From an Associated Press dispatch appearing on December 30, 2002. The study report appeared in the *Journal of Adolescent Health*.

12. Douglas G. Altman, Steven N. Goodman, and Sara Schroter, "How statistical expertise is used in medical research," *Journal of the American Medical Association*, 287 (2002), pp. 2817–2820.

13. Arne L. Kalleberg and Kevin T. Leicht, "Gender and organizational performance: determinants of small business survival and success," *The Academy of Management Journal*, 34 (1991), pp. 136–161.

14. François Gaudet et al., "Induction of tumors in mice by genomic hypomethylation," *Science*, 300 (2003), pp. 489–492.

15. See Note 13 for Chapter 18.

16. Richard M. Felder et al., "Who gets it and who doesn't: a study of student performance in an introductory chemical engineering course," *1992 ASEE Annual Conference Proceedings*, American Society for Engineering Education, Washington, D.C., 1992, pp. 1516–1519.

17. Douglas E. Jorenby et al., "A controlled trial of sustained-release bupropion, a nicotine patch, or both for smoking cessation," *New England Journal of Medicine*, 340 (1999), pp. 685–691.

18. Data courtesy of Raymond Dumett, Purdue University.

19. Based on Alan G. Sanfey et al., "The neural basis of economic decision-making in the ultimatum game," *Science*, 300 (2003), pp. 1755–1758. The paper reports a chi-square test (equivalent to a two-sided z test). This analysis is incorrect for the paper's data, as there were in fact only 19 participants, each appearing twice in each row of the table given in the exercise. Exercise 19.27 therefore amends the data, assuming 76 participants, so that the elementary analysis is correct.

20. See Note 18 for Chapter 18.

21. Clive G. Jones et al., "Chain reactions linking acorns to gypsy moth outbreaks and Lyme disease risk," *Science*, 279 (1998), pp. 1023–1026.

22. The study is reported in William Celis III, "Study suggests Head Start helps beyond school," *New York Times*, April 20, 1993. See www.highscope.org.

23. Karen M. Herbert, "Does impulse buying vary by mode of payment?" MS thesis, Purdue University, 1994.

Chapter 20

1. Lee Rainie and Bill Tancer, "36% of online American adults consult Wikipedia," Pew Internet and American Life Project, 2007, at www.pewinternet.org.

2. See Note 4 for Chapter 19.

3. See Note 7 for Chapter 13.

4. K. S. Oberhauser, "Fecundity, lifespan and egg mass in butterflies: effects of male-derived nutrients and female size," *Functional Ecology*, 11 (1997), pp. 166–175.

5. See Note 3 for Chapter 19.

6. Michael R. Dohm, Jack P. Hayes, and Theodore Garland, Jr., "Quantitative genetics of sprint running speed and swimming endurance in laboratory house mice (*Mus domesticus*)," *Evolution*, 50 (1996), pp. 1688–1701.

7. Marianne Perle, Rebecca Moran, and Anthony D. Lutkus, *NAEP 2004 Trends in Academic Progress: Three Decades of Student Performance in Reading and Mathematics*, National Center for Education Statistics, 2005, at nces.ed.gov. The data given are approximate due to rounding in the study report.

8. See Note 8 for Chapter 15. The exercises are simplified, in that the measures reported in this paper have been statistically adjusted for "sociodemographic status."

9. See Note 9 for Chapter 19. It is oversimplified to treat these complex samples as SRSs. The report gives 18.9% to 23.1% as the 95% confidence interval for Canada, a bit wider than the SRS interval.

10. V. D. Bass, W. E. Hoffmann, and J. L. Dorner, "Normal canine lipid profiles and effects of experimentally induced pancreatitis and hepatic necrosis on lipids," *American Journal of Veterinary Research*, 37 (1976), pp. 1355–1357.

11. Jin Ha Lee and J. Stephen Downie, "Survey of music information needs, uses, and seeking behaviors: preliminary findings," online Proceedings of the 5th International Conference on Music Information Retrieval, 2004, at ismir2004.ismir.net.

12. Josh McDermott and Marc D. Hauser, "Nonhuman primates prefer slow tempos but dislike music overall," *Cognition*, 104 (2007), pp. 654–668. Failure to take account of repeated measures on the same subjects is one of the most common errors observed in statistical analysis.

13. These data were originally collected by L. M. Linde of UCLA but were first published by M. R. Mickey, O. J. Dunn, and V. Clark, "Note on the use of stepwise regression in detecting outliers," *Computers and Biomedical Research*, 1 (1967), pp. 105–111. The data have been

used by several authors. I found them in N. R. Draper and J. A. John, "Influential observations and outliers in regression," *Technometrics*, 23 (1981), pp. 21–26.

14. Jacqueline T. Ngai and Diane S. Srivastava, "Predators accelerate nutrient cycling in a bromeliad ecosystem," *Science*, 314 (2006), p. 963. I thank Jacqueline Ngai for providing the data.

15. Yvan R. Germain, "The dyeing of ramie with fiber reactive dyes using the cold pad-batch method," MS thesis, Purdue University, 1988.

16. Data provided by Marigene Arnold, Kalamazoo College.

17. Data provided by Corinne Lim, Purdue University, from a student project supervised by Professor Joseph Vanable.

18. Saiyad S. Ahmed, "Effects of microwave drying on checking and mechanical strength of low-moisture baked products," MS thesis, Purdue University, 1994.

19. Michael O. Finkelstein and Bruce Levin, "Statistical proof of discrimination in peremptory challenges," *Chance*, 17, No. 1 (2004), pp. 35–38.

Chapter 21

1. See Note 4 for Chapter 9.

2. Lien-Ti Bei, "Consumers' purchase behavior toward recycled products: an acquisition-transaction utility theory perspective," MS thesis, Purdue University, 1993.

3. Pennsylvania State University Division of Student Affairs, "Net behaviors November 2006," *Penn State Pulse*, at www.sa.psu.edu.

4. There are many computer studies of the accuracy of chi-square critical values for χ^2. Our guideline goes back to W. G. Cochran (1954). Later work has shown that it is often conservative in the sense that, if the expected cell counts are all similar and the degrees of freedom exceed 1, the chi-square approximation works well for an average expected count as small as 1 or 2. Our guideline protects against dissimilar expected counts. It has the added advantage that it is safe in the 2×2 case, where the chi-square approximation is least good. So our guideline is helpful for beginners—there is no single condition that is not conservative and applies to 2×2 and larger tables with similar and dissimilar expected cell counts.

5. All General Social Survey exercises in this chapter present tables constructed using the search function at the GSS archive, sda.berkeley.edu/archive.htm. Most concern data from the 2006 GSS.

6. Pew Research Center for the People and the Press, "The cell phone challenge to survey research," news release for May 15, 2006, at www.people-press.org.

7. Based on a news item in *Science*, 305 (2004), p. 1560. The study, by Daniel Klem, appeared in the *Wilson Journal*.

8. David W. Eby et al., "The effect of changing from secondary to primary safety belt enforcement on police harassment," *Accident Analysis and Prevention*, 36 (2000), pp. 819–828.

9. Public use data available on the Web site of the Carolina Population Center, www.cpc.unc.edu.

10. Based on John B. Horrigan and Aaron Smith, "Home broadband adoption 2007," Pew Internet and American Life Project, 2007, at www.pewinternet.org. The exercise is slightly modified because the data in the paper are not consistent: the authors claim both that 47% have home broadband and that 966 in their sample of 2200 have home broadband.

11. Modified from Felicity Barringer, "Measuring sexuality through polls can be shaky," *New York Times*, April 25, 1993.

12. Virgilio P. Carnielli et al., "Intestinal absorption of long-chain polyunsaturated fatty acids in preterm infants fed breast milk or formula," *American Journal of Clinical Nutrition*, 67 (1998), pp. 97–103.

13. Adapted from M. A. Visintainer, J. R. Volpicelli, and M. E. P. Seligman, "Tumor rejection in rats after inescapable or escapable shock," *Science*, 216 (1982), pp. 437–439.

14. See Note 4 for Chapter 9.

15. Tom Reichert, "The prevalence of sexual imagery in ads targeted to young adults," *Journal of Consumer Affairs*, 37 (2003), pp. 403–412.

16. Mark A. Sabbagh and Dare A. Baldwin, "Learning words from knowledgeable versus ignorant speakers: links between preschoolers' theory of mind and semantic development," *Child Development*, 72 (2001), pp. 1054–1070. Many statistical software packages offer "exact tests" that are valid even when there are small expected counts.

17. U.S. Department of Commerce, Office of Travel and Tourism Industries, in-flight survey, 2007, at `tinet.ita.doc.gov`.

18. See Note 2 for Chapter 15. I have simplified slightly: the table in the paper is exactly as in the exercise but contains data for 63 subjects plus data from one type of bar for 3 subjects who dropped out. Although the authors say that their chi-square refers to this table, they give a nonsignificant value that contradicts what the table shows.

19. Karine Marangon et al., "Diet, antioxidant status, and smoking habits in French men," *American Journal of Clinical Nutrition*, 67 (1998), pp. 231–239.

20. See Note 9 for Chapter 19. As in that exercise, the counts given are only approximate.

21. Data compiled from a table of percents in "Americans view higher education as key to the American dream," press release by the National Center for Public Policy and Higher Education, May 3, 2000, at `www.highereducation.org`.

22. Claudia Braga et al., "Olive oil, other seasoning fats, and the risk of colorectal carcinoma," *Cancer*, 82 (1998), pp. 448–453.

23. Data produced by Ries and Smith, found in William D. Johnson and Gary G. Koch, "A note on the weighted least squares analysis of the Ries-Smith contingency table data," *Technometrics*, 13 (1971), pp. 438–447.

Chapter 22

1. Samuel Karelitz et al., "Relation of crying activity in early infancy to speech and intellectual development at age three years," *Child Development*, 35 (1964), pp. 769–777.

2. See Note 4 for Chapter 4.

3. See Note 12 for Chapter 4.

4. From a graph in Bruce J. Peterson et al., "Increasing river discharge to the Arctic Ocean," *Science*, 298 (2002), pp. 2171–2173.

5. Electronic Encyclopedia of Statistical Examples and Exercises (EESEE) at the text Web site, `www.whfreeman.com/essentialstats`.

6. From a graph in Allison L. Perry et al., "Climate change and distribution shifts in marine fishes," *Science*, 308

(2005), pp. 1912–1915. The explanatory variable is the five-year running mean of winter (December to March) sea-bottom temperature.

7. Data for the building at 1800 Ben Franklin Drive, Sarasota, Florida, starting in March 2003. From the Web site of the Sarasota County Property Appraiser, `www.sarasotaproperty.net`.

8. Carly J. Stevens et al., "Impact of nitrogen deposition on the species richness of grasslands," *Science*, 303 (2004), pp. 1876–1879.

9. Based on Marion E. Dunshee, "A study of factors affecting the amount and kind of food eaten by nursery school children," *Child Development*, 2 (1931), pp. 163–183. This article gives the means, standard deviations, and correlation for 37 children, from which the data in the exercise are simulated.

10. From Table S2 in the online supplement to Antonio Dell'Anno and Roberto Danovaro, "Extracellular DNA plays a key role in deep-sea ecosystem functioning," *Science*, 309 (2005), p. 2179.

11. See Note 20 for Chapter 6.

Chapter 23

1. See Note 8 for Chapter 2.

2. Amandine Cournil, Jean-Marie Legay, and François Schächter, "Evidence of sex-linked effects on the inheritance of human longevity: a population-based study in the Valserine valley (French Jura), 18–20th centuries," *Proceedings of the Royal Society of London: Biological Sciences*, 267 (2000), pp. 1021–1025.

3. Elisabeth Wells-Parker et al., "An exploratory study of the relationship between road rage and crash experience in a representative sample of US drivers," *Accident Analysis and Prevention*, 34 (2002), pp. 271–278.

4. See Note 9 for Chapter 2.

5. See Note 15 for Chapter 2.

6. See Note 18 for Chapter 17.

7. See Note 14 for Chapter 20.

8. David B. Wooten, "One-of-a-kind in a full house: some consequences of ethnic and gender distinctiveness," *Journal of Consumer Psychology*, 4 (1995), 205–224.

9. See Note 7 for Chapter 2.

10. Annie C. St.-Pierre et al., "Insulin resistance syndrome, body mass index and the risk of ischemic heart disease," *Canadian Medical Association Journal*, 172 (2005), pp. 1301–1305.

11. Data from the online supplement to André Kessler and Ian T. Baldwin, "Defensive function of herbivore-induced plant volatile emissions in nature," *Science*, 291 (2001), pp. 2141–2144.

12. The data and the full story can be found in the Data and Story Library at `lib.stat.cmu.edu`. The orig-inal study is by Faith Loven, "A study of interlist equivalency of the CID W-22 word list presented in quiet and in noise," MS thesis, University of Iowa, 1981.

13. See Note 5 for Chapter 8. I thank Kenwyn Suttle for providing these data, for the year 2003.

14. See Note 15 for Chapter 20.

15. See Note 3 for Chapter 13.

16. See Note 5 for Chapter 17.

17. See Note 3 for Chapter 10.

18. See Note 5 for Chapter 8.

TABLES

Table A   Standard Normal Probabilities

Table B   Random Digits

Table C   *t* Distribution Critical Values

Table D   Chi-square Distribution Critical Values

Table entry for z is the area under the standard Normal curve to the left of z.

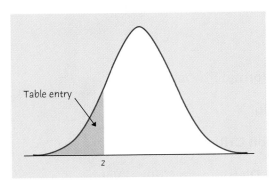

Table entry

z

TABLE A Standard Normal cumulative proportions

z	.00	.01	.02	.03	.04	.05	.06	.07	.08	.09
−3.4	.0003	.0003	.0003	.0003	.0003	.0003	.0003	.0003	.0003	.0002
−3.3	.0005	.0005	.0005	.0004	.0004	.0004	.0004	.0004	.0004	.0003
−3.2	.0007	.0007	.0006	.0006	.0006	.0006	.0006	.0005	.0005	.0005
−3.1	.0010	.0009	.0009	.0009	.0008	.0008	.0008	.0008	.0007	.0007
−3.0	.0013	.0013	.0013	.0012	.0012	.0011	.0011	.0011	.0010	.0010
−2.9	.0019	.0018	.0018	.0017	.0016	.0016	.0015	.0015	.0014	.0014
−2.8	.0026	.0025	.0024	.0023	.0023	.0022	.0021	.0021	.0020	.0019
−2.7	.0035	.0034	.0033	.0032	.0031	.0030	.0029	.0028	.0027	.0026
−2.6	.0047	.0045	.0044	.0043	.0041	.0040	.0039	.0038	.0037	.0036
−2.5	.0062	.0060	.0059	.0057	.0055	.0054	.0052	.0051	.0049	.0048
−2.4	.0082	.0080	.0078	.0075	.0073	.0071	.0069	.0068	.0066	.0064
−2.3	.0107	.0104	.0102	.0099	.0096	.0094	.0091	.0089	.0087	.0084
−2.2	.0139	.0136	.0132	.0129	.0125	.0122	.0119	.0116	.0113	.0110
−2.1	.0179	.0174	.0170	.0166	.0162	.0158	.0154	.0150	.0146	.0143
−2.0	.0228	.0222	.0217	.0212	.0207	.0202	.0197	.0192	.0188	.0183
−1.9	.0287	.0281	.0274	.0268	.0262	.0256	.0250	.0244	.0239	.0233
−1.8	.0359	.0351	.0344	.0336	.0329	.0322	.0314	.0307	.0301	.0294
−1.7	.0446	.0436	.0427	.0418	.0409	.0401	.0392	.0384	.0375	.0367
−1.6	.0548	.0537	.0526	.0516	.0505	.0495	.0485	.0475	.0465	.0455
−1.5	.0668	.0655	.0643	.0630	.0618	.0606	.0594	.0582	.0571	.0559
−1.4	.0808	.0793	.0778	.0764	.0749	.0735	.0721	.0708	.0694	.0681
−1.3	.0968	.0951	.0934	.0918	.0901	.0885	.0869	.0853	.0838	.0823
−1.2	.1151	.1131	.1112	.1093	.1075	.1056	.1038	.1020	.1003	.0985
−1.1	.1357	.1335	.1314	.1292	.1271	.1251	.1230	.1210	.1190	.1170
−1.0	.1587	.1562	.1539	.1515	.1492	.1469	.1446	.1423	.1401	.1379
−0.9	.1841	.1814	.1788	.1762	.1736	.1711	.1685	.1660	.1635	.1611
−0.8	.2119	.2090	.2061	.2033	.2005	.1977	.1949	.1922	.1894	.1867
−0.7	.2420	.2389	.2358	.2327	.2296	.2266	.2236	.2206	.2177	.2148
−0.6	.2743	.2709	.2676	.2643	.2611	.2578	.2546	.2514	.2483	.2451
−0.5	.3085	.3050	.3015	.2981	.2946	.2912	.2877	.2843	.2810	.2776
−0.4	.3446	.3409	.3372	.3336	.3300	.3264	.3228	.3192	.3156	.3121
−0.3	.3821	.3783	.3745	.3707	.3669	.3632	.3594	.3557	.3520	.3483
−0.2	.4207	.4168	.4129	.4090	.4052	.4013	.3974	.3936	.3897	.3859
−0.1	.4602	.4562	.4522	.4483	.4443	.4404	.4364	.4325	.4286	.4247
−0.0	.5000	.4960	.4920	.4880	.4840	.4801	.4761	.4721	.4681	.4641

Table entry for z is the area under the standard Normal curve to the left of z.

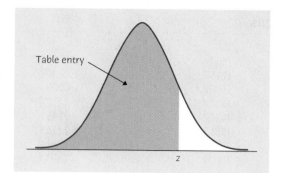

Table entry

z

TABLE A Standard Normal cumulative proportions (*continued*)

z	.00	.01	.02	.03	.04	.05	.06	.07	.08	.09
0.0	.5000	.5040	.5080	.5120	.5160	.5199	.5239	.5279	.5319	.5359
0.1	.5398	.5438	.5478	.5517	.5557	.5596	.5636	.5675	.5714	.5753
0.2	.5793	.5832	.5871	.5910	.5948	.5987	.6026	.6064	.6103	.6141
0.3	.6179	.6217	.6255	.6293	.6331	.6368	.6406	.6443	.6480	.6517
0.4	.6554	.6591	.6628	.6664	.6700	.6736	.6772	.6808	.6844	.6879
0.5	.6915	.6950	.6985	.7019	.7054	.7088	.7123	.7157	.7190	.7224
0.6	.7257	.7291	.7324	.7357	.7389	.7422	.7454	.7486	.7517	.7549
0.7	.7580	.7611	.7642	.7673	.7704	.7734	.7764	.7794	.7823	.7852
0.8	.7881	.7910	.7939	.7967	.7995	.8023	.8051	.8078	.8106	.8133
0.9	.8159	.8186	.8212	.8238	.8264	.8289	.8315	.8340	.8365	.8389
1.0	.8413	.8438	.8461	.8485	.8508	.8531	.8554	.8577	.8599	.8621
1.1	.8643	.8665	.8686	.8708	.8729	.8749	.8770	.8790	.8810	.8830
1.2	.8849	.8869	.8888	.8907	.8925	.8944	.8962	.8980	.8997	.9015
1.3	.9032	.9049	.9066	.9082	.9099	.9115	.9131	.9147	.9162	.9177
1.4	.9192	.9207	.9222	.9236	.9251	.9265	.9279	.9292	.9306	.9319
1.5	.9332	.9345	.9357	.9370	.9382	.9394	.9406	.9418	.9429	.9441
1.6	.9452	.9463	.9474	.9484	.9495	.9505	.9515	.9525	.9535	.9545
1.7	.9554	.9564	.9573	.9582	.9591	.9599	.9608	.9616	.9625	.9633
1.8	.9641	.9649	.9656	.9664	.9671	.9678	.9686	.9693	.9699	.9706
1.9	.9713	.9719	.9726	.9732	.9738	.9744	.9750	.9756	.9761	.9767
2.0	.9772	.9778	.9783	.9788	.9793	.9798	.9803	.9808	.9812	.9817
2.1	.9821	.9826	.9830	.9834	.9838	.9842	.9846	.9850	.9854	.9857
2.2	.9861	.9864	.9868	.9871	.9875	.9878	.9881	.9884	.9887	.9890
2.3	.9893	.9896	.9898	.9901	.9904	.9906	.9909	.9911	.9913	.9916
2.4	.9918	.9920	.9922	.9925	.9927	.9929	.9931	.9932	.9934	.9936
2.5	.9938	.9940	.9941	.9943	.9945	.9946	.9948	.9949	.9951	.9952
2.6	.9953	.9955	.9956	.9957	.9959	.9960	.9961	.9962	.9963	.9964
2.7	.9965	.9966	.9967	.9968	.9969	.9970	.9971	.9972	.9973	.9974
2.8	.9974	.9975	.9976	.9977	.9977	.9978	.9979	.9979	.9980	.9981
2.9	.9981	.9982	.9982	.9983	.9984	.9984	.9985	.9985	.9986	.9986
3.0	.9987	.9987	.9987	.9988	.9988	.9989	.9989	.9989	.9990	.9990
3.1	.9990	.9991	.9991	.9991	.9992	.9992	.9992	.9992	.9993	.9993
3.2	.9993	.9993	.9994	.9994	.9994	.9994	.9994	.9995	.9995	.9995
3.3	.9995	.9995	.9995	.9996	.9996	.9996	.9996	.9996	.9996	.9997
3.4	.9997	.9997	.9997	.9997	.9997	.9997	.9997	.9997	.9997	.9998

TABLE B Random digits

LINE								
101	19223	95034	05756	28713	96409	12531	42544	82853
102	73676	47150	99400	01927	27754	42648	82425	36290
103	45467	71709	77558	00095	32863	29485	82226	90056
104	52711	38889	93074	60227	40011	85848	48767	52573
105	95592	94007	69971	91481	60779	53791	17297	59335
106	68417	35013	15529	72765	85089	57067	50211	47487
107	82739	57890	20807	47511	81676	55300	94383	14893
108	60940	72024	17868	24943	61790	90656	87964	18883
109	36009	19365	15412	39638	85453	46816	83485	41979
110	38448	48789	18338	24697	39364	42006	76688	08708
111	81486	69487	60513	09297	00412	71238	27649	39950
112	59636	88804	04634	71197	19352	73089	84898	45785
113	62568	70206	40325	03699	71080	22553	11486	11776
114	45149	32992	75730	66280	03819	56202	02938	70915
115	61041	77684	94322	24709	73698	14526	31893	32592
116	14459	26056	31424	80371	65103	62253	50490	61181
117	38167	98532	62183	70632	23417	26185	41448	75532
118	73190	32533	04470	29669	84407	90785	65956	86382
119	95857	07118	87664	92099	58806	66979	98624	84826
120	35476	55972	39421	65850	04266	35435	43742	11937
121	71487	09984	29077	14863	61683	47052	62224	51025
122	13873	81598	95052	90908	73592	75186	87136	95761
123	54580	81507	27102	56027	55892	33063	41842	81868
124	71035	09001	43367	49497	72719	96758	27611	91596
125	96746	12149	37823	71868	18442	35119	62103	39244
126	96927	19931	36809	74192	77567	88741	48409	41903
127	43909	99477	25330	64359	40085	16925	85117	36071
128	15689	14227	06565	14374	13352	49367	81982	87209
129	36759	58984	68288	22913	18638	54303	00795	08727
130	69051	64817	87174	09517	84534	06489	87201	97245
131	05007	16632	81194	14873	04197	85576	45195	96565
132	68732	55259	84292	08796	43165	93739	31685	97150
133	45740	41807	65561	33302	07051	93623	18132	09547
134	27816	78416	18329	21337	35213	37741	04312	68508
135	66925	55658	39100	78458	11206	19876	87151	31260
136	08421	44753	77377	28744	75592	08563	79140	92454
137	53645	66812	61421	47836	12609	15373	98481	14592
138	66831	68908	40772	21558	47781	33586	79177	06928
139	55588	99404	70708	41098	43563	56934	48394	51719
140	12975	13258	13048	45144	72321	81940	00360	02428
141	96767	35964	23822	96012	94591	65194	50842	53372
142	72829	50232	97892	63408	77919	44575	24870	04178
143	88565	42628	17797	49376	61762	16953	88604	12724
144	62964	88145	83083	69453	46109	59505	69680	00900
145	19687	12633	57857	95806	09931	02150	43163	58636
146	37609	59057	66967	83401	60705	02384	90597	93600
147	54973	86278	88737	74351	47500	84552	19909	67181
148	00694	05977	19664	65441	20903	62371	22725	53340
149	71546	05233	53946	68743	72460	27601	45403	88692
150	07511	88915	41267	16853	84569	79367	32337	03316

Table entry for C is the critical value t^* required for confidence level C. To approximate one- and two-sided P-values, compare the value of the t statistic with the critical values of t^* that match the P-values given at the bottom of the table.

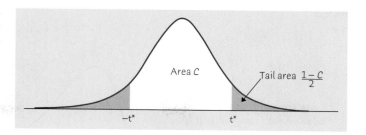

Area C

Tail area $\frac{1-C}{2}$

$-t^*$ t^*

TABLE C t distribution critical values

DEGREES OF FREEDOM	CONFIDENCE LEVEL C											
	50%	60%	70%	80%	90%	95%	96%	98%	99%	99.5%	99.8%	99.9%
1	1.000	1.376	1.963	3.078	6.314	12.71	15.89	31.82	63.66	127.3	318.3	636.6
2	0.816	1.061	1.386	1.886	2.920	4.303	4.849	6.965	9.925	14.09	22.33	31.60
3	0.765	0.978	1.250	1.638	2.353	3.182	3.482	4.541	5.841	7.453	10.21	12.92
4	0.741	0.941	1.190	1.533	2.132	2.776	2.999	3.747	4.604	5.598	7.173	8.610
5	0.727	0.920	1.156	1.476	2.015	2.571	2.757	3.365	4.032	4.773	5.893	6.869
6	0.718	0.906	1.134	1.440	1.943	2.447	2.612	3.143	3.707	4.317	5.208	5.959
7	0.711	0.896	1.119	1.415	1.895	2.365	2.517	2.998	3.499	4.029	4.785	5.408
8	0.706	0.889	1.108	1.397	1.860	2.306	2.449	2.896	3.355	3.833	4.501	5.041
9	0.703	0.883	1.100	1.383	1.833	2.262	2.398	2.821	3.250	3.690	4.297	4.781
10	0.700	0.879	1.093	1.372	1.812	2.228	2.359	2.764	3.169	3.581	4.144	4.587
11	0.697	0.876	1.088	1.363	1.796	2.201	2.328	2.718	3.106	3.497	4.025	4.437
12	0.695	0.873	1.083	1.356	1.782	2.179	2.303	2.681	3.055	3.428	3.930	4.318
13	0.694	0.870	1.079	1.350	1.771	2.160	2.282	2.650	3.012	3.372	3.852	4.221
14	0.692	0.868	1.076	1.345	1.761	2.145	2.264	2.624	2.977	3.326	3.787	4.140
15	0.691	0.866	1.074	1.341	1.753	2.131	2.249	2.602	2.947	3.286	3.733	4.073
16	0.690	0.865	1.071	1.337	1.746	2.120	2.235	2.583	2.921	3.252	3.686	4.015
17	0.689	0.863	1.069	1.333	1.740	2.110	2.224	2.567	2.898	3.222	3.646	3.965
18	0.688	0.862	1.067	1.330	1.734	2.101	2.214	2.552	2.878	3.197	3.611	3.922
19	0.688	0.861	1.066	1.328	1.729	2.093	2.205	2.539	2.861	3.174	3.579	3.883
20	0.687	0.860	1.064	1.325	1.725	2.086	2.197	2.528	2.845	3.153	3.552	3.850
21	0.686	0.859	1.063	1.323	1.721	2.080	2.189	2.518	2.831	3.135	3.527	3.819
22	0.686	0.858	1.061	1.321	1.717	2.074	2.183	2.508	2.819	3.119	3.505	3.792
23	0.685	0.858	1.060	1.319	1.714	2.069	2.177	2.500	2.807	3.104	3.485	3.768
24	0.685	0.857	1.059	1.318	1.711	2.064	2.172	2.492	2.797	3.091	3.467	3.745
25	0.684	0.856	1.058	1.316	1.708	2.060	2.167	2.485	2.787	3.078	3.450	3.725
26	0.684	0.856	1.058	1.315	1.706	2.056	2.162	2.479	2.779	3.067	3.435	3.707
27	0.684	0.855	1.057	1.314	1.703	2.052	2.158	2.473	2.771	3.057	3.421	3.690
28	0.683	0.855	1.056	1.313	1.701	2.048	2.154	2.467	2.763	3.047	3.408	3.674
29	0.683	0.854	1.055	1.311	1.699	2.045	2.150	2.462	2.756	3.038	3.396	3.659
30	0.683	0.854	1.055	1.310	1.697	2.042	2.147	2.457	2.750	3.030	3.385	3.646
40	0.681	0.851	1.050	1.303	1.684	2.021	2.123	2.423	2.704	2.971	3.307	3.551
50	0.679	0.849	1.047	1.299	1.676	2.009	2.109	2.403	2.678	2.937	3.261	3.496
60	0.679	0.848	1.045	1.296	1.671	2.000	2.099	2.390	2.660	2.915	3.232	3.460
80	0.678	0.846	1.043	1.292	1.664	1.990	2.088	2.374	2.639	2.887	3.195	3.416
100	0.677	0.845	1.042	1.290	1.660	1.984	2.081	2.364	2.626	2.871	3.174	3.390
1000	0.675	0.842	1.037	1.282	1.646	1.962	2.056	2.330	2.581	2.813	3.098	3.300
z^*	0.674	0.841	1.036	1.282	1.645	1.960	2.054	2.326	2.576	2.807	3.091	3.291
One-sided P	.25	.20	.15	.10	.05	.025	.02	.01	.005	.0025	.001	.0005
Two-sided P	.50	.40	.30	.20	.10	.05	.04	.02	.01	.005	.002	.001

Table entry for p is the critical value χ^* with probability p lying to its right.

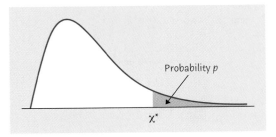

Probability p

χ^*

TABLE D Chi-square distribution critical values

df	.25	.20	.15	.10	.05	.025	.02	.01	.005	.0025	.001	.0005
1	1.32	1.64	2.07	2.71	3.84	5.02	5.41	6.63	7.88	9.14	10.83	12.12
2	2.77	3.22	3.79	4.61	5.99	7.38	7.82	9.21	10.60	11.98	13.82	15.20
3	4.11	4.64	5.32	6.25	7.81	9.35	9.84	11.34	12.84	14.32	16.27	17.73
4	5.39	5.99	6.74	7.78	9.49	11.14	11.67	13.28	14.86	16.42	18.47	20.00
5	6.63	7.29	8.12	9.24	11.07	12.83	13.39	15.09	16.75	18.39	20.51	22.11
6	7.84	8.56	9.45	10.64	12.59	14.45	15.03	16.81	18.55	20.25	22.46	24.10
7	9.04	9.80	10.75	12.02	14.07	16.01	16.62	18.48	20.28	22.04	24.32	26.02
8	10.22	11.03	12.03	13.36	15.51	17.53	18.17	20.09	21.95	23.77	26.12	27.87
9	11.39	12.24	13.29	14.68	16.92	19.02	19.68	21.67	23.59	25.46	27.88	29.67
10	12.55	13.44	14.53	15.99	18.31	20.48	21.16	23.21	25.19	27.11	29.59	31.42
11	13.70	14.63	15.77	17.28	19.68	21.92	22.62	24.72	26.76	28.73	31.26	33.14
12	14.85	15.81	16.99	18.55	21.03	23.34	24.05	26.22	28.30	30.32	32.91	34.82
13	15.98	16.98	18.20	19.81	22.36	24.74	25.47	27.69	29.82	31.88	34.53	36.48
14	17.12	18.15	19.41	21.06	23.68	26.12	26.87	29.14	31.32	33.43	36.12	38.11
15	18.25	19.31	20.60	22.31	25.00	27.49	28.26	30.58	32.80	34.95	37.70	39.72
16	19.37	20.47	21.79	23.54	26.30	28.85	29.63	32.00	34.27	36.46	39.25	41.31
17	20.49	21.61	22.98	24.77	27.59	30.19	31.00	33.41	35.72	37.95	40.79	42.88
18	21.60	22.76	24.16	25.99	28.87	31.53	32.35	34.81	37.16	39.42	42.31	44.43
19	22.72	23.90	25.33	27.20	30.14	32.85	33.69	36.19	38.58	40.88	43.82	45.97
20	23.83	25.04	26.50	28.41	31.41	34.17	35.02	37.57	40.00	42.34	45.31	47.50
21	24.93	26.17	27.66	29.62	32.67	35.48	36.34	38.93	41.40	43.78	46.80	49.01
22	26.04	27.30	28.82	30.81	33.92	36.78	37.66	40.29	42.80	45.20	48.27	50.51
23	27.14	28.43	29.98	32.01	35.17	38.08	38.97	41.64	44.18	46.62	49.73	52.00
24	28.24	29.55	31.13	33.20	36.42	39.36	40.27	42.98	45.56	48.03	51.18	53.48
25	29.34	30.68	32.28	34.38	37.65	40.65	41.57	44.31	46.93	49.44	52.62	54.95
26	30.43	31.79	33.43	35.56	38.89	41.92	42.86	45.64	48.29	50.83	54.05	56.41
27	31.53	32.91	34.57	36.74	40.11	43.19	44.14	46.96	49.64	52.22	55.48	57.86
28	32.62	34.03	35.71	37.92	41.34	44.46	45.42	48.28	50.99	53.59	56.89	59.30
29	33.71	35.14	36.85	39.09	42.56	45.72	46.69	49.59	52.34	54.97	58.30	60.73
30	34.80	36.25	37.99	40.26	43.77	46.98	47.96	50.89	53.67	56.33	59.70	62.16
40	45.62	47.27	49.24	51.81	55.76	59.34	60.44	63.69	66.77	69.70	73.40	76.09
50	56.33	58.16	60.35	63.17	67.50	71.42	72.61	76.15	79.49	82.66	86.66	89.56
60	66.98	68.97	71.34	74.40	79.08	83.30	84.58	88.38	91.95	95.34	99.61	102.7
80	88.13	90.41	93.11	96.58	101.9	106.6	108.1	112.3	116.3	120.1	124.8	128.3
100	109.1	111.7	114.7	118.5	124.3	129.6	131.1	135.8	140.2	144.3	149.4	153.2

Chapter 1

1.1 **(a)** Vehicles. **(b)** Make/model, vehicle type, transmission type (all categorical); number of cylinders, city mpg, highway mpg (all quantitative).

1.3 **(a)** 61.6%; 38.4% listen to other formats. **(c)** A pie chart could be used.

1.5 A pie chart could be used. Perhaps induced or C-section births are often scheduled for weekdays.

1.7 The distribution is roughly symmetric; the center is near 23 minutes, and the spread is from 15.5 to 30.9 minutes.

1.9 The midpoint is 23.4 minutes, and the times range from 15.5 to 30.9 minutes.

1.11 **(b)** Tuition and fees have increased, apart from a slight dip in the late 1970s. **(c)** There are no outliers. Charges decreased at the beginning of this time period and increased more rapidly from about 2000 to 2004.

1.12 (c)   **1.13** (c)   **1.14** (b)   **1.15** (a)   **1.16** (a)   **1.17** (b)   **1.18** (c)

1.19 **(a)** Medical students. **(b)** Five variables; medical school, sex, and specialty are categorical, while age and USMLE are quantitative.

1.21 5% are other colors. Either a bar graph or a pie chart could be used.

1.23 **(b)** To make a pie chart, we need to know the total number of deaths in this age group.

1.25 The distribution is skewed to the right, spread from 0 to 8 servings, and the center is about 2 or 3 servings. About 35% ate fewer than 2 servings of fruit.

1.27 (a) 4, (b) 2, (c) 1, (d) 3.

1.29 **(a)** States with large populations need more doctors to serve that population. **(b)** Right-skewed, with D.C. a high outlier.

1.31 The distribution is right-skewed with a high outlier. The center is around 700 million, and the spread is from 173 million to 4700 million (2809 million, if we omit the outlier).

1.33 The number of recruits peaked in the mid-1980s, and in recent years has fallen back to levels similar to those in the 1970s.

1.35 Newer coins are more common than older coins.

1.37 With most software that can create such plots, the mouse can be used to resize the plot.

1.39 **(a)** The midpoint is 13 people. **(b)** The number of bites has exceeded the midpoint 15 times since 1986.

Chapter 2

2.1   30,841 pounds; only 6 pieces of wood had breaking strengths below the mean. The mean is made smaller by the left-skew of the distribution.

2.3   The mean (31.25 minutes) is larger than the median (22.5 minutes), as we expect for a right-skewed distribution.

2.5   The mean (0.7607) is larger than the median (0.075) because of the sharp right skew.

2.7   **(a)** About −3.5% and 3.0%. **(b)** About 0% or 0.1%. **(c)** The stock fund is much more variable.

2.9   Both data sets have $\bar{x} \doteq 7.50$ and $s \doteq 2.03$; set A is left-skewed, while set B has a high outlier.

2.11   The means and the stemplots appear to suggest that logging reduces the number of trees per plot and that recovery is slow (the 1-year-after and 8-years-after means and stemplots are similar).

2.13   (c)   **2.14**   (b)   **2.15**   (a)   **2.16**   (c)   **2.17**   (b)   **2.18**   (b)   **2.19**   (a)

2.21   These distributions are sharply right-skewed, because while many have not saved very much, a few have saved hundreds of thousands or even millions.

2.23   **(a)** 23,040, 30,315, 31,975, 32,710, and 33,650 pounds. **(b)** The gaps between the minimum and Q_1 and between Q_1 and M are larger than the other two gaps.

2.25 $M = 2$, $Q_1 = 1$, and $Q_3 = 4$ servings.

2.27   **(a)** Symmetric distributions with no outliers. **(b)** Women: $\bar{x}$ changes from 165.2 to 158.4 minutes; s from 56.5 to 43.7 minutes. Men: $\bar{x}$ from 117.2 to 110.9 minutes; s from 74.2 to 66.9 minutes.

2.29   Weekend births are less common, and births are less common on Monday than on the rest of the weekdays.

2.31   If we list the credit card debt figures for all American households, more than half of the numbers in that list equal zero (for households with no credit cards and those who pay off their balance each month).

2.33   Answers will vary; 9 to 15 digits is typical.

2.37   The five-number summary is −37.23%, 0.06%, 15.69%, 24.4%, 37.38%. Returns have typically been positive, but with much variability and no clear pattern over time.

2.39   Compare each pair of distributions using graphs (stemplots, boxplots, or histograms) and numerical summaries. Lean subjects had more active time ($\bar{x} \doteq 525.8$, $s \doteq 107.1$ min) than obese subjects ($\bar{x} \doteq 373.3$, $s \doteq 67.5$ min). There was little difference in time spent lying down (lean: $\bar{x} \doteq 501.6$, $s \doteq 52.0$ min; obese: $\bar{x} \doteq 491.7$, $s \doteq 46.6$ min).

2.41   Compare, for example, the means: −3.59% and 0.31%.

Chapter 3

3.3 Both are 1.5.

3.7 **(a)** 688 to 1016 mm. **(b)** Less than 688 mm.

3.9 Women: $z = 2.96$. Men: $z = 0.96$.

3.11 **(a)** About 2.94%. **(b)** About 96.11%.

3.13 **(a)** $z \doteq -0.84$. **(b)** $z \doteq 0.25$.

3.15 **(a)** **3.16** (b) **3.17** (b) **3.18** (b) **3.19** (c) **3.20** (a) **3.21** (b)

3.23 About 2.5%.

3.25 **(a)** $z \doteq 0.84$. **(b)** $z \doteq 0.39$.

3.27 About 0.2296.

3.29 About 0.9876.

3.31 About 92.92%.

3.33 About 15.8 and 21.6 mpg.

3.35 15th percentile.

3.37 About 2.5%.

3.39 Mean 250, standard deviation 175.8.

3.41 **(a)** The stemplot looks Normal, although there are two low values. **(b)** $\bar{x} = 105.84$ and $s = 14.27$. The proportions are about 74.2% and 94.5%; a Normal distribution would have 68% and 95%.

3.43 **(a)** The mean (5.43) is close to the median (5.44), and the quartiles are similar distances from the median ($M - Q_1 = 0.39$ and $Q_3 - M = 0.35$), suggesting that the distribution is reasonably symmetric. **(b)** Less than 5.05: about 0.2420. Less than 5.79: about 0.7486. These are close to what we would expect for the quartiles (0.25 and 0.75), so this is consistent with the distribution being close to Normal.

3.45 **(a)** $\bar{x} \doteq 847.58$ mm, $M = 860.8$ mm. **(b)** The histogram shows a left-skew, which makes the mean lower than the median.

Chapter 4

4.1 **(a)** Explanatory: time spent studying. Response: grade. **(b)** Explore the relationship. **(c)** Explanatory: time spent on extracurricular activities. Response: GPA. **(d)** Explore the relationship.

4.3 Lean body mass should be on the horizontal axis.

4.5 The scatterplot shows a positive linear moderately strong association.

4.7 **(b)** The association is linear and positive, stronger for women. Males typically have larger values for both variables.

4.9   No; units do not affect correlation.

4.11 These variables do not have a straight-line relationship; the association is neither positive nor negative.

4.12 (a)   **4.13** (c)   **4.14** (a)   **4.15** (c)   **4.16** (b)   **4.17** (b)   **4.18** (a)

4.19 (a) The lowest first-round score was 69, achieved by two golfers; they shot 73 and 75 in the second round. (b) Villegas shot 85 (second round) and 80 (first round). (c) Closest to 0.2.

4.21 (a) Positive, but not close to 1. (b) $r = 0.5653$.

4.23 Linear, negative, fairly weak; sparrowhawks are long-lived and territorial.

4.25 (a) SRD should be on the horizontal axis. (b) The scatterplot shows a positive linear association; $r \doteq 0.9685$.

4.27 (a) Planting rate is explanatory. (b) The pattern is curved. The association is not linear, and is neither positive nor negative, so $r \doteq 0.1349$ is not helpful. (c) 131.025, 143.15, 146.225, 143.07, and 134.75 bushels/acre. At or around 20,000 plants/acre is best.

4.29 (a) r would not change. (b) r would not change; it does not tell us that the men were generally taller. (c) 1.

4.31 (a) Small-cap stocks. (b) A negative correlation.

4.33 (a) Gender is not quantitative. (b) r cannot exceed 1. (c) r has no units.

4.35 The new points are generally slightly lower than the old points, suggesting that gas usage has dropped slightly.

4.37 A fairly strong positive linear association ($r \doteq 0.8782$); social exclusion does appear to trigger a pain response.

Chapter 5

5.1   (a) The slope is 1.109. On average, highway mileage increases by 1.109 mpg for each 1 mpg change in city mileage. (b) The intercept is 4.62 mpg. (c) 22.36 and 35.67 mpg.

5.3   (a) $\bar{x} = 3.5$, $s_x \doteq 1.3784$, $\bar{y} = 31.3333$, $s_y \doteq 16.1328$, and $r \doteq 0.9623$. $\hat{y} \doteq -8.088 + 11.26x$.

5.5   A correlation close to 1 (or -1) means a strong linear relationship.

5.7   (a) The residuals are 0.8246, -4.7018, -3.9649, 4.0351, 6.0351, and -2.2281.

5.9   (b) $r \doteq 0.4765$ with all points, and 0.4838 with the outlier removed. (c) With all points, $\hat{y} \doteq 4.73 + 0.3868x$, and the prediction is 34.13%. With Hawaiian Airlines removed, $\hat{y} \doteq 10.88 + 0.2495x$, and the prediction is 29.84%.

5.11 For example, a student's general intelligence, problem-solving ability, or self-confidence.

5.13 For example, social status and ethnic background.

5.15 (b) **5.16** (c) **5.17** (b) **5.18** (a) **5.19** (b) **5.20** (a) **5.21** (c)

5.22 (b)

5.23 (a) 0.0138 minutes per meter. On the average, if the depth of the dive is increased by 1 meter, it adds 0.0138 minutes (about 0.83 seconds) to the time spent underwater. (b) 5.45 minutes. (c) To plot the line, compute DD (y) when $x = 40$ and when $x = 300$, then connect those points.

5.25 (a) $\hat{y} = -0.126 + 0.0608x$; $\hat{y} = -0.0044$ when $x = 2.0$. (b) 77.1%. (c) $r \doteq 0.88$; it is positive because the slope is positive.

5.27 (a) Slope, 0.5185; intercept, 36.115. (b) The prediction is about 70.85 inches. (c) This regression explains only 25% of the variation in the husband's height.

5.29 $r = 0.40$.

5.31 (a) $\hat{y} = 31.9 - 0.304x$. (b) On the average, for every 1% increase in returning birds, the number of new birds joining the colony decreases by 0.304. (c) We predict $\hat{y} \doteq 13.69$ new birds.

5.33 (a) $r \doteq 0.9999$, so recalibration is not necessary. (b) $\hat{y} = 8.825x - 14.52$; when $x = 40$, $\hat{y} \doteq 338.5$ mg/l. (c) The relationship is strong, so the prediction should be very accurate.

5.35 (b) For all points, $r \doteq 0.4819$. Removing Subject 15 increases r to 0.5684, because its presence makes the scatterplot less linear. Removing Subject 18 decreases r to 0.3837, because its presence decreases the relative scatter about the linear pattern.

5.37 $\hat{y} \doteq 66.4 + 10.4x$ (all observations), $\hat{y} \doteq 69.5 + 8.92x$ (without Subject 15), $\hat{y} \doteq 52.3 + 12.1x$ (without Subject 18). Neither point is particularly influential. Outliers in the y direction (like Subject 15) are typically not very influential; Subject 18 is consistent with the linear pattern suggested by the other points.

5.39 For example, students might differ in self-motivation or computer skills.

5.41 The predictions are 76.33 and 74.53.

5.43 The right-hand points lie below the left-hand points. Regression on the right hand gives $\hat{y} = 99.4 + 0.0283x$ ($r = 0.305$, $r^2 = 9.3\%$); on the left hand, $\hat{y} = 172 + 0.262x$ ($r = 0.318$, $r^2 = 10.1\%$). Neither is very good for prediction.

5.45 The scatterplot suggests a negative linear association, with correlation $r \doteq -0.9179$.

5.47 Scatterplots of female life expectancy and infant mortality against health care spending (the explanatory variable) suggest that regression lines might be appropriate, if the outliers are excluded. Health care spending allows some prediction of the response variables, but those predictions are not very reliable unless the outliers are excluded—and even then are not too good for infant mortality.

Chapter 6

6.1 (a) Quantitative. (b) Categorical. (c) Categorical. (d) Quantitative.

6.3 A bar graph is the best choice.

6.5 Use either a histogram or a stemplot. The distribution is sharply right-skewed, with several possible high outliers. The five-number summary is 0.1, 3.5, 5.4, 9, 33.8.

6.7 (b) A pie chart cannot be used because each percent represents a different whole.

6.9 The five-number summaries are 7.2, 8.5, 9.3, 10.9, 12.8 for Aleppo pines and 21.2, 23.7, 26.7, 29.7, 33.7 for Torrey pines. It should be easy to tell which species a needle comes from.

6.11 (a) The Aleppo distribution looks more Normal. (b) For Aleppo pines, $\bar{x} = 9.593$ and M = 9.3 cm, and for Torrey pines, $\bar{x} = 27$ and M = 26.7 cm. The means are similar to the medians because both distributions are relatively symmetric.

6.13 95% are between 6.4 and 12.8 cm; 2.5% are less than 6.4 cm.

6.15 (a) About 6%. (b) About 73%.

6.17 The plot shows a strong negative association; $r \doteq -0.998$.

6.19 −56.1 grams; prediction outside the range of the available data is risky.

6.21 (a) Lean monkeys: $\bar{x} = 8.6833$ kg. Obese monkeys: $\bar{x} = 10.5167$ kg. (b) Lean monkeys: $\hat{y} = 0.541 + 0.0826x$. Obese monkeys: $\hat{y} = 0.371 + 0.0852x$. Energy increases at about the same rate for both types of monkeys, but obese monkeys have a lower intercept, meaning that they expend less energy overall.

6.23 A scatterplot shows a moderately strong positive association (correlation 0.7565), and the regression line is $\hat{y} = 1.4146 + 0.4399x$.

6.25 (a) 31 neurons. (b) The correlation is 0.6386; the relationship is moderately strong.

6.27 (a) Fidelity Technology Fund. (b) No.

6.29 Incorrect; it should be $r^2 = 64\%$.

6.31 (a) $\hat{y} = 166 - 1.10x$. Each additional lamb's-quarter per meter decreases yield by about 1.1 bushels/acre. (b) We predict 159.4 bushels/acre.

6.33 The time plot shows a lot of fluctuation from year to year, but also shows a recent increase: prior to 1972, the discharge rarely rose above 600 km^3, but since then, it has exceeded that level more than half the time.

6.35 (b) $\hat{y} = 156.92 - 0.07211x$. (c) $r^2 = 0.1048$.

6.37 (a) and (b) Leaving out the three highest countries (Eritrea, São Tomé and Príncipe, and Georgia), the distribution is relatively symmetrical. (c) $\bar{x} \doteq 18.2447\%$ and $s \doteq 7.0451\%$. (d) The U.S. government's share of GDP is small compared to the shares of the other countries in this list.

6.39 The distribution seems to be fairly Normal apart from a high outlier. The five-number summary is Min = 13, $Q_1 = 20$, M = 25, $Q_3 = 30$, Max = 50 degrees, while $\bar{x} = 25.42$ degrees and $s = 7.47$ degrees.

6.41 A scatterplot shows a moderate-to-weak positive linear association, with one clear outlier. MA angle can be used to give (very rough) estimates of HAV angle, but the spread is wide enough that they would not be too reliable.

6.43 A scatterplot shows a moderate positive linear association. The regression line is $\hat{y} = 70.44 + 274.78x$.

6.45 (a) $\hat{y} = 93.9 + 0.778x$. The third point is A; the first point is B. (b) The correlation drops only slightly (from 0.6386 to 0.6101) when A is removed; it drops more drastically (to 0.4793) without B. (c) Without A: $\hat{y} = 98.4 + 0.679x$. Without B: $\hat{y} = 101 + 0.693x$.

Chapter 7

7.1 (a) All college students. (b) 104 students.

7.3 Population: all 45,000 people who made credit card purchases. Sample: the 137 people who returned the survey form.

7.5 Possible answers: (a) A call-in poll. (b) Interviewing students as they enter the student center.

7.7 Number from 01 to 28 and choose 04, 10, 17, 19, 12, 13.

7.9 Larger samples provide better information about the population.

7.11 The higher no-answer was probably the second period—more families are likely to be gone for vacations, etc. High nonresponse rates are problematic because we do not know what information we are missing.

7.13 (b) **7.14** (a) **7.15** (b) **7.16** (a) **7.17** (c) **7.18** (a) **7.19** (b)

7.21 Population: the 1000 envelopes stuffed during a given hour. Sample: the 40 envelopes selected.

7.23 Label the codes 001 to 341; Table B gives 288, 229, 131, 303, and 007.

7.25 (a) Label from 0001 to 7500. (b) From Table B, choose 7282, 3297, 3408, 4178, 5426, 2817, 6176, 2169, 5388, and 6041.

7.27 (a) False. (b) True. (c) False.

7.29 Online polls tend to attract responses from those who have strong opinions on the subject and therefore are often not representative of the population as a whole.

7.31 (a) 1388, 0746, 0227, 4001, 1858. (b) More than 171 respondents have run red lights.

7.33 Each student has a 10% chance of being interviewed, but each sample must contain exactly 3 older and 2 younger students.

7.35 Assign labels 001 through 290 to the men, and 001 through 110 to the women. From Table B, the first three men are 174, 095, and 178, and the first three women are 019, 007, and 041.

7.37 (a) Dialing a randomly chosen phone number can conceivably contact any person who has a telephone. (b) "Phone answerers" and "non-phone answerers" might have different characteristics; a good survey should fairly represent both groups.

7.41 (a) Smaller sample sizes give less information about the population. (b) The margin of error was so large that the results could not be viewed as an accurate reflection of the population of Cubans.

Chapter 8

8.1   This is an observational study. Explanatory variable: cell phone usage. Response variable: presence/absence of brain cancer.

8.3   For ideas, ask: what else might binge-drinking students do that might lead to lower grades?

8.5   Individuals: pine seedlings. Factor: amount of light. Treatments: full light, 25% light, or 5% light. Response variable: dry weight at the end of the study.

8.7   Over a year, many things can change: the state of the economy, hiring costs (due to an increasing minimum wage or the cost of employee benefits), etc.

8.9   **(a)** Assign 6 plots to each treatment. **(b)** If using Table B, label 01 to 36 and take two digits at a time.

8.11   The effects of factors other than the nonphysical treatment have been eliminated or accounted for, so that the differences in improvement observed between the subjects can be attributed to the differences in treatments.

8.13   **(a)** The researchers simply observed the existing arsenic levels; they did not alter them. **(b)** For example: the increased lung cancer mortality rate is greater than would be likely to occur by chance if arsenic had no effect.

8.15   The experimenter knows which subjects were taught to meditate; if he or she has some expectations about the effect of meditation, this could influence the diagnosis.

8.17   **(a)** Randomly assign 15 students to Group 1 (easy mazes) and the other 15 to Group (hard mazes). Compare each group's time estimates. **(b)** Each student does the activity twice, once with the easy mazes and once with the hard mazes, in a randomly determined order. Compare each student's "easy" and "hard" time estimate.

8.18   (a)   **8.19**   (b)   **8.20**   (a)   **8.21**   (a)   **8.22.**   (b)   **8.23**   (a)   **8.24**   (b)

8.25   **(a)** An observational study; the explanatory variable is alcohol consumption, and the response variable is whether or not a subject dies. **(b)** For example, some non-drinkers might avoid drinking because of other health concerns.

8.29   Assign 272 subjects to each treatment (the two descriptions of Jim), then compare the opinions of the two groups.

8.31   **(a)** Assign 10 subjects to each group, then compare work output and earnings. **(b)** From line 131, we choose 05, 19, 04, 20, 16, 18, 07, 13, 02, and 08.

8.33   **(a)** Three factors (roller type, dyeing cycle time, and temperature), each with two levels, for a total of eight treatments. The experiment requires 24 fabric specimens. **(b)** Note that because there are eight treatments, this diagram is quite large.

8.35   **(a)** Assign subjects as described, and observe length of sinus infection. **(b)** Assign labels from 001 to 240. **(c)** Randomly select the 53 subjects for Treatment 1, then 64 for Treatment 2, etc.

8.37   While there almost certainly were *some* differences in these variables between the four groups, those differences were no bigger than we might expect from true random allocation.

8.39 (a) Randomly assign three circles to get extra carbon dioxide; the others are a control group. (b) Place pairs of circles close together, and randomly choose one of each pair for treatment.

8.41 (a) Explanatory variable: beta-carotene/vitamin(s) taken each day (or not). Response variable: whether or not colon cancer develops. (b) Assign 216 subjects to each treatment. (c) and (d) See the definitions in this chapter. (e) Perhaps the benefit of fruits and vegetables is the fiber those foods contain. Also, persons who eat lots of fruits and vegetables may have healthier diets overall.

Chapter 9

9.1 Considering many hands in which you are dealt a pair, the proportion of times that you get four of a kind is about 0.088. This does not mean that, if you've been dealt a pair 999 times and gotten four of a kind 87 times, you are guaranteed to get four of a kind from your next pair.

9.3 (a) 0.075, 0.125, 0.15, 0.1, and 0.075. (b) 0.105.

9.5 (a) The sample space consists of the 16 possible pairs of rolls. (b) Each outcome has probability 1/16.

9.7 (a) 35%; Rule 3. (b) 80%; Rule 4.

9.9 (a) 0.09. (b) 0.37. (c) 0.15.

9.11 (a) 0.155. (b) 0.609. (c) 0.660.

9.13 (a) 0.4. (b) 0.4. (c) 0.2.

9.15 (a) $\{X \geq 10\}$. (b) Either 0.025 (68–95–99.7 rule) or 0.0228 (Table A).

9.17 (a) $Y \geq 8$ means the student runs the mile in 8 minutes or more. $P(Y \geq 8) \doteq 0.1151$. (b) $P(Y < 6) \doteq 0.0668$.

9.18 (a)   **9.19** (b)   **9.21** (b)   **9.22** (c)   **9.23** (a)   **9.24** (c)

9.25 (a) 16 possible outcomes (all possible sequences of hits and misses). (b) $\{0, 1, 2, 3, 4\}$.

9.27 (a) 0.28. (b) 0.87.

9.29 (a) All probabilities are between 0 and 1 and add to 1. (b) 0.41. (c) 0.38.

9.31 (a) 3/7. (b) 2/7. (c) 5/7.

9.33 The probability is 42/90.

9.35 (a) Every person must fall into exactly one category, and the probabilities add to 1. (b) 0.04. (c) 0.18. (d) 0.42.

9.37 (a) 0.56. (b) 0.54.

9.39 (a) Each digit 1 to 9 has probability 1/9. (b) $P(W \geq 6) = 4/9$—twice as big as the Benford's law probability.

9.41 (a) Each arrangement has probability 1/8. (b) 0.375. (c) X can be 0, 1, 2, 3 with probabilities 0.125, 0.375, 0.375, 0.125.

9.43   **(a)** 0.4. **(b)** 0.6.

9.45   0.8164.

9.47   **(a)** 1/10,000. **(b)** 24/10,000.

Chapter 10

10.1   Both are statistics.

10.3   If 1 of the 12 homes were lost, it would cost more than the collected premiums. For many policies, the average claim should be close to $250.

10.5   **(a)** 69.4. **(b)** Answers will vary. **(c)** Answers will vary.

10.7   **(a)** $N(188, 12.9653)$.

10.9   We can be about 99.4% certain that average losses will not exceed $275 per policy.

10.10   (c)   **10.11**   (b)   **10.12**   (b)   **10.13**   (a)   **10.14**   (c)   **10.15**   (c)   **10.16**   (b)

10.17   1 is a parameter and 1.09 is a statistic.

10.19   In the long run, the gambler loses an average of about 5.3 cents per bet.

10.21   **(a)** 0.2812. **(b)** $N(70, 0.56)$. **(c)** 0.9266.

10.23   **(a)** Nearly 1. **(b)** Nearly 0.

10.25   **(a)** Approximately $N(2.2, 0.1941)$. **(b)** 0.1515. **(c)** 0.0764.

10.27   About 0.0052.

10.29   **(a)** 1/6 inch. **(b)** $n = 283$.

10.31   **(a)** Mean $0.60 and standard deviation $0.1602. **(b)** $P(\$0.50 < \bar{x} < \$0.70) \doteq$ 0.4648.

Chapter 11

11.1   Independence is not a reasonable assumption.

11.3   About 0.38 (0.3773).

11.5   **(b)** For example, "A and not B" is "student is at least 25 and not local." **(c)** The first is given; the other three are 0.20, 0.65, and 0.10.

11.7   2/3.

11.9   4% of adults go to health clubs at least twice per week.

11.11   **(a)** 0.25; 0.2353. **(b)** 0.22; 0.2041; 0.1875. **(c)** The general multiplication rule applies; the probability is about 0.0004952. **(d)** About 0.001981.

11.13   **(a)** The first branch is for the presence of antibodies, and the second is for the outcome of the test. **(b)** 0.015925.

11.15   About 0.6270.

11.16 (b) **11.17** (b) **11.18** (a) **11.19** (b) **11.20** (c) **11.21** (c) **11.22** (c)

11.23 0.1001.

11.25 (a) 0.001125. (b) The other symbol can show up on the middle wheel (probability 0.001375) or on either of the outside wheels (probability 0.021375 each). (c) 0.044125.

11.27 (a) 0.3. (b) 0.3. (c) Yes.

11.29 $P(D) = 0.4$.

11.31 (a) 0.334. (b) 0.3503.

11.33 (a) 1/3. (b) 1/2.

11.35 (a) $P(M) \doteq 0.4090$. (b) $P(B|M) \doteq 0.6761$. (c) $P(M \text{ and } B) \doteq 0.2765$.

11.37 65.07%.

11.39 1.

11.41 $P(B \mid C) = 0.25$. $P(C \mid B) = 0.125$.

11.43 $0.4307 + 0.208034 \doteq 0.6387$.

11.45 About 67.43%.

11.47 (a) 25.7%. (b) About 14%.

11.49 (a) A, B, or AB. (b) $P(\text{type A}) = P(\text{type B}) = 0.25$, and $P(\text{type AB}) = 0.5$.

11.51 (a) 0.25. (b) 0.375.

Chapter 12

12.1 Yes.

12.3 No; p does not remain fixed.

12.5 (a) Caught: binomial, $n = 10$, $p = 0.7$. Missed: binomial, $n = 10$, $p = 0.3$. (b) 0.2668; 0.6172.

12.7 (a) X is binomial with $n = 10$ and $p = 0.3$; Y is binomial with $n = 10$ and $p = 0.7$. (b) 7 errors caught, 3 missed. (c) 1.4491 errors.

12.9 $P(X \le 29) \doteq P(Z \le -2.94) = 0.0016$.

12.11 (a) $\mu = 180$ and $\sigma = 12.5857$ blacks. (b) $P(165 \le X \le 195) \doteq 0.7660$.

12.12 (b) **12.13** (c) **12.14** (c) **12.15** (b) **12.16** (c) **12.17** (a) **12.18** (b)

12.19 (a) There is no fixed number of observations. (b) A "large city" will have a population much larger than 1000, and each randomly selected juror has the same (unknown) probability p of opposing the death penalty. (c) Joe has the same chance of winning every week, so if a year consists of 52 weeks, this would be binomial.

12.21 (a) $n = 20$ and $p = 0.25$. (b) 5 correct guesses. (c) $P(X = 5) \doteq 0.2023$.

12.23 (a) Binomial with $n = 12$ and $p = 0.5$. (b) $P(X = 8) \doteq 0.1208$; $P(X \geq 8) \doteq$ 0.1938.

12.25 About 0.91.

12.27 (a) Each drive must be independent, and he must have a 60% chance of hitting the fairway each time. (b) With $n = 14$ and $p = 0.6$, 8 and 9 each have probability 0.2066.

12.29 (a) Binomial with $n = 1000$ and $p = 0.004$. (b) 4 positive tests. (c) Because $np = 4$.

12.31 (a) $\mu = 156$ and $\sigma \doteq 11.6499$ Hispanics. (b) 132 to 180. (c) At least 1539 adults.

12.33 0.1802; this is not unreasonable behavior for a fair coin.

12.35 The probability is nearly 1.

12.37 (a) $P(1$ of the vaccinated children$) \doteq 0.3741$. $P(1$ of the unvaccinated children$) \doteq 0.0960$. $P(1$ of each$) \doteq 0.0359$. (b) Total probability: 0.1977.

Chapter 13

13.1 (a) 2.0702. (b) 4.1404. (c) About 268 to 276.

13.3 $z^* = 2.24$.

13.5 (a) Aside from two low outliers, the distribution is close to Normal. (b) 98.90 to 112.78 IQ points.

13.7 (a) $N(5, 0.0816)$. (b) 4.98 is less than 0.25 standard deviations below the presumed mean, while 4.7 is about 3.67 standard deviations below.

13.9 $H_0: \mu = 5$; $H_a: \mu \neq 5$.

13.11 (a) $N(0, 0.3162)$. (b) $P = 0.1711$.

13.13 (a) $z \doteq 0.95$. (b) $z \doteq 3.23$. (c) $z \doteq 1.20$.

13.15 We test $H_0: \mu = 22$ seconds versus $H_a: \mu > 22$ seconds, and find $\bar{x} = 27.088$ seconds, $z \doteq 4.24$, and $P \doteq 0$.

13.17 Significant at 5% but not at 1%.

13.19 (a) $z \doteq -2.20$. (b) Significant at the 5% level. (c) Not significant at the 1% level. (d) z is between 2.054 and 2.326, so P is between 0.02 and 0.04.

13.20 (a) **13.21** (c) **13.22** (c) **13.23** (a) **13.24** (b) **13.25** (b) **13.26** (c)

13.27 $H_0: \mu = 64.2$ inches; $H_a: \mu \neq 64.2$ inches.

13.29 (a) 126.8 to 147.2 minutes. (b) Can the students in this class be considered an SRS of the population of all first-year students at this university?

13.31 237.8 to 258.2 minutes.

13.33 (a) $H_0: \mu = 120$ minutes; $H_a: \mu > 120$ minutes. (b) $z \doteq 4.29$. (c) $P < 0.0001$; we have very strong evidence against H_0.

13.35 (a) H_0: $\mu = 5.19$; H_a: $\mu \neq 5.19$. (b) $z \doteq 1.56$. (c) $P = 0.1188$; we should not reject H_0.

13.37 The differences observed would occur less than 1% of the time if pig skulls had no special meaning.

13.39 The differences in richness and total stem densities between the two areas were so small that they could easily occur by chance if population means were identical.

13.41 (a) The alternative hypothesis should be formulated without looking at the data. Before looking at the data, we had no reason to expect that women would rate a movie more highly. (b) $P = 0.0358$.

13.43 (a) The distribution is skewed to the left; the data do not appear to follow a Normal distribution. (b) 29,737 to 31,945 pounds.

13.45 (a) Because 32,000 pounds is not in the interval, we reject H_0: $\mu = 32{,}000$ pounds. (b) Because $31{,}500$ pounds is in the interval, we cannot reject H_0.

13.47 (a) We assume that the 10 students can be considered to be an SRS of the population of students, and that odor thresholds are Normally distributed. The latter condition is supported by a stemplot. (b) 26.06 to 34.74 μg/l.

13.49 We test H_0: $\mu = 25$ μg/l versus H_a: $\mu > 25$ μg/l, for which $\bar{x} = 30.4\mu$g/l, $z \doteq 2.44$, and $P = 0.0073$.

13.51 (a) No. (b) Yes.

Chapter 14

14.1 The most important reason is (c).

14.3 Because this survey was conducted on a Sunday morning, certain types of shoppers would or would not be present.

14.5 (a) 1.47. (b) $n = 400$: 0.735. $n = 1600$: 0.3675. (c) Margin of error decreases as n increases. (Specifically, it is halved each time n quadruples.)

14.7 Use $n = 217$.

14.9 (a) $z = 1.61$ is not significant. (b) $z = 1.67$ is significant.

14.11 The confidence intervals are 4.362 to 5.238, 4.547 to 5.053, and 4.645 to 4.955.

14.13 (a) **14.14** (c) **14.15** (b) **14.16** (c) **14.17** (a) **14.18** (a) **14.19** (c)

14.21 Were the 148 respondents chosen at random from the population? What was the rate of nonresponse?

14.23 $n = 101$.

14.25 $n = 35$.

14.27 The effect is greater if the sample is small.

14.29 B, A, C

14.31 (a) Margin of error decreases. (b) The P-value decreases.

14.33 (a) $z \doteq 1.70$, $P = 0.0891$. (b) The sample size is small, so a test like this one will often mistakenly fail to reject H_0.

14.35 (a) The differences observed might occur by chance even if SES had no effect. (b) This tells us that the test was insignificant not merely because of a small sample size.

Chapter 15

15.1 This is an experiment; students were randomly (at the time they visited the site) assigned to a treatment. The explanatory variable is the log-in box (genuine or not), and the response is the student's action (logging in or not).

15.3 (a) Label from 0001 to 3478. (b) 2940, 0769, 1481, 2975, 1315. (c) The response variable is how much money the students earn in the summer.

15.5 (a) The control group should have 24 trees with no beehives. (b) Table B gives 53, 64, 56, and 68. (c) The response variable is elephant damage.

15.7 (a) For example: Did subject get a job? Did subject keep the job? For the design, randomly assign about one-third of the group to each treatment, and observe the chosen response variables after a suitable amount of time. (b) Label from 00001 through 10065 and choose 06565, 00795, and 08727.

15.9 This is a convenience sample.

15.11 $H_0: \mu = 48$; $H_a: \mu < 48$.

15.13 4.0043 to 4.7957 mmol/l.

15.15 Cut in half: $n = 56$. ± 0.1 mmol/dl: $n = 220$.

15.17 322.35 to 391.65 ng/g.

15.19 80%: 334.35 to 379.65 ng/g; 90%: 327.92 to 386.08 ng/g; margin of error grows with increasing confidence.

15.21 $H_0: \mu = 100$; $H_a: \mu < 100$. $z \doteq -8.79$, $P \doteq 0$.

15.23 (a) {F, M}. (b) {6, 7,..., 20}. (c) All numbers between 2.5 and 6.1 l/min. (d) Upper limits will vary.

15.25 (a) $P(Y > 1) = 0.74$. (b) 0.31. (c) 0.67.

15.27 (a) Mean 445 ms, standard deviation 21.1723 ($n = 15$) or 6.6953 ($n = 150$) ms. (b) Large sample sizes overcome skewness. (c) 0.2266.

15.29 The first result would happen frequently when chocolate and carob have identical effects; the second would rarely happen in that event.

15.31 (a) For example: all full-time undergraduate students in the fall term on a list provided by the registrar. (b) For example: a stratified sample with 125 students from each year. (c) Consider issues of cost, ease of contacting subjects, and reluctance to respond to questions about sexual harassment.

15.33   Parents who fail to return the consent form may be more likely to place less priority on education; including those children in the control group may lower that group's score.

15.35   (a) There are six treatments: three levels of discount and two levels of fraction of shoes on sale. (b) Assign 10 subjects to each group. From Table B, the first group is 48, 60, 51, 30, 41, 27, 12, 38, 50, and 59.

15.37   A and B must be able to occur together.

15.39   (a) Nearly all should be in the range 4.5 to 49.5. (b) $\bar{x}$ will nearly always fall in the range 24.75 to 29.25.

15.41   (a) An observational study; no treatment is imposed. (b) This means unlikely to happen by chance if alcohol consumption were unrelated to death rate. (c) For example, some nondrinkers might avoid drinking because of other health concerns.

15.43   (b) $z \doteq -2.54$, $P = 0.0110$.

15.45   97.95° to 98.46°.

15.47   62% do neither.

15.49   0.1622.

15.51   (a) Binomial with $n = 12$ and $p = 0.67$. (b) $P(N \geq 9) \doteq 0.4027$ and $P(N \geq 8) \doteq 0.6410$.

15.53   (a) Approximately binomial with $n = 211$ and $p = 0.7$. (b) $P(X \geq 150) \doteq 0.3632$.

15.55   0.036.

15.57   27.2%.

15.59   0.2586.

Chapter 16

16.1   4.8925 minutes.

16.3   (a) 2.015. (b) 2.518.

16.5   (a) 2.262. (b) 2.861. (c) 1.943.

16.7   The distribution is slightly, but not unreasonably, left-skewed, with no outliers. The interval is 55.71% to 63.47%.

16.9   (a) 24. (b) t is between 1.059 and 1.318, so $0.20 < P < 0.30$. (c) $t = 1.12$ is not significant at either level.

16.11   This is a matched pairs setting; compute the call minus pure-tone differences. $\bar{x} \doteq 70.378$, $s \doteq 88.447$, $t \doteq 4.84$, df $= 36$, $P < 0.0001$.

16.13   The distribution of nitrogen concentration is too skewed—and the sample size too small—to use t procedures.

16.15 (b) **16.16** (c) **16.17** (a) **16.18** (c) **16.19** (a) **16.20** (a) **16.21** (b)

16.23 26.2244 to 27.3756.

16.25 (a) 111.2 to 118.6 mm Hg. (b) The important assumption is that this is an SRS from some population. We also assume a Normal distribution, but this is not crucial provided there are no outliers and little skewness.

16.27 (a) A stemplot shows no particular cause for concern. (b) 1.089 to 1.148. (c) The interval does not include 1, so we can conclude that $\mu \neq 1$.

16.29 22.95 and 27.89 degrees.

16.31 (a) 22.6 to 26.9 degrees. (b) This interval is narrower.

16.33 (a) A stemplot of differences is sharply skewed, with one or two high outliers, so the t procedures are not safe.

16.35 (a) Weather conditions that change from day to day can affect spore counts. (b) Take the differences, kill room count minus processing count. The interval is 843.2 to 2805.8 CFUs/m^3. (c) The data are counts, that are at best only approximately Normally distributed, and we have only a small sample.

16.37 (a) 38.19 to 58.30 thousand barrels. (b) The width is similar, but the new interval is higher (by 2000 barrels).

16.39 μ is the mean difference in healing rates. H_0: $\mu = 0$, and H_a is either $\mu < 0$ or $\mu > 0$, depending on the order of subtraction. A stemplot is roughly Normal. $t = 2.02$, df $= 13$, and $P = 0.032$.

16.41 (a) Fund and index performances are certainly not independent. (b) We test H_0: $\mu = 0$; H_a: $\mu \neq 0$. $t \doteq -0.05$, for which $P > 0.5$, so we have very little reason to doubt that $\mu = 0$.

16.43 $t = 0.15$, df $= 19$, $P = 0.88$.

Chapter 17

17.1 Matched pairs.

17.3 Single sample.

17.5 (a) If the loggers had known that a study would be done, they might have (consciously or subconsciously) altered their behavior. (b) With all points: $t \doteq 2.11$, for which $0.25 < P < 0.05$ (df $= 7$) or $P = 0.026$ (df $= 14.8$). With the low outlier removed from the logged data: $t \doteq 1.832$, for which $0.05 < P < 0.1$ (df $= 7$) or $P = 0.042$ (df $= 17.2$).

17.7 0.46 to 7.20 species (df $= 8$) or 0.65 to 7.02 species (df $= 14.8$).

17.9 (a) The time data are reasonably Normal. $t = -3.98$, for which $P < 0.0005$ (df $= 29$) or $P = 0.0001$ (df $= 57.041$). (b) The spending data are skewed and have many gaps. $t = -5.945$, for which $P < 0.0005$ (df $= 29$) or P is very small (df $= 57.998$).

17.11 With such small samples, t procedures are not reliable unless both distributions are Normal.

17.13 (a) **17.14** (c) **17.15** (a) **17.16** (b) **17.17** (c) **17.18** (a) **17.19** (b)

17.21 4.30 to 49.70 g (df = 8) or 5.77 to 48.23 g (df = 17.08); significant at 10%.

17.23 Test H_0: $\mu_1 = \mu_2$ versus H_a: $\mu_1 \neq \mu_2$. Both tests are significant: for reliability, $t \doteq 3.892$ and $P < 0.001$; for empathy, $t \doteq -3.595$ and $P < 0.001$. There is strong evidence that Anglos value reliability more than Hispanics do, and Hispanics value empathy more than Anglos do.

17.25 (a) Use a matched pairs test. (b) $t = 10.16$, $P < 0.0005$. Coached students do improve their scores. (c) 21.5 to 36.5 points (or 21.6 to 36.4, with software).

17.27 This was an observational study, not an experiment.

17.29 (a) The stemplots suggest that t procedures should be safe. It appears that customers stayed a bit longer when there was no odor. (b) To test H_0: $\mu_N = \mu_L$ versus H_a: $\mu_N \neq \mu_L$, we find $t \doteq 0.371$ and $P > 0.5$.

17.31 (a) The sample means suggest that the Permafresh swatches are slightly stronger. (b) The stemplots also suggest that the Permafresh swatches are stronger. (c) With all points, $t \doteq 3.33$ and $P \doteq 0.0184$. With the outlier removed, $t \doteq 3.96$ and $P \doteq 0.0147$.

17.33 1.56 to 7.12 pounds (df = 4) or 1.76 to 6.92 pounds (df = 5.476).

17.35 A two-sample t statistic, with conservative df = 5, for which $0.30 < P < 0.40$.

17.37 Paired t statistics, with df = 5 for the control group and df = 6 for the supplemented group. $t = 0.63$ is not significant, but $t = -2.63$ has one-sided $P = 0.0195$.

17.39 H_0: $\mu_A = \mu_P$; H_a: $\mu_A > \mu_P$; $t \doteq 4.28$, $P < 0.0005$. Active learning results in more correct identifications.

17.41 (a) 3.9 to 9.2 Blissymbols. (b) 22.2 to 26.6 Blissymbols.

17.43 (a) A 95% confidence interval for μ_w is 3.84 to 4.71 drinks. (b) A 95% confidence interval for μ_m is 5.78 to 7.26 drinks. (c) To test H_0: $\mu_w = \mu_m$ versus H_a: $\mu_w \neq \mu_m$, we find $t \doteq -5.193$, $P < 0.001$. A 95% confidence interval for $\mu_m - \mu_w$ tells us that, on the average, sophomore men who drink claim an additional 1.4 to 3.1 drinks per day.

Chapter 18

18.1 (a) p is the proportion of the population (all college students) who say they pray at least once in a while. (b) $\hat{p} = 0.8425$.

18.3 (a) N(0.75, 0.01369). (b) N(0.75, 0.00685).

18.5 0.1194 to 0.1508.

18.7 There were only 5 or 6 "successes" in the sample.

18.9 $n = 318$.

18.11 $z \doteq 2.12$ and $P = 0.0169$.

18.13 (c) **18.14** (c) **18.15** (a) **18.16** (a) **18.17** (c) **18.18** (c) **18.19** (a)

18.21 (a) The survey excludes those who have no phones or have only cell phone service. (b) 0.8170 to 0.8622.

18.23 (a) 2.26%. (b) 3.08%. (c) For samples of about this size, the margin of error is no more than about $\pm 3\%$ no matter what $\hat{p}$ is.

18.25 The failure count (5) is too small.

18.27 (a) 0.1682 to 0.2205. (b) More than 171 respondents have run red lights.

18.29 (a) Use $n = 4719$. (b) 0.01125.

18.31 0.6601 to 0.6799.

18.33 0.3753 to 0.4252.

18.35 Yes: $z = -7.68$, $P < 0.0001$.

18.37 Use $n = 375$ Hispanic female drivers.

Chapter 19

19.1 0.1800 to 0.3804.

19.3 The male proportion is higher by 0.1394 to 0.1806.

19.5 Yes: $z = -2.87$, $P = 0.0021$.

19.7 (b) **19.8** (a) **19.9** (c) **19.10** (b) **19.11** (b) **19.12** (a) **19.13** (b)

19.15 (a) $H_0: p_1 = p_2$; $H_a: p_1 < p_2$; $z = -3.53$, $P = 0.0002$. (b) One count is only 7.

19.17 0.6973 to 0.7629.

19.19 (a) $\hat{p}_1 \doteq 0.1415$, $\hat{p}_2 \doteq 0.1667$; $z \doteq -0.39$, $P = 0.6966$. (b) $z \doteq -2.12$ and $P = 0.0340$. (c) For (a): -0.1559 to 0.1056. For (b): -0.04904 to -0.001278. Larger samples make the margin of error smaller.

19.21 The two samples are not independent, because the same 23 facilities were used for both.

19.23 $H_0: p_1 = p_2$; $H_a: p_1 \neq p_2$; $z \doteq 0.02$, $P = 0.9840$ (no evidence of a difference).

19.25 0.0915 to 0.2908.

19.27 $H_0: p_1 = p_2$; $H_a: p_1 > p_2$; $z \doteq 2.96$, $P = 0.0015$.

19.29 $H_0: p_1 = p_2$; $H_a: p_1 \neq p_2$; $z \doteq 1.33$, $P \doteq 0.1836$.

19.31 The confidence interval for the proportion of all customers who pay by credit card is 0.3953 to 0.5943. The difference is not significant: $z \doteq -1.02$, $P = 0.3078$.

Chapter 20

20.1 0.3357 to 0.3843.

20.3 $H_0: p = 0.5$; $H_a: p \neq 0.5$; $z \doteq 1.90$, $P = 0.0578$.

20.5 2.00 to 2.70 kg/m^2.

20.7 $H_0: \mu_1 = \mu_2$; $H_a: \mu_1 > \mu_2$; $t \doteq 10.4$, $P < 0.0001$ (df = 19 or 32.39).

20.9 0.1654 to 0.2746.

20.11 (a) With large samples, the t procedures are fairly safe even with non-Normal data. (b) Yes: $t \doteq 2.207$, for which $0.01 < P < 0.02$ (df = 134) or $P = 0.0143$ (df = 186.02).

20.13 Either 0.48 to 8.92 minutes (df = 100) or 0.50 to 8.90 minutes (df = 186.02).

20.15 0.4422 to 0.4976.

20.17 315.24 to 318.76 points (using either df = 100 or 1013).

20.19 (a) This is an observational study (one cannot "assign" a baby's birth weight). (b) Yes: $z \doteq -2.34$, $P = 0.0096$.

20.21 Both differences are significant. For drug use, $z \doteq -2.08$, $P = 0.0376$. For IQ scores, $t \doteq -2.08$, $0.04 < P < 0.05$ (df = 100) or $P = 0.0389$ (df = 247.1).

20.23 $H_0: p_1 = p_2$; $H_a: p_1 > p_2$; $z \doteq 2.54$, $P \doteq 0.0055$.

20.25 −14.57 to 52.57 mg/dl (df = 22) or −13.64 to 51.64 mg/dl (df = 43.3).

20.27 We assume two SRSs from Normal populations. It is unlikely we have random samples from either population, especially among pets.

20.29 Estimate one proportion (line 6).

20.31 No procedure is appropriate: we have information about all players, not just a sample.

20.33 (a) Estimate one proportion (line 6). (b) Compare two means (line 3). (c) Compare two percents (line 4).

20.35 The response rate was only 0.2033.

20.37 $t \doteq 0.907$, df = 19, $P = 0.1879$.

20.39 11.09 to 14.91 months.

20.41 (a) Randomly assign 8 pieces of fabric to each method, then compare color. (b) $t \doteq -8.79$, for which P is very small (using either df = 7 or df = 13.73). However, we cannot tell if the difference is important in practice.

20.43 0.5981 to 0.7849.

20.45 $t \doteq 6.914$, P is very small (using either df = 19 or df = 33.27). The confidence interval is either 43.65 to 81.55 psi (df = 19) or 44.18 to 81.02 psi (df = 33.27).

20.47 Two of the counts are too small to allow us to perform a significance test safely.

Chapter 21

21.1 (a) We have the opinions of 133 people, of which 36 buy the recycled product. (b) 36.8% (higher), 24.1% (the same), 39.1% (lower). 60.9% think that the recycled product is no worse than the other filters. (c) For example, 55.6% of those who buy recycled filters believe the quality is higher, compared to 29.9% of non-buyers. (d) Perhaps actual use convinces people that the recycled filters are high quality, or perhaps people use recycled filters because they think in advance that their quality is high.

21.3   Start by setting a equal to any number from 10 to 50.

21.5   (a) 13.26, 8.66, 14.08, 35.74, 23.34, and 37.92. (b) The largest differences between observed and expected counts are in the "Higher" and "Lower" columns.

21.7   (a) The smallest expected count is 8.66. (b) $\chi^2 \doteq 7.638$, $P \doteq 0.022$. Rejecting H_0 means that we have evidence that buyers and nonbuyers of recycled coffee filters have different opinions about the quality of those products. (c) Buyers are more likely to say "higher" and less likely to say "lower."

21.9 $\chi^2 = 127.385$, df $= 3$, and $P < 0.0005$. We have strong evidence that there is a relationship. About 47% of the youngest age group rely entirely on a cell phone; that proportion drops as age increases.

21.11 (a) df $= (2-1)(3-1) = 2$. (b) $7.38 < \chi^2 < 7.82$, so $0.02 < P < 0.025$. (c) If H_0 is true, the mean would be 2; the observed value is quite a bit larger than this.

21.13 (a) Under H_0, $p_1 = p_2 = \cdots = p_7 = 1/7$, and we would expect 100 births on each day. (b) $\chi^2 = 19.12$. (c) df $= 6$, $P = 0.004$.

21.15 (a) 24.2%, 41.8%, 22.0%, 12.1%. Fewer A's, more D/F's. (b) 29.12, 37.31, 18.20, 6.37. (c) H_0: $p_1 = 0.32$, $p_2 = 0.41$, $p_3 = 0.20$, $p_4 = 0.07$; H_a: at least one of these probabilities is different. All expected counts are more than 5. $\chi^2 = 5.297$, df $= 3$, $P = 0.1513$.

21.17 (a)   **21.18** (c)   **21.19** (c)   **21.20** (a)   **21.21** (a)   **21.22** (b)   **21.23** (a)

21.24 (c)

21.25 (a) 0.1547 to 0.2666. (b) $\hat{p}_u \doteq 0.5208$, $\hat{p}_r \doteq 0.3102$, and $\hat{p}_s \doteq 0.4901$. Testing H_0: $p_r = p_s = p_u$ versus H_a: some proportion is different, we find $\chi^2 = 62.813$, df $= 2$, and $P < 0.0005$.

21.27 Testing H_0: all proportions are equal versus H_a: some proportions are different, we find $\chi^2 = 10.619$, df $= 2$, and $P < 0.005$.

21.29 (a) Testing H_0: $p_h = p_b$ versus H_a: $p_h \neq p_b$, we find $\hat{p}_h \doteq 0.7324$, $\hat{p}_b \doteq 0.6329$, $z \doteq 4.19$, and $P < 0.00005$. (b) $\chi^2 = 17.590$, df $= 1$, $P < 0.0005$. (c) The test statistics and P-values agree, up to rounding.

21.31 The differences between men and women are highly significant: $\chi^2 = 43.946$, df $= 4$, $P < 0.0005$. Overall, men give themselves a better chance of being rich.

21.33 (a) Compute the percents across each row. (b) The expected counts are too small. (c) Most statistical software should give a warning.

21.35 Each respondent could have participated in more than one—or even none—of the categories of Internet use.

21.37 (a) Add up the columns (516 men and 636 women). Men are generally more likely to agree or strongly agree. (b) $\chi^2 = 47.547$, df $= 4$, and $P < 0.0005$. (c) The largest contributions to χ^2 come from the "Agree," "Disagree," and "Strongly disagree" rows of the table.

21.39 Canadians are generally less satisfied than Americans. The overall difference is significant: $\chi^2 = 60.375$, df $= 4$, $P < 0.0005$.

21.41 (a) This is not an experiment, because treatments were not assigned. (b) A high nonresponse rate might mean that our random sample was undermined by non-participation. (c) High olive oil consumption is *not* more common among those without cancer: $\chi^2 = 1.552$, df $= 4$, $P = 0.817$. Within each group (colon cancer, rectal cancer, control), roughly one-third fall in each olive oil consumption category.

Chapter 22

22.1 (a) $r \doteq 0.9623$. (b) β is the average number of additional days before the first death for each unit increase in distance. We estimate $b \doteq 11.263$ and $a \doteq -8.088$. (c) The residuals are 0.825, -4.702, -3.965, 4.035, 6.035, and -2.228. The estimated standard deviation is $s \doteq 4.903$.

22.3 (a) $r^2 = 11.2\%$. (b) $\hat{y} = -2057 + 1.97x$, $s = 104.0$ km^3 of water.

22.5 $t \doteq 2.79$, df $= 62$, $P = 0.007$.

22.7 $r \doteq 0.8782$, $P \doteq 0.00004$.

22.9 0.1507 to 0.1662 cm/min. The slope is the average rate at which icicles grow under the conditions of this experiment.

22.11 (a) Use a prediction interval: -1.69 to 30.57 days. (b) 7.81 to 21.07 days.

22.13 (a) One residual may be a high outlier, but the stemplot does not show any other deviations from Normality. (b) The scatterplot shows no striking features (other than the outlier). (c) We have measurements for 38 infants.

22.15 (b)   **22.16** (b)   **22.17** (b)   **22.18** (b)   **22.19** (a)   **22.20** (a)   **22.21** (b)

22.23 Testing $H_0: \beta = 0$ versus $H_a: \beta \neq 0$, we find $t \doteq 3.116$, df $= 10$, and $0.01 < P < 0.02$.

22.25 (a) The scatterplot shows no obvious problems. (b) The residuals are quite spread out but are not strikingly non-Normal. (c) Results change slightly but perhaps not enough to be considered influential.

22.27 Testing $H_0: \beta = 0$ versus $H_a: \beta > 0$, we find $t \doteq 15.89$ and df $= 29$, so P is very small.

22.29 (a) $t \doteq -4.64$ and $P < 0.0005$. (b) -0.00475 to -0.00214 kg/cal. (c) 0.488 to 3.789 kg.

22.31 (a) $\hat{y} = 31.9 - 0.304x$. The estimated slope is significantly negative, which supports the conjecture. (b) 11.43 to 15.95 new birds.

22.33 (a) No obvious pattern. (b) No clear lack of Normality. (c) They come from 13 unrelated colonies. (d) Possibly wider in the middle but not markedly so.

22.35 (a) $\hat{y} = 560.65 - 3.0771x$. (b) The distribution of residuals has a slightly irregular appearance but is not markedly non-Normal. The scatterplot does not suggest that the standard deviation changes. (c) -4.8625 to -1.2917 calories per minute.

22.37 386 to 489 calories.

22.39 $\hat{y} \doteq 1.4146 + 0.4399x$. The evidence for a relationship is very strong: $t = 4.33$, $P = 0.001$. The residuals show no obvious causes for concern.

22.41   The evidence of a relationship is strong ($t \doteq 10.47$, $P < 0.0005$). The 95% confidence interval for the slope is 9.53 to 14.26 clusters per stump.

22.43 $P = 0.3320$; we cannot conclude that the intercept is not 0.

Chapter 23

23.1   (a) $H_0: \mu_A = \mu_B = \mu_C = \mu_D$; H_a: at least one mean is different. (b) A child's life expectancy increases by about 2 years for each long-lived parent.

23.3   (a) The stemplots show no extreme outliers or strong skewness (given the small sample sizes). (b) The means suggest that logging reduces the number of trees per plot, and that recovery is slow. (c) $F = 11.43$, $P = 0.000205$; $H_0: \mu_1 = \mu_2 = \mu_3$; H_a: not all means are the same.

23.5   (a) $541.44/2.09 \doteq 259.12$. (b) $\sqrt{2.09} \doteq 1.446$.

23.7   (a) The ratio of standard deviations is about 1.16. (b) The ratio of standard deviations is about 1.18.

23.9   The differences among the groups were significant ($F = 3.44$, df = 3 and 27, $P = 0.031$). Nitrogen had a positive effect, the phosphorus and control groups were similar, and the plants that got both nutrients fell between the others.

23.11   (a) df = 2 and 93. (b) df = 2 and 87.

23.13   (c)   **23.14** (b)   **23.15** (b)   **23.16** (a)   **23.17** (a)   **23.18** (a)

23.19   Populations: morning people, evening people, neither. Response variable: difference in memorization scores. $H_0: \mu_m = \mu_e = \mu_n$ versus H_a: at least one mean is different.

23.21   There are four populations: learning-disabled children with each of the four treatments. The response variable is the scores on the state math exam. H_0: $\mu_1 = \mu_2 = \mu_3 = \mu_4$ versus H_a: at least one mean is different.

23.23   (a) Yes; the mean control emission rate is half the smallest of the others. (b) H_0: all groups have the same mean emission rate; H_a: at least one group has a different mean emission rate. (c) Are the data Normally distributed? Were these random samples? (d) $s = \text{SEM} \times \sqrt{8}$. The four standard deviations are 16.77, 24.75, 18.78, and 24.38; the rule-of-thumb ratio is 1.48.

23.25   (a) Winter: $\bar{x} = 205.17$, $s = 58.77$. Spring: $\bar{x} = 315.39$, $s = 37.34$. Control: $\bar{x} = 136.65$, $s = 21.69$. It appears that extra water in the spring has the greatest effect on biomass, with a lesser effect from added water in the winter. ANOVA is risky with these data; the standard deviation ratio is nearly 3, and the winter and spring distributions may have skewness or outliers. (b) $H_0 : \mu_w = \mu_s = \mu_c$; H_a: at least one mean is different. (c) The differences are significant ($F = 27.52$, df 2 and 15, $P < 0.0005$), but we must keep in mind that the conditions for ANOVA are not satisfied.

23.27   (a) Randomly assign 8 pieces of cloth to each treatment, then compare lightness scores. (b) Method C is lightest and Method B is darkest. The differences in mean lightness are small but highly significant ($F = 22.77$, $P < 0.001$).

23.29   The means are 123.8, 123.6, and 134.4 lb; they do not consistently decrease. The standard deviations are 4.6043, 6.5422, and 9.5289 lb. $9.5289/4.6043 \doteq 2.07$; ANOVA is risky. If we do ANOVA anyway, $F = 3.70$ (df = 2 and 12) and $P = 0.056$; the differences are not significant.

23.31   The means are 134.8, 134.2, and 143.2 degrees, and the standard deviations are 1.92, 10.16, and 2.28 degrees (for Permafresh 55, Permafresh 48, and Hylite LF). Hylite LF, which had the lowest breaking strength, has the highest wrinkle resistance. ANOVA gives $F = 3.39$ and $P = 0.068$, but this cannot be trusted because there is evidence that the standard deviations are different.

23.33   (a) There is a slight increase in growth when water is added in the wet season, but a much greater increase when it is added during the dry season. (b) The means differ significantly during the first three years. (c) The year 2005 is the only one for which the winter biomass was higher than the spring biomass.

23.35   In addition to a high standard deviation ratio, the spring biomass distribution has a high outlier.

TABLE 1.1	Percent of state population born outside the United States	10
TABLE 1.2	Average travel time to work, by state	12
TABLE 1.3	Annual spending per person on health care	19
TABLE 1.4	Omega-3 fatty acids as a fraction of omega-6 fatty acids in food oils	25
TABLE 1.5	Medical doctors per 100,000 people, by state	25
TABLE 1.6	Carbon dioxide emissions, by country	26
TABLE 1.7	Recruitment of rock sole in the Bering Sea	26
TABLE 2.1	Flower lengths for three *Heliconia* varieties	42
TABLE 2.2	Salaries for the Boston Red Sox	47
TABLE 2.3	Amount spent by customers in a restaurant	48
TABLE 2.4	Time active and lying down by lean and obese subjects	48
TABLE 2.5	Penetrability of soil at three compression levels	48
TABLE 2.6	Earnings of a sample of Canadians in 1901	49
TABLE 4.1	Florida boat registrations and manatees killed by boats	77
TABLE 4.2	Growth of icicles over time	87
TABLE 5.1	Four data sets for exploring correlation and regression	112
TABLE 5.2	Two measures of glucose level in diabetics	112
TABLE 5.3	Reaction times in a computer game	114
TABLE 6.1	Neuron response to tones and monkey calls	120
TABLE 6.2	Yearly discharge of the Mississippi river	122
TABLE 6.3	Days from April 20 for the Tanana River tripod to fall	122
TABLE 6.4	Angle of deformity for two types of foot deformity	124
TABLE 16.1	Trials on which chimpanzees recruited a partner	295
TABLE 16.2	Neuron response to tones and monkey calls	297
TABLE 16.3	Nitrogen and carbon-13 in a sample of diamonds	300
TABLE 16.4	A mutual fund versus its benchmark index	305
TABLE 16.5	Performance times using right-hand and left-hand threads	305
TABLE 16.6	Absorption extent for two versions of a drug	306
TABLE 17.1	Time spent in three different postures by lean and obese subjects	310
TABLE 17.2	Time and spending by restaurant customers	318
TABLE 17.3	Mathematics skills scores before and after a subliminal message	325
TABLE 17.4	Drinks per session claimed by female and male students	325
TABLE 20.1	Drinks per session by female students	360
TABLE 21.1	Young adults by age and living arrangement	366
TABLE 21.2	Young adults by age and living arrangement: expected cell counts	371
TABLE 22.1	Infants' crying and IQ scores	394
TABLE 22.2	Arctic river discharge, 1936 to 1999	401
TABLE 22.3	Winter temperature and anglerfish latitude	410
TABLE 22.4	Appraised value and selling price for condominium units	415
TABLE 23.1	Flower lengths three *Heliconia* varieties	422
TABLE 23.2	Data from a study of logging in Borneo	427
TABLE 23.3	Time that customers remain in a restaurant	428
TABLE 23.4	Time until subjects ask for help with a puzzle	433
TABLE 23.5	Effect of electrical field on healing rate in newts	441
TABLE 23.6	Plant biomass for three water conditions	442

ACT, 15, 60, 70, 195
Addition rule for probabilities, 169–170, 178, 199, 202, 203–204, 212
Alternative hypothesis, 241–242, 251, 265
  many-sided, 370, 373, 382, 423, 430
  one-sided, 241, 243, 251
  two-sided, 241–242, 244, 251
American Community Survey, 4, 137–138
Analysis of variance (ANOVA), 423, Chapter 23
  idea of, 429–430
  one-way, 430, 437
Anscombe, Frank, 111
Association, 146
  explaining, 104, 105–107, 146–147
  negative, 77, 80, 83
  positive, 77–78, 80, 83

Bar graph, 7–8, 11, 21
Benford's law, 171, 225
Bias, 131, 189–190. See also Unbiased estimator
  in experiment, 148, 150, 155, 158
  in sample, 131–132, 134, 136, 137–139, 140, 163
Binomial coefficient, 221
Binomial distribution. See Distribution, binomial
Binomial setting, 217–219, 226
Boggs, Rex, 119
Boxplot, 35–36, 44, 354, 429

Canada, 9, 46, 49, 118, 125, 137, 143, 170, 179, 203, 218, 228, 277, 304, 322, 332, 338, 348, 358, 390, 438
Cannon, Charles, 43
Categorical data. See Variable, categorical
Causation, 105–107, 108, 145–147, 156
Cautions
  confidence intervals, 262, 268, 331–332
  correlation and regression, 81–83, 103–104
  experiments, 154–156
  inference, 257–260, 268
  sample surveys, 137–139
  significance tests, 249, 264–267, 268–269, 314, 404, 429
Cell, in a two-way table, 365
Cell counts for chi-square, 373, 386
Center of a distribution, 12–15, 18, 21, 33, 44, 51, 116, 188, 354. See also Mean; Median
Central limit theorem, 190–193, 194, 259, 298, 300, 319, 432
Chi-square distribution. See Distribution, chi-square

Chi-square statistic, 372, 386
  goodness of fit, 382–384
  terms of, 373, 374–375, 386
Clusters, 76
Conditional distribution. See Distribution, conditional
Conditional probability. See Probability, conditional
Conditions for inference
  analysis of variance, 423, 431–434
  about a mean, 285–286, 289, 291, 296
  comparing two means, 308, 309, 313–314
  regression, 395, 408–412, 414
Confidence interval, 231, 232–234, 251, 261–262, 274, 354
  cautions about, 262, 268, 331–332
  four-step process, 236
  reasoning of, 232–234, 354
  relationship to tests, 255
  t for difference of means, 311–314, 319, 355
  t for matched pairs, 295
  t for one mean, 288–290, 301, 355
  t for regression intercept, 420
  t for regression mean response, 406–407, 414
  t for regression slope, 404–405, 414
  z for difference of proportions, 343–344, 349, 355
  z for one mean, 235–237, 251, 257
  z for one proportion, 330–332, 336, 355
Confidence level, 233–234, 251, 274, 354
Confounding, 146–147, 149–150, 155, 157, 353
Continuity correction, 229
Control, experimental, 149–152, 153, 158, 259
Control group, 150–152, 155
Convenience sample, 131
Correlation, 79–83, 84, 92, 101, 116, 354, 394
  cautions about, 81–83, 103–104
  squared, 97, 108, 395
  test for, 403–404, 414
Critical value
  of chi-square distribution, 380–381, Table D
  of standard Normal distribution, 235, 249, 251, 331, 333, 343, 347, Table C
  of t distribution, 288, 289, 292, 296, 301, 312, 313, 404, Table C
Cumulative proportion. See Proportion, cumulative
Current Population Survey, 130, 136, 183, 184
Cycle, in a time plot, 20, 21

Data, vii, xviii
Data analysis, vii, xviii, 1, 115–116, 260, 268, 273, 353–354, 370, 374–375. See also Exploratory data analysis

Data production, xviii–xix, 129, 273, 353, Chapter 7, Chapter 8
Degrees of freedom
  of ANOVA F statistic, 425, 436, 437
  of chi-square distribution, 380
  of chi-square test, 380, 383, 386
  of F distribution, 435–436
  of regression s and t, 397–398, 414
  of standard deviation s, 38, 287
  of t distribution, 287–288, 301
  of two-sample t, 311, 315, 319
Density curve, 51–53, 67, 116, 173–175, 178, 287, 354
Design, 129, 273
  experimental, 147–148, 150–152, 153, 156–157, 158
  sampling, 130, 140
Deviation
  from distribution pattern, 12, 21, 51
  from mean, 38
  from scatterplot pattern, 76–78, 98
Direction of a relationship, 76–78, 83, 116, 354
Disjoint events, 169–170, 178, 199–202, 203, 212
Distribution, 6, 21, 51
  binomial, 218, 226, Chapter 12
    Normal approximation for, 223–225, 226
  of categorical variable, 6, 7, 21, 365–369, 382–383
  chi-square, 372, 373, 380–381, 386, Table D
  conditional, 366–369, 385
  exponential, 191–192
  F, 435–436, 437
  geometric, 215
  marginal, 366–369, 385
  Normal, 55–58, 67, 116, 188, 190–193, 232, 237, 247, 259–260, 285, 308, 395, 431, 437
    as probability distribution, 175
    standard, 59–60, 68, 235, 245, 286, 287, Table A
  population. See Population distribution
  probability. See Probability distribution
  of quantitative variable, 10–12, 21
  of random variable, 176–177, 178
  sampling. See Sampling distribution
  skewed, 14, 17, 18, 21, 32, 36, 44, 54, 67, 291, 296, 298, 299, 380
  symmetric, 14, 21, 32, 35, 44, 54, 56, 60, 67, 285, 287
  t, 286–288, 300, Table C
  uniform, 173–174
Dobbs, Lou, 132
Dotplot, 296
Double-blind experiment, 155, 158

Effect size, 266, 354
Estimation, 184–186. *See also* Confidence
   interval
Event, 166–167, 178
Excel, ix, 40–41, 95–96, 293–295, 315–316,
   344, 399–400, 425–426, 427
Expected cell count, 370–371, 374, 382–383,
   386
Experiment, 106, 108, 145–147, 157, 356,
   Chapter 8
   cautions about, 149–150, 154–156
   completely randomized, 151–152, 156–157
   design of, 147–148, 150–152, 153, 156–157,
      158
   matched pairs design, 156–157, 158, 295–297
   randomized comparative, 150–152, 153–154,
      258, 274
Explanatory variable. *See* Variable, explanatory
Exploratory data analysis, 5–6, 21, 127
Extrapolation, 104, 108

F distribution. *See* Distribution, *F*
F statistic, 430
Factor, experimental, 147–148, 151–152
Factorial, 220, 226
Five-number summary, 34–36, 39, 44, 116,
   354
Form of a relationship, 76–78, 83–84, 116,
   354
Four-step process, xix, 42–43, 44, 74–78, 92,
   192, 202, 207, 209, 210, 236–237, 246–247,
   283, 289, 291, 295, 309, 312, 313, 331, 333,
   335, 341, 346, 367, 378, 393, 405, 410, 421,
   432
   for confidence interval, 236
   for significance test, 246

General Social Survey, 138, 377, 385, 387,
   388, 390
Geometric distribution. *See* Distribution,
   geometric
Goodness of fit, 382–384
Gray, William, 81, 113, 418
Guéguen, Nicolas, 47, 427

Histogram, 10–12, 21, 51, 52–53, 116, 222, 354
   interpreting, 12–15

Independence
   of events, 199–202, 206, 212
   of observations, 217, 226, 395, 409–410
   of random digits, 133
   of samples, 308, 431, 437
Individuals, 3, 21, 147, 158, 353
Inference, statistical, xix, 127, 136, 184–186,
   231, 274, 354, 363. *See also* Confidence
   interval, Test of significance
   cautions about, 257–260, 268, 314, 354

Influential observation, 101–103, 108, 354,
   394, 412
Intercept of a line, 93
Iowa Test of Basic Skills, 14, 51–53, 56, 57–58
IQ, 23, 68, 70, 84, 108, 238, 277, 278, 322, 358,
   393–395

Kerrich, John, 228
Kress, John, 42, 421

Large numbers, law of, 184–186, 194
Leaf, in a stemplot, 16–18
Least-squares regression line, 94–98, 108,
   394, 414
   equation of, 94, 108
Levine, James, 309
Linear relationship, 78, 84, 91–92, 98, 103, 116,
   354, 393, 409–410. *See also* Correlation
   testing, 401–402
Lurking variable. *See* Variable, lurking

Margin of error, 233, 261–262, 268, 332, 354,
   407
   choosing sample size, 263–264, 268,
      332–334, 336
Marginal distribution. *See* Distribution,
   marginal
Matched pairs design, 156–157, 158, 295, 307
Mean, 29–30, 32, 39, 44, 82, 116, 184
   of binomial distribution, 221–222, 226
   of chi-square distribution, 381
   of density curve, 54–55, 67
   of difference of sample proportions, 342–343,
      349
   of Normal distribution, 55–56, 67
   of a population, 184, 185, 189, 194, 232,
      245, 285
   of residuals, 100
   response in regression, 395–396
   of sample mean, 189–190, 194
   of sample proportion, 328–329, 336
Mean square, 425, 430
Median, 31–32, 39, 44
   of density curve, 54, 67
Mendel, Gregor, 216
Minitab, ix, 40–41, 62, 65, 95–96, 109, 110,
   220, 224, 288, 293–294, 315–316, 344–345,
   367–368, 374, 376, 377, 378–379, 388, 389,
   399–400, 405, 407, 408, 413, 416, 417,
   425–426, 428, 434, 439, 440
Multiplication rule for probabilities, 201–202,
   207–208, 212, 219–221

Ngai, Jacqueline, 359, 434
Nonresponse, 137–138, 140, 259, 262
Normal curve, 55–56, 67
Normal distribution. *See* Distribution, Normal
Null hypothesis, 241–242, 251

Observational study, 145–147, 157, 356
Outlier, 12–13, 16, 21, 29, 39, 51, 52, 76, 82,
   83, 259–260, 298, 354, 394, 411–412
   in regression, 101–103, 354

Parameter, 183–184, 194, 218, 395, 414
Pattern
   of a distribution, 12–15, 21, 51
   of a scatterplot, 76–78
   of a time plot, 20
Percentile, 69
Pie chart, 7, 21
Placebo, 155, 158
Pooled estimator
   of population proportion, 346–347, 349, 355
   of standard deviation in ANOVA, 430
Population, 129–130, 140, 184
Population distribution, 187–188, 190–191,
   232, 259–260
Population regression line, 395–396, 409, 414
Prediction, 92–93, 94, 97, 104, 393, 402
   inference for, 405–407, 409
Prediction interval, 407, 409, 414
Probability, 136, 165, 177, 185, 273, Chapter 9,
   Chapter 10, Chapter 11
   binomial, 219–221, 226
   conditional, 205–206, 211, 212
   equally likely outcomes, 167
   idea of, 164–165
   rules of, 168–170, 178, 199, 212, Chapter 11
Probability distribution, 176–177, 178
Probability model, 166–167, 178, 207, 208
   continuous, 172–175, 177, 178
   discrete, 171, 177, 178
Proportion, cumulative, 61–62, 68
   standard Normal, 62–64, Table A
Proportion, population, 163, 327
Proportion, sample, 163, 328
   distribution of, 328–329
   Normal approximation for, 328–329
   pooled, 346–347, 349, 355
P-value, 242–244, 246–247, 251, 264–265, 268,
   275, 354

Quartiles, 33–34, 40, 44
   of a density curve, 54, 67
Quintile, 69

Random digit dialing, 134–135, 137, 140,
   378–379
Random digits, 133, 140, 150–151
   table of, 133–134, 150–151, 158, 166,
      Table B
Random phenomenon, 165, 177
Random variable, 176–177, 178
   continuous, 177, 178
   discrete, 177, 178
Randomization, experimental, 150–152,
   153–154, 157, 158

Regression, Chapter 5
  cautions about, 103–104
  inference for, Chapter 22
Regression line, 91–93, 107, 116, 354. *See also*
  Least-squares regression line
  intercept of, 93, 108, 396
  population, 395–396
  slope of, 93, 107, 396, 404–405
Regression to the mean, 113
Regression standard error. *See* Standard error,
  regression
Residual, 98–101, 396–398, 411–412
  plot, 100–101, 409–412
Resistant measure, 30, 32, 34, 38, 44, 82,
  103, 259
Response bias, 138, 140
Response variable. *See* Variable, response
Robustness, 297–299, 301, 317, 432, 437
Rounding data, 18, 42, 309
Roundoff error, 6, 175, 193, 366, 371, 375

Sample, 129–130, 140, 184, 218–219
  cautions about, 137–139, 314
  design of, 130, 140
  random, 134–135, 140, 163, 258
  simple random, 132–135, 140, 218–219, 232,
    237, 247, 258–259, 273, 285, 308, 431
  stratified, 142
  systematic, 142
Sample size, choosing
  confidence interval for a mean, 263–264, 268
  confidence interval for a proportion,
    332–334, 337
Sample space, 166–167, 178
Sample survey, 130, 135, 140
Sampling design. *See* Sample, design of
Sampling distribution, 187–188, 194
  of difference of proportions, 342–343, 349
  of sample count, 219, 223–225
  of sample mean, 187–188, 190–193,
    232–233, 239
  of sample proportion, 328–329, 336
SAT, 14–15, 56, 60, 61–64, 65–66, 69, 70,
  74–75, 195, 265, 322, 332
Scatterplot, 74–75, 83, 92, 116, 354, 394
  interpreting, 76–78
Shape, of a distribution, 12–15, 21, 51, 116,
  188, 259–260, 354
Significance, statistical, 154, 248–249, 251,
  264–266, 354
Significance level, 248–249
Significance test. *See* Test of significance
Simple conditions, 232, 257–260
Simple random sample. *See* Sample, simple
  random
Simulation, 187
68–95–99.7 rule, 57–58, 68, 232, 235
Skewed distribution. *See* Distribution, skewed
Slope, of a line, 93, 393

Spread, of a distribution, 12–15, 18, 21, 33, 44,
  116, 188, 354. *See also* Quartiles, Standard
  deviation
Spreadsheet, 4. *See also* Excel
Srivastava, Diane, 359, 434
Standard deviation, 37–38, 39, 44, 82, 116
  of binomial distribution, 221–222, 226
  of a density curve, 55, 67
  of difference of sample means, 310
  of difference of sample proportions, 342–343,
    349
  of Normal distribution, 55–56
  of a population, 232, 237, 261, 300, 310, 431,
    432, 437
  of sample mean, 189–190, 194, 232, 286,
    288, 300
  of sample proportion, 328–329, 336
  about population regression line, 395–396,
    409–410
Standard error, 286
  of difference of sample means, 310–311, 319
  of difference of sample proportions, 343–344,
    349
  of individual regression response, 407, 414
  of least-squares slope, 402, 404
  of mean regression response, 407, 414
  regression, 397–398, 412, 414
  of sample mean, 286, 288, 290, 300
  of sample proportion, 330
Standard Normal distribution. *See* Distribution,
  Normal, standard
Standardized value, 59–60, 63–64, 66–67,
  79–80
Statistic, 183–184, 187–188, 194
Stem and leaf plot. *See* Stemplot
Stemplot, 16–18, 21, 51, 116, 354
  back-to-back, 26, 309
  splitting stems in, 18
Straight lines, review of, 93
Strength of a relationship, 76–78, 83–84, 116,
  354. *See also* Correlation
Subjects, experimental, 147–148, 158, 353
Sums of squares, 425
Suttle, Kenwin, 152, 439, 442
Symmetric distribution. *See* Distribution,
  symmetric

t distribution. *See* Distribution, *t*
t inference procedures
  for matched pairs, 295–297, 301
  for one mean, 288–290, 291–292, 301
  for prediction in regression, 405–407, 414
  for regression slope, 401–402, 404–405, 414
  for two means, 310–314, 319
t statistic
  one-sample, 287, 291, 300
  regression slope, 402
  two-sample, 310–314, 319
Temeles, Ethan, 42, 421
Test of significance, 231, 238–244, 251, 275, 354

  cautions about, 249, 264–267, 268–269, 314,
    404, 429
  chi-square for two-way table, 372–374, 386
  chi-square for goodness of fit, 382–384
  correlation, 403–404
  F test in ANOVA, 423, 430, 437
  four-step process, 246
  reasoning of, 238–240, 354
  t test for matched pairs, 295–297, 301
  t test for one mean, 291–292, 301, 355
  t test for regression intercept, 420
  t test for regression slope, 401–402, 414
  t test for two means, 310–314, 319, 355
  z test for one mean, 245–247, 251, 257
  z test for one proportion, 334–336, 337, 355
  z test for two proportions, 346–348, 349, 355
Test statistic, 242, 246, 251
Testing hypotheses. *See* Test of significance
TI graphing calculator, ix, 40–41, 95–96,
  293–294, 315–316, 344–345, 399–400,
  425–426
Time plot, 19–20, 21
Treatment, experimental, 147–148, 158
Tree diagram, 208–211, 212
Trend, in a time plot, 20, 21
Tukey, John, ix
Two-sample problems, 307, 317, 319, 341, 349
Two-way table, 365–369, 385

Unbiased estimator, 189, 194, 328, 396, 404
Undercoverage, 137, 140, 262
Units of measurement, 4, 38, 80, 353

Variability, 33, 44, 163. *See also* Spread of a
  distribution
Variable, 3, 21, 353. *See also* Random variable
  categorical, 4, 21, 353, 355, 363, 365,
    382–383
  explanatory, 73–74, 80, 83, 91–93, 97, 147,
    353, 363, 395, 414
  lurking, 104, 105, 108, 146–147, 149–150,
    354, 412
  quantitative, 4, 10, 16, 21, 80, 353, 355, 363
  response, 73–74, 80, 83, 91–93, 97, 148, 353,
    355, 363, 395, 414
  row and column, 385
Variance, 37–38, 44
Venn diagram, 200, 203
Vohs, Kathleen, 324, 432
Voluntary response sample, 132, 140, 259, 353

Wording of questions, 138–139, 140

z-score, 59
z statistic
  for one proportion, 334, 337
  one-sample for mean, 245–247, 251
  for two proportions, 347, 349

Table entry for C is the critical value t^* required for confidence level C. To approximate one- and two-sided P-values, compare the value of the t statistic with the critical values of t^* that match the P-values given at the bottom of the table.

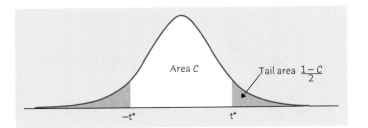

Area C

Tail area $\frac{1-C}{2}$

$-t^*$ t^*

TABLE C t distribution critical values

DEGREES OF FREEDOM	CONFIDENCE LEVEL C											
	50%	60%	70%	80%	90%	95%	96%	98%	99%	99.5%	99.8%	99.9%
1	1.000	1.376	1.963	3.078	6.314	12.71	15.89	31.82	63.66	127.3	318.3	636.6
2	0.816	1.061	1.386	1.886	2.920	4.303	4.849	6.965	9.925	14.09	22.33	31.60
3	0.765	0.978	1.250	1.638	2.353	3.182	3.482	4.541	5.841	7.453	10.21	12.92
4	0.741	0.941	1.190	1.533	2.132	2.776	2.999	3.747	4.604	5.598	7.173	8.610
5	0.727	0.920	1.156	1.476	2.015	2.571	2.757	3.365	4.032	4.773	5.893	6.869
6	0.718	0.906	1.134	1.440	1.943	2.447	2.612	3.143	3.707	4.317	5.208	5.959
7	0.711	0.896	1.119	1.415	1.895	2.365	2.517	2.998	3.499	4.029	4.785	5.408
8	0.706	0.889	1.108	1.397	1.860	2.306	2.449	2.896	3.355	3.833	4.501	5.041
9	0.703	0.883	1.100	1.383	1.833	2.262	2.398	2.821	3.250	3.690	4.297	4.781
10	0.700	0.879	1.093	1.372	1.812	2.228	2.359	2.764	3.169	3.581	4.144	4.587
11	0.697	0.876	1.088	1.363	1.796	2.201	2.328	2.718	3.106	3.497	4.025	4.437
12	0.695	0.873	1.083	1.356	1.782	2.179	2.303	2.681	3.055	3.428	3.930	4.318
13	0.694	0.870	1.079	1.350	1.771	2.160	2.282	2.650	3.012	3.372	3.852	4.221
14	0.692	0.868	1.076	1.345	1.761	2.145	2.264	2.624	2.977	3.326	3.787	4.140
15	0.691	0.866	1.074	1.341	1.753	2.131	2.249	2.602	2.947	3.286	3.733	4.073
16	0.690	0.865	1.071	1.337	1.746	2.120	2.235	2.583	2.921	3.252	3.686	4.015
17	0.689	0.863	1.069	1.333	1.740	2.110	2.224	2.567	2.898	3.222	3.646	3.965
18	0.688	0.862	1.067	1.330	1.734	2.101	2.214	2.552	2.878	3.197	3.611	3.922
19	0.688	0.861	1.066	1.328	1.729	2.093	2.205	2.539	2.861	3.174	3.579	3.883
20	0.687	0.860	1.064	1.325	1.725	2.086	2.197	2.528	2.845	3.153	3.552	3.850
21	0.686	0.859	1.063	1.323	1.721	2.080	2.189	2.518	2.831	3.135	3.527	3.819
22	0.686	0.858	1.061	1.321	1.717	2.074	2.183	2.508	2.819	3.119	3.505	3.792
23	0.685	0.858	1.060	1.319	1.714	2.069	2.177	2.500	2.807	3.104	3.485	3.768
24	0.685	0.857	1.059	1.318	1.711	2.064	2.172	2.492	2.797	3.091	3.467	3.745
25	0.684	0.856	1.058	1.316	1.708	2.060	2.167	2.485	2.787	3.078	3.450	3.725
26	0.684	0.856	1.058	1.315	1.706	2.056	2.162	2.479	2.779	3.067	3.435	3.707
27	0.684	0.855	1.057	1.314	1.703	2.052	2.158	2.473	2.771	3.057	3.421	3.690
28	0.683	0.855	1.056	1.313	1.701	2.048	2.154	2.467	2.763	3.047	3.408	3.674
29	0.683	0.854	1.055	1.311	1.699	2.045	2.150	2.462	2.756	3.038	3.396	3.659
30	0.683	0.854	1.055	1.310	1.697	2.042	2.147	2.457	2.750	3.030	3.385	3.646
40	0.681	0.851	1.050	1.303	1.684	2.021	2.123	2.423	2.704	2.971	3.307	3.551
50	0.679	0.849	1.047	1.299	1.676	2.009	2.109	2.403	2.678	2.937	3.261	3.496
60	0.679	0.848	1.045	1.296	1.671	2.000	2.099	2.390	2.660	2.915	3.232	3.460
80	0.678	0.846	1.043	1.292	1.664	1.990	2.088	2.374	2.639	2.887	3.195	3.416
100	0.677	0.845	1.042	1.290	1.660	1.984	2.081	2.364	2.626	2.871	3.174	3.390
1000	0.675	0.842	1.037	1.282	1.646	1.962	2.056	2.330	2.581	2.813	3.098	3.300
z^*	0.674	0.841	1.036	1.282	1.645	1.960	2.054	2.326	2.576	2.807	3.091	3.291
One-sided P	.25	.20	.15	.10	.05	.025	.02	.01	.005	.0025	.001	.0005
Two-sided P	.50	.40	.30	.20	.10	.05	.04	.02	.01	.005	.002	.001